PP 1990:2010

Structural Eurocodes

Extracts from the Structural Eurocodes for students of structural design

Third Edition

First published in the UK in 2004
Second edition published in 2007
Third edition published in 2010

by
BSI
389 Chiswick High Road
London W4 4AL

British Library Cataloguing in Publication Data
A catalogue record for this book is available from the British Library

ISBN 978 0 580 69454 7

Typeset in Verdana by Monolith – www.monolith.uk.com
Printed in Great Britain by Berforts Group, www.berforts.co.uk

Acknowledgments

Compilers

BSI thanks Professor Norman Bright and Professor John Roberts for overseeing the authoring of the first edition of this guide (2004), and Professor John Roberts for co-ordinating the update for the second edition (2007) and third edition (2010).

Contributors

Chapter 0	Professor Haig Gulvanessian (all editions)
Chapter 1	Professor Haig Gulvanessian (all editions)
Chapter 2	Anthony Threlfall (first edition); Professor Norman Bright (second edition) Owen Booker (third edition)
Chapter 3	Dr Mike Gardner (first and second editions) Professor Gerry Parke (third edition)
Chapter 4	Dr J B (Buick) Davidson (all editions)
Chapter 5	Christopher Mettem (first edition); Professor Norman Bright (second edition) Peter Watt (third edition)
Chapter 6	Professor John Roberts (all editions)
Chapter 7	Dr Andrew Bond and Andrew Harris (all editions)
Chapter 8	Costas Georgopoulos (all editions)
Chapter 9	Dr Anton Fried (all editions)

Introduction

This guide

This guide contains extracts from some of the principal parts of each of the Eurocodes. It is intended to be a suitable teaching tool for lecturers of students of structural design, and to be suitable as guidance material for undergraduate design projects. The extracts chosen are as concise as possible, focussing on the essential principles in the Eurocodes. Commentary is kept to a minimum and only made on parts of the text that require explanation. The commentary in each chapter is shown as boxed text with a grey background, in order to distinguish it from the Eurocode extracts. This guide does not deal with fire design.

Each chapter in this guide corresponds to a particular Eurocode, and has been numbered in accordance with that Eurocode e.g. chapter 1 contains extracts from Eurocode 1: Actions on structures. For consistency with the Eurocodes, EN 1990: Eurocode — Basis of structural design, has been labelled as "Eurocode" (not "Eurocode 0"). In order to facilitate future amendments to this guide, the page numbers in each chapter reflect the chapter that they belong to e.g. the page numbers in chapter 0 are preceded by "0-", whilst the page numbers in chapter 6 are preceded by "6-".

The guide is written for students at UK universities and for English-speaking universities worldwide. It is a "stand alone" publication. However, it is expected that the reader has access to the full published versions of the Eurocodes, either in hard copy in the university library, or electronically through, for example, the university's membership of BSI, that provides access to all published British Standards.

Symbols and definitions are covered in each chapter of the guide in the same way they are dealt with in the individual chapter of the Eurocodes. This is because it is recognized that there are differences between each chapter. However, the following note is important:

IMPORTANT NOTE: The distinction between Principles and Application Rules described in Clause 1.4 of the Eurocode for Basis of Design (Chapter 0) applies to all parts of the suite of Eurocodes.

In the guide the extracts have been taken from the latest version of the Eurocode at the time of writing. The parts of the Eurocodes each have a corresponding National Annex for each Member State, which provides the Nationally Determined Parameters and various allowable choices, such as which Informative Annexes may be used in that Member State.

National Annex content that is included in this guide is inserted at the corresponding points of the Eurocode to which the National Annex text refers. All National Annex content is labelled "NA.*x*".

Complete list of parts of the Eurocodes

The following is a complete list of all parts of the Eurocodes. The parts included in this guide are indicated in **bold**.

EN 1990:2002 – Eurocode, *Basis of structural design*

EN1991 – Eurocode 1: Actions on structures

- **EN 1991-1-1:2002, *General actions — Densities, self-weight, imposed loads for buildings***
- EN1991-1-2:2002, *Actions on structures exposed to fire*
- **EN1991-1-3:2003, *General actions — Snow loads***
- **EN1991-1-4:2005, *General actions — Wind actions***
- EN1991-1-5:2003, *General actions — Thermal actions*
- EN1991-1-6:2005, *General actions — Actions during execution*
- EN1991-1-7:2006, *General actions — Accidental actions*
- EN1991-2:2003, *Traffic loads on bridges*
- EN1991-3:2006, *Actions induced by cranes and machinery*
- EN1991-4:2006, *Silos and tanks*

EN 1992 – Eurocode 2: *Design of concrete structures*

- **EN1992-1-1:2004, *General rules and rules for buildings***
- EN1992-1-2:2004, *General rules — Structural fire design*
- EN1992-2:2005, *Concrete bridges — Design and detailing*
- EN1992-3:2006, *Liquid retaining and containment structures*
- PD 6687-2:2008, *Recommendations for the design of structures to BS EN 1992-2:2005*

EN 1993 – Eurocode 3: *Design of steel structures*

- **EN1993-1-1:2005, *General rules and rules for buildings***
- EN1993-1-2:2005, *General rules — Structural fire design*
- EN1993-1-3:2006, *General rules — Supplementary rules for cold-formed members and sheeting*
- EN1993-1-4:2006, *General rules — Supplementary rules for stainless steel*
- EN1993-1-5:2006, *Strength and stability of planar plated structures without transverse loading*
- EN1993-1-6:2007, *Strength and stability of shell structures*
- EN1993-1-7:2007, *Plated structures subject to out of plane loading*
- **EN1993-1-8:2005, *Design of joints***
- EN1993-1-9:2005, *Fatigue*
- EN1993-1-10:2005, *Material toughness and through-thickness properties*
- EN1993-1-11:2006, *Design of structures with tension components*
- EN 1993-1-12:2007, *Additional rules for the extension of EN 1993 up to steel grades S 700*
- EN1993-2:2006, *Steel bridges*
- EN1993-3-1:2006, *Towers, masts and chimneys — Towers and masts*
- EN 1993-3-2:2006, *Towers, masts and chimneys — Chimneys*
- EN 1090-2:2008, *Execution of steel structures and aluminium structures — Technical requirements for the execution of steel structures*
- PD 6695-2:2008, *Recommendations for the design of bridges to BS EN 1993*
- EN1993-4-1:2007, *Silos*
- EN1993-4-2:2007, *Tanks*
- EN1993-4-3:2007, *Pipelines*
- EN1993-5:2007, *Piling*
- EN1993-6:2007, *Crane supporting structures*

EN 1994 – Eurocode 4: *Design of composite steel and concrete structures*

- **EN1994-1-1:2004, *General rules and rules for buildings***
- EN1994-1-2:2005, *General rules — Structural fire design*
- EN1994-2:2005, *General rules and rules for bridges*
- PD 6696-2:2007, *Background paper to BS EN 1994-2 and the UK National Annex to BS EN 1994-2 — Eurocode 4 — Design and composite steel and concrete structures — General rules and rules for bridges*

EN 1995 – Eurocode 5: *Design of timber structures*
EN1995-1-1:2004, *General — Common rules and rules for buildings*
EN1995-1-2:2004, *General — Structural fire design*
EN1995-2:2004, *Bridges*

EN 1996 – Eurocode 6: *Design of masonry structures*
EN1996-1-1:2005, *General rules for reinforced and unreinforced masonry structures*
EN1996-1-2:2005, *General rules — Structural fire design*
EN1996-2:2006, *Design considerations, selection of materials and execution of masonry*
EN 1996-3:2006, *Simplified calculation methods and simple rules for masonry structures*

EN 1997 – Eurocode 7: *Geotechnical design*
EN1997-1:2004, *General rules*
EN1997-2:2007, *Ground investigation and testing*

EN 1998 – Eurocode 8: *Design of structures for earthquake resistance*
EN1998-1:2004, *General rules, seismic actions and rules for buildings*
EN1998-2:2005, *Bridges*
EN1998-3:2005, *Assessment and retrofitting of buildings*
EN1998-4:2006, *Silos, tanks and pipelines*
EN1998-5:2004, *Foundations, retaining structures and geotechnical aspects*
EN1998-6:2005, *Towers, masts and chimneys*

EN 1999 – Eurocode 9: *Design of aluminium structures*
EN1999-1-1:2007, *General structural rules*
EN1999-1-2:2007, *Structural fire design*
EN 1999-1-3:2007, *Structures susceptible to fatigue*
EN 1999-1-4:2007, *Cold-formed structural sheeting*
EN 1999-1-5:2007, *Shell structures*
EN 1090-3:2008, *Execution of steel structures and aluminium structures — Technical requirements for aluminium structures*

Chapter 0 — Extracts from Eurocode: Basis of structural design

The Eurocode extracts in this chapter are taken from EN 1990:2002+A1:2005 (incorporating corrigendum December 2008 and corrigendum No 2 October 2009), *Eurocode: Basis of structural design*.

Text altered by CEN amendment A1 is indicated by [A1) (A1]. Text altered by CEN corrigendum December 2008 is indicated in the text by [AC1) (AC1]. Text altered by CEN corrigendum No 2 October 2009 is indicated in the text by [AC2) (AC2].

The National Annex extracts are taken from NA to BS EN 1990:2002+A1:2005 (Incorporating National Amendment No. 1), *UK National Annex for Eurocode Basis of Structural Design*.

For the design of new structures, EN 1990 is intended to be used for direct application, together with Eurocodes EN 1991 to 1999.

All material independent clauses have been removed from EN 1992 to EN 1999 and included only in EN 1990, thus making EN 1990 the head Eurocode.

The full list of the contents of EN 1990 follows, and is given for reference purposes. (Bold items are covered in this chapter.)

The National Annex text is taken from the Foreword of EN 1990.

National Annex for EN 1990

This standard gives alternative procedures, values and recommendations for classes with notes indicating where national choices may have to be made. Therefore the national standard implementing EN 1990 should have a National Annex containing all Nationally Determined Parameters to be used for the design of buildings and civil engineering works to be constructed in the relevant country.

Section 1 General

The scope for EN 1990 is given in full. (Bold items are covered in this chapter.)

1.1 Scope

(1) EN 1990 establishes Principles and requirements for the safety, serviceability and durability of structures, describes the basis for their design and verification and gives guidelines for related aspects of structural reliability.

(2) EN 1990 is intended to be used in conjunction with EN 1991 to EN 1999 for the structural design of buildings and civil engineering works, including geotechnical aspects, structural fire design, situations involving earthquakes, execution and temporary structures.

NOTE For the design of special construction works (e.g. nuclear installations, dams, etc.), other provisions than those in EN 1990 to EN 1999 might be necessary.

(3) EN 1990 is applicable for the design of structures where other materials or other actions outside the scope of EN 1991 to EN 1999 are involved.

(4) EN 1990 is applicable for the structural appraisal of existing construction, in developing the design of repairs and alterations or in assessing changes of use.

NOTE Additional or amended provisions might be necessary where appropriate.

1.3 Assumptions

(1) Design which employs the Principles and Application Rules is deemed to meet the requirements provided the assumptions given in EN 1990 to EN 1999 are satisfied (see Section 2).

(2) The general assumptions of EN 1990 are:

- the choice of the structural system and the design of the structure is made by appropriately qualified and experienced personnel;
- execution is carried out by personnel having the appropriate skill and experience;
- AC2) adequate supervision and quality control is provided during design and during execution of the work, i.e. in factories, plants, and on site; (AC2
- the construction materials and products are used as specified in EN 1990 or in EN 1991 to EN 1999 or in the relevant execution standards, or reference material or product specifications;
- the structure will be adequately maintained;
- the structure will be used in accordance with the design assumptions.

NOTE There may be cases when the above assumptions need to be supplemented.

1.4 Distinction between Principles and Application Rules

(1) Depending on the character of the individual clauses, distinction is made in EN 1990 between Principles and Application Rules.

(2) The Principles comprise :

- general statements and definitions for which there is no alternative, as well as;
- requirements and analytical models for which no alternative is permitted unless specifically stated.

(3) The Principles are identified by the letter P following the paragraph number.

(4) The Application Rules are generally recognised rules which comply with the Principles and satisfy their requirements.

(5) It is permissible to use alternative design rules different from the Application Rules given in EN 1990 for works, provided that it is shown that the alternative rules accord with the relevant Principles and are at least equivalent with regard to the structural safety, serviceability and durability which would be expected when using the Eurocodes.

NOTE If an alternative design rule is substituted for an application rule, the resulting design cannot be claimed to be wholly in accordance with EN 1990 although the design will remain in accordance with the Principles of EN 1990. When EN 1990 is used in respect of a property listed in an Annex Z of a product standard or an ETAG, the use of an alternative design rule may not be acceptable for CE marking.

(6) In EN 1990, the Application Rules are identified by a number in brackets e.g. as this clause.

1.5 Terms and definitions

NOTE For the purposes of this European Standard, the terms and definitions are derived from ISO 2394, ISO 3898, ISO 8930 and ISO 8402.

1.5.1 Common terms used in EN 1990 to EN 1999

1.5.1.1
construction works
everything that is constructed or results from construction operations

NOTE This definition accords with ISO 6707-1. The term covers both building and civil engineering works. It refers to the complete construction works comprising structural, non-structural and geotechnical elements.

1.5.1.2
type of building or civil engineering works
type of construction works designating its intended purpose, e.g. dwelling house, retaining wall, industrial building, road bridge

1.5.1.3
type of construction
indication of the principal structural material, e.g. reinforced concrete construction, steel construction, timber construction, masonry construction, steel and concrete composite construction

1.5.1.4
method of construction
manner in which the execution will be carried out, e.g. cast in place, prefabricated, cantilevered

1.5.1.5
construction material
material used in construction work, e.g. concrete, steel, timber, masonry

1.5.1.6
structure
organised combination of connected parts designed to carry loads and provide adequate rigidity

1.5.1.7
structural member
physically distinguishable part of a structure, e.g. a column, a beam, a slab, a foundation pile

1.5.1.8
form of structure
arrangement of structural members

NOTE Forms of structure are, for example, frames, suspension bridges.

1.5.1.9
structural system
load-bearing members of a building or civil engineering works and the way in which these members function together

1.5.1.10
structural model
idealisation of the structural system used for the purposes of analysis, design and verification

1.5.1.11
execution
all activities carried out for the physical completion of the work including procurement, the inspection and documentation thereof

NOTE The term covers work on site; it may also signify the fabrication of components off site and their subsequent erection on site.

1.5.2 Special terms relating to design in general

1.5.2.1
design criteria
quantitative formulations that describe for each limit state the conditions to be fulfilled

1.5.2.2
design situations
sets of physical conditions representing the real conditions occurring during a certain time interval for which the design will demonstrate that relevant limit states are not exceeded

1.5.2.3
transient design situation
design situation that is relevant during a period much shorter than the design working life of the structure and which has a high probability of occurrence

NOTE A transient design situation refers to temporary conditions of the structure, of use, or exposure, e.g. during construction or repair.

1.5.2.4
persistent design situation
design situation that is relevant during a period of the same order as the design working life of the structure

NOTE Generally it refers to conditions of normal use.

1.5.2.5
accidental design situation
design situation involving exceptional conditions of the structure or its exposure, including fire, explosion, impact or local failure

1.5.2.6
fire design
design of a structure to fulfil the required performance in case of fire

1.5.2.7
seismic design situation
design situation involving exceptional conditions of the structure when subjected to a seismic event

1.5.2.8
design working life
assumed period for which a structure or part of it is to be used for its intended purpose with anticipated maintenance but without major repair being necessary

1.5.2.9
hazard
for the purpose of EN 1990 to EN 1999, an unusual and severe event, e.g. an abnormal action or environmental influence, insufficient strength or resistance, or excessive deviation from intended dimensions

1.5.2.10
load arrangement
identification of the position, magnitude and direction of a free action

1.5.2.11
load case
compatible load arrangements, sets of deformations and imperfections considered simultaneously with fixed variable actions and permanent actions for a particular verification

1.5.2.12
limit states
states beyond which the structure no longer fulfils the relevant design criteria

1.5.2.13
ultimate limit states
states associated with collapse or with other similar forms of structural failure

NOTE They generally correspond to the maximum load-carrying resistance of a structure or structural member.

1.5.2.14
serviceability limit states
states that correspond to conditions beyond which specified service requirements for a structure or structural member are no longer met

1.5.2.14.1
irreversible serviceability limit states
serviceability limit states where some consequences of actions exceeding the specified service requirements will remain when the actions are removed

1.5.2.14.2
reversible serviceability limit states
serviceability limit states where no consequences of actions exceeding the specified service requirements will remain when the actions are removed

1.5.2.14.3
serviceability criterion
design criterion for a serviceability limit state

1.5.2.15
resistance
capacity of a member or component, or a cross-section of a member or component of a structure, to withstand actions without mechanical failure e.g. bending resistance, buckling resistance, tension resistance

1.5.2.16
strength
mechanical property of a material indicating its ability to resist actions, usually given in units of stress

1.5.2.17
reliability
ability of a structure or a structural member to fulfil the specified requirements, including the design working life, for which it has been designed. Reliability is usually expressed in probabilistic terms

NOTE Reliability covers safety, serviceability and durability of a structure.

1.5.2.18
reliability differentiation
measures intended for the socio-economic optimisation of the resources to be used to build construction works, taking into account all the expected consequences of failures and the cost of the construction works

1.5.2.19
basic variable
part of a specified set of variables representing physical quantities which characterise actions and environmental influences, geometrical quantities, and material properties including soil properties

1.5.2.20
maintenance
set of activities performed during the working life of the structure in order to enable it to fulfil the requirements for reliability

NOTE Activities to restore the structure after an accidental or seismic event are normally outside the scope of maintenance.

1.5.2.21
repair
activities performed to preserve or to restore the function of a structure that fall outside the definition of maintenance

1.5.2.22
nominal value
value fixed on non-statistical bases, for instance on acquired experience or on physical conditions

1.5.3 Terms relating to actions

1.5.3.1
action (*F*)

a) set of forces (loads) applied to the structure (direct action);
b) set of imposed deformations or accelerations caused for example, by temperature changes, moisture variation, uneven settlement or earthquakes (indirect action).

1.5.3.2
effect of action (E)
effect of actions (or action effect) on structural members, (e.g. internal force, moment, stress, strain) or on the whole structure (e.g. deflection, rotation)

1.5.3.3
permanent action (G)
action that is likely to act throughout a given reference period and for which the variation in magnitude with time is negligible, or for which the variation is always in the same direction (monotonic) until the action attains a certain limit value

1.5.3.4
variable action (Q)
action for which the variation in magnitude with time is neither negligible nor monotonic

1.5.3.5
accidental action (A)
action, usually of short duration but of significant magnitude, that is unlikely to occur on a given structure during the design working life

NOTE 1 An accidental action can be expected in many cases to cause severe consequences unless appropriate measures are taken.

NOTE 2 Impact, snow, wind and seismic actions may be variable or accidental actions, depending on the available information on statistical distributions.

1.5.3.6
seismic action (A_E)
action that arises due to earthquake ground motions

1.5.3.7
geotechnical action
action transmitted to the structure by the ground, fill or groundwater

1.5.3.8
fixed action
action that has a fixed distribution and position over the structure or structural member such that the magnitude and direction of the action are determined unambiguously for the whole structure or structural member if this magnitude and direction are determined at one point on the structure or structural member

1.5.3.9
free action
action that may have various spatial distributions over the structure

1.5.3.10
single action
action that can be assumed to be statistically independent in time and space of any other action acting on the structure

1.5.3.11
static action
action that does not cause significant acceleration of the structure or structural members

1.5.3.12
dynamic action
action that causes significant acceleration of the structure or structural members

1.5.3.13
quasi-static action
dynamic action represented by an equivalent static action in a static model

1.5.3.14
characteristic value of an action (F_k)
principal representative value of an action

NOTE In so far as a characteristic value can be fixed on statistical bases, it is chosen so as to correspond to a prescribed probability of not being exceeded on the unfavourable side during a "reference period" taking into account the design working life of the structure and the duration of the design situation.

1.5.3.15
reference period
chosen period of time that is used as a basis for assessing statistically variable actions, and possibly for accidental actions

1.5.3.16
combination value of a variable action ($\psi_0 Q_k$)
value chosen – in so far as it can be fixed on statistical bases – so that the probability that the effects caused by the combination will be exceeded is approximately the same as by the characteristic value of an individual action. It may be expressed as a determined part of the characteristic value by using a factor $\psi_0 \leq 1$

1.5.3.17
frequent value of a variable action ($\psi_1 Q_k$)
value determined – in so far as it can be fixed on statistical bases – so that either the total time, within the reference period, during which it is exceeded is only a small given part of the reference period, or the frequency of it being exceeded is limited to a given value. It may be expressed as a determined part of the characteristic value by using a factor $\psi_1 \leq 1$

AC2 NOTE For the frequent value of multi-component traffic actions see load groups in EN 1991-2. AC2

1.5.3.18
quasi-permanent value of a variable action ($\psi_2 Q_k$)
value determined so that the total period of time for which it will be exceeded is a large fraction of the reference period. It may be expressed as a determined part of the characteristic value by using a factor $\psi_2 \leq 1$

1.5.3.19
accompanying value of a variable action (ψQ_k)
value of a variable action that accompanies the leading action in a combination

NOTE The accompanying value of a variable action may be the combination value, the frequent value or the quasi-permanent value.

1.5.3.20
representative value of an action (F_{rep})
value used for the verification of a limit state. A representative value may be the characteristic value (F_k) or an accompanying value (ψF_k)

1.5.3.21
design value of an action (F_d)
value obtained by multiplying the representative value by the partial factor γ_f

NOTE The product of the representative value multiplied by the partial factor $\gamma_F = \gamma_{Sd} \times \gamma_f$ may also be designated as the design value of the action (See 6.3.2).

1.5.3.22
combination of actions
set of design values used for the verification of the structural reliability for a limit state under the simultaneous influence of different actions

1.5.4 Terms relating to material and product properties

1.5.4.1
characteristic value (X_k or R_k)
value of a material or product property having a prescribed probability of not being attained in a hypothetical unlimited test series. This value generally corresponds to a specified fractile of the assumed statistical distribution of the particular property of the material or product. A nominal value is used as the characteristic value in some circumstances

1.5.4.2
design value of a material or product property (X_d or R_d)
value obtained by dividing the characteristic value by a partial factor γ_m or γ_M, or, in special circumstances, by direct determination

1.5.4.3
nominal value of a material or product property (X_{nom} or R_{nom})
value normally used as a characteristic value and established from an appropriate document such as a European Standard or Prestandard

1.5.5 Terms relating to geometrical data

1.5.5.1
characteristic value of a geometrical property (a_k)
value usually corresponding to the dimensions specified in the design. Where relevant, values of geometrical quantities may correspond to some prescribed fractiles of the statistical distribution

1.5.5.2
design value of a geometrical property (a_d)
generally a nominal value. Where relevant, values of geometrical quantities may correspond to some prescribed fractile of the statistical distribution

NOTE The design value of a geometrical property is generally equal to the characteristic value. However, it may be treated differently in cases where the limit state under consideration is very sensitive to the value of the geometrical property, for example when considering the effect of geometrical imperfections on buckling. In such cases, the design value will normally be established as a value specified directly, for example in an appropriate European Standard or Prestandard. Alternatively, it can be established from a statistical basis, with a value corresponding to a more appropriate fractile (e.g. a rarer value) than applies to the characteristic value.

1.6 Symbols

For the purposes of this European Standard, the following symbols apply.

NOTE The notation used is based on ISO 3898:1987.

Latin upper case letters

A	Accidental action
A_d	Design value of an accidental action
A_{Ed}	Design value of seismic action $A_{Ed} = \gamma_I A_{Ek}$
A_{Ek}	Characteristic value of seismic action
C_d	Nominal value, or a function of certain design properties of materials
E	Effect of actions
E_d	Design value of effect of actions
$E_{d,dst}$	Design value of effect of destabilising actions
$E_{d,stb}$	Design value of effect of stabilising actions
F	Action
F_d	Design value of an action
F_k	Characteristic value of an action

F_{rep}	Representative value of an action
AC2) F_w	Wind force (general symbol)
F_{wk}	Characteristic value of the wind force
F_w^*	Wind force compatible with road traffic
F_w^{**}	Wind force compatible with railway traffic (AC2
G	Permanent action
G_{d}	Design value of a permanent action
$G_{\mathrm{d,inf}}$	Lower design value of a permanent action
$G_{\mathrm{d,sup}}$	Upper design value of a permanent action
G_{k}	Characteristic value of a permanent action
$G_{\mathrm{k,j}}$	Characteristic value of permanent action *j*
$G_{\mathrm{k,j,sup}}/G_{\mathrm{k,j,inf}}$	Upper/lower characteristic value of permanent action *j*
AC2) G_{set}	Permanent action due to uneven settlements (AC2
P	Relevant representative value of a prestressing action (see EN 1992 to EN 1996 and EN 1998 to EN 1999)
P_{d}	Design value of a prestressing action
P_{k}	Characteristic value of a prestressing action
P_{m}	Mean value of a prestressing action
Q	Variable action
Q_{d}	Design value of a variable action
Q_{k}	Characteristic value of a single variable action
$Q_{\mathrm{k,1}}$	Characteristic value of the leading variable action *1*
AC1) $Q_{\mathrm{k,i}}$ (AC1	Characteristic value of the accompanying variable action *i*
R	Resistance
R_{d}	Design value of the resistance
R_{k}	Characteristic value of the resistance
AC2) T	Thermal climatic action (general symbol)
T_k	Characteristic value of the thermal climatic action (AC2
X	Material property
X_{d}	Design value of a material property
X_{k}	Characteristic value of a material property

Latin lower case letters

a_{d}	Design values of geometrical data
a_{k}	Characteristic values of geometrical data
a_{nom}	Nominal value of geometrical data
AC2) d_{set}	Difference in settlement of an individual foundation or part of a foundation compared to a reference level (AC2
u	Horizontal displacement of a structure or structural member
w	Vertical deflection of a structural member

Greek upper case letters

Δa	Change made to nominal geometrical data for particular design purposes, e.g. assessment of effects of imperfections
AC2) Δd_{set}	Uncertainty attached to the assessment of the settlement of a foundation or part of a foundation (AC2

Greek lower case letters

γ	Partial factor (safety or serviceability)
γ_{bt}	Maximum peak value of bridge deck acceleration for ballasted track
γ_{df}	Maximum peak value of bridge deck acceleration for direct fastened track
γ_{Gset}	Partial factor for permanent actions due to settlements, also accounting for model uncertainties
γ_{f}	Partial factor for actions, which takes account of the possibility of unfavourable deviations of the action values from the representative values
γ_{F}	Partial factor for actions, also accounting for model uncertainties and dimensional variations
γ_{g}	Partial factor for permanent actions, which takes account of the possibility of unfavourable deviations of the action values from the representative values

γ_G Partial factor for permanent actions, also accounting for model uncertainties and dimensional variations

$\gamma_{G,j}$ Partial factor for permanent action *j*

$\gamma_{Gj,sup}/\gamma_{Gj,inf}$ Partial factor for permanent action *j* in calculating upper/lower design values

[AC2) γ_I Importance factor (see EN 1998) (AC2]

γ_m Partial factor for a material property

γ_M Partial factor for a material property, also accounting for model uncertainties and dimensional variations

γ_P Partial factor for prestressing actions (see EN 1992 to EN 1996 and EN 1998 to EN 1999)

γ_q Partial factor for variable actions, which takes account of the possibility of unfavourable deviations of the action values from the representative values

γ_Q Partial factor for variable actions, also accounting for model uncertainties and dimensional variations

$\gamma_{Q,i}$ Partial factor for variable action *i*

γ_{Rd} Partial factor associated with the uncertainty of the resistance model

γ_{Sd} Partial factor associated with the uncertainty of the action and/or action effect model

η Conversion factor

ξ Reduction factor

ψ_0 Factor for combination value of a variable action

ψ_1 Factor for frequent value of a variable action

ψ_2 Factor for quasi-permanent value of a variable action

Section 2 Requirements

2.1 Basic requirements

(1)P A structure shall be designed and executed in such a way that it will, during its intended life, with appropriate degrees of reliability and in an economical way:

- sustain all actions and influences likely to occur during execution and use; and
- AC1 meet the specified serviceability requirements for a structure or a structural element.

NOTE See also 1.3, 2.1(7) and 2.4(1) P. AC1

(2)P A structure shall be designed to have adequate:

- structural resistance,
- serviceability, and
- durability.

(3)P In the case of fire, the structural resistance shall be adequate for the required period of time.

NOTE See also EN 1991-1-2.

(4)P A structure shall be designed and executed in such a way that it will not be damaged by events such as:

- explosion,
- impact, and
- the consequences of human errors,

to an extent disproportionate to the original cause.

NOTE 1 The events to be taken into account are those agreed for an individual project with the client and the relevant authority.

NOTE 2 Further information is given in EN 1991-1-7.

(5)P Potential damage shall be avoided or limited by appropriate choice of one or more of the following:

- avoiding, eliminating or reducing the hazards to which the structure can be subjected;
- selecting a structural form which has low sensitivity to the hazards considered;
- selecting a structural form and design that can survive adequately the accidental removal of an individual member or a limited part of the structure, or the occurrence of acceptable localised damage;
- avoiding as far as possible structural systems that can collapse without warning;
- tying the structural members together.

(6) The basic requirements should be met:

- by the choice of suitable materials,
- by appropriate design and detailing, and
- by specifying control procedures for design, production, execution, and use

relevant to the particular project.

(7) The provisions of Section 2 should be interpreted on the basis that due skill and care appropriate to the circumstances is exercised in the design, based on such knowledge and good practice as is generally available at the time that the design of the structure is carried out.

2.2 Reliability management

(1)P The reliability required for structures within the scope of EN 1990 shall be achieved:
a) by design in accordance with EN 1990 to EN 1999 and
b) by
   - appropriate execution and
   - quality management measures.

NOTE See 2.2(5) and Annex B.

(2) Different levels of reliability may be adopted *inter alia*:
- for structural resistance;
- for serviceability.

(3) The choice of the levels of reliability for a particular structure should take account of the relevant factors, including:
- the possible cause and /or mode of attaining a limit state;
- the possible consequences of failure in terms of risk to life, injury, potential economical losses;
- public aversion to failure;
- the expense and procedures necessary to reduce the risk of failure.

The table below gives a possible classification.

Degree of reliability	**Risk of life, economic and social losses**	**Examples of buildings and civil engineering works**
Extremely high	High	Nuclear power reactors Major dams and barriers Strategic defence structures etc.
Higher than normal	High	Significant bridges Grandstands Public buildings where consequences of failure are high etc.
Normal (obtained by using EN 1990 clause 2.2(1) and Table B2)	Medium	Residential and office buildings Public buildings where consequences of failure are medium etc.
Lower than normal	Low	Agricultural buildings where people do not normally enter Greenhouses Lighting columns etc.

For a detailed presentation of reliability differentiation see EN 1990 2.2 and Annexes B and C.

2.3 Design working life

(1) The design working life should be specified.

See A1.1, which is reproduced on 0-31.

2.4 Durability

(1)P The structure shall be designed such that deterioration over its design working life does not impair the performance of the structure below that intended, having due regard to its environment and the anticipated level of maintenance.

(2) In order to achieve an adequately durable structure, the following should be taken into account:
- the intended or foreseeable use of the structure;
- the required design criteria;
- the expected environmental conditions;
- the composition, properties and performance of the materials and products;
- the properties of the soil;
- the choice of the structural system;
- the shape of members and the structural detailing;
- the quality of workmanship, and the level of control;
- the particular protective measures;
- the intended maintenance during the design working life.

NOTE The relevant EN 1992 to EN 1999 specify appropriate measures to reduce deterioration.

(3)P The environmental conditions shall be identified at the design stage so that their significance can be assessed in relation to durability and adequate provisions can be made for protection of the materials used in the structure.

(4) The degree of any deterioration may be estimated on the basis of calculations, experimental investigation, experience from earlier constructions, or a combination of these considerations.

2.5 Quality management

(1) In order to provide a structure that corresponds to the requirements and to the assumptions made in the design, appropriate quality management measures should be in place. These measures comprise:
- definition of the reliability requirements,
- organisational measures, and
- controls at the stages of design, execution, use and maintenance.

NOTE EN ISO 9001:2000 is an acceptable basis for quality management measures, where relevant.

Section 3 Principles of limit states design

3.1 General

(1)P A distinction shall be made between ultimate limit states and serviceability limit states.

NOTE In some cases, additional verifications may be needed, for example to ensure traffic safety.

(3)P Limit states shall be related to design situations, see 3.2.

(4) Design situations should be classified as persistent, transient or accidental, see 3.2.

3.2 Design situations

(1)P The relevant design situations shall be selected taking into account the circumstances under which the structure is required to fulfil its function.

(2)P Design situations shall be classified as follows:
- persistent design situations, which refer to the conditions of normal use;
- transient design situations, which refer to temporary conditions applicable to the structure, e.g. during execution or repair;
- accidental design situations, which refer to exceptional conditions applicable to the structure or to its exposure, e.g. to fire, explosion, impact or the consequences of localised failure;
- seismic design situations, which refer to conditions applicable to the structure when subjected to seismic events.

NOTE Information on specific design situations within each of these classes is given in EN 1991 to EN 1999.

Seismic design will not be covered further in this document. Reference may be made to EN 1990 and EN 1998 for detailed information.

(3)P The selected design situations shall be sufficiently severe and varied so as to encompass all conditions that can reasonably be foreseen to occur during the execution and use of the structure.

3.3 Ultimate limit states

(1)P The limit states that concern:
- the safety of people; and/or
- the safety of the structure

shall be classified as ultimate limit states.

(2) In some circumstances, the limit states that concern the protection of the contents should be classified as ultimate limit states.

NOTE The circumstances are those agreed for a particular project with the client and the relevant authority.

(3) States prior to structural collapse, which, for simplicity, are considered in place of the collapse itself, may be treated as ultimate limit states.

(4)P The following ultimate limit states shall be verified where they are relevant:
- loss of equilibrium of the structure or any part of it, considered as a rigid body;
- failure by excessive deformation, transformation of the structure or any part of it into a mechanism, rupture, loss of stability of the structure or any part of it, including supports and foundations;
- failure caused by fatigue or other time-dependent effects.

NOTE Different sets of partial factors are associated with the various ultimate limit states, see 6.4.1.

3.4 Serviceability limit states

(1)P The limit states that concern:
- the functioning of the structure or structural members under normal use;
- the comfort of people;
- the appearance of the construction works,

shall be classified as serviceability limit states.

NOTE 1 In the context of serviceability, the term "appearance" is concerned with such criteria as high deflection and extensive cracking, rather than aesthetics.

NOTE 2 Usually the serviceability requirements are agreed for each individual project.

(2)P A distinction shall be made between reversible and irreversible serviceability limit states.

(3) The verification of serviceability limit states should be based on criteria concerning the following aspects:

a) deformations that affect
   - the appearance,
   - the comfort of users, or
   - the functioning of the structure (including the functioning of machines or services),

or that cause damage to finishes or non-structural members;

b) vibrations
   - that cause discomfort to people, or
   - that limit the functional effectiveness of the structure;

c) damage that is likely to adversely affect
   - the appearance,
   - the durability, or
   - the functioning of the structure.

NOTE Additional provisions related to serviceability criteria are given in the relevant EN 1992 to EN 1999.

3.5 Limit state design

(1)P Design for limit states shall be based on the use of structural and load models for relevant limit states.

(2)P It shall be verified that no limit state is exceeded when relevant design values for
- actions,
- material properties, or
- product properties, and
- geometrical data

are used in these models.

(3)P The verifications shall be carried out for all relevant design situations and load cases.

Section 4 Basic variables

4.1 Actions and environmental influences

4.1.1 Classification of actions

(1)P Actions shall be classified by their variation in time as follows:

- permanent actions *(G)*, e.g. self-weight of structures, fixed equipment and road surfacing, and indirect actions caused by shrinkage and uneven settlements;
- variable actions *(Q)*, e.g. imposed loads on building floors, beams and roofs, wind actions or snow loads;
- accidental actions *(A)*, e.g. explosions, or impact from vehicles.

NOTE Indirect actions caused by imposed deformations can be either permanent or variable.

(2) Certain actions, such as seismic actions and snow loads, may be considered as either accidental and/or variable actions depending on the site location, see EN 1991 and EN 1998.

(3) Actions caused by water may be considered as permanent and/or variable actions depending on the variation of their magnitude with time.

(4)P Actions shall also be classified

- by their origin, as direct or indirect,
- by their spatial variation, as fixed or free, or
- by their nature and/or the structural response, as static or dynamic.

(5) An action should be described by a model, its magnitude being represented in the most common cases by one scalar which may have several representative values.

NOTE For some actions and some verifications, a more complex representation of the magnitudes of some actions may be necessary.

The table below gives a classification.

Permanent action	**Variable action**	**Accidental action**
(a) Self-weight of structures, fittings and fixed equipment (b) Prestressing force (c) Water and earth pressure (d) Indirect action, e.g. settlement of supports	(a) Imposed floor loads (b) Snow loads (c) Wind loads (d) Indirect action, e.g. temperature effects	(a) Explosions (b) Fire (c) Impact from vehicles

4.1.2 Characteristic values of actions

(1)P The characteristic value F_k of an action is its main representative value and shall be specified:

- as a mean value, an upper or lower value, or a nominal value (which does not refer to a known statistical distribution) (see EN 1991);
- in the project documentation, provided that consistency is achieved with methods given in EN 1991.

(2)P The characteristic value of a permanent action shall be assessed as follows:

- if the variability of G can be considered as small, one single value G_k may be used;
- if the variability of G cannot be considered as small, two values shall be used: an upper value $G_{k,sup}$ and a lower value $G_{k,inf}$.

(3) The variability of G may be neglected if G does not vary significantly during the design working life of the structure and its coefficient of variation is small. G_k should then be taken equal to the mean value.

NOTE This coefficient of variation can be in the range of 0,05 to 0,10 depending on the type of structure.

(4) In cases when the structure is very sensitive to variations in G (e.g. some types of prestressed concrete structures), two values should be used even if the coefficient of variation is small. Then $G_{k,inf}$ is the 5% fractile and $G_{k,sup}$ is the 95% fractile of the statistical distribution for G, which may be assumed to be Gaussian.

(5) The self-weight of the structure may be represented by a single characteristic value and be calculated on the basis of the nominal dimensions and mean unit masses, see EN 1991-1-1.

NOTE For the settlement of foundations, see EN 1997.

(6) Prestressing (P) should be classified as a permanent action caused by either controlled forces and/or controlled deformations imposed on a structure. These types of prestress should be distinguished from each other as relevant (e.g. prestress by tendons, prestress by imposed deformation at supports).

NOTE The characteristic values of prestress, at a given time t, may be an upper value $P_{k,sup}(t)$ and a lower value $P_{k,inf}(t)$. For ultimate limit states, a mean value $P_m(t)$ can be used. Detailed information is given in EN 1992 to EN 1996 and EN 1999.

(7)P For variable actions, the characteristic value (Q_k) shall correspond to either:
- an upper value with an intended probability of not being exceeded or a lower value with an intended probability of being achieved, during some specific reference period;
- a nominal value, which may be specified in cases where a statistical distribution is not known.

NOTE 1 Values are given in the various Parts of EN 1991.

NOTE 2 The characteristic value of climatic actions is based upon the probability of 0,02 of its time-varying part being exceeded for a reference period of one year. This is equivalent to a mean return period of 50 years for the time-varying part. However in some cases the character of the action and/or the selected design situation makes another fractile and/or return period more appropriate.

(8) For accidental actions the design value A_d should be specified for individual projects.

NOTE See also EN 1991-1-7.

4.1.3 Other representative values of variable actions

(1)P Other representative values of a variable action shall be as follows:

(a) the combination value, represented as a product $\psi_0 Q_k$, used for the verification of ultimate limit states and irreversible serviceability limit states (see section 6 and Annex C);

(b) the frequent value, represented as a product $\psi_1 Q_k$, used for the verification of ultimate limit states involving accidental actions and for verifications of reversible serviceability limit states;

NOTE 1 For buildings, for example, the frequent value is chosen so that the time it is exceeded is 0,01 of the reference period; for road traffic loads on bridges, the frequent value is assessed on the basis of a return period of one week.

AC2 NOTE 2 The infrequent value, represented as a product $\psi_{1,\text{infq}}Q_k$, may be used only for the verification of certain serviceability limit states specifically for concrete bridges. The infrequent value which is defined only for road traffic loads (see EN 1991-2) is based on a return period of one year.

NOTE 3 For the frequent value of multi-component traffic actions see EN 1991-2. AC2

(c) the quasi-permanent value, represented as a product ψ_2Q_k, used for the verification of ultimate limit states involving accidental actions and for the verification of reversible serviceability limit states. Quasi-permanent values are also used for the calculation of long-term effects.

NOTE For loads on building floors, the quasi-permanent value is usually chosen so that the proportion of the time it is exceeded is 0,50 of the reference period. The quasi-permanent value can alternatively be determined as the value averaged over a chosen period of time. In the case of wind actions or road traffic loads, the quasi-permanent value is generally taken as zero.

Figure A provides a diagrammatical explanation. Note that representation of fatigue and dynamic actions is omitted.

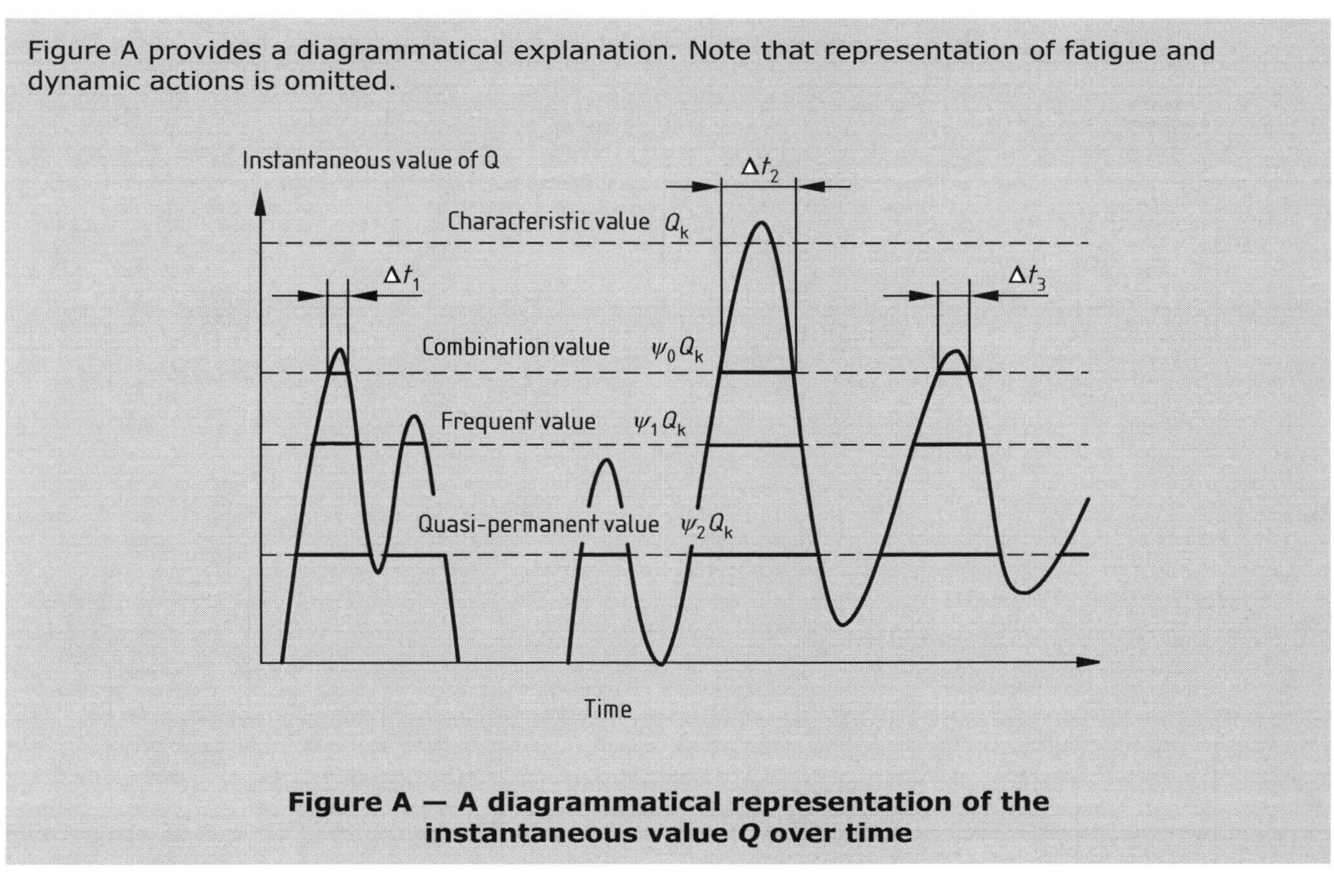

Figure A — A diagrammatical representation of the instantaneous value Q over time

4.2 Material and product properties

(1) Properties of materials (including soil and rock) or products should be represented by characteristic values (see 1.5.4.1).

(2) When a limit state verification is sensitive to the variability of a material property, upper and lower characteristic values of the material property should be taken into account.

(3) Unless otherwise stated in EN 1991 to EN 1999:

- where a low value of material or product property is unfavourable, the characteristic value should be defined as the 5% fractile value;
- where a high value of material or product property is unfavourable, the characteristic value should be defined as the 95% fractile value.

A detailed explanation of 4.2 and 4.3 is given in the *Designers' Handbook to EN 1990: Eurocode: Basis of Structural Design* [1].

4.3 Geometrical data

(1)P Geometrical data shall be represented by their characteristic values, or (e.g. the case of imperfections) directly by their design values.

(2) The dimensions specified in the design may be taken as characteristic values.

Section 5 Structural analysis and design assisted by testing

Very brief extracts are given in the following section, and the Sections on *Fire design* and *Design assisted by testing* are omitted.

5.1 Structural analysis

5.1.1 Structural modelling

(1)P Calculations shall be carried out using appropriate structural models involving relevant variables.

5.1.2 Static actions

(1)P The modelling for static actions shall be based on an appropriate choice of the force-deformation relationships of the members and their connections and between members and the ground.

5.1.3 Dynamic actions

(1)P The structural model to be used for determining the action effects shall be established taking account of all relevant structural members, their masses, strengths, stiffnesses and damping characteristics, and all relevant non structural members with their properties.

(3) When it is appropriate to consider dynamic actions as quasi-static, the dynamic parts may be considered either by including them in the static values or by applying equivalent dynamic amplification factors to the static actions.

NOTE For some equivalent dynamic amplification factors, the natural frequencies are determined.

Section 6 Verification by the partial factor method

6.1 General

(1)P When using the partial factor method, it shall be verified that, in all relevant design situations, no relevant limit state is exceeded when design values for actions or effects of actions and resistances are used in the design models.

(2) For the selected design situations and the relevant limit states the individual actions for the critical load cases should be combined as detailed in this section. However actions that cannot occur simultaneously, for example due to physical reasons, should not be considered together in combination.

(3) Design values should be obtained by using:
- the characteristic, or
- other representative values,
- in combination with partial and other factors as defined in this section and EN 1991 to EN 1999.

6.3 Design values

6.3.1 Design values of actions

(1) The design value F_d of an action F can be expressed in general terms as:

$$F_d = \gamma_f F_{rep} \qquad (6.1a)$$

with:

$$F_{rep} = \psi F_k \qquad (6.1b)$$

where:

F_k is the characteristic value of the action.

F_{rep} is the relevant representative value of the action.

γ_f is a partial factor for the action which takes account of the possibility of unfavourable deviations of the action values from the representative values.

ψ is either 1,00 or ψ_0, ψ_1 or ψ_2.

6.3.2 Design values of the effects of actions

(2) In most cases, the following simplification can be made:

$$E_d = E\left\{\gamma_{F,i} F_{rep,i}\,;\, a_d\right\} \qquad i \geq 1 \qquad (6.2a)$$

with:

$$\gamma_{F,i} = \gamma_{Sd} \times \gamma_{f,i} \qquad (6.2b)$$

where a_d is the design value of the geometric data

NOTE When relevant, e.g. where geotechnical actions are involved, partial factors $\gamma_{F,i}$ can be applied to the effects of individual actions or only one particular factor γ_F can be globally applied to the effect of the combination of actions with appropriate partial factors.

(3)P Where a distinction has to be made between favourable and unfavourable effects of permanent actions, two different partial factors shall be used ($\gamma_{G,inf}$ and $\gamma_{G,sup}$).

6.3.3 Design values of material or product properties

The following text simplifies and combines EN 1990, 6.3.3(1) and (2).

The design value X_d of a material or product property can be expressed as:

$X_d = X_k/\gamma_M$

where:

X_k is the characteristic value of the material or product property;

γ_M is the partial factor for the material or the product property to take account of the possibility of a unfavourable deviation from its characteristic value and model uncertainties.

6.3.4 Design values of geometrical data

(1) Design values of geometrical data such as dimensions of members that are used to assess action effects and/or resistances may be represented by nominal values:

$$a_d = a_{nom} \tag{6.4}$$

(3) Effects of other deviations should be covered by partial factors
- on the action side (γ_F), and/or
- resistance side (γ_M).

NOTE Tolerances are defined in the relevant standards on execution referred to in EN 1990 to EN 1999.

6.3.5 Design resistance

(3) Alternatively to expression (6.6a) the design resistance may be obtained directly from the characteristic value of a material or product resistance, without explicit determination of design values for individual basic variables, using :

$$R_d = \frac{R_k}{\gamma_M} \tag{6.6c}$$

NOTE This is applicable to products or members made of a single material (e.g. steel) and is also used in connection with Annex D "Design assisted by testing".

This expression is a simplification from the general case and is normally applicable to products or members of a single material (e.g. steel, timber). See EN 1990, 6.3.5 for the general expressions.

6.4 Ultimate limit states

6.4.1 General

(1)P The following ultimate limit states shall be verified as relevant:

a) EQU: Loss of static equilibrium of the structure or any part of it considered as a rigid body, where:

[AC2] – minor variations in the value or the spatial distribution of permanent actions from a single source are significant, and [AC2]

– the strengths of construction materials or ground are generally not governing;

b) STR: Internal failure or excessive deformation of the structure or structural members, including footings, piles, basement walls, etc., where the strength of construction materials of the structure governs;

c) GEO: Failure or excessive deformation of the ground where the strengths of soil or rock are significant in providing resistance;

d) FAT: Fatigue failure of the structure or structural members.

[AC2] NOTE For fatigue design, the combinations of actions are given in EN 1992 to EN 1995, EN 1998 and EN 1999.

e) UPL: loss of equilibrium of the structure or the ground due to uplift by water pressure (buoyancy) or other vertical actions;

NOTE See EN 1997.

f) HYD: hydraulic heave, internal erosion and piping in the ground caused by hydraulic gradients.

NOTE See EN 1997. [AC2]

The ultimate limit states EQU, STR and GEO are illustrated in Figure B.

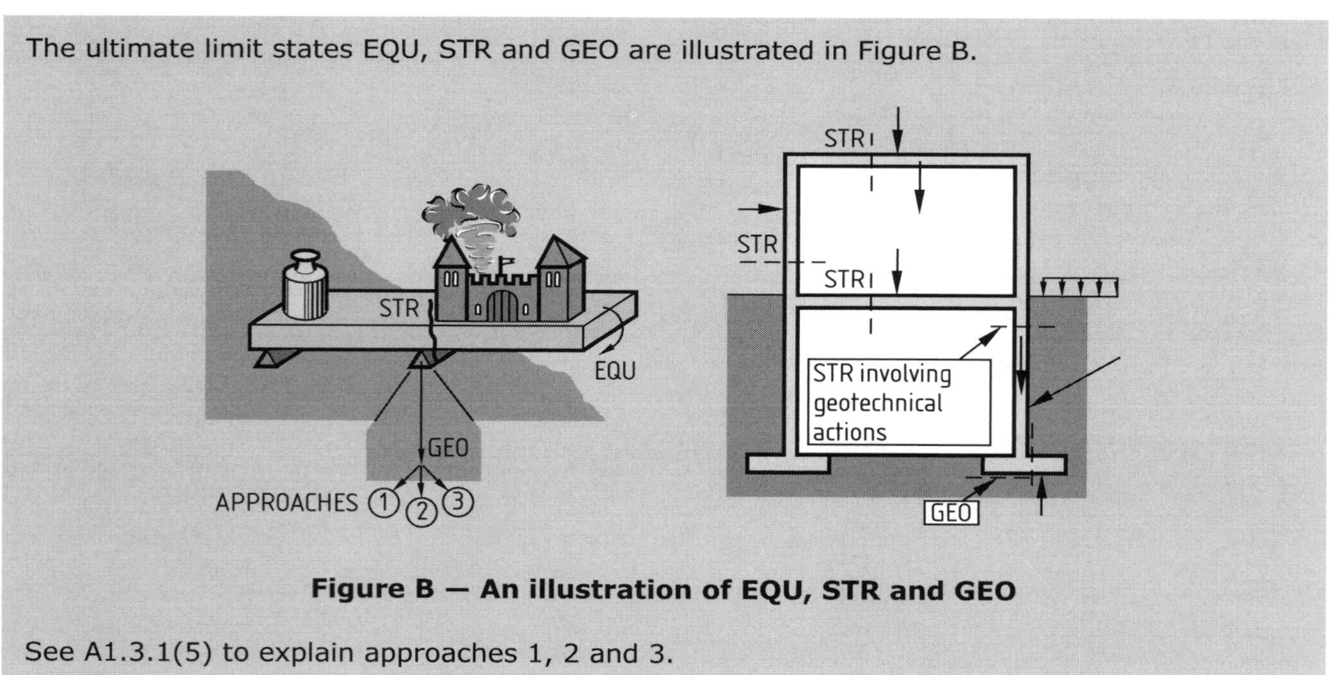

Figure B — An illustration of EQU, STR and GEO

See A1.3.1(5) to explain approaches 1, 2 and 3.

(2)P The design values of actions shall be in accordance with Annex A.

6.4.2 Verifications of static equilibrium and resistance

(1)P When considering a limit state of static equilibrium of the structure (EQU), it shall be verified that:

$$E_{d,dst} \leq E_{d,stb} \tag{6.7}$$

where:

$E_{d,dst}$ is the design value of the effect of destabilising actions;

$E_{d,stb}$ is the design value of the effect of stabilising actions.

(3)P When considering a limit state of rupture or excessive deformation of a section, member or connection (STR and/or GEO), it shall be verified that:

$$E_d \leq R_d \tag{6.8}$$

where:

E_d is the design value of the effect of actions such as internal force, moment or a vector representing several internal forces or moments;

R_d is the design value of the corresponding resistance.

NOTE 1 Details for the methods STR and GEO are given in Annex A.

NOTE 2 Expression (6.8) does not cover all verification formats concerning buckling, i.e. failure that happens where second order effects cannot be limited by the structural response, or by an acceptable structural response. See EN 1992 to EN 1999.

6.4.3 Combination of actions (fatigue verifications excluded)

6.4.3.1 General

(1)P For each critical load case, the design values of the effects of actions (E_d) shall be determined by combining the values of actions that are considered to occur simultaneously.

(2) Each combination of actions should include:
a leading variable action, or
an accidental action.

(3) The combinations of actions should be in accordance with 6.4.3.2 to 6.4.3.4.

(4)P Where the results of a verification are very sensitive to variations of the magnitude of a permanent action from place to place in the structure, the unfavourable and the favourable parts of this action shall be considered as individual actions.

NOTE This applies in particular to the verification of static equilibrium and analogous limit states, see 6.4.2(2).

6.4.3.2 Combinations of actions for persistent or transient design situations (fundamental combinations)

(2) The combination of effects of actions to be considered should be based on the design value of the leading variable action, and the design combination values of accompanying variable actions :

NOTE See also 6.4.3.2(4).

$$E_d = E\{\gamma_{G,j} G_{k,j} ; \gamma_P P ; \gamma_{Q,1} Q_{k,1} ; \gamma_{Q,i} \psi_{0,i} Q_{k,i}\} \qquad j \geq 1 ; i > 1 \tag{6.9b}$$

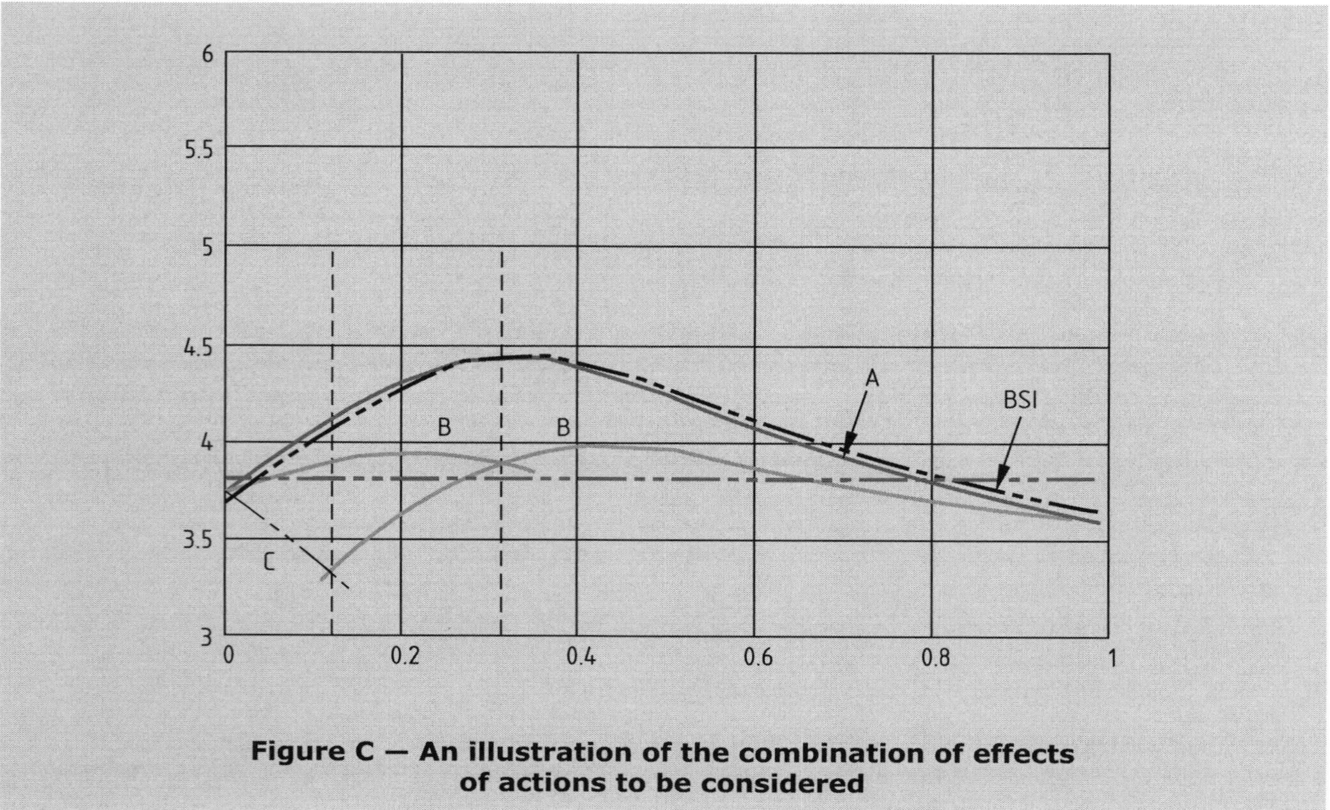

Figure C — An illustration of the combination of effects of actions to be considered

(3) The combination of actions in brackets { }, in 6.9b to determine E_d may either be expressed as:

$$\sum_{j\geq 1}\gamma_{G,j}G_{k,j}\ "+"\ \gamma_P P\ "+"\ \gamma_{Q,1}Q_{k,1}\ "+"\ \sum_{i>1}\gamma_{Q,i}\psi_{0,i}Q_{k,i} \qquad (6.10)$$

or, alternatively for STR and GEO limit states, the less favourable of the two following expressions:

$$\begin{cases}\sum_{j\geq 1}\gamma_{G,j}G_{k,j}\ "+"\ \gamma_P P\ "+"\ \gamma_{Q,1}\psi_{0,1}Q_{k,1}\ "+"\ \sum_{i>1}\gamma_{Q,i}\psi_{0,i}Q_{k,i} & (6.10a)\\ \sum_{j\geq 1}\xi_{G,j}G_{k,j}\ "+"\ \gamma_P P\ "+"\ \gamma_{Q,1}Q_{k,1}\ "+"\ \sum_{i>1}\gamma_{Q,i}\psi_{0,i}Q_{k,i} & (6.10b)\end{cases}$$

where:

"+" implies "to be combined with"
Σ implies "the combined effect of"
ξ is a reduction factor for unfavourable permanent actions *G*.

Figure C has been taken from a very comprehensive study that shows the differences in levels of safety when applying expression (6.10) or twin expressions (6.10a and 6.10b) and BSI Codes of Practice (e.g. BS 8110, BS 5950 and BS 5628). For EN 1990, combination rules A and B apply (γ_R = 1.15, γ_G = 1.35, γ_Q = 1.5), and for BSI, rules (γ_R = 1.10, γ_G = 1.4, γ_Q = 1.6) apply. For explanation of β (vertical axis) see EN 1990, C5. As an example, β = 3.8 is equivalent to a probability of failure of 1 in 10 000 over 50 years. χ is the ratio of the variable actions to the total load acting on a member. γ_R is the partial factor associated with resistance.

6.4.3.3 Combinations of actions for accidental design situations

(2) The combination of actions in brackets { } to determine E_d can be expressed as:

$$\sum_{j\geq 1} G_{k,j} \text{"+"} P \text{"+"} A_d \text{"+"} (\psi_{1,1} \text{ or } \psi_{2,1}) Q_{k,1} \text{"+"} \sum_{i>1} \psi_{2,i} Q_{k,i} \qquad (6.11b)$$

(3) The choice between $\psi_{1,1}Q_{k,1}$ or $\psi_{2,1}Q_{k,1}$ should be related to the relevant accidental design situation (impact, fire or survival after an accidental event or situation).

NOTE Guidance is given in the relevant Parts of EN 1991 to EN 1999.

Seismic design situations are not covered in this guide.

6.4.4 Partial factors for actions and combinations of actions

(1) The values of the γ and ψ factors for actions should be obtained from EN 1991 and from Annex A.

6.4.5 Partial factors for materials and products

(1) The partial factors for properties of materials and products should be obtained from EN 1992 to EN 1999.

6.5 Serviceability limit states

6.5.1 Verifications

(1)P It shall be verified that:

$$E_d \leq C_d \qquad (6.13)$$

where:

C_d is the limiting design value of the relevant serviceability criterion.

E_d is the design value of the effects of actions specified in the serviceability criterion, determined on the basis of the relevant combination.

6.5.2 Serviceability criteria

(1) The deformations to be taken into account in relation to serviceability requirements should be as detailed in the relevant Annex A according to the type of construction works, or agreed with the client or the National authority.

NOTE For other specific serviceability criteria such as crack width, stress or strain limitation, slip resistance, see EN 1991 to EN 1999.

6.5.3 Combination of actions

(1) The combinations of actions to be taken into account in the relevant design situations should be appropriate for the serviceability requirements and performance criteria being verified.

(2) The combinations of actions for serviceability limit states are defined symbolically by the following expressions (see also 6.5.4):

NOTE It is assumed, in these expressions, that all partial factors are equal to 1. See Annex A and EN 1991 to EN 1999.

a) Characteristic combination:

$$E_d = \{G_{k,j} ; P ; Q_{k,1} ; \psi_{0,i} Q_{k,1}\} \qquad j \geq 1 ; i > 1 \tag{6.14a}$$

in which the combination of actions in brackets { } to determine E_d (called the characteristic combination) can be expressed as:

$$\sum_{j \geq 1} G_{k,j} \text{"+"} P \text{"+"} Q_{k,1} \text{"+"} \sum_{i > 1} \psi_{0,i} Q_{k,i} \tag{6.14b}$$

NOTE The characteristic combination is normally used for irreversible limit states.

b) Frequent combination :

$$E_d = E\{G_{k,j} ; P ; \psi_{1,1} Q_{k,1} ; \psi_{2,i} Q_{k,1}\} \qquad j \geq 1 ; i > 1 \tag{6.15a}$$

in which the combination of actions in brackets { } to determine E_d (called the frequent combination) can be expressed as:

$$\sum_{j \geq 1} G_{k,j} \text{"+"} P \text{"+"} \psi_{1,1} Q_{k,1} \text{"+"} \sum_{i > 1} \psi_{2,i} Q_{k,i} \tag{6.15b}$$

NOTE The frequent combination is normally used for reversible limit states.

c) Quasi-permanent combination:

$$E_d = E\{G_{k,j} ; P ; \psi_{2,i} Q_{k,j}\} \qquad j \geq 1 ; i > 1 \tag{6.16a}$$

in which the combination of actions in brackets { } to determine E_d (called the quasi-permanent combination) can be expressed as:

$$\sum_{j \geq 1} G_{k,j} \text{"+"} P \text{"+"} \sum_{i \geq 1} \psi_{2,i} Q_{k,i} \tag{6.16b}$$

where the notation is as given in 1.6 and 6.4.3(1).

NOTE The quasi-permanent combination is normally used for long-term effects and the appearance of the structure.

6.5.4 Partial factors for materials

(1) For serviceability limit states the partial factors γ_M for the properties of materials should be taken as 1,0 except if differently specified in EN 1992 to EN 1999.

Annex A1 (normative) Application for Buildings

A1.1 Field of application

(1) This annex A1 gives rules and methods for establishing combinations of actions for buildings. It also gives the recommended design values of permanent, variable and accidental actions and ψ factors to be used in the design of buildings.

NOTE Guidance may be given in the National Annex with regard to the use of Table 2.1 (design working life).

NA.2.1 Nationally determined parameters for buildings and civil engineering works

NA.2.1.1 EN 1990 clause A.1.1 Field of Application

Table NA.2.1 Provides modified values for the design working life given in Table 2.1 of EN 1990.

[A1) NOTE The values of design working life in Table NA.2.1 are indicative. Alternative values of design working life may be determined for the individual project. (A1]

Table NA.2.1 — Indicative Design Working Life

Design working life category	Indicative design working life (years)	Examples
1	10	Temporary structures[a]
2	10 to 30	Replaceable structural parts, e.g. gantry girders, bearings
3	15 to 25	Agricultural and similar structures
4	50	Building structures and other common structures, not listed elsewhere in this table
5	120	Monumental building structures, highway and railway bridges, and other civil engineering structures

[a] Structures or parts of structures that can be dismantled with a view of being re-used should not be considered as temporary

A1.2 Combinations of actions

A1.2.1 General

(1) Effects of actions that cannot exist simultaneously due to physical or functional reasons should not be considered together in combinations of actions.

NOTE 1 Depending on its uses and the form and the location of a building, the combinations of actions may be based on not more than two variable actions.

NOTE 2 Where modifications of A1.2.1(2) and A1.2.1(3) are necessary for geographical reasons, these can be defined in the National Annex.

(2) The combinations of actions given in expressions (6.9a) to (6.12b) should be used when verifying ultimate limit states.

(3) The combinations of actions given in expressions (6.14a) to (6.16b) should be used when verifying serviceability limit states.

NA.2.2.1 Clause A.1.2.1 (1)

a) All effects of actions that can exist simultaneously should be considered together in combination of actions
b) With regard to Note 2 of clause A 1.2.1(1) of EN 1990 no modifications are allowed through the National Annex for A1.2.1 (2) and (3)

A1.2.2 Values of ψ factors

(1) Values of ψ factors should be specified.

[AC2) NOTE Recommended values of ψ factors for the more common actions may be obtained from Table A1.1. For ψ factors during execution see EN 1991-1-6 Annex A1. (AC2]

Table A1.1 — Recommended values of ψ factors for buildings

Action	ψ_0	ψ_1	ψ_2
Imposed loads in buildings, category (see EN 1991-1-1)			
Category A: domestic, residential areas	0,7	0,5	0,3
Category B: office areas	0,7	0,5	0,3
Category C: congregation areas	0,7	0,7	0,6
Category D: shopping areas	0,7	0,7	0,6
Category E: storage areas	1,0	0,9	0,8
Category F: traffic area, vehicle weight ≤ 30 kN	0,7	0,7	0,6
Category G: traffic area, 30 kN < vehicle weight ≤ 160 kN	0,7	0,5	0,3
Category H: roofs	0	0	0
Snow loads on buildings (see EN 1991-1-3)*			
Finland, Iceland, Norway, Sweden	0,70	0,50	0,20
Remainder of CEN Member States, for sites located at altitude H > 1000 m a.s.l.	0,70	0,50	0,20
Remainder of CEN Member States, for sites located at altitude H ≤ 1000 m a.s.l.	0,50	0,20	0
Wind loads on buildings (see EN 1991-1-4)	0,6	0,2	0
Temperature (non-fire) in buildings (see EN 1991-1-5)	0,6	0,5	0

NOTE The ψ values may be set by the National Annex.
* For countries not mentioned below, see relevant local conditions.

NA.2.2.2 Clause A.1.2.2

Table NA.A1.1 provides values for the symbols of Table A1.1 of EN 1990.

Table NA.A1.1 — Values of ψ factors for buildings

Action	ψ_0	ψ_1	ψ_2
Imposed loads in buildings, category (see EN 1991-1-1)			
Category A: domestic, residential areas	0,7	0,5	0,3
Category B: office areas	0,7	0,5	0,3
Category C: congregation areas	0,7	0,7	0,6
Category D: shopping areas	0,7	0,7	0,6
Category E: storage areas	1,0	0,9	0,8
Category F: traffic area, vehicle weight ≤ 30 kN	0,7	0,7	0,6
Category G: traffic area, 30 kN < vehicle weight ≤ 160 kN	0,7	0,5	0,3
Category H: roofs[a]	0,7	0	0
Snow loads on buildings (see EN 1991-3)			
— for sites located at altitude H > 1000 m a.s.l.	0,70	0,50	0,20
— for sites located at altitude H ≤ 1000 m a.s.l.	0,50	0,20	0
Wind loads on buildings (see EN 1991-1-4)	0,5	0,2	0
Temperature (non-fire) in buildings (see EN 1991-1-5)	0,6	0,5	0
[a] see also EN 1991-1-1: clause 3.3.2.(1)			

A1.3 Ultimate limit states

A1.3.1 Design values of actions in persistent and transient design situations

(1) The design values of actions for ultimate limit states in the persistent and transient design situations (expressions 6.9a to 6.10b) should be in accordance with Tables A1.2(A) to (C).

NOTE The values in Tables A1.2 ((A) to (C)) can be altered e.g. for different reliability levels in the National Annex (see Section 2 and Annex B).

(2) In applying Tables A1.2(A) to A1.2(C) in cases when the limit state is very sensitive to variations in the magnitude of permanent actions, the upper and lower characteristic values of actions should be taken according to 4.1.2(2)P.

(3) Static equilibrium (EQU, see 6.4.1) for building structures should be verified using the design values of actions in Table A1.2(A).

(4) Design of structural members (STR, see 6.4.1) not involving geotechnical actions should be verified using the design values of actions from Table A1.2(B).

(5) Design of structural members (footings, piles, basement walls, etc.) (STR) involving geotechnical actions and the resistance of the ground (GEO, see 6.4.1) should be verified using one of the following three approaches supplemented, for geotechnical actions and resistances, by EN 1997:

- Approach 1: Applying in separate calculations design values from Table A1.2(C) and Table A1.2(B) to the geotechnical actions as well as the other actions on/from the structure. In common cases, the sizing of foundations is governed by Table A1.2(C) and the structural resistance is governed by Table A1.2(B);

NOTE In some cases, application of these tables is more complex, see EN 1997.

- Approach 2: Applying design values from Table A1.2(B) to the geotechnical actions as well as the other actions on/from the structure;

- Approach 3: Applying design values from Table A1.2(C) to the geotechnical actions and, simultaneously, applying partial factors from Table A1.2(B) to the other actions on/from the structure.

NOTE The use of Approaches 1, 2 or 3 is chosen in the National Annex.

NA.2.2.4 Clause A.1.3.1 (5)

Approach 1 should be used for the design of buildings in the UK.

The National Annex to EN 1990 uses all the recommended values given in Tables A1.2(A), A1.2(B), (except ξ = 0.925 instead of 0.85), A1.2(C) and Table 1.3. For Table 1.2(B) both choices (i.e. either using expression (6.10) or expressions (6.10a) and (6.10b)) are given in this document as appropriate national authorities may use either.

Figure D explains Table A1.2(B), NOTE 3 in simple terms.

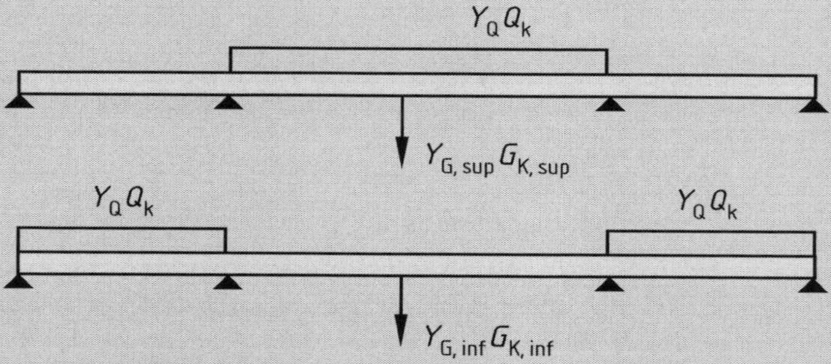

Figure D — A simple explanation of Table A1.2(*B*), NOTE 3

Considering verification using expression 6.10, the use of $\gamma_{G,sup}G_{K,sup}$ or $\gamma_{G,inf}G_{K,inf}$ and the load arrangements for permanent and variable actions are illustrated in Figure D.

In the top diagram all three spans are loaded with $\gamma_{G,sup}G_{K,sup}$, and in the lower diagram all three spans are loaded with $\gamma_{G,inf}G_{K,inf}$.

The top diagram will give the maximum sagging moment in the central span and the lower diagram will give the hogging moment in the central span. The top diagram with $\gamma_{G,inf}G_{K,inf}$ instead of $\gamma_{G,sup}G_{K,sup}$ will give the hogging moment in the end spans and the lower diagram with $\gamma_{G,sup}G_{K,sup}$ instead $\gamma_{G,inf}G_{K,inf}$ will give the sagging moment in the end spans.

Table A1.2(A) — Design values of actions (EQU) (Set A)

Persistent and transient design situations	Permanent actions		Leading variable action (*)	Accompanying variable actions	
	Unfavourable	Favourable		Main (if any)	Others
(Eq. 6.10)	$\gamma_{G,j,sup}G_{k,j,sup}$	$\gamma_{G,j,inf}G_{k,j,inf}$	$\gamma_{Q,1}\ Q_{k,1}$		$\gamma_{Q,i}\psi_{0,i}Q_{k,i}$

(*) Variable actions are those considered in Table A1.1

NOTE 1 The γ values may be set by the National Annex. The recommended set of values for γ are:

$\gamma_{G,j,sup} = 1{,}10$
$\gamma_{G,j,inf} = 0{,}90$
$\gamma_{Q,1} = 1{,}50$ where unfavourable (0 where favourable)
$\gamma_{Q,i} = 1{,}50$ where unfavourable (0 where favourable)

NOTE 2 In cases where the verification of static equilibrium also involves the resistance of structural members, as an alternative to two separate verifications based on Tables A1.2(A) and A1.2(B), a combined verification, based on Table A1.2(A), may be adopted, if allowed by the National Annex, with the following set of recommended values. The recommended values may be altered by the National Annex.

$\gamma_{G,j,sup} = 1{,}35$
$\gamma_{G,j,inf} = 1{,}15$
$\gamma_{Q,1} = 1{,}50$ where unfavourable (0 where favourable)
$\gamma_{Q,i} = 1{,}50$ where unfavourable (0 where favourable)

provided that applying $\gamma_{G,j,inf} = 1{,}00$ both to the favourable part and to the unfavourable part of permanent actions does not give a more unfavourable effect.

Table A1.2(B) — Design values of actions (STR/GEO) (Set B)

Persistent and transient design situations	Permanent actions		Leading variable action	Accompanying variable actions (*)	
	Unfavourable	Favourable		Main (if any)	Others
(Eq. 6.10)	$\gamma_{G,j,sup}G_{k,j,sup}$	$\gamma_{G,j,inf}G_{k,j,inf}$	$\gamma_{Q,1}Q_{k,1}$		$\gamma_{Q,i}\psi_{0,i}Q_{k,i}$

Persistent and transient design situations	Permanent actions		Leading variable action (*)	Accompanying variable actions (*)	
	Unfavourable	Favourable	Action	Main	Others
(Eq. 6.10a)	$\gamma_{G,j,sup}G_{k,j,sup}$	$\gamma_{G,j,inf}G_{k,j,inf}$		$\gamma_{Q,1}\psi_{0,1}Q_{k,1}$	$\gamma_{Q,i}\psi_{0,i}Q_{k,i}$
(Eq. 6.10b)	$\xi\gamma_{G,j,sup}G_{k,j,sup}$	$\gamma_{G,j,inf}G_{k,j,inf}$	$\gamma_{Q,1}Q_{k,1}$		$\gamma_{Q,i}\psi_{0,i}Q_{k,i}$

(*) Variable actions are those considered in Table A1.1

NOTE 1 The choice between (6.10), or (6.10a) and (6.10b) will be in the National Annex. In case of (6.10a) and (6.10b), the National Annex may in addition modify (6.10a) to include permanent actions only.

NOTE 2 The γ and ξ values may be set by the National Annex. The following values for γ and ξ are recommended when using expressions (6.10), or (6.10a) and (6.10b).
$\gamma_{G,j,sup}$ = 1,35
$\gamma_{G,j,inf}$ = 1,00
$\gamma_{Q,1}$ = 1,50 where unfavourable (0 where favourable)
$\gamma_{Q,i}$ = 1,50 where unfavourable (0 where favourable)
ξ = 0,85 (so that $\xi\gamma_{G,j,sup}$ = 0,85 × 1,35 ≅ 1,15). In the BSI National Annex, ξ = 0.925.
See also EN 1991 to EN 1999 for γ values to be used for imposed deformations.

NOTE 3 The characteristic values of all permanent actions from one source are multiplied by $\gamma_{G,sup}$ if the total resulting action effect is unfavourable and $\gamma_{G,inf}$ if the total resulting action effect is favourable. For example, all actions originating from the self weight of the structure may be considered as coming from one source; this also applies if different materials are involved.

Table A1.2(C) — Design values of actions (STR/GEO) (Set C)

Persistent and transient design situations	Permanent actions		Leading variable action (*)	Accompanying variable actions	
	Unfavourable	Favourable		Main (if any)	Others
(Eq. 6.10)	$\gamma_{G,j,sup} G_{k,j,sup}$	$\gamma_{G,j,inf} G_{k,j,inf}$	$\gamma_{Q,1}\ Q_{k,1}$		$\gamma_{Q,i} \psi_{0,i} Q_{k,i}$

(*) Variable actions are those considered in Table A1.1

NOTE The γ values may be set by the National Annex. The recommended set of values for γ are:

$\gamma_{G,j,sup}$ = 1,00
$\gamma_{G,j,inf}$ = 1,00
$\gamma_{Q,1}$ = 1,30 where unfavourable (0 where favourable)
$\gamma_{Q,i}$ = 1,30 where unfavourable (0 where favourable)

NA.2.2.3 Clause A.1.3

NA.2.2.3.1 Values for the symbols γ of Table A1.2(A)

Table NA.A1.2 (A) provides the values for the symbols γ of Table A1.2(A). The values chosen are:

$\gamma_{G,j,sup}$ = 1,10
$\gamma_{G,j,inf}$ = 0,90
$\gamma_{Q,1}$ = 1,50 where unfavourable (0 where favourable)
$\gamma_{Q,i}$ = 1,50 where unfavourable (0 where favourable)

NOTE For ψ values see Table A1.1(BS)

Table NA.A1.2 (A) — Design values of actions (EQU) (Set A)

Persistent and transient design situations	Permanent actions		Leading variable action[a]	Accompanying variable actions	
	Unfavourable	Favourable		Main (if any)	Others
(Exp. 6.10)	1,10 $G_{k,j,sup}$	0,90 $G_{k,j,inf}$	1,50 $Q_{k,1}$ (0 where favourable)		1,50 $\psi_{0,i} Q_{k,I}$ (0 where favourable)

[a] Variable actions are those considered in Table A1.1

In cases where the verification of static equilibrium also involves the resistance of structural members, as an alternative to two separate verifications based on Tables NA.A1.2 (A) and A1.2 (B), a combined verification, based on Table NA.A1.2(A), should be adopted, with the following set of values.

$\gamma_{G,j,sup}$ = 1,35
$\gamma_{G,j,inf}$ = 1,15
$\gamma_{Q,1}$ = 1,50 where unfavourable (0 where favourable)
$\gamma_{Q,i}$ = 1,50 where unfavourable (0 where favourable)
provided that applying $\gamma_{G,j,inf}$ = 1,00 both to the favourable part and to the unfavourable part of permanent actions does not give a more unfavourable effect.

NA.2.2.3.2 Values for the symbols γ and ξ of Table A1.2(B)

Table NA.A1.2 (B) provides the values for the symbols γ and ξ of Table A1.2 (B). The values chosen are:

$\gamma_{G,j,sup}$ = 1,35
$\gamma_{G,j,inf}$ = 1,00
$\gamma_{Q,1}$ = 1,50 where unfavourable (0 where favourable)
$\gamma_{Q,i}$ = 1,50 where unfavourable (0 where favourable)
ξ = 0,925

NOTE For ψ values see Table NA.A1.1

Table NA. A1.2(B) — Design values of actions (STR/GEO) (Set B)

Persistent and transient design situations	Permanent actions		Leading variable action	Accompanying variable actions[a]	
	Unfavourable	Favourable		Main (if any)	Others
(Exp. 6.10)	1,35 $G_{k,j,sup}$	1,00 $G_{k,j,inf}$	1,5 $Q_{k,1}$		1,5 $\psi_{0,I}Q_{k,i}$

Persistent and transient design situations	Permanent actions		Leading variable action[a]	Accompanying variable actions[a]	
	Unfavourable	Favourable	Action	Main	Others
(Exp. 6.10a)	1,35 $G_{k,j,sup}$	1,00 $G_{k,j,inf}$		1,5 $\psi_{0,1}Q_{k,1}$	1,5 $\psi_{0,i}Q_{k,i}$
(Eq. 6.10b)	0,925*1,35 $G_{k,j,sup}$	1,00 $G_{k,j,inf}$	1,5 $Q_{k,1}$		1,5 $\psi_{0,i}Q_{k,i}$

NOTE 1 Either expression 6.10, or expression 6.10a together with and 6.10b may be made, as desired.

NOTE 3 The characteristic values of all permanent actions from one source are multiplied by $\gamma_{G,sup}$ if the total resulting action effect is unfavourable and $\gamma_{G,inf}$ if the total resulting action effect is favourable. For example, all actions originating from the self weight of the structure may be considered as coming from one source; this also applies if different materials are involved.

NOTE 4 For particular verifications, the values for γ_G and γ_Q may be subdivided into γ_g and γ_q and the model uncertainty factor γ_{Sd}. A value of γ_{Sd} in the range 1,05 to 1,15 can be used in most common cases and can be modified in the National Annex

NOTE 5 When variable actions are favourable Q_k should be taken as 0.

[a] Variable actions are those considered in Table NA.A1.1

NA.2.2.3.3 Values for the symbols γ of Table A1.2(C)

Table NA.A1.2(C) provides the values for the symbols γ of Table A1.2(C). The values chosen are:

$\gamma_{G,j,sup}$ = 1,00
$\gamma_{G,j,inf}$ = 1,00
$\gamma_{Q,1}$ = 1,30 where unfavourable (0 where favourable)
$\gamma_{Q,i}$ = 1,30 where unfavourable (0 where favourable)

NOTE For ψ values see Table NA.A1.1

Table NA.A1.2(C) — Design values of actions (STR/GEO) (Set C)

Persistent and transient design situation	Permanent actions		Leading variable action[a]	Accompanying variable actions[a]	
	Unfavourable	Favourable		Main (if any)	Others
(Eq. 6.10)	1,0 $G_{k,j,sup}$	1,0 $G_{k,j,inf}$	1,3 $Q_{k,1}$ (0 where favourable)		1,3 $\psi_{0,i}Q_{k,I}$ (0 where favourable)

[a] Variable actions are those considered in Table NA.A1.1

A1.3.2 Design values of actions in the accidental design situations

(1) The partial factors for actions for the ultimate limit states in the accidental design situations (expressions 6.11a) should be 1,0. ψ values are given in Table A1.1.

NOTE For the seismic design situation see also EN 1998.

AC2 Table A1.3 — Design values of actions for use in accidental and seismic combinations of actions

Design situation	Permanent actions		Leading accidental or seismic action	Accompanying variable actions (**)	
	Unfavourable	Favourable		Main (if any)	Others
Accidental (*) (Eq. 6.11a/b)	$G_{k,j,sup}$	$G_{k,j,inf}$	A_d	$\psi_{1,1}$ or $\psi_{2,1}Q_{k,1}$	$\psi_{2,i}\ Q_{k,i}$
Seismic (Eq. 6.12a/b)	$G_{k,j,sup}$	$G_{k,j,inf}$	$A_{Ed} = \gamma_1 A_{Ek}$		$\psi_{2,i}\ Q_{k,i}$

(*) In the case of accidental design situations, the main variable action may be taken with its frequent or, as in seismic combinations of actions, its quasi-permanent values. The choice will be in the National Annex, depending on the accidental action under consideration. See also EN 1991-1-2.

(**) Variable actions are those considered in Table A1.1.

NA.2.2.5 Clause A.1.3.2

Table NA.A1.3 provides the values for the symbols of Table A1.3 of EN 1990. All γ factors are equal to 1,00. Coefficient ψ_{11} is selected for the main accompanying variable action for the accidental design situation.

NOTE For ψ values see Table NA. A1.1

Table NA.A1.3 — Design values of actions for use in accidental and seismic combinations of actions

Design situation	Permanent actions		Leading accidental or seismic action	Accompanying variable actions[b]	
	Unfavourable	Favourable		Main (if any)	Others
Accidental (Eq. 6.11a/b)	$G_{k,j,sup}$	$G_{k,j,inf}$	A_d	$\psi_{11}\ Q_{k1}$	$\psi_{2,i}\ Q_{k,i}$
Seismic[a] (Eq. 6.12a/b)	$G_{k,j,sup}$	$G_{k,j,inf}$	$\gamma_I A_{Ek}$ or A_{Ed}		$\psi_{2,i}\ Q_{k,i}$

[a] The seismic design situation should be used only when specified by the client. See also Eurocode 8

[b] Variable actions are those considered in Table NA.A1.1.

A1.4 Serviceability limit states

A1.4.1 Partial factors for actions

(1) For serviceability limit states the partial factors for actions should be taken as 1,0 except if differently specified in EN 1991 to EN 1999.

Table A1.4 — Design values of actions for use in the combination of actions

Combination	Permanent actions G_d		Variable actions Q_d	
	Unfavourable	Favourable	Leading	Others
Characteristic	$G_{k,j,sup}$	$G_{k,j,inf}$	$Q_{k,1}$	$\psi_{0,i}Q_{k,i}$
Frequent	$G_{k,j,sup}$	$G_{k,j,inf}$	$\psi_{1,1}Q_{k,1}$	$\psi_{2,i}Q_{k,i}$
Quasi-permanent	$G_{k,j,sup}$	$G_{k,j,inf}$	$\psi_{2,1}Q_{k,1}$	$\psi_{2,i}Q_{k,i}$

A1.4.2 Serviceability criteria

(1) Serviceability limit states in buildings should take into account criteria related, for example, to floor stiffness, differential floor levels, storey sway or/and building sway and roof stiffness. Stiffness criteria may be expressed in terms of limits for vertical deflections and for vibrations. Sway criteria may be expressed in terms of limits for horizontal displacements.

(2) The serviceability criteria should be specified for each project and agreed with the client.

NOTE The serviceability criteria may be defined in the National Annex.

(3)P The serviceability criteria for deformations and vibrations shall be defined:
- depending on the intended use;
- in relation to the serviceability requirements in accordance with 3.4;
- independently of the materials used for supporting structural member.

NA.2.2.6 Clause A1.4.2

Clause A1.4.2 of EN 1990, states that the serviceability criteria should be specified for each project and agreed with the client. In the absence of specific requirements in EN 1992 to EN 1999 or their National Annexes it is recommended that the following Combination of Action expressions are used with particular serviceability requirements.

- For function and damage to structural and non-structural elements (e.g. partition walls etc) the characteristic combination (i.e. expression 6.14b of EN 1990).
- For comfort to user, use of machinery, avoiding ponding of water etc the frequent combination (i.e. expression 6.15b of EN 1990).
- For appearance of the structure the quasi-permanent combination (i.e. expression 6.15c of EN 1990).

Separate consideration should be given to serviceability related to appearance and that related to user comfort which may be affected by structural deformation or vibration.

Nationally determined parameters for Basis of Design information for other planned annexes to EN 1990 (e.g. cranes and machinery, silos and tanks, towers and masts) will be provided when these annexes are incorporated into EN 1990.

A1.4.3 Deformations and horizontal displacements

(1) Vertical and horizontal deformations should be calculated in accordance with EN 1992 to EN 1999, by using the appropriate combinations of actions according to expressions (6.14a) to (6.16b) taking into account the serviceability requirements given in 3.4(1). Special attention should be given to the distinction between reversible and irreversible limit states.

(2) Vertical deflections are represented schematically in Figure A1.1.

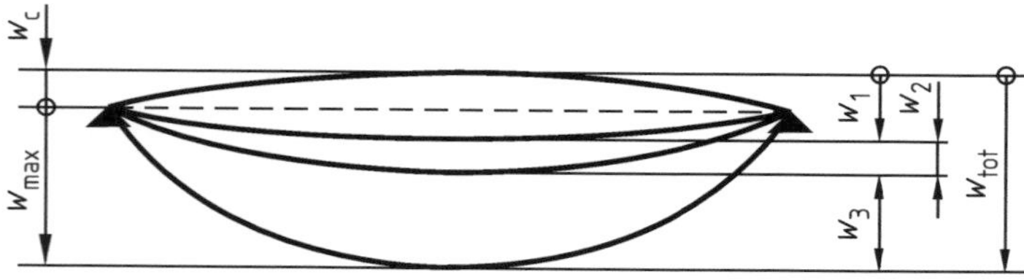

Figure A1.1 — Definitions of vertical deflections

Key :

w_c Precamber in the unloaded structural member

w_1 Initial part of the deflection under permanent loads of the relevant combination of actions according to expressions (6.14a) to (6.16b)

w_2 Long-term part of the deflection under permanent loads

w_3 Additional part of the deflection due to the variable actions of the relevant combination of actions according to expressions (6.14a) to (6.16b)

w_{tot} Total deflection as sum of w_1 , w_2 , w_3

w_{max} Remaining total deflection taking into account the precamber

(3) If the functioning or damage of the structure or to finishes, or to non-structural members (e.g. partition walls, claddings) is being considered, the verification for deflection should take account of those effects of permanent and variable actions that occur after the execution of the member or finish concerned.

NOTE Guidance on which expression (6.14a) to (6.16b) to use is given in 6.5.3 and EN 1992 to EN 1999.

(4) If the appearance of the structure is being considered, the quasi-permanent combination (expression 6.16b) should be used.

(5) If the comfort of the user, or the functioning of machinery are being considered, the verification should take account of the effects of the relevant variable actions.

(6) Long term deformations due to shrinkage, relaxation or creep should be considered where relevant, and calculated by using the effects of the permanent actions and quasi-permanent values of the variable actions.

(7) Horizontal displacements are represented schematically in Figure A1.2.

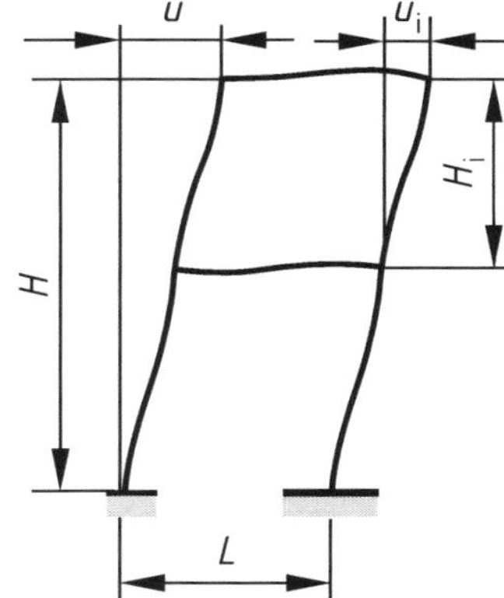

Figure A1.2 — Definition of horizontal displacements

Key:

u Overall horizontal displacement over the building height H
u_i Horizontal displacement over a storey height H_i

A1.4.4 Vibrations

(1) To achieve satisfactory vibration behaviour of buildings and their structural members under serviceability conditions, the following aspects, amongst others, should be considered:

a) the comfort of the user;
b) the functioning of the structure or its structural members (e.g. cracks in partitions, damage to cladding, sensitivity of building contents to vibrations).

Other aspects should be considered for each project and agreed with the client.

Bibliography

ISO 2394	General principles on reliability for structures
ISO 2631:1997	Mechanical vibration and shock – Evaluation of human exposure to whole-body vibration
ISO 3898	Basis for design of structures – Notations – General symbols
ISO 6707-1	Building and civil engineering – Vocabulary – Part 1: General terms
ISO 8930	General principles on reliability for structures – List of equivalent terms
EN ISO 9001:2000	Quality management systems – Requirements (ISO 9001:2000)
ISO 10137	Basis for design of structures – Serviceability of buildings against vibrations
ISO 8402	Quality management and quality assurance – Vocabulary

[A1) Bibliography

BS EN 1991 (all parts), *Eurocode 1 – Actions on structures*

BS EN 1997-1:2004, *Eurocode 7 – Geotechnical design – Part 1: General rules*

NA to BS EN 1991-1-1:2002, *UK National Annex to Eurocode 1 – Actions on structures – Part 1-1: General actions – Densities, self-weight, imposed loads for buildings*

NA to BS EN 1991-1-3, *UK National Annex to Eurocode 1 – Actions on structures – Part 1-3: General actions – Snow loads*

NA to BS EN 1991-1-4:2005, *UK National Annex to Eurocode 1 – Actions on structures – Part 1-4: General actions – Wind actions*

NA to BS EN 1991-1-5:2003, *UK National Annex to Eurocode 1 – Actions on structures – Part 1-5: General actions – Thermal actions*

NA to BS EN 1991-1-6:2005, *UK National Annex to Eurocode 1 – Actions on structures – Part 1-6: General actions – Actions during execution*

NA to BS EN 1991-2:2003, *UK National Annex to Eurocode 1 – Actions on structures – Part 2: Traffic loads on bridges*

NA to BS EN 1997-1:2004, *UK National Annex to Eurocode 7 – Geotechnical design – Part 1: General rules* (A1]

Useful references

[1] Gulvanessian H, Calgaro J A, Holicky M, *Designer's Handbook to EN 1990: Eurocode Basis of Structural Design*. London, England: Thomas Telford Publications; 2002.

Chapter 1 — Extracts from Eurocode 1: Actions on structures

The Eurocode extracts in this chapter are taken from:

EN 1991-1-1:2002 (incorporating corrigendum No 1 and corrigendum No 2 March 2009), *Eurocode 1: Actions on structures — Part 1-1: General actions — Densities, self-weight, imposed loads for buildings*;

EN 1991-1-3:2003 (incorporating corrigenda December 2004 and March 2009), *Eurocode 1: Actions on structures — Part 1-3: General actions — Snow loads*;

and EN 1991-1-4:2005 (incorporating corrigendum July 2009), *Eurocode 1: Actions on structures — Part 1-4: General actions — Wind actions.*

The National Annex extracts are taken from:

NA to BS EN 1991-1-1:2002, *UK National Annex to Eurocode 1: Actions on structures — Part 1-1: General actions — Densities, self-weight, imposed loads for buildings*

NA to BS EN 1991-1-3:2003 (Incorporating corrigendum No 1), *UK National Annex to Eurocode 1: Actions on structures — Part 1-3: General actions — Snow loads*

NA to BS EN 1991-1-4:2005, *UK National Annex to Eurocode 1 — Actions on structures — Part 1-4: General actions — Wind actions*

Extracts from EN 1991-1-1

The extracts in this part of Chapter 1 are taken from EN 1991-1-1:2002 (incorporating corrigendum No 1 and corrigendum No 2 March 2009), *Eurocode 1: Actions on structures — Part 1-1: General actions — Densities, self-weight, imposed loads for buildings.*

Text altered by CEN corrigendum March 2009 is indicated in the text by [AC1) (AC1].

The full list of the contents of EN 1991-1-1 follows, and is given for reference purposes. (Bold items are included in this chapter.)

Section 3 Design situations
3.1 General
3.2 Permanent loads
3.3 Imposed loads
3.3.1 General
3.3.2 Additional provisions for buildings
Section 4 Densities of construction and stored materials
4.1 General
Section 5 Self-weight of construction works
5.1 Representation of actions
5.2 Characteristic values of self-weight
5.2.1 General
5.2.2 Additional provisions for buildings
5.2.3 Additional provisions specific for bridges
Section 6 Imposed loads on buildings
6.1 Representation of actions
6.2 Load arrangements
6.2.1 Floors, beams and roofs
6.2.2 Columns and walls
6.3 Characteristic values of Imposed Loads
6.3.1 Residential, social, commercial and administration areas
6.3.1.1 Categories
6.3.1.2 Values of actions
6.3.2 Areas for storage and industrial activities
6.3.2.1 Categories
6.3.2.2 Values for Actions
6.3.2.3 Actions induced by forklifts
6.3.2.4 Actions induced by transport vehicles
6.3.2.5 Actions induced by special devices for maintenance
6.3.3 Garages and vehicle traffic areas (excluding bridges)
6.3.3.1 Categories
6.3.3.2 Values of actions
6.3.4 Roofs
6.3.4.1 Categories
6.3.4.2 Values of actions
6.4 Horizontal loads on parapets and partition walls acting as barriers
Loaded areas
Annex A (informative) Tables for nominal density of construction materials, and nominal density and angles of repose for stored materials
Annex B (informative) Vehicle barriers and parapets for car parks

Foreword

Additional information specific for EN 1991-1-1

EN 1991-1-1 gives design guidance and actions for the structural design of buildings and civil engineering works, including the following aspects:

- densities of construction materials and stored materials;
- self-weight of construction elements; and
- imposed loads for buildings.

EN 1991-1-1 is intended for clients, designers, contractors and public authorities. EN 1991-1-1 is intended to be used with EN 1990, the other Parts of EN 1991 and EN 1992 to EN 1999 for the design of structures.

See Chapter 0 – Extracts from Eurocode: Basis of structural design.

The following text is a brief summary of the scope and field of application for the Parts of Eurocode 1 that are outside the scope of this guide.

EN 1991-1-2, *Actions on structures exposed to fire*

EN 1991-1-2 covers the actions to be used in the structural design of buildings and civil engineering works where they are required to give adequate performance in fire exposure. It is intended for use with EN 1990 and with the Parts on structural fire design in Eurocodes 2 to 6 and 9. For fire design, fire actions are the dominant action.

EN 1991-1-5, *Thermal actions*

EN 1991-1-5 gives principles, rules and methods of calculating thermal actions on buildings, bridges and other structures including their structural components. Principles for determining thermal actions for claddings and other appendages on the building are also provided.

Characteristic values of thermal actions are provided for the design of structures which are exposed to daily and seasonal climatic changes. Structures in which thermal actions are mainly a function of their use (e.g. chimneys, cooling towers, silos, tanks, warm and cold storage facilities, hot and cold services) are also treated. The characteristic values of isotherms of national minimum and maximum shade air temperatures are provided in the form of maps or in other forms.

EN 1991-1-6, *Actions during execution*

EN 1991-1-6 covers assessment of actions, combinations of actions and environmental influences during the execution stage, including those actions applied to auxiliary construction works, e.g. scaffolding, propping and bracing, for use in structural design of buildings and bridges. The safety of people on construction sites is not within the scope of this Eurocode.

EN 1991-1-7, *Accidental actions*

EN 1991-1-7 describes safety strategies for accidental design situations. It recommends design values for the most common cases of accidental actions from impact and explosion; it gives design models and also detailing provisions which may be used as alternatives to design verifications. It also provides more advanced impact and explosion design concepts.

External explosion, warfare, sabotage or actions due to natural phenomena such as tornadoes, extreme erosion or rock falls are not in the scope of the Eurocode.

EN 1991-2, *Traffic loads on bridges*

EN 1991-2 specifies imposed loads (models and representative values) associated with road traffic, pedestrian actions and rail traffic that include, when relevant, dynamic effects and centrifugal, braking, acceleration and accidental forces. It also includes guidance on combinations with non-traffic loads on road and railway bridges, and on loads on parapets. Actions for the design of road bridges with individual spans less than 200 m and with carriageway widths not greater than 42 m are defined.

EN 1991-3, *Actions induced by cranes and machinery*

EN 1991-3 specifies actions, self-weights and imposed loads (models and representative values) associated with hoists, crabs and cranes on runway beams and static and dynamic actions induced in supporting structures by machinery.

EN 1991-4, *Actions in silos and tanks*

EN 1991-4 gives general principles and rules for determining actions arising from the storage of bulk materials and liquids in silos and tanks. The scope is restricted to:

- silos with limited eccentricity of inlet and outlet, with small impact effects caused by filling, and with discharge devices which do not cause shock or eccentricities beyond the given limitations;
- silos containing particulate materials which are free-flowing and have a low cohesion;
- tanks with liquids stored at normal atmospheric pressure.

Section 1 General

1.1 Scope

The scope of EN 1991-1-1 is given in full. (Bold items are covered in this chapter.)

(1) EN 1991-1-1 gives design guidance and actions for the structural design of buildings and civil engineering works including some geotechnical aspects for the following subjects:
- **Densities of construction materials and stored materials;**
- **Self-weight of construction works;**
- **Imposed loads for buildings.**

(2) Section 4 and Annex A give nominal values for densities of specific building materials, additional materials for bridges and stored materials. In addition for specific materials the angle of repose is provided.

(3) Section 5 provides methods for the assessment of the characteristic values of self-weight of construction works.

(4) Section 6 gives characteristic values of imposed loads for floors and roofs according to category of use in the following areas in buildings:
- **residential, social, commercial and administration areas;**
- **garage and vehicle traffic areas;**
- **areas for storage and industrial activities;**
- **roofs;**
- **helicopter landing areas.**

(5) The loads on traffic areas given in Section 6 refer to vehicles up to a gross vehicle weight of 160 kN. The design for traffic areas for heavy vehicles of more than 160 kN gross weight needs to be agreed with the relevant authority. Further information may be obtained from EN 1991-2.

(6) For barriers or walls having the function of barriers, horizontal forces are given in Section 6. Annex B gives additional guidance for vehicle barriers in car parks.

NOTE Forces due to vehicle impact are specified in EN 1991-1-7 and EN 1991-2.

(7) For the design situations and effects of actions in silos and tanks caused by water or other materials see EN 1991-3.

1.3 Distinction between principles and application rules

See Chapter 0 – Extracts from Eurocode: Basis of structural design.

1.4 Terms and definitions

For the purposes of this European Standard, the terms and definitions given in ISO 2394, ISO 3898, ISO 8930 and the following apply. Additionally, for the purposes of this standard a basic list of terms and definitions is provided in EN 1990, 1.5.

1.4.1
bulk weight density
the bulk weight density is the overall weight per unit volume of a material, including a normal distribution of micro-voids, voids and pores

NOTE In everyday usage this term is frequently abbreviated to "density" (which is strictly mass per unit volume).

1.4.2
angle of repose
the angle of repose is the angle which the natural slope of the sides of a heaped pile of loose material makes to the horizontal

1.4.3
gross weight of vehicle
the gross weight of a vehicle includes the self-weight of the vehicle together with the maximum weight of the goods it is permitted to carry

1.4.4
structural elements
structural elements comprise the primary structural frame and supporting structures. For bridges, structural elements comprise girders, structural slabs and elements providing support such as cable stays

1.4.5
non-structural elements
non structural elements are those that include completion and finishing elements connected with the structure, including road surfacing and non-structural parapets. They also include services and machinery fixed permanently to, or within, the structure

1.4.6
partitions
non load bearing walls

1.4.7
movable partitions
movable partitions are those which can be moved on the floor, be added or removed or re-built at another place

1.5 Symbols

(1) For the purposes of this European standard, the following symbols apply.

NOTE The notation used is based on ISO 3898: 1997.

(2) A basic list of symbols is provided in EN 1990 clause 1.6 and the additional notations below are specific to this part of EN 1991.

Latin upper case letters

A	Loaded area
A_0	Basic area
Q_k	Characteristic value of a variable concentrated load

Latin lower case letters

g_k	Weight per unit area, or weight per unit length
n	Number of storeys
q_k	Characteristic value of a uniformly distributed load, or line load

Lower case Greek letters

α_A	Reduction factor
α_n	Reduction factor
γ	Bulk weight density
φ	Dynamic magnification factor
ψ_0	Factor for combination value of a variable action, see Table A.1.1 of EN 1990
ϕ	Angle of repose (degrees)

Section 2 Classification of actions

2.1 Self-weight

(1) The self-weight of construction works should be classified as a permanent fixed action, see EN 1990, 1.5.3 and 4.1.1.

(4)P The earth loads on roofs and terraces shall be considered as permanent actions.

(5) With regard to 2.1(4)P, the design should consider variations in moisture content and variation in depth, that may be caused by uncontrolled accumulation during the design life of the structure.

NOTE For detailed information on earth pressures see EN 1997.

Where there is doubt as to the permanency of an action, the action should be treated as an imposed load. This applies in particular when the effect of the permanent action is favourable.

2.2 Imposed loads

(1)P Imposed loads shall be classified as variable free actions, unless otherwise specified in this standard, see EN 1990, 1.5.3 and 4.1.1.

NOTE For imposed loads on bridges see EN 1991-2.

Section 3 Design situations

3.1 General

(1)P The relevant permanent and imposed loads shall be determined for each design situation identified in accordance with EN 1990, 3.2.

3.2 Permanent loads

(1) The total self-weight of structural and non-structural members should be taken into account in combinations of actions as a single action.

See Chapter 0, Table A1.2(B), Note 3. (Page 0-36)

(2) For areas where it is intended to remove or add structural or non-structural elements, the critical load cases should be taken into account in the design.

(3) The self-weight of new coatings and/or distribution conduits that are intended to be added after execution should be taken into account in design situations (see 5.2).

(5) The source and moisture content of bulk materials should be considered in design situations of buildings used for storage purposes.

NOTE The values for the densities provided in Annex A are for materials in the dry state.

3.3 Imposed loads

3.3.1 General

(1)P For areas which are intended to be subjected to different categories of loadings the design shall consider the most critical load case.

(2)P In design situations when imposed loads act simultaneously with other variable actions (e.g actions induced by wind, snow, cranes or machinery), the total imposed loads considered in the load case shall be considered as a single action.

3.3.2 Additional provisions for buildings

[AC1) (1) On roofs (particularly for category H roofs), imposed loads need not be applied in combination with either snowloads and/or wind actions. (AC1]

(2)P When the imposed load is considered as an accompanying action, in accordance with EN 1990, only one of the two factors ψ (EN 1990, Table A1.1) and α_n (6.3.1.2 (11)) shall be applied.

(4) The imposed loads to be considered for serviceability limit state verifications should be specified in accordance with the service conditions and the requirements concerning the performance of the structure.

Section 4 Densities of construction and stored materials

4.1 General

(1) Characteristic values of densities of construction and stored materials should be specified. Mean values should be used as characteristic values. See however 4.1(2) and 4.1(3).

NOTE Annex A gives mean values for densities and angles of repose for stored materials. When a range is given it is assumed that the mean value will be highly dependent on the source of the material and may be selected considering each individual project.

The following tables are extracts from tables in Annex A of EN 1991-1-1 for key construction materials.

Table A.1 — Construction materials-concrete and mortar

Materials	**Density** γ **[kN/m³]**
concrete	
lightweight	
density class LC 1,6	14,0 to 16,0[1)2)]
normal weight	24,0[1)2)]

[1)] Increase by 1 kN/m³ for normal percentage of reinforcing and pre-stressing steel.
[2)] Increase by 1 kN/m³ for unhardened concrete.

Table A.2 — Construction materials-masonry

Materials	**Density** γ **[kN/m³]**
masonry units	
clay masonry units	see EN 771-1
aggregate concrete masonry units	see EN 771-3
autoclaved aerated masonry units	see EN 771-4

Table A.3 — Construction materials-wood

Materials	Density γ [kN/m^3]
wood	
timber strength class C16	3,7
timber strength class C24	4,2
glued laminated timber	
homogeneous glulam GL28h	4,0
combined glulam GL28c	3,7
plywood	
softwood plywood	5,0
birch plywood	7,0
particle boards	
chipboard	7,0 to 8,0
oriented strand board	7,0

Table A.4 — Construction materials-metals

Materials	Density γ [kN/m^3]
metals	
aluminium	27,0
steel	77,0 to 78,5

(2) For materials (e.g. new and innovative materials) which are not covered by the tables in Annex A, the characteristic value of the density should be determined in accordance with EN 1990 clause 4.1.2 and agreed for each individual project.

(3) Where materials are used with a significant scatter of densities e.g. due to their source, water content etc, the characteristic value of these densities should be assessed in accordance with EN 1990 clause 4.1.2.

Section 5 Self-weight of construction works

5.1 Representation of actions

(1) The self-weight of the construction works should in most cases, be represented by a single characteristic value and be calculated on the basis of the nominal dimensions and the characteristic values of the densities.

(2) The self-weight of the construction works includes the structure and non-structural elements including fixed services as well as the weight of earth and ballast.

(3) Non-structural elements include:
- roofing;
- surfacing and coverings;
- partitions and linings;
- hand rails, safety barriers, parapets and kerbs;
- wall cladding;
- suspended ceilings;
- thermal insulation;
- fixed services (see 5.1(4)).

NOTE For information on fixed machinery see EN 1991-3. For other industrial equipment (e.g. safes) the manufacturer should be consulted.

(4) Fixed services include:
- equipments for lifts and moving stairways;
- heating, ventilating and air conditioning equipment;
- electrical equipment;
- pipes without their contents;
- cable trunking and conduits.

(5)P Loads due to movable partitions shall be treated as imposed loads, see 5.2.2(2)P and 6.3.1.2(8).

5.2 Characteristic values of self-weight

5.2.1 General

(1)P The determination of the characteristic values of self-weight, and of the dimensions and densities shall be in accordance with EN 1990, 4.1.2.

(2) Nominal dimensions should be those as shown on the drawings.

5.2.2 Additional provisions for buildings

(1) For manufactured elements such as flooring systems, facades and ceilings, lifts and equipment for buildings, data may be provided by the manufacturer.

(2)P For determining the effect of the self-weight due to movable partitions, an equivalent uniformly distributed load shall be used and added to the imposed load, see 6.3.1.2 (8).

Additional provisions that are specific for bridges (see EN 1991-1-1, 5.2.2) are omitted from this guide.

Section 6 Imposed loads on buildings

6.1 Representation of actions

(1) Imposed loads on buildings are those arising from occupancy. Values given in this section include:

- normal use by persons;
- furniture and moveable objects (e.g. moveable partitions, storage, the contents of containers);
- vehicles;
- anticipating rare events, such as concentrations of persons or of furniture, or the moving or stacking of objects which may occur during reorganization or redecoration.

(2) The imposed loads specified in this part are modelled by uniformly distributed loads, line loads or concentrated loads or combinations of these loads.

(3) For the determination of the imposed loads, floor and roof areas in buildings should be sub-divided into categories according to their use.

(4) Heavy equipment (e.g. in communal kitchens, radiology rooms, boiler rooms etc) are not included in the loads given in this section. Loads for heavy equipment should be agreed between the client and/or the relevant Authority.

6.2 Load arrangements

6.2.1 Floors, beams and roofs

(1)P For the design of a floor structure within one storey or a roof, the imposed load shall be taken into account as a free action applied at the most unfavourable part of the influence area of the action effects considered.

(2) Where the loads on other storeys are relevant, they may be assumed to be distributed uniformly (fixed actions).

As a practical example the horizontal beam at the second storey of the frame shown in the figure below is considered. In accordance with the two subclauses above (6.1 and 6.2) for determining the bending resistance at the points (a) and (b), the load arrangement for the imposed load q should be as demonstrated in Figure A.

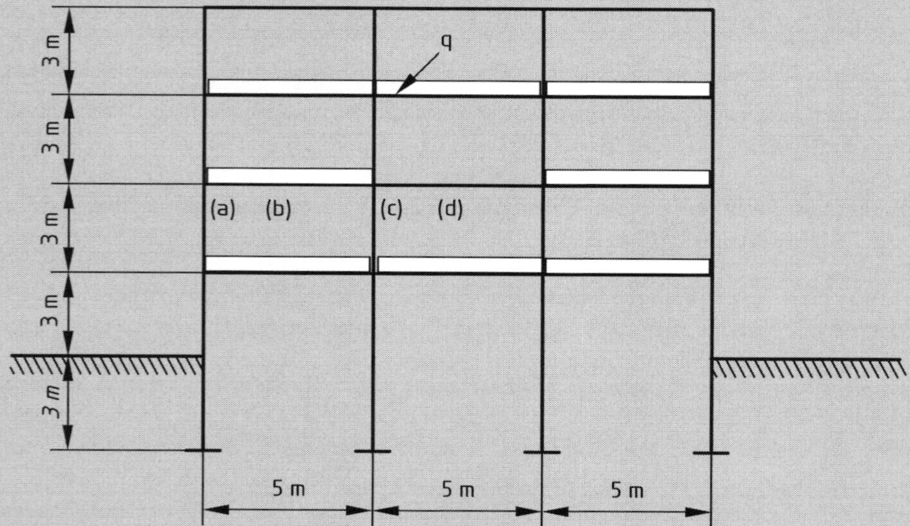

Figure A — An example of the load arrangement for the imposed load *q*

(3)P To ensure a minimum local resistance of the floor structure a separate verification shall be performed with a concentrated load that, unless stated otherwise, shall not be combined with the uniformly distributed loads or other variable actions.

(4) Imposed loads from a single category may be reduced according to the areas supported by the appropriate member, by a reduction factor α_A according to 6.3.1.2(10).

6.2.2 Columns and walls

AC1⟩ (1) For the design of columns and walls, the imposed load should be placed at all unfavourable locations.

NOTE The National Annex may introduce further simplifying rules. It is recommended that the maximum axial force may be calculated assuming the total imposed load on the floor of each story to be uniformly distributed. ⟨AC1

(2) Where imposed loads from several storeys act on columns and walls, the total imposed loads may be reduced by a factor α_n according to 6.3.1.2(11) and 3.3.1(2)P.

6.3 Characteristic values of imposed loads

6.3.1 Residential, social, commercial and administration areas

6.3.1.1 Categories

(1)P Areas in residential, social, commercial and administration buildings shall be divided into categories according to their specific uses shown in Table 6.1.

Table 6.1 — Categories of use

Category	Specific Use	Example
A	Areas for domestic and residential activities	Rooms in residential buildings and houses; bedrooms and wards in hospitals; bedrooms in hotels and hostels; kitchens and toilets.
B	Office areas	
C	Areas where people may congregate (with the exception of areas defined under category A, B, and D[1)])	**C1**: Areas with tables, etc. e.g. areas in schools, cafés, restaurants, dining halls, reading rooms, receptions. **C2**: Areas with fixed seats, e.g. areas in churches, theatres or cinemas, conference rooms, lecture halls, assembly halls, waiting rooms, railway waiting rooms. **C3**: Areas without obstacles for moving people, e.g. areas in museums, exhibition rooms, etc. and access areas in public and administration buildings, hotels, hospitals, railway station forecourts. **C4**: Areas with possible physical activities, e.g. dance halls, gymnastic rooms, stages. **C5**: Areas susceptible to large crowds, e.g. in buildings for public events like concert halls, sports halls including stands, terraces and access areas and railway platforms.
D	Shopping areas	**D1**: Areas in general retail shops **D2**: Areas in department stores
[1)] Attention is drawn to 6.3.1.1(2), in particular for C4 and C5. See EN 1990 when dynamic effects need to be considered. For Category E, see Table 6.3.		
NOTE 1 Depending on their anticipated uses, areas likely to be categorised as C2, C3, C4 may be categorized as C5 by decision of the client and/or National Annex. NOTE 2 The National Annex may provide sub categories to A, B, C1 to C5, D1 and D2. NOTE 3 See 6.3.2 for storage or industrial activity.		

The National Annex for EN 1991-1-1 sub-categorizes A, B, C1, C2, C3, C4, C5.

NA.2.3 Categories for residential, social, commercial and administration areas [BS EN 1991-1-1:2002, 6.3.1.1]

The categories for residential, social, commercial and administration areas are given in BS EN 1991-1-1:2002, Table 6.1. These categories have been expanded in Table NA.2 to include additional sub-categories for the UK.

Table NA.2 of EN 1991-1-1 — Categories for residential, social, commercial and administration areas including additional sub-categories for the UK

Category of loaded area	Specific use	Sub-category	Example
A	Areas for domestic and residential activities	A1	All usages within self-contained dwelling units (a unit occupied by a single family or a modular student accommodation unit with a secure door and comprising not more than six single bedrooms and an internal corridor) Communal areas (including kitchens) in blocks of flats with limited use (see Note 1). For communal areas in other blocks of flats, see A5, A6 and C3
		A2	Bedrooms and dormitories except those in self-contained single family dwelling units and in hotels and motels
		A3	Bedrooms in hotels and motels; hospital wards; toilet areas
		A4	Billiard/snooker rooms
		A5	Balconies in single family dwelling units and communal areas in blocks of flats with limited use (see Note 1)
		A6	Balconies in hostels, guest houses, residential clubs and communal areas in blocks of flats except those covered by Note 1
		A7	Balconies in hotels and motels
B	Office areas	B1	General use other than in B2
		B2	At or below ground floor level
C	Areas where people may congregate (with the exception of areas defined under category A, B and D)	C1	Areas with tables
		C11	Public, institutional and communal dining rooms and lounges, cafes and restaurants (see Note 2)
		C12	Reading rooms with no book storage
		C13	Classrooms
		C2	Areas with fixed seats

Category of loaded area	Specific use	Sub-category	Example
		C21	Assembly areas with fixed seating (see Note 3)
		C22	Places of worship
		C3	Areas without obstacles for moving people
		C31	Corridors, hallways, aisles in institutional type buildings not subjected to crowds or wheeled vehicles, hostels, guest houses, residential clubs, and communal areas in blocks of flats not covered by Note 1
		C32	Stairs, landings in institutional type buildings not subjected to crowds or wheeled vehicles, hostels, guest houses, residential clubs, and communal areas in blocks of flats not covered by Note 1
		C33	Corridors, hallways, aisles in all buildings not covered by C31 and C32, including hotels and motels and institutional buildings subjected to crowds
		C34	Corridors, hallways, aisles in all buildings not covered by C31 and C32, including hotels and motels and institutional buildings subjected to wheeled vehicles, including trolleys
		C35	Stairs, landings in all buildings not covered by C31 and C32, including hotels and motels and institutional buildings subjected to crowds
		C36	Walkways — Light duty (access suitable for one person, walkway width approx 600 mm)
		C37	Walkways — General duty (regular two-way pedestrian traffic)
		C38	Walkways — Heavy duty (high density pedestrian traffic including escape routes)
		C39	Museum floors and art galleries for exhibition purposes
		C4	Areas with possible physical activities
		C41	Dance halls and studios, gymnasia, stages (see Note 5)
		C42	Drill halls and drill rooms (Note 5)
		C5	Areas susceptible to large crowds
		C51	Assembly areas without fixed seating, concert halls, bars and places of worship (see Note 4 and Note 5)
		C52	Stages in public assembly areas (see Note 5)

Category of loaded area	Specific use	Sub-category	Example
D	Shopping areas	D1	Areas in general retail shops
		D2	Areas in department stores
NOTE 1 Communal areas in blocks of flats with limited use are blocks of flats not more than three storeys in height and with not more than four self-contained dwelling units per floor accessible from one staircase. NOTE 2 Where the areas described by C11 might be subjected to loads due to physical activities or overcrowding, e.g. a hotel dining room used as a dance floor, imposed loads should be based on C4 or C5 as appropriate. Reference should also be made to Note 5. NOTE 3 Fixed seating is seating where its removal and the use of the space for other purposes is improbable. NOTE 4 For grandstands and stadia, reference should be made to the requirements of the appropriate certifying authority. NOTE 5 For structures that might be susceptible to resonance effects, reference should be made to **NA.2.1**.			

6.3.1.2 Values of actions

(1)P The categories of loaded areas, as specified in Table 6.1, shall be designed by using characteristic values q_k (uniformly distributed load) and Q_k (concentrated load).

NOTE Values for q_k and Q_k are given in Table 6.2 below. Where a range is given in this table, the value may be set by the National Annex. The recommended values, intended for separate application, are underlined. q_k is intended for determination of general effects and Q_k for local effects. The National Annex may define different conditions of use of this table.

Table 6.2 — Imposed loads on floors, balconies and stairs in buildings

Categories of loaded areas	q_k [kN/m²]	Q_k [kN]
Category A		
– Floors	1,5 to <u>2,0</u>	<u>2,0</u> to 3,0
– Stairs	<u>2,0</u> to 4,0	<u>2,0</u> to 4,0
– Balconies	<u>2,5</u> to 4,0	<u>2,0</u> to 3,0
Category B	2,0 to <u>3,0</u>	1,5 to <u>4,5</u>
Category C		
– C1	2,0 to <u>3,0</u>	3,0 to <u>4,0</u>
– C2	3,0 to <u>4,0</u>	2,5 to 7,0 <u>(4,0)</u>
– C3	3,0 to <u>5,0</u>	<u>4,0</u> to 7,0
– C4	4,5 to <u>5,0</u>	3,5 to <u>7,0</u>
– C5	<u>5,0</u> to 7,5	3,5 to <u>4,5</u>
Category D		
– D1	<u>4,0</u> to 5,0	3,5 to 7,0 <u>(4,0)</u>
– D2	4,0 to <u>5,0</u>	3,5 to <u>7,0</u>

The National Annex to EN 1991-1-1 comprehensively categorizes A, B, C and D. The values adopted by the National Annex are within the ranges above. For educational purposes the underlined values above may be used.

NA.2.4 Imposed loads on floors, balconies and stairs in buildings [BS EN 1991-1-1:2002, 6.3.1.2 (1)P]

Values for minimum imposed loads on floors, balconies and stairs in buildings should be taken from Table NA.3 of EN 1991-1-1 for the categories of residential, social, commercial and administration areas described in Table NA.2.

Table NA.3 of EN 1991-1-1 — Imposed loads on floors, balconies and stairs in buildings

Category of loaded area		q_k kN/m²	Q_k kN
Category A	A1	1,5	2,0
	A2	1,5	2,0
	A3	2,0	2,0
	A4	2,0	2,7
	A5	2,5	2,0
	A6	Same as the rooms to which they give access but with a minimum of 3,0	2,0 (concentrated at the outer edge)
	A7	Same as the rooms to which they give access but with a minimum of 4,0	2,0 (concentrated at the outer edge)
Category B	B1	2,5	2,7
	B2	3,0	2,7
Category C	C11	2,0	3,0
	C12	2,5	4,0
	C13	3,0	3,0
	C21	4,0	3,6
	C22	3,0	2,7
	C31	3,0	4,5
	C32	3,0	4,0
	C33	4,0	4,5
	C34	5,0	4,5
	C35	4,0	4,0
	C36	3,0	2,0
	C37	5,0	3,6
	C38	7,5	4,5
	C39	4,0	4,5
	C41	5,0	3,6

Category of loaded area		q_k kN/m²	Q_k kN
	C42	5,0	7,0
	C51	5,0	3,6
	C52	7,5	4,5
Category D	D1/D2	4,0	3,6

(2) Where necessary q_k and Q_k should be increased in the design (e.g. for stairs and balconies depending on the occupancy and on dimensions).

(3) For local verifications a concentrated load Q_k acting alone should be taken into account.

The shape on which the load acts may normally be assumed as a square with a width of 500 mm.

(7)P Where floors are subjected to multiple use, they shall be designed for the most unfavourable category of loading which produces the highest effects of actions (e.g. forces or deflection) in the member under consideration.

(8) Provided that a floor allows a lateral distribution of loads, the self-weight of movable partitions may be taken into account by a uniformly distributed load q_k which should be added to the imposed loads of floors obtained from Table 6.2. This defined uniformly distributed load is dependent on the self-weight of the partitions as follows:
- for movable partitions with a self-weight ≤ 1,0 kN/m wall length: q_k =0,5 kN/m²;
- AC1) for movable partitions with a self-weight > 1,0 and ≤ 2,0 kN/m wall length: q_k =0,8 kN/m²;
- for movable partitions with a self-weight > 2,0 and ≤ 3,0 kN/m wall length: q_k =1,2 kN/m². (AC1

(9) Heavier partitions should be considered in the design taking account of:
- the locations and directions of the partitions;
- the structural form of the floors.

AC1) (10) In accordance with 6.2.1(4) a reduction factor α_A may be applied to the q_k values for imposed loads for floors (see Table 6.2 and sub-clauses (8) and (9)), and for accessible roofs, Category I (see Table 6.9). (AC1

NOTE 1 The recommended value for the reduction factor α_A for categories AC1) A to D (AC1 is determined as follows:

$$\alpha_A = \frac{5}{7}\psi_0 + \frac{A_0}{A} \leq 1,0 \qquad (6.1)$$

with the restriction for categories C and D: $\alpha_A \geq 0,6$

where:
ψ_0 is the factor according to EN 1990 Annex A1 Table A1.1
A_0 = 10,0 m²
A is the loaded area.

NOTE 2 The National Annex may give an alternative method.

NA.2.5 Reduction factor for imposed loads for floors and accessible roofs [BS EN 1991-1-1:2002, 6.3.1.2 (10)]

The reduction factor α_A should be determined using Equation (NA.1) instead of BS EN 1991-1-1:2002, Equation (6.1):

$$\alpha_A = 1,0 - A/1\,000 \geq 0,75 \qquad \text{(NA.1)}$$

where:
A is the area (m^2) supported.

NOTE Loads that have been specifically determined from knowledge of the proposed use of the structure do not qualify for reduction.

The tabulated values obtained from NA 2.5 are given below.

Reduction factor, α_A (Reference NA 2.5)

Area supported (see note), m^2	**Reduction factor,** α_A
0	1,00
50	0,95
100	0,90
150	0,85
200	0,80
above 250	0,75 max
NOTE Reductions for intermediate areas may be calculated by linear interpolation.	

(11) In accordance with 6.2.2(2) and provided that the area is classified according to Table 6.1 into the categories A to D, for columns and walls the total imposed loads from several storeys may be multiplied by the reduction factor α_n.

NOTE 1 The recommended values for α_n are given below.

$$\alpha_n = \frac{2 + (n-2)\,\psi_0}{n} \qquad (6.2)$$

where:
n is the number of storeys (> 2) above the loaded structural elements from the same category.
ψ_0 is in accordance with EN 1990, Annex A1, Table A1.1.

NOTE 2 The National Annex may give an alternative method.

NA.2.6 Reduction factors for imposed loads from several storeys [BS EN 1991-1-1:2002, 6.3.1.2 (11)]

The reduction factor α_n should be determined using Equation (NA.2) instead of BS EN 1991-1-1:2002, Equation (6.2):

$$\alpha_n = 1{,}1 - n/10 \quad \text{for } 1 \leq n \leq 5$$
$$\alpha_n = 0{,}6 \quad \text{for } 5 < n \leq 10 \qquad \text{(NA.2)}$$
$$\alpha_n = 0{,}5 \quad \text{for } n > 10$$

where:
n is the number of storeys with loads qualifying for reduction (see Note).

Load reductions based on area in NA.2.5 may be applied if $\alpha_A < \alpha_n$. However, the reductions given by Equation (NA.1) cannot be used in combination with those determined from Equation (NA.2).

NOTE Loads that have been specifically determined from knowledge of the proposed use of the structure do not qualify for reduction.

The tabulated values from NA 2.6 are given below.

Reduction factor, α_n (Reference NA 2.6)

Number of storeys with loads qualifying for reduction	Reduction factor, α_n, for total imposed load from several storeys carried by the column or wall
1	1,0
2	0,90
3	0,80
4	0,70
5 to 10	0,60
over 10	0,5 max

6.3.2 Areas for storage and industrial activities

Storage is not discussed in this document. See EN 1991-1-1 and the UK National Annex to EN 1991-1-1.

6.3.3 Garages and vehicle traffic areas (excluding bridges)

6.3.3.1 Categories

(1)P Traffic and parking areas in buildings shall be divided into two categories according to their accessibility for vehicles as shown in Table 6.7.

Table 6.7 — Traffic and parking areas in buildings

Categories of traffic areas	Specific use	Examples
F	Traffic and parking areas for light vehicles (≤ 30 kN gross vehicle weight and ≤ 8 seats not including driver)	garages; parking areas, parking halls
G	Traffic and parking areas for medium vehicles (> 30 kN, ≤ 160 kN gross vehicle weight, on 2 axles)	access routes; delivery zones; zones accessible to fire engines (≤ 160 kN gross vehicle weight)
NOTE 1 Access to areas designed to category F should be limited by physical means built into the structure. NOTE 2 Areas designed to categories F and G should be posted with the appropriate warning signs.		

6.3.3.2 Values of actions

(1) The load model which should be used is a single axle with a load Q_k with dimensions according to Figure 6.2 and a uniformly distributed load q_k. The characteristic values for q_k and Q_k are given in Table 6.8.

NOTE q_k is intended for determination of general effects and Q_k for local effects. The National Annex may define different conditions of use of this table.

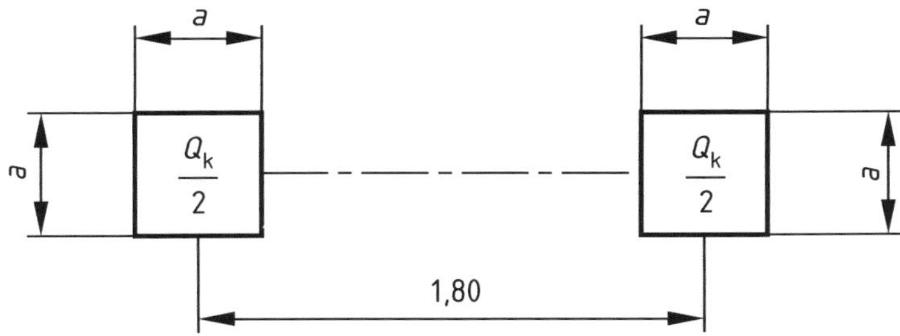

NOTE For category F (see Table 6.8) the width of the square surface is 100 mm and for category G (see Table 6.8) the width of a square surface is 200 mm.

Figure 6.2 — Dimensions of axle load

Table 6.8 — Imposed loads on garages and vehicle traffic areas

Categories of traffic areas	q_k [kN/m²]	Q_k [kN]
Category F Gross vehicle weight: ≤ 30 kN	q_k	Q_k
Category G 30 kN < gross vehicle weight ≤ 160 kN	5,0	Q_k
NOTE 1 For category F, q_k may be selected within the range 1,5 to 2,5 kN/m² and Q_k may be selected within the range 10 to 20 kN. NOTE 2 For category G, Q_k may be selected within the range 40 to 90 kN. NOTE 3 Where a range of values are given in Notes 1 & 2, the value may be set by the National Annex. The recommended values are underlined.		

NA.2.9 Imposed loads on garages and vehicle traffic areas [BS EN 1991-1-1:2002, 6.3.3.2 (1)]

Values for imposed loads on garages and vehicle traffic areas should be taken from Table NA.6 (as a replacement for BS EN 1991-1-1:2002, Table 6.8) for categories F and G described in BS EN 1991-1-1:2002, Table 6.7.

Table NA.6 of EN 1991-1-1 — Imposed loads on garages and vehicle traffic areas

Categories of traffic areas	q_k kN/m^2	Q_k kN
Category F (Gross vehicle weight: ≤ 30 kN)	2,5	10,0
Category G (30 kN < gross vehicle weight ≤ 160 kN)	5,0	To be determined for specific use
NOTE q_k and Q_k should not be applied simultaneously.		

(2) The axle load should be applied on two square surfaces with a 100 mm side for category F and a 200 mm side for category G in the possible positions which will produce the most adverse effects of the action.

6.3.4 Roofs

6.3.4.1 Categories

(1)P Roofs shall be categorised according to their accessibility into three categories as shown in Table 6.9.

Table 6.9 — Categorization of roofs

Categories of loaded area	Specific use
H	Roofs not accessible except for normal maintenance and repair
I	Roofs accessible with occupancy according to categories [AC1) A to G (AC1]
K	Roofs accessible for special services, such as helicopter landing areas

(2) Imposed loads for roofs of category H should be those given in Table 6.10. Imposed loads for roofs of category I are given in Tables 6.2, 6.4 and 6.8 according to the specific use.

(3) The loads for roofs of category K which provide areas for helicopter landing areas should be for the helicopter classes HC, see Table 6.11.

6.3.4.2 Values of actions

(1) For roofs of category H the minimum characteristic values Q_k and q_k that should be used are given in Table 6.10. They are related to the projected area of the roof under consideration.

Table 6.10 — Imposed loads on roofs of category H

<table>
<tr><th>Roof</th><th>q_k
[kN/m²]</th><th>Q_k
[kN]</th></tr>
<tr><td>Category H</td><td>q_k</td><td>Q_k</td></tr>
<tr><td colspan="3">NOTE 1 For category H q_k may be selected within the range 0,00 kN/m² to 1,0 kN/m² and Q_k may be selected within the range 0,9 kN to 1,5 kN.

Where a range is given the values may be set by the National Annex. The recommended values are:

q_k = 0,4 kN/m², Q_k = 1,0 kN

NOTE 2 q_k may be varied by the National Annex dependent upon the roof slope.

NOTE 3 q_k may be assumed to act on an area A which may be set by the National Annex. The recommended value for A is 10 m², within the range of zero to the whole area of the roof.

NOTE 4 See also 3.3.2 (1).</td></tr>
</table>

NA.2.10 Imposed loads on roofs [BS EN 1991-1-1:2002, 6.3.4.2]

Values for imposed loads on roofs not accessible except for normal maintenance and repair should be taken from Table NA.7 of EN 1991-1-1 for category H described in BS EN 1991-1-1:2002, Table 6.9.

Table NA.7 of EN 1991-1-1 — Imposed loads on roofs not accessible except for normal maintenance and repair

<table>
<tr><th>Roof slope, α
(degrees)</th><th>q_k
kN/m²</th><th>Q_k
kN</th></tr>
<tr><td>α < 30°</td><td>0,6</td><td rowspan="3">0,9</td></tr>
<tr><td>30° ≤ α < 60°</td><td>0,6 [(60 - α)/30]</td></tr>
<tr><td>α ≥ 60°</td><td>0</td></tr>
<tr><td colspan="3">NOTE 1 All roof slopes α are measured from the horizontal and all loads should be applied vertically.
NOTE 2 In evaluating Table NA.6 for curved roofs the roofs should be divided into not less than five equal segments and the mean slope of each segment considered to be equivalent to the roof slope, α.
NOTE 3 BS EN 1991-1-1:2002, Note 3 to Table 6.10 states that q_k may be assumed to act on an area A. It is recommended that the value of A should be the whole area of the roof.</td></tr>
</table>

(2) The minimum values given in Table 6.10 do not take into account uncontrolled accumulations of construction materials that may occur during maintenance.

NOTE See also EN 1991-1-6: Actions during execution.

(3)P For roofs separate verifications shall be performed for the concentrated load Q_k and the uniformly distributed load q_k, acting independently.

(4) Roofs, other than those with roof sheeting, should be designed to resist 1,5 kN on an area based on a 50 mm sided square. Roof elements with a profiled or discontinuously laid surface should be designed so that the concentrated load Q_k acts over the effective area provided by load spreading arrangements.

(5) For roofs of category K the actions from helicopters on landing areas should be determined in accordance with Table 6.11, and using the dynamic factors given in 6.3.4.2 (6) and expression 6.3.

Table 6.11 — Imposed loads on roofs of category K for helicopters

Class of helicopter	Take-off load Q of helicopter	Take-off load Q_k	Dimension of the loaded area (m x m)
HC1 HC2	$Q \leq 20$ kN 20 kN< $Q \leq 60$ kN	$Q_k = 20$ kN $Q_k = 60$ kN	0,2 x 0,2 0,3 x 0,3

(6) The dynamic factor φ to be applied to the take-off load Q_k to take account of impact effects may be taken as $\varphi = 1{,}40$.

(7) Access ladders and walkways should be assumed to be loaded according to Table 6.10 for a roof slope < 20°. For walkways which are part of a designated escape route, q_k should be according to Table 6.2. For walkways for service a minimum characteristic value Q_k of 1,5 kN should be taken.

(8) The following loads should be used for the design of frames and coverings of access hatches (other than glazing), the supports of ceilings and similar structures:

a) without access: no imposed load;

b) with access: 0,25 kN/m^2 distributed over the whole area or the area supported, and the concentrated load of 0,9 kN so placed so as to produce maximum stresses in the affected member.

6.4 Horizontal loads on parapets and partition walls acting as barriers

Horizontal loads on parapets are not discussed in this document. See EN 1991-1-1 and the UK National Annex to EN 1991-1-1.

Bibliography

ISO 2394 General principles on reliability for structures

ISO 3898 Basis of design of structures – Notations. General symbols

ISO 8930 General principles on reliability for structures. List of equivalent terms

Bibliography

Standards publications

BS EN 1991-1-3, *Eurocode 1: Actions on structures — Part 1-3: General actions — Snow loads.*

BS EN 1991-1-4, *Eurocode 1: Actions on structures — Part 1-4: General actions — Wind actions.*

BS EN 1991-1-5, *Eurocode 1: Actions on structures — Part 1-5: General actions — Thermal actions.*

BS EN 1991-2, *Eurocode 1: Actions on structures — Part 2: Traffic loads on bridges.*

BS EN 1991-3, *Eurocode 1: Actions on structures — Part 3: Actions induced by cranes and machinery.*

PD 6688, *Background paper to the UK National Annexes to BS EN 1991-1.*

Other publications

[1] BRE Digest 426, *The response of structures to dynamic crowd loads*. BRE: Watford, 2004.

Useful references

[1] Gulvanessian H., Formichi P. and Calgaro J.A. *Designers' Guide to Eurocode 1: Actions on Buildings*, Thomas Telford, London, 2009

Extracts from EN 1991-1-3

The extracts in this part of Chapter 1 are taken from EN 1991-1-3:2003 (incorporating corrigenda December 2004 and March 2009), *Eurocode 1: Actions on structures — Part 1-3: General actions — Snow loads.*

The start and finish of text introduced or altered by corrigendum is indicated in the text by tags. Text altered by CEN corrigendum March 2009 is indicated in the text by [AC1) (AC1].

Foreword

Introduction – Additional information specific for EN 1991-1-3

EN 1991-1-3 gives design guidance and actions from snow for the structural design of buildings and civil engineering works. EN 1991-1-3 is intended for clients, designers, contractors and public authorities. EN 1991-1-3 is intended to be used with EN 1990, the other Parts of EN 1991 and EN 1992-1999 for the design of structures.

See Chapter 0 – Extracts from Eurocode 0: Basis of structural design.

The full list of the contents of EN 1991-1-3 follows, and is given for reference purposes. (Bold items are included in this chapter.)

Section 1 General

1.1 Scope

The scope of EN 1991-1-3 is given in full. (Bold items are covered in this chapter.)

(1) EN 1991-1-3 gives guidance to determine the values of loads due to snow to be used for the structural design of buildings and civil engineering works.

(2) This Part does not apply for sites at altitudes above 1 500 m, unless otherwise specified.

[AC1) **NOTE Advice for the treatment of snow loads for altitudes above 1 500 m may be found in the National Annex.** (AC1]

NA.2.1 Altitudes greater than 1 500 m [BS EN 1991-1-3:2003, 1.1 (2)]

The scope of BS EN 1991-1-3 does not include sites at altitudes above 1 500 m. For altitudes greater than 1 500 m specialist advice should be sought from the Meteorological Office on the snow loads likely to occur at the site.

(3) Annex A gives information on design situations and load arrangements to be used for different locations.

NOTE These different locations may be identified by the National Annex.

NA.2.2 Design situations and load arrangements to be used for different locations [BS EN 1991-1-3:2003, 1.1 (3)]

The scope of BS EN 1991-1-3 states that information on design situations and load arrangements to be used for different locations is given in BS EN 1991-1-3:2003, Annex A.

The design situations summarized as case B2 in BS EN 1991-1-3:2003, Table A.1 should be the only exceptional condition to be checked for determining imposed roof snow loads in the UK.

(4) Annex B gives shape coefficients to be used for the treatment of exceptional snow drifts.

NOTE The use of Annex B is allowed through the National Annex.

NA.2.3 Snow load shape coefficients for exceptional snow drifts [BS EN 1991-1-3:2003, 1.1 (4)]

The scope of BS EN 1991-1-3 states that information on snow load shape coefficients for exceptional snow drifts is given in BS EN 1991-1-3:2003, Annex B.

BS EN 1991-1-3:2003, Annex B should be used in the UK in order to determine exceptional snow drift loads.

(5) Annex C gives characteristic values of snow load on the ground based on the results of work carried out under a contract specific to this Eurocode, to DGIII / D3 of the European Commission. The objectives of this Annex are:

- to give information to National Competent Authorities to help them to redraft and update their national maps;
- to help to ensure that the established harmonised procedures used to produce the maps in this Annex are used in the member states for treating their basic snow data.

(6) Annex D gives guidance for adjusting the ground snow loads according to the return period.

(7) Annex E gives information on the bulk weight density of snow.

(8) This Part does not give guidance on specialist aspects of snow loading, for example:
- impact snow loads resulting from snow sliding off or falling from a higher roof;
- the additional wind loads which could result from changes in shape or size of the construction works due to the presence of snow or the accretion of ice;
- loads in areas where snow is present all year round;
- ice loading;
- lateral loading due to snow (e.g. lateral loads exerted by drifts);
- snow loads on bridges.

1.3 Assumptions

See Chapter 0 – Extracts from Eurocode: Basis of structural design.

1.4 Distinction between principles and application rules

See Chapter 0 – Extracts from Eurocode: Basis of structural design.

1.6 Terms and definitions

For the purposes of this European standard, a basic list of terms and definitions given in EN 1990:2002, 1.5 apply together with the following.

1.6.1
characteristic value of snow load on the ground
snow load on the ground based on an annual probability of exceedence of 0,02, excluding exceptional snow loads

1.6.2
altitude of the site
height above mean sea level of the site where the structure is to be located, or is already located for an existing structure

1.6.3
exceptional snow load on the ground
load of the snow layer on the ground resulting from a snow fall which has an exceptionally infrequent likelihood of occurring

NOTE See notes to 2(3) and 4.3(1).

1.6.4
characteristic value of snow load on the roof
product of the characteristic snow load on the ground and appropriate coefficients

NOTE These coefficients are chosen so that the probability of the calculated snow load on the roof does not exceed the probability of the characteristic value of the snow load on the ground

1.6.5
undrifted snow load on the roof
load arrangement which describes the uniformly distributed snow load on the roof, affected only by the shape of the roof, before any redistribution of snow due to other climatic actions

1.6.6
drifted snow load on the roof
load arrangement which describes the snow load distribution resulting from snow having been moved from one location to another location on a roof, e.g. by the action of the wind

1.6.7
roof snow load shape coefficient
ratio of the snow load on the roof to the undrifted snow load on the ground, without the influence of exposure and thermal effects

1.6.8
thermal coefficient
coefficient defining the reduction of snow load on roofs as a function of the heat flux through the roof, causing snow melting

1.6.9
exposure coefficient
coefficient defining the reduction or increase of load on a roof of an unheated building, as a fraction of the characteristic snow load on the ground

1.6.10
load due to exceptional snow drift
load arrangement which describes the load of the snow layer on the roof resulting from a snow deposition pattern which has an exceptionally infrequent likelihood of occurring

1.7 Symbols

(1) For the purpose of this European standard, the following symbols apply.

NOTE The notation used is based on ISO 3898.

(2) A basic list of notations is given in EN 1990:2002 1.6, and the additional notations below are specific to this Part.

Latin upper case letters

C_e Exposure coefficient
C_t Thermal coefficient
C_{esl} Coefficient for exceptional snow loads
A Site altitude above sea level [m]
S_e Snow load per metre length due to overhang [kN/m]
F_s Force per metre length exerted by a sliding mass of snow [kN/m]

Latin lower case letters

b Width of construction work [m]
d Depth of the snow layer [m]
h Height of construction work [m]
k Coefficient to take account of the irregular shape of snow (see also 6.3)
l_s Length of snow drift or snow loaded area [m]
s Snow load on the roof [kN/m^2]
s_k Characteristic value of snow on the ground at the relevant site [kN/m^2]
s_{Ad} Design value of exceptional snow load on the ground [kN/m^2]

Greek lower case letters

α Pitch of roof, measured from horizontal [°]
β Angle between the horizontal and the tangent to the curve for a cylindrical roof [°]
γ Weight density of snow [kN/m^3]
μ Snow load shape coefficient
ψ_0 Factor for combination value of a variable action
ψ_1 Factor for frequent value of a variable action
ψ_2 Factor for quasi-permanent value of a variable action

NOTE For the purpose of this standard the units specified in the above list apply.

Section 2 Classification of actions

(1)P Snow loads shall be classified as variable, fixed actions (see also 5.2), unless otherwise specified in this standard, see EN 1990:2002, 4.1.1 (1)P and 4.1.1 (4).

(2) Snow loads covered in this standard should be classified as static actions, see EN 1990:2002, 4.1.1 (4).

(3) In accordance with EN 1990:2002, 4.1.1 (2), for the particular condition defined in 1.6.3, exceptional snow loads may be treated as accidental actions depending on geographical locations.

NOTE The National Annex may give the conditions of use (which may include geographical locations) of this clause.

NA.2.4 Exceptional snow load on the ground [BS EN 1991–1–3:2003, 2 (3)]

Exceptional snow load on the ground should be treated as accidental actions.

(4) In accordance with EN 1990:2002, 4.1.1 (2), for the particular condition defined in 1.6.10, loads due to exceptional snow drifts may be treated as accidental actions, depending on geographical locations.

NOTE The National Annex may give the conditions of use (which may include geographical locations) of this clause.

NA.2.5 Load due to exceptional snow drift [BS EN 1991–1–3:2003, 2 (4)]

Drift loads determined using the guidance given in BS EN 1991-1-3:2003, Annex B should be treated as accidental actions.

Section 3 Design situations

3.1 General

(1)P The relevant snow loads shall be determined for each design situation identified, in accordance with EN 1990:2002, 3.5.

(2) For local effects described in Section 6 the persistent/transient design situation should be used.

The table in Annex A (reproduced after Section 6 of this part of Chapter 1) recommends the design situations to be used for:

- no exceptional falls, no exceptional drifts;
- exceptional falls, no exceptional drifts;
- no exceptional falls, exceptional drifts;
- exceptional falls, exceptional drifts.

EN 1991-1-3, Annex B should be used in place of EN 1991-1-3, **6.2** in order to determine the load case due to drifting in the UK.

Section 4 Snow load on the ground

4.1 Characteristic values

(1) The characteristic value of snow load on the ground (s_k) should be determined in accordance with EN 1990:2002, 4.1.2 (7)P and the definition for characteristic snow load on the ground given in 1.6.1.

NOTE 1 The National Annex specifies the characteristic values to be used. To cover unusual local conditions the National Annex may additionally allow the client and the relevant authority to agree upon a different characteristic value from that specified for an individual project.

NOTE 2 Annex C gives the European ground snow load map, resulting from studies commissioned by DGIII/D-3. The National Annex may make reference to this map in order to eliminate, or to reduce, inconsistencies occurring at borderlines between countries.

NA.2.8 Characteristic value of snow load on the ground [BS EN 1991-1-3:2003, 4.1 (1)]

The characteristic ground snow loads s_k to be used in the UK should be obtained from the map shown in Figure NA.1 and Equation (NA.1).

$$s_k = [0{,}15 + (0{,}1Z + 0{,}05)] + [(A - 100)/525] \qquad \text{(NA.1)}$$

where:

s_k is the characteristic ground snow load (kN/m^2);
Z is the zone number obtained from the map in Figure NA.1;
A is the site altitude (m).

Unusual local effects may not have been accounted for in the analysis undertaken to produce the ground snow load map given in Figure NA.1. These include local shelter from the wind, which can result in increased local snow loads and local configurations in mountainous areas, which may funnel the snow and give increased local loading. If the designer suspects that there are unusual local conditions that need to be taken into account, then for coastal sites below 100 m the map value should be used without the altitude modification. Alternatively, and in other cases, the Meteorological Office should be consulted.

NA.2.9 Refined characteristic value of snow load on the ground [BS EN 1991-1-3:2003, 4.1 (2)]

Where a more refined characteristic ground snow load value s_k is required, the Meteorological Office should be consulted.

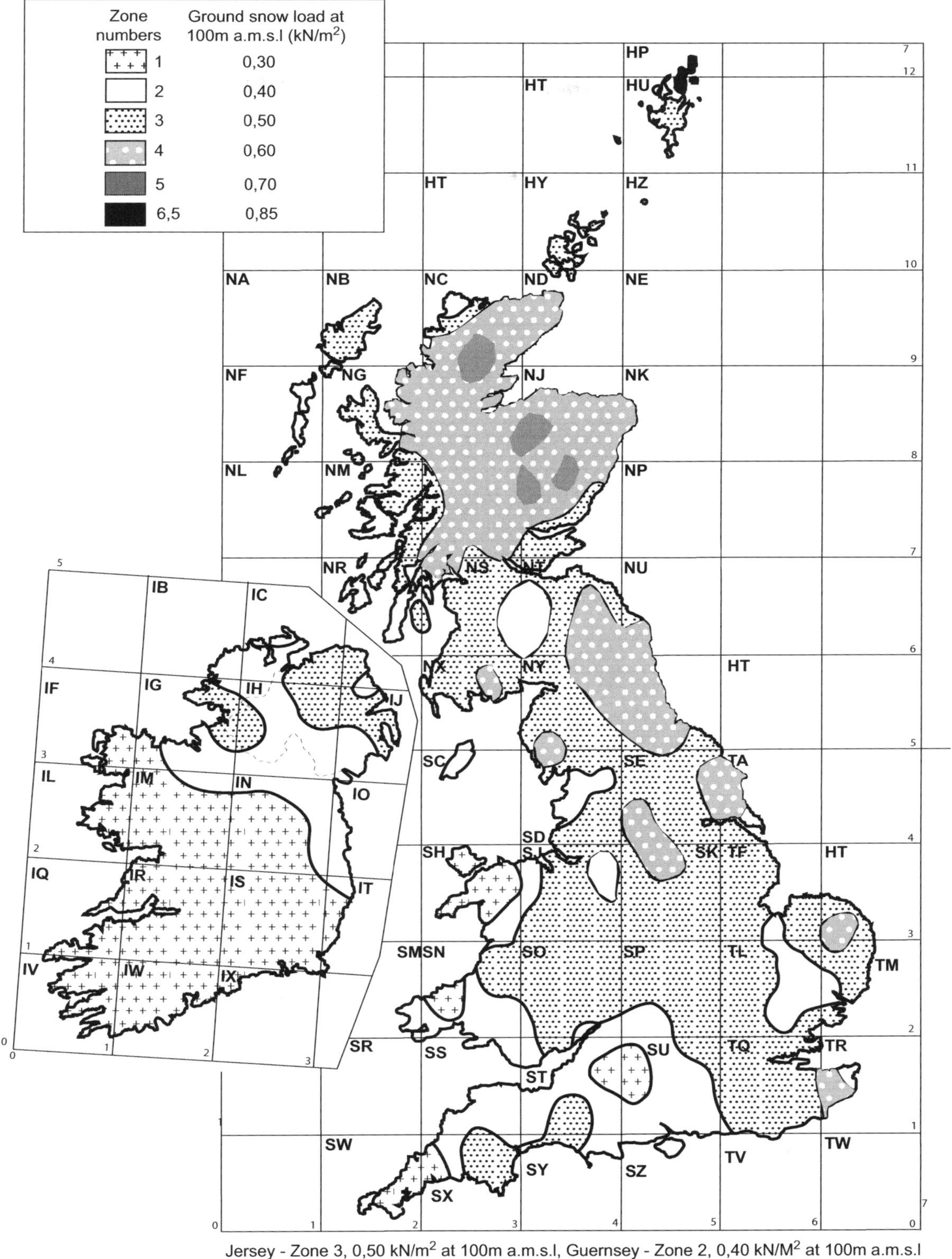

Figure NA.1 — Characteristic ground snow load map

4.2 Other representative values

See Chapter 0, Table A.1.1.

4.3 Treatment of exceptional snow loads on the ground

(1) For locations where exceptional snow loads on the ground can occur, they may be determined by:

$$s_{Ad} = C_{esl}\, s_k \qquad (4.1)$$

where:

s_{Ad} is the design value of exceptional snow load on the ground for the given location;
C_{esl} is the coefficient for exceptional snow loads;
s_k is the characteristic value of snow load on the ground for a given location.

NOTE The coefficient C_{esl} may be set by the National Annex. The recommended value for C_{esl} is 2,0 (see also 2(3))

NA.2.11 Treatment of exceptional snow load on the ground [BS EN 1991-1-3:2003, 4.3 (1)]

The coefficient for exceptional snow loads C_{esl} should take a value of 2,0 as recommended in BS EN 1991-1-3.

Section 5 Snow load on roofs

5.1 Nature of the load

(1) P The design shall recognise that snow can be deposited on a roof in many different patterns.

(2) Properties of a roof or other factors causing different patterns can include:

a) the shape of the roof;
b) its thermal properties;
c) the roughness of its surface;
d) the amount of heat generated under the roof;
e) the proximity of nearby buildings;
f) the surrounding terrain;
g) the local meteorological climate, in particular its windiness, temperature variations, and likelihood of precipitation (either as rain or as snow).

5.2 Load arrangements

(1)P The following two primary load arrangements shall be taken into account:

- undrifted snow load on roofs (see 1.6.5);
- drifted snow load on roofs (see 1.6.6).

(2) The load arrangements should be determined using 5.3; and Annex B, where specified in accordance with 3.3.

NOTE The National Annex may specify the use of Annex B for the roof shapes described in 5.3.4, 5.3.6 and 6.2, and will normally apply to specific locations where all the snow usually melts and clears between the individual weather systems and where moderate to high wind speeds occur during the individual weather system.

> The National Annex to EN 1991-1-3 specifies the use of Annex B for the roof shapes described in 5.3.4, 5.3.6 and 6.2.

(3)P Snow loads on roofs shall be determined as follows:

a) for the persistent / transient design situations

$$s = \mu_i \, C_e \, C_t \, s_k \tag{5.1}$$

b) for the accidental design situations where exceptional snow load is the accidental action (except for the cases covered in 5.2 (3) P c)

$$s = \mu_i \, C_e \, C_t \, s_{Ad} \tag{5.2}$$

NOTE See 2(3).

c) for the accidental design situations where exceptional snow drift is the accidental action and where Annex B applies

$$s = \mu_i \, s_k \tag{5.3}$$

NOTE See 2(4).

where:

μ_i is the snow load shape coefficient (see Section 5.3 and Annex B)
s_k is the characteristic value of snow load on the ground
s_{Ad} is the design value of exceptional snow load on the ground for a given location (see 4.3)
C_e is the exposure coefficient
C_t is the thermal coefficient

(4) The load should be assumed to act vertically and refer to a horizontal projection of the roof area.

(5) When artificial removal or redistribution of snow on a roof is anticipated the roof should be designed for suitable load arrangements.

NOTE 1 Load arrangements according to this Section have been derived for natural deposition patterns only.

NOTE 2 Further guidance may be given in the National Annex.

NA.2.13 Load arrangements for artificial removal or redistribution of snow on a roof [BS EN 1991-1-3:2003, 5.2 (5)]

In certain cases, snow may be artificially removed from or redistributed on a roof, e.g. due to excessive heat loss through a small section of roof or manually to maintain access to a service door. This can result in more severe load imbalances occurring than those resulting from BS EN 1991-1-3:2003, **5.3** and Annex B (which have been derived for natural deposition patterns). To provide for these situations, if they are likely to occur and other information is not available, a load case should be considered comprising the minimum imposed uniformly distributed load (BS EN 1991-1-3:2003, **5.3**) on any portion of the roof area and zero load on the remainder of the area.

(7) The exposure coefficient C_e should be used for determining the snow load on the roof. The choice for C_e should consider the future development around the site. C_e should be taken as 1,0 unless otherwise specified for different topographies.

NOTE The National Annex may give the values of C_e for different topographies. The recommended values are given in Table 5.1 below.

Table 5.1 — Recommended values of C_e for different topographies

Topography	C_e
Windswept[a]	0,8
Normal[b]	1,0
Sheltered[c]	1,2

[a] *Windswept topography*: flat unobstructed areas exposed on all sides without, or little shelter afforded by terrain, higher construction works or trees.

[b] *Normal topography*: areas where there is no significant removal of snow by wind on construction work, because of terrain, other construction works or trees.

[c] *Sheltered topography*: areas in which the construction work being considered is considerably lower than the surrounding terrain or surrounded by high trees and/or surrounded by higher construction works.

NA.2.15 Exposure coefficient used for determining snow load on a roof [BS EN 1991-1-3:2003, 5.2 (7)]

The recommended value for exposure coefficient C_e in the UK is 1,0 for all topographies.

(8) The thermal coefficient C_t should be used to account for the reduction of snow loads on roofs with high thermal transmittance (> 1 W/m^{2}K), in particular for some glass covered roofs, because of melting caused by heat loss.

For all other cases:

C_t = 1,0

NOTE 1 Based on the thermal insulating properties of the material and the shape of the construction work, the use of a reduced C_t value may be permitted through the National Annex.

NOTE 2 Further guidance may be obtained from ISO 4355.

NA.2.16 Thermal coefficient used to account for the reduction of snow load on roofs with high thermal transmittance [BS EN 1991-1-3:2003, 5.2 (8)]

The recommended value for thermal coefficient C_t in the UK is 1,0 for all roofing materials.

5.3 Roof shape coefficients

5.3.1 General

(1) 5.3 gives roof shape coefficients for undrifted and drifted snow load arrangements for all types of roofs identified in this standard, with the exception of the consideration of exceptional snow drifts defined in Annex B, where its use is allowed.

(2) Special consideration should be given to the snow load shape coefficients to be used where the roof has an external geometry which may lead to increases in snow load, that are considered significant in comparison with that of a roof with linear profile.

(3) Shape coefficients for roof shapes in 5.3.2, 5.3.3 and 5.3.4 are given in Figure 5.1.

5.3.2 Monopitch roofs

(1) The snow load shape coefficient μ_1 that should be used for monopitch roofs is given in Table 5.2 and shown in Figure 5.1 and Figure 5.2.

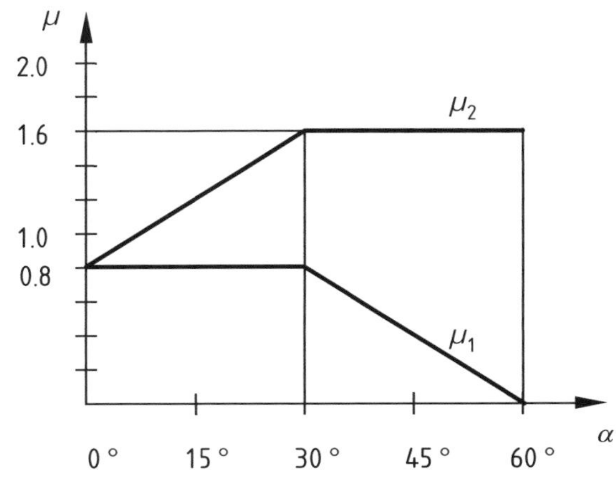

Figure 5.1 — Snow load shape coefficients

(2) The values given in Table 5.2 apply when the snow is not prevented from sliding off the roof. Where snow fences or other obstructions exist or where the lower edge of the roof is terminated with a parapet, then the snow load shape coefficient should not be reduced below 0,8.

Table 5.2 — Snow load shape coefficients

Angle of pitch of roof α	$0° \leq \alpha \leq 30°$	$30° < \alpha < 60°$	$\alpha \geq 60°$
μ_1	0,8	$0,8(60 - \alpha)/30$	0,0
μ_2	$0,8 + 0,8\ \alpha/30$	1,6	--

(3) The load arrangement of Figure 5.2 should be used for both the undrifted and drifted load arrangements.

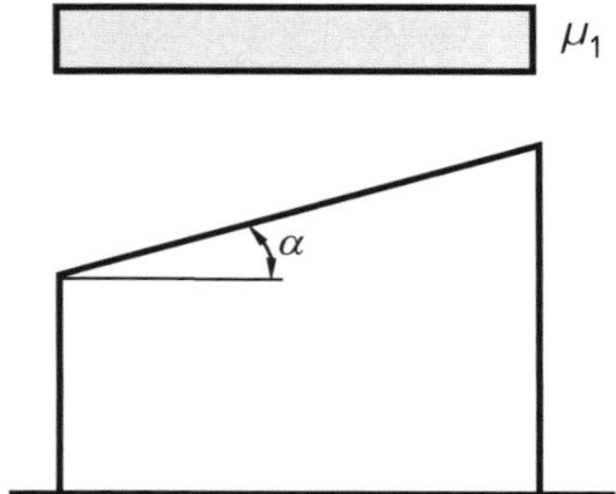

Figure 5.2 — Snow load shape coefficient – monopitch roof

5.3.3 Pitched roofs

(1) The snow load shape coefficients that should be used for pitched roofs are given in Figure 5.3, where μ_1 is given in Table 5.2 and shown in Figure 5.1.

(2) The values given in Table 5.2 apply when snow is not prevented from sliding off the roof. Where snow fences or other obstructions exist or where the lower edge of the roof is terminated with a parapet, then the snow load shape coefficient should not be reduced below 0,8.

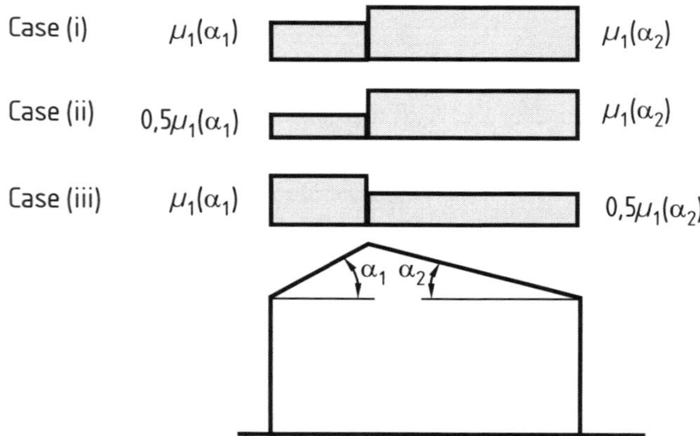

Figure 5.3 — Snow load shape coefficients – pitched roofs

(3) The undrifted load arrangement which should be used is shown in Figure 5.3, case (i).

(4) The drifted load arrangements which should be used are shown in Figure 5.3, cases (ii) and (iii), unless [AC1) otherwise (AC1] specified for local conditions.

NOTE Based on local conditions, an alternative drifting load arrangement may be given in the National Annex.

NA.2.17 Drifted snow load arrangement for pitched roofs [BS EN 1991-1-3:2003, 5.3.3 (4)]

The load arrangement given in Figure NA.2 and Table NA.1 of EN 1991-1-3 should be used in place of BS EN 1991-1-3:2003, 5.3.3 (4) to determine the drifted snow load on a duo-pitched roof in the UK.

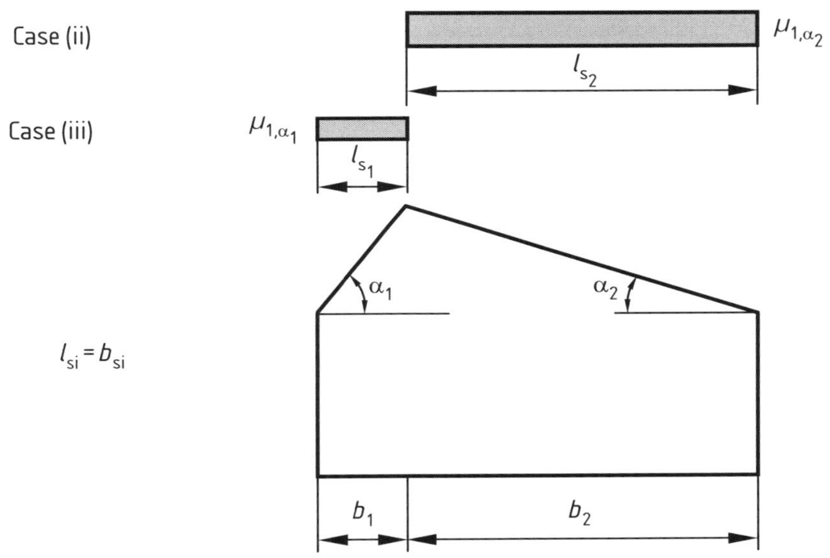

Figure NA.2 — Drifted snow load arrangement for a duo-pitched roof in the UK

Table NA.1 — Drifted snow load shape coefficient for a duo-pitched roof in the UK

Snow load shape coefficent	Angle of pitch of roof (α_i, i =1,2)			
	$0° \leq \alpha_i \leq 15°$	$15° < \alpha_i \leq 30°$	$30° < \alpha_i < 60°$	$\alpha_i \geq 60°$
μ_1	0,8	0,8+0,4(α–15)/15	1,2(60–α)/30	0,0

5.3.4 Multi-span roofs

(1) For multi-span roofs the snow load shape coefficients are given in Table 5.2 and shown in Figure [AC1) 5.4 (AC1].

(2) The undrifted load arrangement which should be used is shown in Figure 5.4, case (i).

(3) The drifted load arrangement which should be used is shown in Figure 5.4, case (ii), unless specified for local conditions.

NOTE Where permitted by the National Annex, Annex B may be used to determine the load case due to drifting.

The National Annex for EN 1991-1-3 specifies the use of Annex B to determine the load case due to drifting.

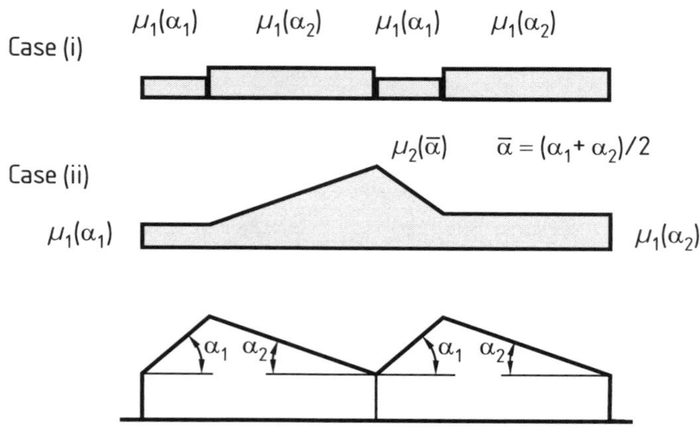

Figure 5.4 — Snow load shape coefficients for multi-span roofs

(4) Special consideration should be given to the snow load shape coefficients for the design of multi-span roofs, where one or both sides of the valley have a slope greater than 60°.

NOTE Guidance may be given in the National Annex.

> **NA.2.18 Drifted snow load arrangement for multi-span roofs [BS EN 1991-1-3:2003, 5.3.4 (3)]**
>
> BS EN 1991-1-3:2003, Annex B should be used in place of the drift load arrangement given in BS EN 1991-1-3:2003, 5.3.4 (3).

5.3.6 Roof abutting and close to taller construction works

(1) The snow load shape coefficients that should be used for roofs abutting to taller construction works are given in the following expressions and shown in Figure 5.7.

μ_1 = 0,8 (assuming the lower roof is flat) (5.6)

$\mu_2 = \mu_s + \mu_w$ (5.7)

where:

μ_s is the snow load shape coefficient due to sliding of snow from the upper roof:
For $\alpha \leq 15°$, $\mu_s = 0$.
For $\alpha > 15°$, μ_s is determined from an additional load amounting to 50 % of the maximum total snow load, on the adjacent slope of the upper roof calculated according to 5.3.3.

μ_w is the snow load shape coefficient due to wind

$$\mu_w = (b_1 + b_2)/2h \leq \gamma\, h/s_k \qquad (5.8)$$

where:

γ is the weight density of snow, which for this calculation may be taken as 2 kN/m^3

An upper and a lower value of μ_w should be specified.

> See EN 1991-1-3, Annex E.

NOTE 1 The range for μ_w may be fixed in the National Annex. The recommended range is $0{,}8 \leq \mu_w \leq 4$.

The drift length is determined as follows:

$$l_s = 2h \qquad (5.9)$$

NOTE 2 A restriction for l_s may be given in the National Annex. The recommended restriction is $5 \leq l_s \leq 15$ m.

NOTE 3 If $b_2 < l_s$ the coefficient at the end of the lower roof is determined by interpolation between μ_1 and μ_2 truncated at the end of the lower roof (see Figure 5.7).

(2) The undrifted load arrangement which should be used is shown in Figure 5.7, case (i).

(3) The drifted load arrangement which should be used is shown in Figure 5.7, case (ii), unless specified for local conditions.

NOTE Where permitted by the National Annex, Annex B may be used to determine the load case due to drifting.

The National Annex for EN 1991-1-3 specifies the use of Annex B to determine the load case due to drifting.

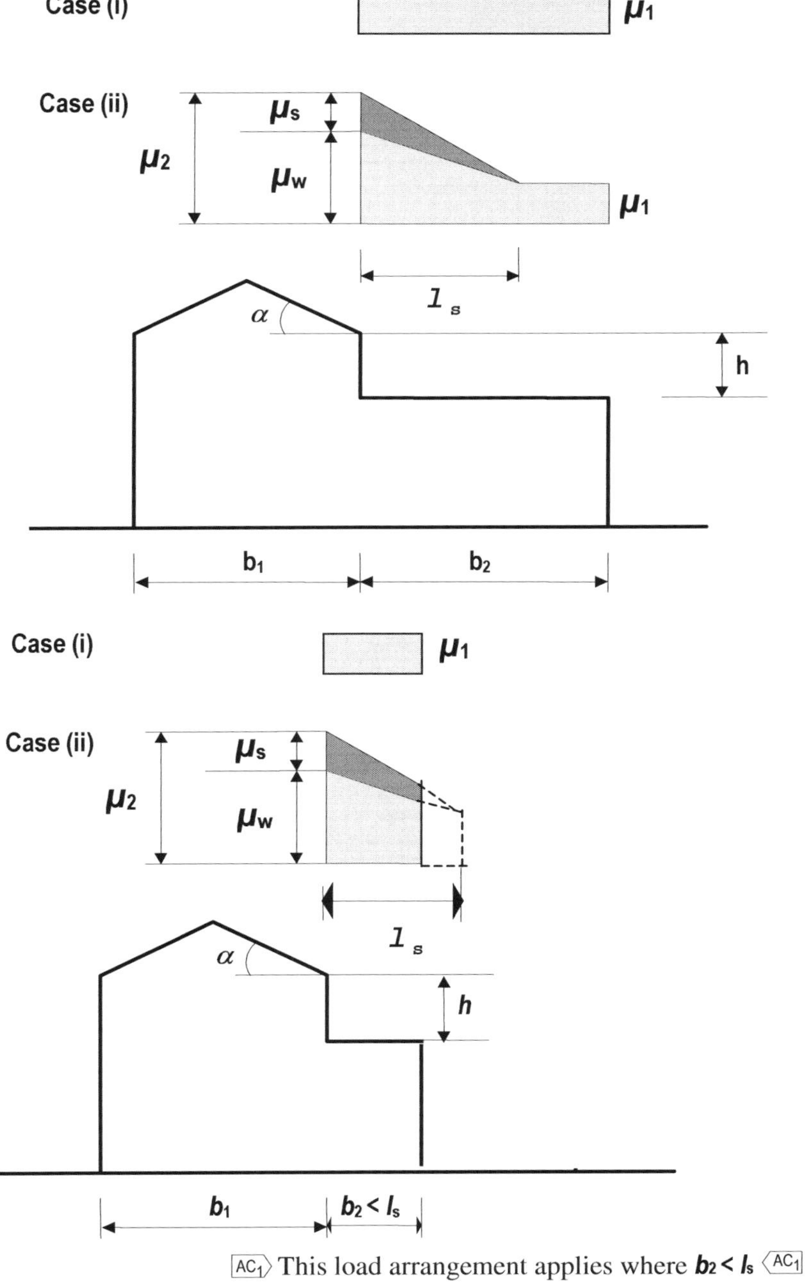

Figure 5.7 — Snow load shape coefficients for roofs abutting to taller construction works

NA.2.21 Snow load shape coeffecient for a roof abutting and close to taller construction works [BS EN 1991-1-3:2003, 5.3.6 (1)]

BS EN 1991-1-3:2003, Annex B should be used to determine the drifted snow load case. This method does not include the snow load shape coefficient μ_w, therefore, no range of values is specified for this coefficient for use in the UK.

NA.2.22 Drifted snow load arrangement for a roof abutting and close to taller construction works [BS EN 1991-1-3:2003, 5.3.6 (3)]

BS EN 1991-1-3:2003, Annex B should be used to determine the drifted snow load case.

Section 6 Local effects

6.1 General

(1) This section gives forces to be applied for the local verifications of:
- drifting at projections and obstructions;
- the edge of the roof;
- snow fences.

(2) The design situations to be considered are persistent/transient.

6.2 Drifting at projections and obstructions

(1) In windy conditions drifting of snow can occur on any roof which has obstructions as these cause areas of aerodynamic shade in which snow accumulates.

(2) The snow load shape coefficients and drift lengths for quasi-horizontal roofs should be taken as follows (see Figure 6.1), unless specified for local conditions:

$\mu_1 = 0,8 \; \mu_2 = \gamma h/s_k$ (6.1)

with the restriction: $0,8 \leq \mu_2 \leq 2,0$ (6.2)

where:

γ is the weight density of snow, may be taken as 2 kN/m^3 See Annex E.

$l_s = 2h$ (6.3)

with the restriction: $5 \leq l_s \leq 15$ m

NOTE Where permitted by the National Annex, Annex B may be used to determine the load case due to drifting.

NA.2.23 Drifting at projections and obstructions [BS EN 1991-1-3:2003, 6.2 (2)]

BS EN 1991-1-3:2003, Annex B should be used to determine the drifted snow load case.

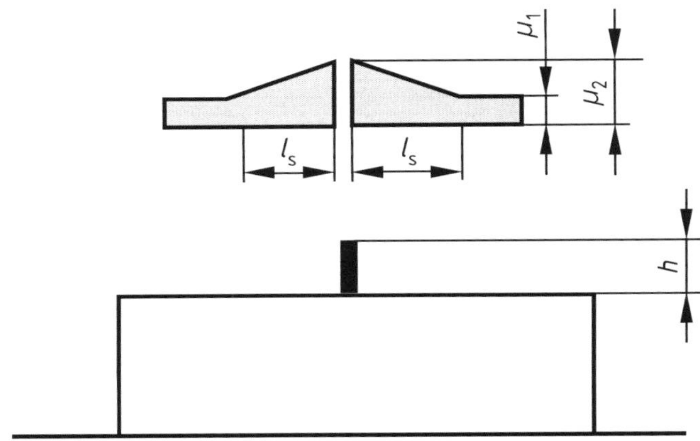

Figure 6.1 — Snow load shape coefficients at projections and obstructions

6.3 Snow overhanging the edge of a roof

(1) Snow overhanging the edge of a roof should be considered.

NOTE The National Annex may specify the conditions of use for this clause. It is recommended that the clause is used for sites above 800 meters above sea level.

See EN 1991-1-3 and NA 2.25 for an explanation.

Table A.1 has been taken from EN 1991-1-3, Annex A (normative), Design situations and load arrangements to be used for different locations.

Table A.1 — Design situations and load arrangements to be used for different locations

Normal	Exceptional conditions		
Case A	Case B1	Case B2	Case B3
No exceptional falls No exceptional drift	Exceptional falls No exceptional drift	No exceptional falls Exceptional drift	Exceptional falls Exceptional drift
3.2(1)	3.3(1)	3.3(2)	3.3(3)
Persistent/transient design situation [1] undrifted μ_i C_eC_t s_k [2] drifted μ_i C_eC_t s_k	*Persistent/transient design situation* [1] undrifted μ_i C_eC_t s_k [2] drifted μ_i C_eC_t s_k *Accidental design situation (where snow is the accidental action)* [3] undrifted μ_i C_eC_t C_{esl} s_k [4] drifted μ_i C_eC_t C_{esl} s_k	*Persistent/transient design situation* [1] undrifted μ_i C_eC_t s_k [2] drifted μ_i C_eC_t s_k (except for roof shapes in Annex B) *Accidental design situation (where snow is the accidental action)* [3] drifted μ_i s_k (for roof shapes in Annex B)	*Persistent/transient design situation* [1] undrifted μ_i C_eC_t s_k [2] drifted μ_i C_eC_t s_k (except for roof shapes in Annex B) *Accidental design situation (where snow is the accidental action)* [3] undrifted μ_i C_eC_t C_{esl} s_k [4] drifted μ_i s_k (for roof shapes in Annex B)

NOTE 1 Exceptional conditions are defined according to the National Annex.

NOTE 2 For cases B1 and B3 the National Annex may define design situations which apply for the particular local effects described in Section 6.

NA.2.26 Design situations and load arrangements to be used for different locations [BS EN 1991-1-3:2003, Annex A]

The localized drifts given in BS EN 1991-1-3:2003, Annex B have been classified as exceptional drifts due to the maritime climate of the UK.

Load case B2 described in BS EN 1991-1-3:2003, Annex A should be used in place of BS EN 1991-1-3:2003, 6.2 for local drifting at projections and obstructions.

ANNEX B (normative) Snow load shape coefficients for exceptional snow drifts

B.1 Scope

(1) This annex gives snow shape coefficients to determine load arrangements due to exceptional snow drifts for the following types of roofs.

a) Multi-span roofs;
b) Roofs abutting and close to taller construction works;
c) Roofs where drifting occurs at projections, obstructions and parapets;
d) For all other load arrangements Section 5 and Section 6 should be used as appropriate.

(2) When considering load cases using snow load shape coefficients obtained from this annex it should be assumed that they are exceptional snow drift loads and that there is no snow elsewhere on the roof.

B.2 Multi-span roofs

(1) The snow load shape coefficient for an exceptional snow drift that should be used for valleys of multi-span roofs is given in Figure B.1 and B.2(2).

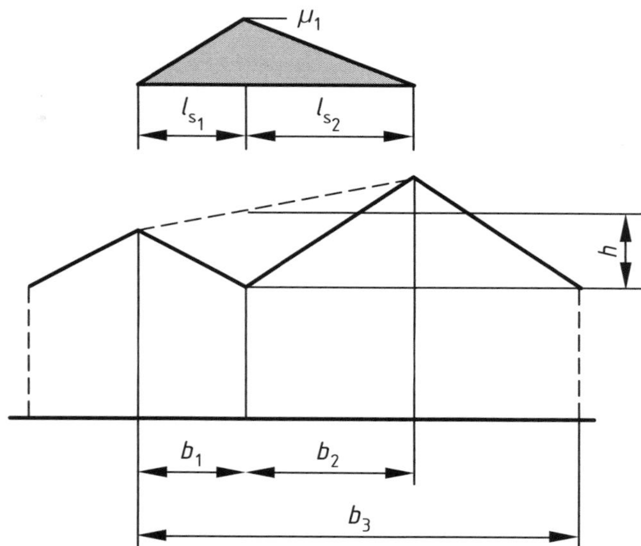

Figure B.1 — Shape coefficient and drift lengths for exceptional snow drifts – valleys of multi-span roofs

(2) The shape coefficient given in Figure B.1 is determined as the least value of:

$\mu_1 = 2h/s_k$

$\mu_1 = 2b_3/(l_{s_1} + l_{s_2})$

$\mu_1 = 5$

The drift lengths are determined as:

$l_{s_1} = b_1$, $l_{s_2} = b_2$

B.3 Roofs abutting and close to taller structures

(1) The snow load shape coefficients for exceptional snow drifts that should be used for roofs abutting a taller construction work are given in Figure B.2 and Table B.1.

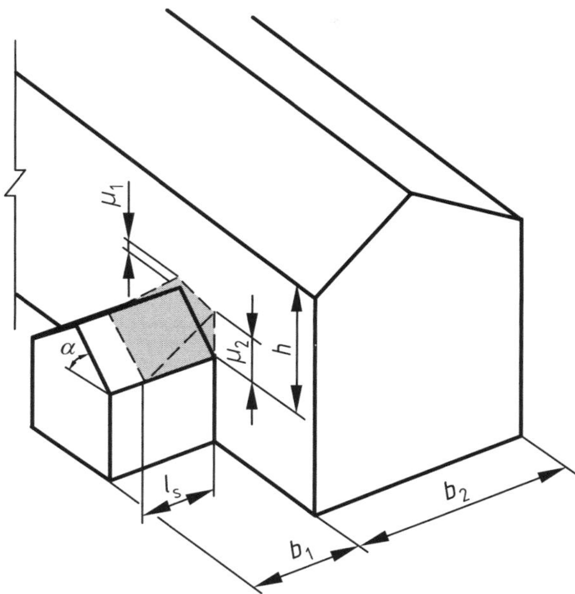

Figure B.2 — Shape coefficients and drift lengths for exceptional snow drifts – Roofs abutting and close to taller structures

(3) The drift length l_s is the least value of $5h$, b_1 or 15 m.

Table B.1 — Shape coefficients for exceptional snow drifts for roofs abutting and close to taller structures

Shape coefficient	Angle of roof pitch α_1			
	$0° \leq \alpha \leq 15°$	$15° < \alpha \leq 30°$	$30° < \alpha < 60°$	$60° \leq \alpha$
μ_1	μ_3	$\mu_3\{[30 - \alpha]/15\}$	0	0
μ_2	μ_3	μ_3	$\mu_3\{[60-\alpha]/30\}$	0
Note 1 μ_3 is the least value of $2h/s_K$, $2b/l_s$ or 8 where b is the larger of b_1 or b_2 and l_s is the least value of $5h$, b_1 or 15 m.				

B.4 Roofs where drifting occurs at projections, obstructions and parapets

(1) The snow load shape coefficients for exceptional snow drifts that should be used for roofs where drifting occurs at projections and obstructions, other than parapets, are given in B.4(2) and Figure B.3. Shape coefficients for drifting behind parapets are given in B4(4).

(2) a) If the vertical elevation against which a drift could form is not greater than [AC1) 1 m, (AC1] the effect of drifting can be ignored.

b) This clause applies to:

- Drifting against obstructions not exceeding 1 m in height.
- Drifting on canopies, projecting not more than 5 m from the face of the building over doors and loading bays, irrespective of the height of the obstruction.

- Slender obstructions over 1 m high but not more than 2 m wide, may be considered as local projections. For this specific case h may be taken as the lesser of the projection height or width perpendicular to the direction of the wind.

c) The shape coefficient given in Figure B.3 is determined as the least value of:
$\mu_1 = 2h_1/s_k$ or 5
$\mu_2 = 2h_2/s_k$ or 5

In addition, for door canopies projecting not more than 5 m from the building, μ_1 should not exceed $2b/l_{s_1}$, where b is the larger of b_1 and b_2.

d) The drift length (l_{s_i}) is taken as the least value of $5h$ or b_i, where i = 1 or 2 and $h \leq$ 1m.

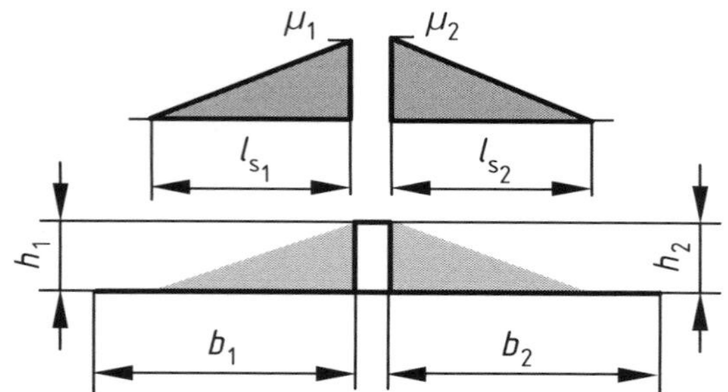

Obstruction on flat roof

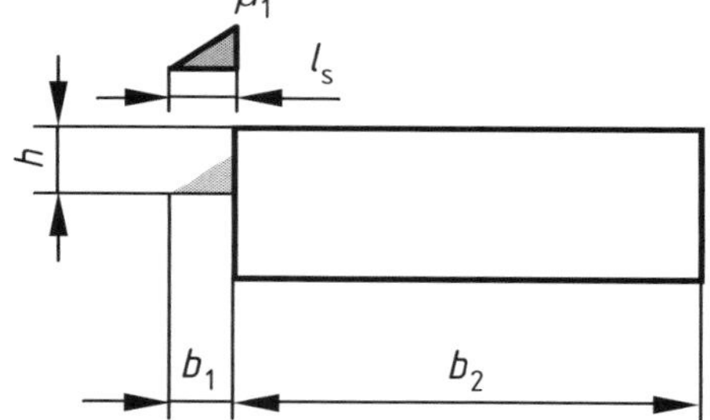

Canopy over door or loading bay where $b_1 \leq 5$ m

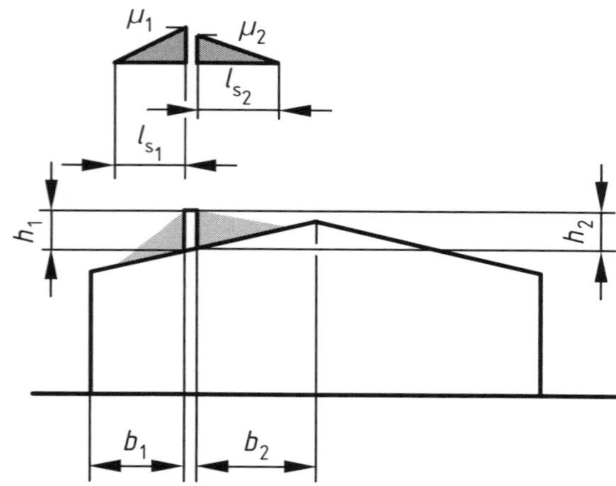

Obstruction on pitched or curved roof

Figure B.3 — Shape coefficients for exceptional snow drifts for roofs where drifting occurs at projections and obstructions

ANNEX E
(informative)
Bulk weight density of snow

(1) The bulk weight density of snow varies. In general it increases with the duration of the snow cover and depends on the site location, climate and altitude.

(2) Except where specified in Sections 1 to 6 indicative values for the mean bulk weight density of snow on the ground given in Table E.1 may be used.

Table E.1 — Mean bulk weight density of snow

Type of snow	Bulk weight density [kN/m^3]
Fresh	1,0
Settled (several hours or days after its fall)	2,0
Old (several weeks or months after its fall)	2,5 - 3,5
Wet	4,0

NA.3.3 Bulk weight density of snow [BS EN 1991-1-3:2003, Annex E]

BS EN 1991-1-3:2003, Annex E may be used in the UK.

Bibliography

ISO 4355 Bases for design of structures – Determination of snow loads on roofs

ISO 3898 Bases for design of structures – Notations – General symbols

Bibliography

Standards publications

BS EN 1990:2002, *Eurocode — Basis of structural design.*

NA to BS EN 1990:2002, *UK National Annex for Eurocode 0 — Basis of structural design.*

NA to BS EN 1991-1-1, *UK National Annex to Eurocode 1: Actions on structures — Part 1-1: General actions — Densities, self-weight, imposed loads for buildings.*

Other publications

[1] BRE Digest 439, *Roof loads due to local drifting of snow*, Watford: BRE, 1999.

Useful references

[1] Sanpaolesi L. 'Snow loading: Scientific basis, problems and challenges', *Progress in Structural Engineering and Materials*, 1998, Vol 1 (4), pp443-451

Extracts from EN 1991-1-4

The extracts in this part of Chapter 1 are taken from EN 1991-1-4:2005 (incorporating corrigendum July 2009), *Eurocode 1: Actions on structure — Part 1-4 General actions — Wind actions*.

The start and finish of text introduced or altered by corrigendum is indicated in the text by tags. Text altered by CEN corrigendum July 2009 is indicated in the text by [AC1) (AC1].

Foreword

Additional information specific for EN 1991-1-4

EN 1991-1-4 gives design guidance and actions for the structural design of buildings and civil engineering works for wind.
EN 1991-1-4 is intended for the use by clients, designers, contractors and relevant authorities.
EN 1991-1-4 is intended to be used with EN 1990, the other Parts of EN 1991 and EN 1992-1999 for the design of structures.

See Chapter 0 – Extracts from Eurocode 0: Basis of structural design.

The full list of the contents of EN 1991-1-4 follows, and is give for reference purposes. (Bold items are included in this chapter.)

Section 1 General

1.1 Scope

The scope for EN 1991-1-4 is given in full. (Bold items are covered in this chapter.)

(1) EN 1991-1-4 gives guidance on the determination of natural wind actions for the structural design of building and civil engineering works for each of the loaded areas under consideration. This includes the whole structure or parts of the structure or elements attached to the structure, e.g. components, cladding units and their fixings, safety and noise barriers.

AC1 (2) This part is applicable to:

- buildings and civil engineering works with heights up to 200 m, see also (11)
- bridges having no span greater than 200 m, provided that they satisfy the criteria for dynamic response, see (12) and 8.2. AC1

(3) This part is intended to predict characteristic wind actions on land-based structures, their components and appendages.

(4) Certain aspects necessary to determine wind actions on a structure are dependent on the location and on the availability and quality of meteorological data, the type of terrain, etc. These need to be provided in the National Annex and Annex A, through National choice by notes in the text as indicated. Default values and methods are given in the main text, where the National Annex does not provide information.

(5) Annex A gives illustrations of the terrain categories and provides rules for the effects of orography including displacement height, roughness change, influence of landscape and influence of neighbouring structures.

(6) Annexes B and C give alternative procedures for calculating the structural factor $c_s c_d$.

(7) Annex D gives $c_s c_d$ factors for different types of structures.

(8) Annex E gives rules for vortex induced response and some guidance on other aeroelastic effects.

(9) Annex F gives dynamic characteristics of structures with linear behaviour.

(10) This part does not give guidance on local thermal effects on the characteristic wind, e.g. strong arctic thermal surface inversion or funnelling or tornadoes.

AC1 (11) Guyed masts and lattice towers are treated in EN 1993-3-1 and lighting columns in EN 40.

(12) This part does not give guidance on the following aspects:

- torsional vibrations, e.g. tall buildings with a central core
- bridge deck vibrations from transverse wind turbulence
- wind actions on cable supported bridges
- vibrations where more than the fundamental mode needs to be considered. AC1

1.3 Assumptions

See Chapter 0.

1.4 Distinction between Principles and Application Rules

See Chapter 0.

1.6 Definitions

For the purposes of this European Standard, the definitions given in ISO 2394, ISO 3898 and ISO 8930 and the following apply. Additionally for the purposes of this Standard a basic list of definitions is provided in EN 1990, 1.5.

1.6.1
fundamental basic wind velocity
the 10 minute mean wind velocity with an annual risk of being exceeded of 0,02, irrespective of wind direction, at a height of 10 m above flat open country terrain and accounting for altitude effects (if required)

1.6.2
basic wind velocity
the fundamental basic wind velocity modified to account for the direction of the wind being considered and the season (if required)

1.6.3
mean wind velocity
the basic wind velocity modified to account for the effect of terrain roughness and orography

1.6.4
pressure coefficient
external pressure coefficients give the effect of the wind on the external surfaces of buildings; internal pressure coefficients give the effect of the wind on the internal surfaces of buildings.

The external pressure coefficients are divided into overall coefficients and local coefficients. Local coefficients give the pressure coefficients for loaded areas of 1 m^2 or less, e.g. for the design of small elements and fixings; overall coefficients give the pressure coefficients for loaded areas larger than 10 m^2.

Net pressure coefficients give the resulting effect of the wind on a structure, structural element or component per unit area

1.6.5
force coefficient
force coefficients give the overall effect of the wind on a structure, structural element or component as a whole, including friction, if not specifically excluded

1.6.6
background response factor
the background factor allowing for the lack of full correlation of the pressure on the structure surface

1.6.7
resonance response factor
the resonance response factor allowing for turbulence in resonance with the vibration mode

1.7 Symbols

(1) For the purposes of this European Standard, the following symbols apply.

NOTE The notation used is based on ISO 3898:1999. In this Part the symbol dot in expressions indicates multiplication sign. This notation has been employed to avoid confusion with functional expressions.

(2) A basic list of notations is provided in EN 1990, 1.6 and the additional notations below are specific to EN 1991-1-4.

Latin upper case letters

A	area
A_{fr}	area swept by the wind
A_{ref}	reference area
B^2	background response part
C	wind load factor for bridges
E	Young's modulus
F_{fr}	resultant friction force
F_j	vortex exciting force at point j of the structure
F_w	resultant wind force
H	height of a topographic feature
I_v	turbulence intensity
K	mode shape factor; shape parameter
[AC1) K_a	aerodynamic damping parameter (AC1]
K_{iv}	interference factor for vortex shedding
K_{rd}	reduction factor for parapets
K_w	correlation length factor
K_x	non dimensional coefficient
L	length of the span of a bridge deck; turbulent length scale
L_d	actual length of a downwind slope
L_e	effective length of an upwind slope
L_j	correlation length
L_u	actual length of an upwind slope
N	number of cycles caused by vortex shedding
N_g	number of loads for gust response
R^2	resonant response part
Re	Reynolds number
R_h, R_b	aerodynamic admittance
S	wind action
Sc	Scruton number
S_L	non dimensional power spectral density function
St	Strouhal number
W_s	weight of the structural parts contributing to the stiffness of a chimney
W_t	total weight of a chimney

Latin lower case letters

a_G	factor of galloping instability
a_{IG}	combined stability parameter for interference galloping
b	width of the structure
c_{alt}	altitude factor
c_d	dynamic factor
c_{dir}	directional factor
$c_e(z)$	exposure factor
c_f	force coefficient
$c_{f,o}$	force coefficient of structures or structural elements without free-end flow
$c_{f,l}$	lift force coefficient
c_{fr}	friction coefficient
c_{lat}	aerodynamic exciting coefficient
c_M	moment coefficient
c_p	pressure coefficient
[AC1) c_{pe}	external pressure coefficient
c_{pi}	internal pressure coefficient
$c_{p,net}$	net pressure coefficient (AC1]
c_{prob}	probability factor
c_r	roughness factor
c_o	orography factor
c_s	size factor
c_{season}	seasonal factor
d	depth of the structure
e	eccentricity of a force or edge distance

f_L non dimensional frequency
h height of the structure
h_{ave} obstruction height
h_{dis} displacement height
k equivalent roughness
[AC1) k_l turbulence factor (AC1]
k_p peak factor
k_r terrain factor
k_Θ torsional stiffness
l length of a horizontal structure
m mass per unit length
m_1 equivalent mass per unit length
n_i natural frequency of the structure of the mode i
$n_{1,x}$ fundamental frequency of along wind vibration
$n_{1,y}$ fundamental frequency of cross-wind vibration
n_0 ovalling frequency
p annual probability of exceedence
q_b reference mean (basic) velocity pressure
q_p peak velocity pressure
r radius
s factor; coordinate
t averaging time of the reference wind speed, plate thickness
v_{CG} onset wind velocity for galloping
v_{CIG} critical wind velocity for interference galloping
v_{crit} critical wind velocity of vortex shedding
v_{div} divergence wind velocity
v_m mean wind velocity
$v_{b,0}$ fundamental value of the basic wind velocity
v_b basic wind velocity
w wind pressure
x horizontal distance of the site from the top of a crest
x-direction horizontal direction, perpendicular to the span
y-direction horizontal direction along the span
y_{max} maximum cross-wind amplitude at critical wind speed
z height above ground
z_{ave} average height
z-direction vertical direction
z_0 roughness length
z_e, z_i reference height for external wind action, internal pressure
z_g distance from the ground to the considered component
z_{max} maximum height
z_{min} minimum height
z_s reference height for determining the structural factor

Greek upper case letters

Φ upwind slope
$\Phi_{1,x}$ fundamental alongwind modal shape

Greek lower case letters

α_G galloping instability parameter
α_{IG} combined stability parameter of interference galloping
δ logarithmic decrement of damping
δ_a [AC1) logarithmic decrement of aerodynamic damping (AC1]
δ_d logarithmic decrement of damping due to special devices
δ_s [AC1) logarithmic decrement of structural damping (AC1]
ε coefficient
ε_0 bandwidth factor
ε_1 frequency factor
η variable
φ solidity ratio, blockage of canopy

λ	slenderness ratio
μ	opening ratio, permeability of a skin
ν	up-crossing frequency; Poisson ratio; kinematic viscosity
θ	torsional angle; wind direction
ρ	air density
σ_{v}	standard deviation of the turbulence
$\sigma_{\mathrm{a,x}}$	standard deviation of alongwind acceleration
ψ_{mc}	reduction factor for multibay canopies
ψ_{r}	reduction factor of force coefficient for square sections with rounded corners
ψ_{λ}	reduction factor of force coefficient for structural elements with end-effects
$\psi_{\lambda\alpha}$	end-effect factor for circular cylinders
ψ_{s}	shelter factor for walls and fences
ζ	exponent of mode shape

Indices

crit	critical
e	external, exposure
fr	friction
i	internal, mode number
j	current number of incremental area or point of a structure
m	mean
p	peak, parapet
ref	reference
v	wind velocity
x	along-wind direction
y	cross-wind direction
z	vertical direction

Section 2 Design situations

(1)P The relevant wind actions shall be determined for each design situation identified in accordance with EN 1990, 3.2.

(2) In accordance with EN 1990, 3.2 (3)P other actions (such as snow, traffic or ice) which will modify the effects due to wind should be taken into account.

AC1 NOTE See also EN 1991-1-3, EN 1991-2 and ISO 12494. AC1

(3) In accordance with EN 1990, 3.2 (3)P, the changes to the structure during stages of execution (such as different stages of the form of the structure, dynamic characteristics, etc.), which may modify the effects due to wind, should be taken into account.

NOTE See also EN 1991-1-6.

(4) Where in design windows and doors are assumed to be shut under storm conditions, the effect of these being open should be treated as an accidental design situation.

NOTE See also EN 1990, 3.2 (2) (P).

Section 3 Modelling of wind actions

3.1 Nature

(1) Wind actions fluctuate with time and act directly as pressures on the external surfaces of enclosed structures and, because of porosity of the external surface, also act indirectly on the internal surfaces. They may also act directly on the internal surface of open structures. Pressures act on areas of the surface resulting in forces normal to the surface of the structure or of individual cladding components. Additionally, when large areas of structures are swept by the wind, friction forces acting tangentially to the surface may be significant.

3.2 Representations of wind actions

(1) The wind action is represented by a simplified set of pressures or forces whose effects are equivalent to the extreme effects of the turbulent wind.

3.3 Classification of wind actions

(1) Unless otherwise specified, wind actions should be classified as variable fixed actions, see EN 1990, 4.1.1.

3.4 Characteristic values

(1) The wind actions calculated using EN 1991-1-4 are characteristic values (see EN 1990, 4.1.2). They are determined from the basic values of wind velocity or the velocity pressure. In accordance with EN 1990 4.1.2 (7)P the basic values are characteristic values having annual probabilities of exceedence of 0,02, which is equivalent to a mean return period of 50 years.

NOTE All coefficients or models, to derive wind actions from basic values, are chosen so that the probability of the calculated wind actions does not exceed the probability of these basic values.

3.5 Models

(1) The effect of the wind on the structure (i.e. the response of the structure) depends on the size, shape and dynamic properties of the structure. This part covers dynamic response due to along-wind turbulence in resonance with the along-wind vibrations of a fundamental flexural mode shape with constant sign.

The response of structures should be calculated according to Section 5 from the peak velocity pressure, q_p, at the reference height in the undisturbed wind field, the force and pressure coefficients and the structural factor $c_s c_d$ (see Section 6). q_p depends on the wind climate, the terrain roughness and orography, and the reference height. q_p is equal to the mean velocity pressure plus a contribution from short-term pressure fluctuations.

(2) Aeroelastic response should be considered for flexible structures such as cables, masts, chimneys and bridges.

NOTE Simplified guidance on aeroelastic response is given in Annex E.

Section 4 Wind velocity and velocity pressure

4.1 Basis for calculation

(1) The wind velocity and the velocity pressure are composed of a mean and a fluctuating component.

The mean wind velocity v_m should be determined from the basic wind velocity v_b which depends on the wind climate as described in 4.2, and the height variation of the wind determined from the terrain roughness and orography as described in 4.3. The peak velocity pressure is determined in 4.5.

The fluctuating component of the wind is represented by the turbulence intensity defined in 4.4.

NOTE The National Annex may provide national climatic information from which the mean wind velocity v_m, the peak velocity pressure q_p and additional values may be directly obtained for the terrain categories considered.

4.2 Basic values

(1)P The fundamental value of the basic wind velocity, $v_{b,0}$, is the characteristic 10 minutes mean wind velocity, irrespective of wind direction and time of year, at 10 m above ground level in open country terrain with low vegetation such as grass and isolated obstacles with separations of at least 20 obstacle heights.

NOTE 1 This terrain corresponds to terrain category II in Table 4.1.

NOTE 2 The fundamental value of the basic wind velocity, $v_{b,0}$, may be given in the National Annex.

> The National Annex to EN 1991-1-4 provides a wind map to determine $v_{b,0}$. See Figure NA.1 on page 1-63.

(2)P The basic wind velocity shall be calculated from expression (4.1).

$$v_b = c_{dir}\, c_{season}\, v_{b,0} \tag{4.1}$$

where:

v_b is the basic wind velocity, defined as a function of wind direction and time of year at 10 m above ground of terrain category II

$v_{b,0}$ is the fundamental value of the basic wind velocity, see (1)P

c_{dir} is the directional factor

c_{season} is the season factor

NOTE 1 Where the influence of altitude on the basic wind velocity v_b is not included in the specified fundamental value $v_{b,0}$ the National Annex may give a procedure to take it into account.

NOTE 2 The value of the directional factor, c_{dir}, for various wind directions may be found in the National Annex. The recommended value is 1,0.

NOTE 3 The value of the season factor, c_{season}, may be given in the National Annex. The recommended value is 1,0.

NOTE 4 The 10 minutes mean wind velocity having the probability p for an annual exceedence is determined by multiplying the basic wind velocity v_b in 4.2 (2)P by the probability factor, c_{prob} given by Expression (4.2). See also EN 1991-1-6.

NA.2.4 The fundamental value of the basic wind velocity $v_{b,0}$
[BS EN 1991-1-4:2005, 4.2 (1)P Note 2]

The fundamental value of the basic wind velocity $v_{b,0}$ should be determined from Equation NA.1.

$$v_{b,0} = v_{b,map} c_{alt} \qquad \text{(NA.1)}$$

where

$v_{b,map}$ is the value of the fundamental basic wind velocity before the altitude correction is applied. $v_{b,map}$ is given in Figure NA.1;
c_{alt} is the altitude factor given in NA.2.5.

NA.2.5 Procedure for determining the influence of altitude
[BS EN 1991-1-4:2005, 4.2 (2)P Note 1]

The altitude factor c_{alt} should be determined from Equations NA.2a) or NA.2b).

$$c_{alt} = 1 + 0{,}001 \cdot A \quad \text{for } z \leq 10 \text{ m} \qquad \text{(NA.2a))}$$
$$c_{alt} = 1 + 0{,}001 \cdot A \cdot (10/z)^{0.2} \quad \text{for } z > 10 \text{ m} \qquad \text{(NA.2b))}$$

where

A is the altitude of the site in metres above mean sea level;
z is either z_s as defined in BS EN 1991-1-4:2005 Figure 6.1 or z_e the height of the part above ground as defined in BS EN 1991-1-4:2005 Figure 7.4.

NOTE Equation NA.2a) may be used conservatively for any building height.

Where there is significant orography, as defined by the shaded zones in Figure NA.2, A should be taken as the altitude of the upwind base of the orographic feature for each wind direction considered.

(3) For temporary structures and for all structures in the execution phase, the seasonal factor c_{season} may be used. For transportable structures, which may be used at any time in the year, c_{season} should be taken equal to 1,0.

NOTE See also EN 1991-1-6.

4.3 Mean wind

4.3.1 Variation with height

(1) The mean wind velocity $v_m(z)$ at a height z above the terrain depends on the terrain roughness and orography and on the basic wind velocity, v_b, and should be determined using expression (4.3)

$$v_m(z) = c_r(z) \cdot c_o(z) \cdot v_b \qquad (4.3)$$

where:

$c_r(z)$ is the roughness factor, given in 4.3.2
$c_o(z)$ is the orography factor, taken as 1,0 unless otherwise specified in 4.3.3

Figure NA.2 defines areas of significant orography.

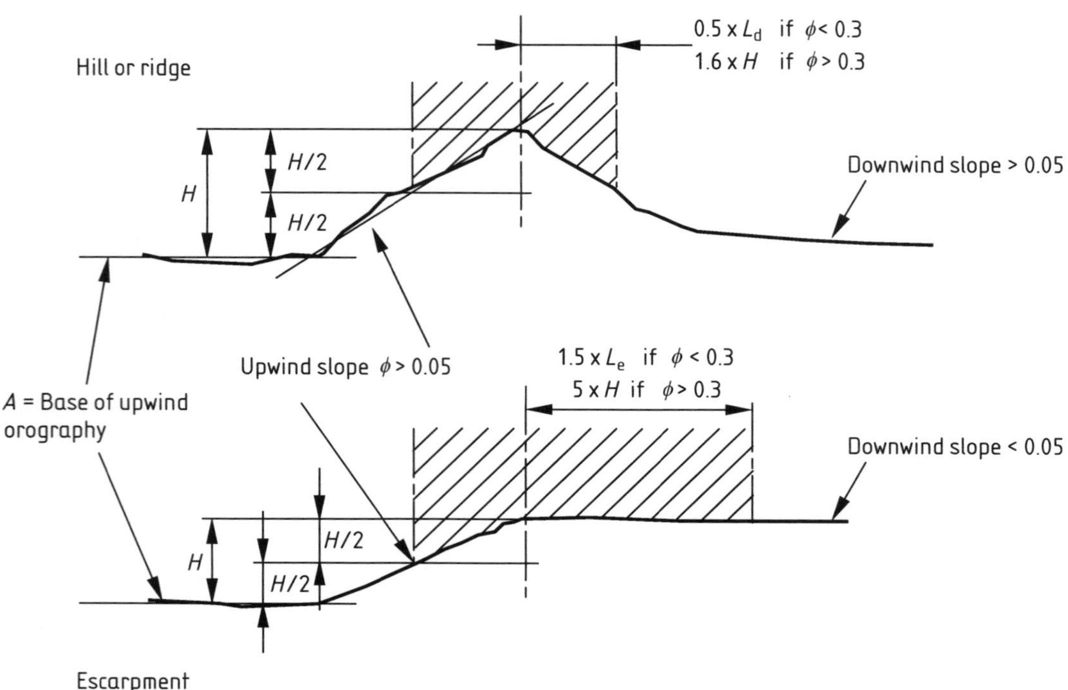

Figure NA.2 — Definition of significant orography (definition of symbols given in A.3(3))

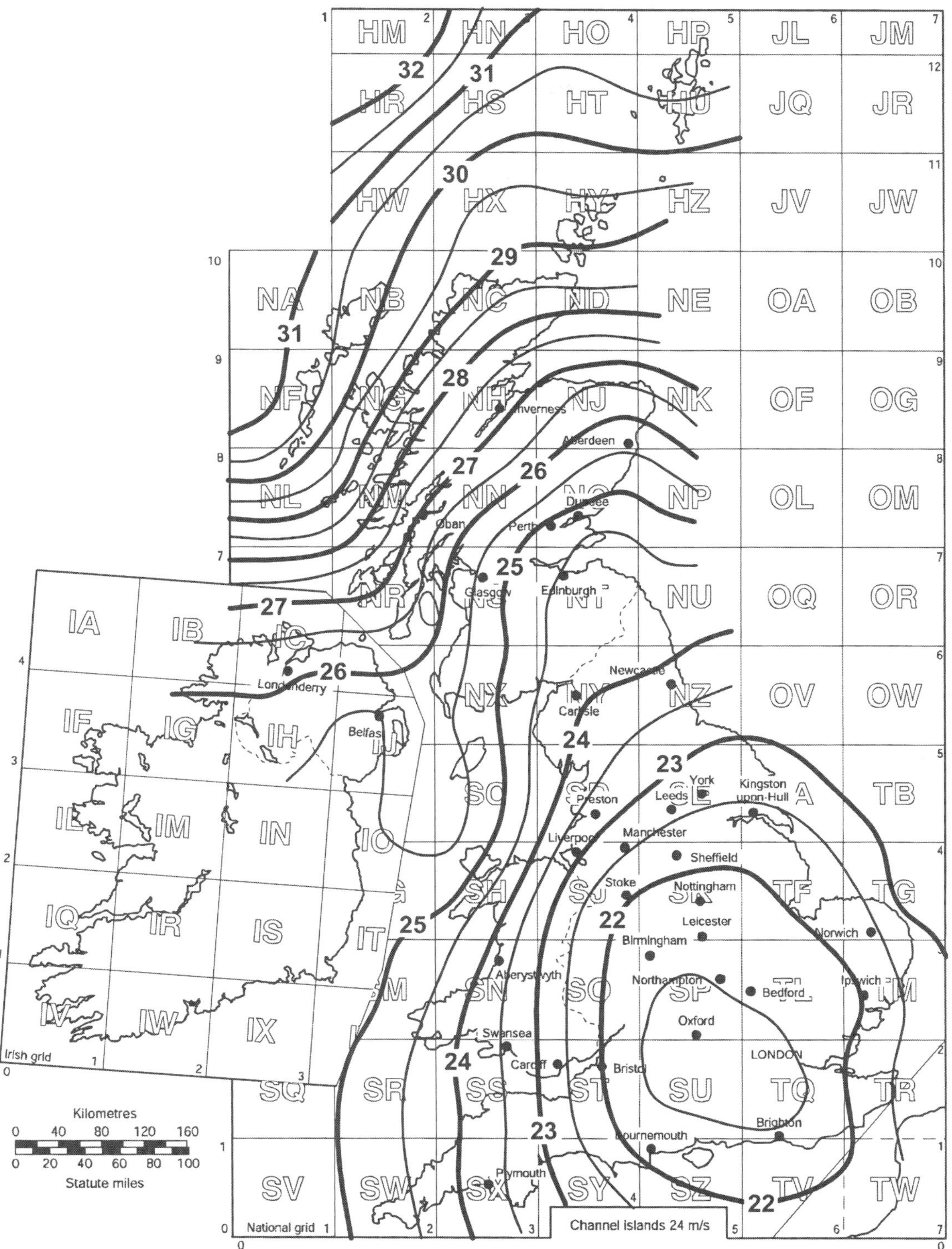

Figure NA.1 — Value of fundamental basic wind velocity $v_{b,map}$ (m/s) before the altitude correction is applied

NOTE 1 Information on $c_o(z)$ may be given in the National Annex. If the orography is accounted for in the basic wind velocity, the recommended value is 1,0.

NOTE 2 Design charts or tables for $v_m(z)$ may be given in the National Annex.

To determine $c_o(z)$ in accordance with the UK National Annex, the recommended procedure in EN 1991-1-4, Annex A should be used. Design charts for $v_m(z)$ are not provided in the UK NA.

The influence of neighbouring structures on the wind velocity should be considered (see 4.3.4).

4.3.2 Terrain roughness

(1) The roughness factor, $c_r(z)$, accounts for the variability of the mean wind velocity at the site of the structure due to:

- the height above ground level
- the ground roughness of the terrain upwind of the structure in the wind direction considered

NOTE The procedure for determining $c_r(z)$ may be given in the National Annex. The recommended procedure for the determination of the roughness factor at height z is given by the expression (4.4) and is based on a logarithmic velocity profile.

The procedure for determining $c_r(z)$ is given in the National Annex and is given below this clause.

$$c_r(z) = k_r \cdot \ln\left(\frac{z}{z_0}\right) \quad \text{for} \quad z_{min} \leq z \leq z_{max}$$

$$c_r(z) = c_r(z_{min}) \quad \text{for} \quad z \leq z_{min} \qquad (4.4)$$

where:
z_0 is the roughness length
k_r is a terrain factor depending on the roughness length z_0 calculated using

$$k_r = 0,19 \cdot \left(\frac{z_0}{z_{0,II}}\right)^{0,07} \qquad (4.5)$$

where $z_{0,II}$ = 0,05 m (terrain category II, Table 4.1)
z_{min} is the minimum height defined in Table 4.1
z_{max} is to be taken as 200 m

z_0, z_{min} depend on the terrain category. Recommended values are given in Table 4.1 depending on five representative terrain categories.

Expression (4.4) is valid when the upstream distance with uniform terrain roughness is long enough to stabilise the profile sufficiently. See (2).

Table 4.1 — Terrain categories and terrain parameters

Terrain category	z_0 m	z_{min} m
0 Sea or coastal area exposed to the open sea	0,003	1
I Lakes or flat and horizontal area with negligible vegetation and without obstacles	0,01	1
II Area with low vegetation such as grass and isolated obstacles (trees, buildings) with separations of at least 20 obstacle heights	0,05	2
III Area with regular cover of vegetation or buildings or with isolated obstacles with separations of maximum 20 obstacle heights (such as villages, suburban terrain, permanent forest)	0,3	5
IV Area in which at least 15 % of the surface is covered with buildings and their average height exceeds 15 m	1,0	10
The terrain categories are illustrated in Annex A.1.		

NA.2.11 Procedure for determining the roughness factor $c_r(z)$ [BS EN 1991-1-4:2005, 4.3.2 (1)]

BS EN 1991-1-4:2005 Expressions (4.4) and (4.5) do not apply.

The classification of roughness categories has been simplified to give the following three terrain categories:

- Terrain category 0 is referred to as Sea;
- Terrain categories I and II have been considered together to give a single terrain category referred to as Country terrain;
- Terrain categories III and IV have been considered together to give a single terrain category referred to as Town terrain.

All inland lakes extending more than 1 km in the direction of wind and closer than 1 km upwind of the site should be treated as Sea.

The roughness factor $c_r(z)$ depends on upwind distance to sea and additionally on the distance upwind to the edge of the urban area for sites in Town terrain.

For sites in Country terrain, the roughness factor $c_r(z)$ given in Figure NA.3 should be used.

For sites adjacent to Sea terrain (sea or large inland lakes), the distance upwind from the shoreline should be taken as 0,1 km.

For sites in Town terrain, the roughness factor $c_r(z)$ given in Figure NA.3 should be multiplied by the roughness correction factor $c_{r,T}$ for Town terrain given in Figure NA.4.

NOTE The appropriate value of h_{dis} is to be used in Figure NA.3 and Figure NA.4. For sites in Country terrain, h_{dis} = 0. For sites in Town terrain, h_{dis} is given by BS EN 1991-1-4:2005 A.5.

BS EN 1991-1-4 A.5 is reproduced after Figure NA.4 on page 1-67.

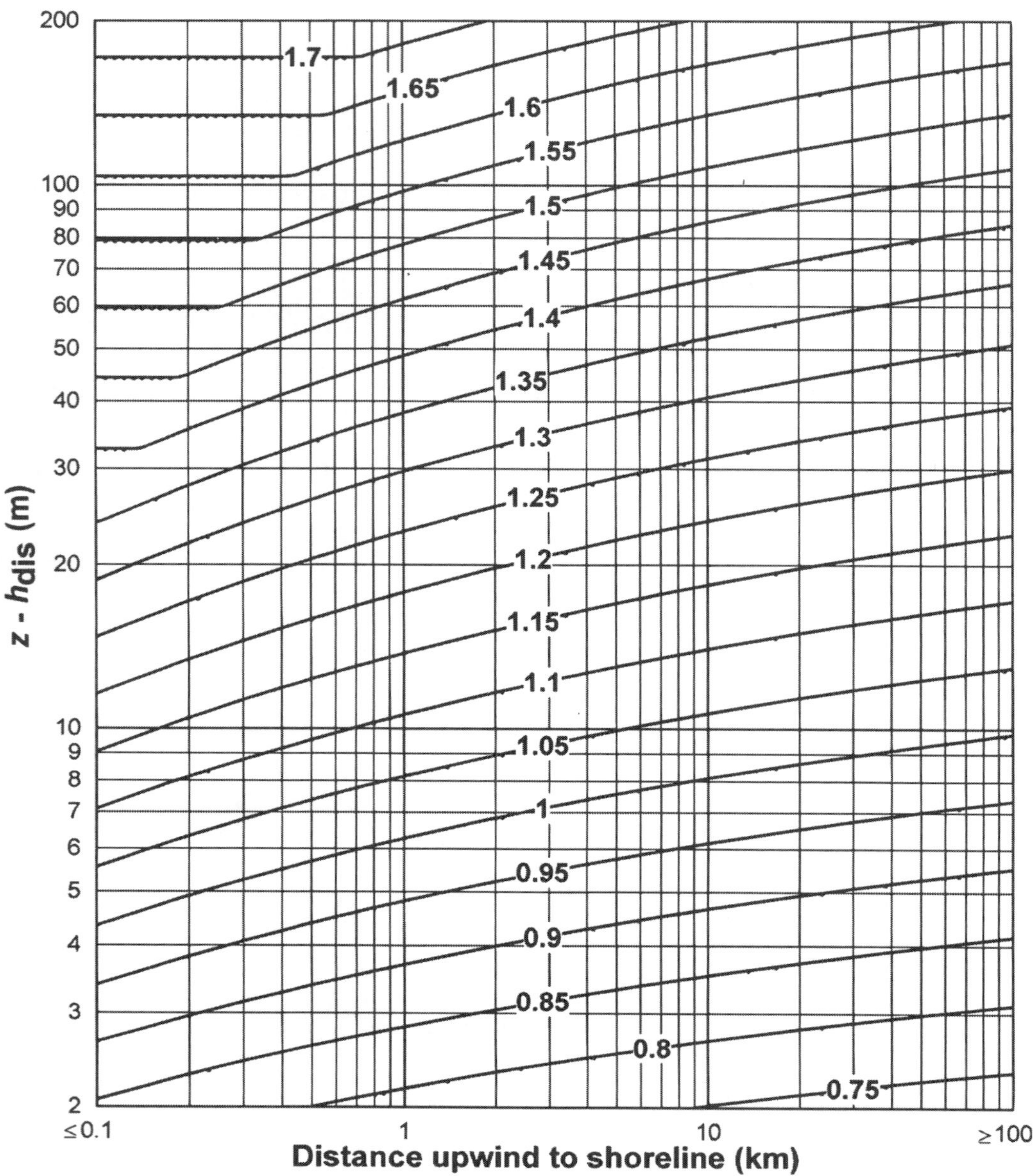

NOTE The height z is the height at which v_m is sought.

Figure NA.3 — Values of $c_r(z)$

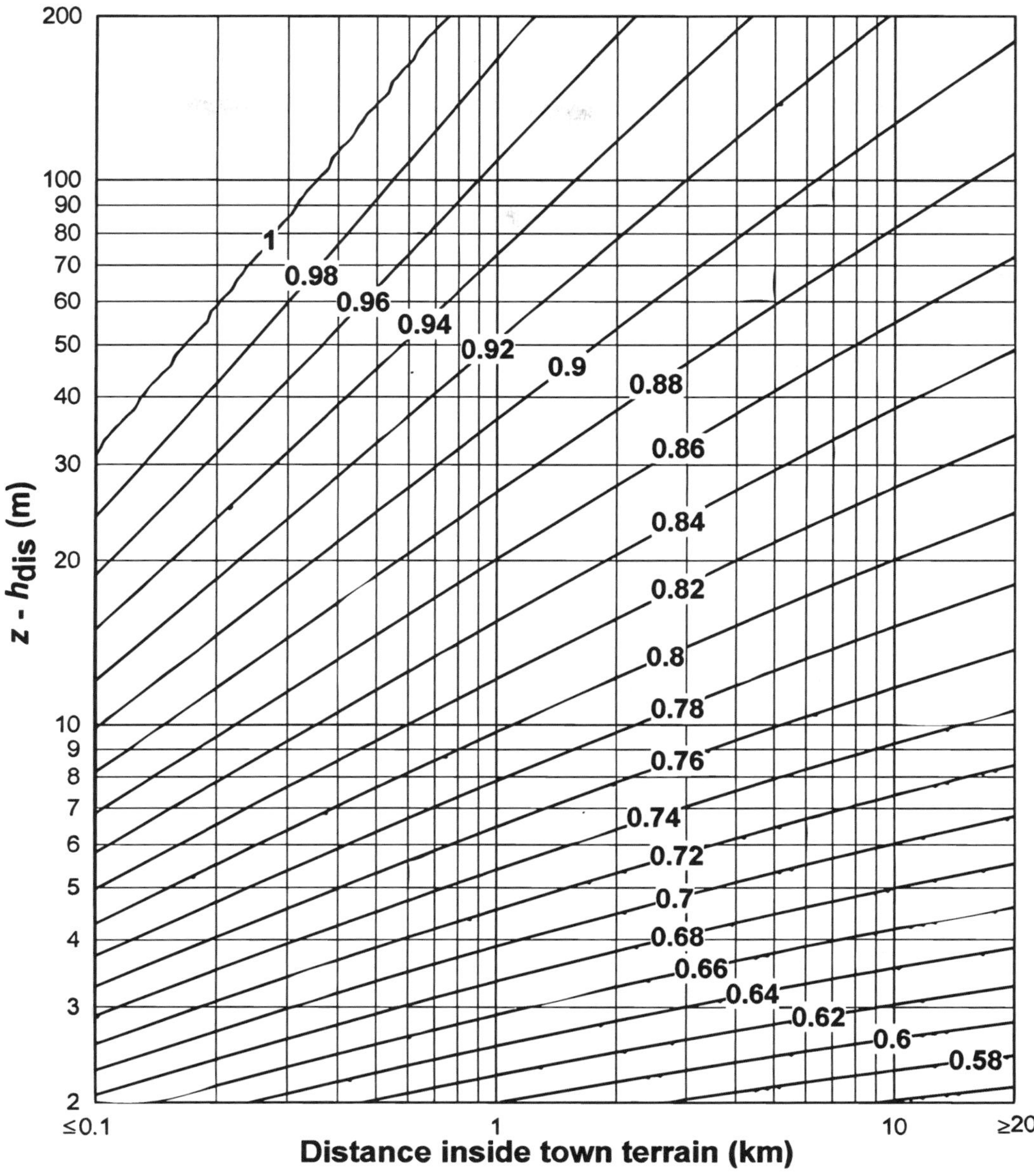

NOTE The height z is the height at which v_m is sought.

Figure NA.4 — Values of correction factor $c_{r,T}$ for sites in Town terrain

A.5 Displacement height

(1) For buildings in terrain category IV, closely spaced buildings and other obstructions cause the wind to behave as if the ground level was raised to a displacement height, h_{dis}. h_{dis} may be determined by Expression (A.15), see Figure A.5. The profile of peak velocity pressure over height (see Figure 4.2) may be lifted by a height h_{dis}.

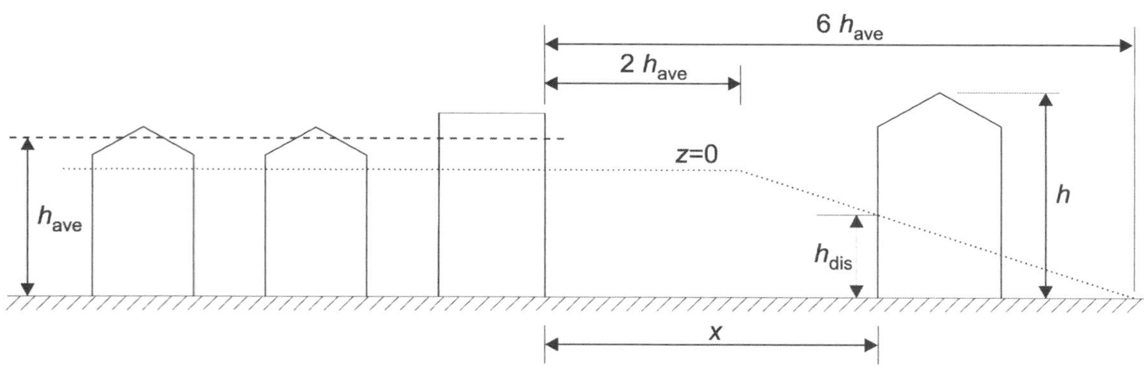

Figure A.5 — Obstruction height and upwind spacing

$x \leq 2 \cdot h_{ave}$	h_{dis} is the lesser of $0{,}8 \cdot h_{ave}$ or $0{,}6 \cdot h$	
$2 \cdot h_{ave} < x < 6 \cdot h_{ave}$	h_{dis} is the lesser of $1{,}2 \cdot h_{ave} - 0{,}2 \cdot x$ or $0{,}6 \cdot h$	(A.15)
$x \geq 6 \cdot h_{ave}$	$h_{dis} = 0$	

In the absence of more accurate information the obstruction height may be taken as h_{ave} = 15 m for terrain category IV. [AC1) These rules are direction dependent, the values of h_{ave} and x should be established for each 30° sector as described in 4.3.2. (AC1]

(2) The terrain roughness to be used for a given wind direction depends on the ground roughness and the distance with uniform terrain roughness in an angular sector around the wind direction. Small areas (less than 10% of the area under consideration) with deviating roughness may be ignored. See Figure 4.1.

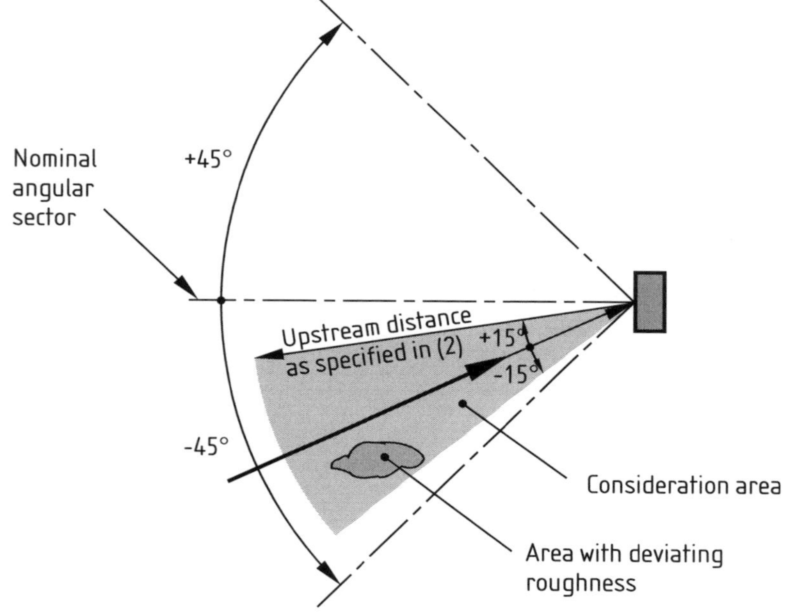

NOTE The National Annex may give definitions of the angular sector and of the upstream distance. The recommended value of the angular sector may be taken as the 30° angular sector within ±15° from the wind direction. The recommended value for the upstream distance may be obtained from Annex A.2.

> The UK NA gives national parameters for the use of Annex A.2.

Figure 4.1 — Assessment of terrain roughness

(3) When a pressure or force coefficient is defined for a nominal angular sector, the lowest roughness length within any 30° angular wind sector should be used.

(4) When there is choice between two or more terrain categories in the definition of a given area, then the area with the lowest roughness length should be used.

4.3.3 Terrain orography

(1) Where orography (e.g. hills, cliffs etc.) increases wind velocities by more than 5 % the effects should be taken into account using the orography factor c_O.

NOTE The procedure to be used for determining c_o may be given in the National Annex. The recommended procedure is given in A.3.

For the purpose of this guide, c_O is taken as 1,0. The National Annex for EN 1991-1-4 gives a procedure to consider terrain orography.

(2) The effects of orography may be neglected when the average slope of the upwind terrain is less than 3°. The upwind terrain may be considered up to a distance of 10 times the height of the isolated orographic feature.

4.3.4 Large and considerably higher neighbouring structures

(1) If the structure is to be located close to another structure, that is at least twice as high as the average height of its neighbouring structures, then it could be exposed (dependent on the properties of the structure) to increased wind velocities for certain wind directions. Such cases should be taken into account.

NOTE The National Annex may give a procedure to take account of this effect. A recommended conservative first approximation is given in A.4.

4.3.5 Closely spaced buildings and obstacles

(1) The effect of closely spaced buildings and other obstacles may be taken into account.

NOTE The National Annex may give a procedure. A recommended first approximation is given in A.5. In rough terrain closely spaced buildings modify the mean wind flow near the ground, as if the ground level was raised to a height called displacement height h_{dis}.

4.4 Wind turbulence

(1) The turbulence intensity $I_v(z)$ at height z is defined as the standard deviation of the turbulence divided by the mean wind velocity.

NOTE 1 The turbulent component of wind velocity has a mean value of 0 and a standard deviation σ_v. The standard deviation of the turbulence σ_v may be determined using expression (4.6).

$$\sigma_v = k_r \cdot v_b \cdot k_I \qquad (4.6)$$

For the terrain factor k_r see expression (4.5), for the basic wind velocity v_b see expression (4.1) and for turbulence factor k_I see Note 2.

NOTE 2 The recommended rules for the determination of $I_v(z)$ are given in expression (4.7)

$$I_v(z) = \frac{\sigma_v}{v_m(z)} = \frac{k_I}{c_o(z) \cdot \ln(z/z_0)} \quad \text{for} \quad z_{min} \le z \le z_{max}$$
$$I_v(z) = I_v(z_{min}) \quad \text{for} \quad z < z_{min} \qquad (4.7)$$

where:

k_I is the turbulence factor. The value of k_I may be given in the National Annex. The recommended value is k_I = 1,0

c_o is the orography factor as described in 4.3.3

z_0 is the roughness length, given in Table 4.1

NA.2.16 Determination of the turbulence factor k_I
[BS EN 1991-1-4:2005, 4.4 (1) Note 2]

Values for turbulence factor k_I on its own are not given. It is incorporated in a new term $I_v(z)_{flat}$.

$I_v(z)_{flat} = k_I/\ln((z - h_{dis})/z_0)$, values of which are given in Figure NA.5.

Where orography is not significant as defined by Figure NA.2: $I_v(z) = I_v(z)_{flat}$ for sites in Country terrain; and

$I_v(z) = I_v(z)_{flat}\ k_{I,T}$, for sites in Town terrain. $k_{I,T}$ is the turbulence correction factor for Town terrain, values of which are given in Figure NA.6.

Where orography is significant, the value obtained from Figure NA.5 should be divided by the orography factor c_o.

NOTE The appropriate value of h_{dis} to be used in Figure NA.5 and Figure NA.6 is defined in BS EN 1991-1-4:2005 A.5.

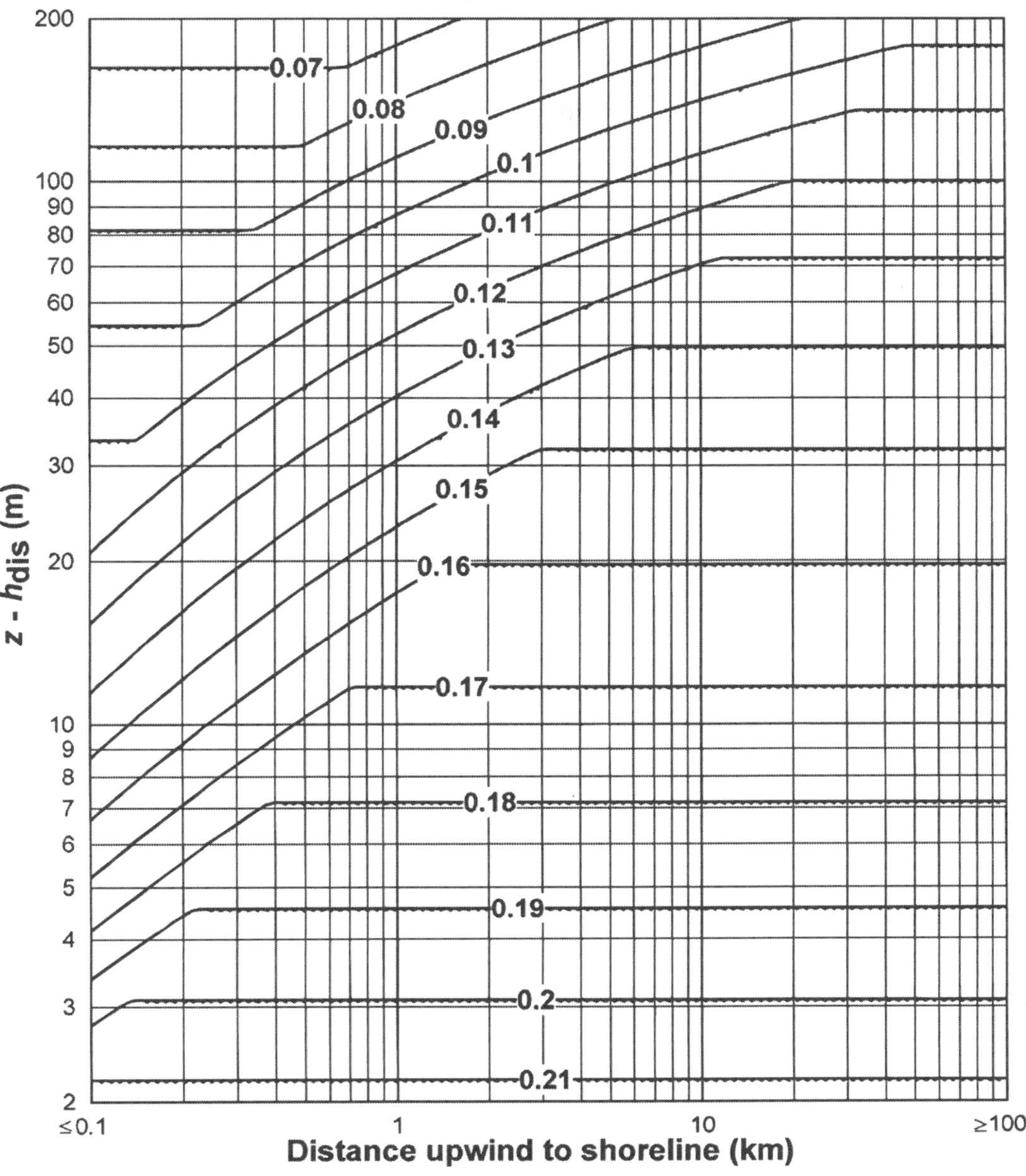

NOTE The height z is the height at which q_p is sought using Expression NA.4b).

Figure NA.5 — Values of $I_v(z)_{flat}$

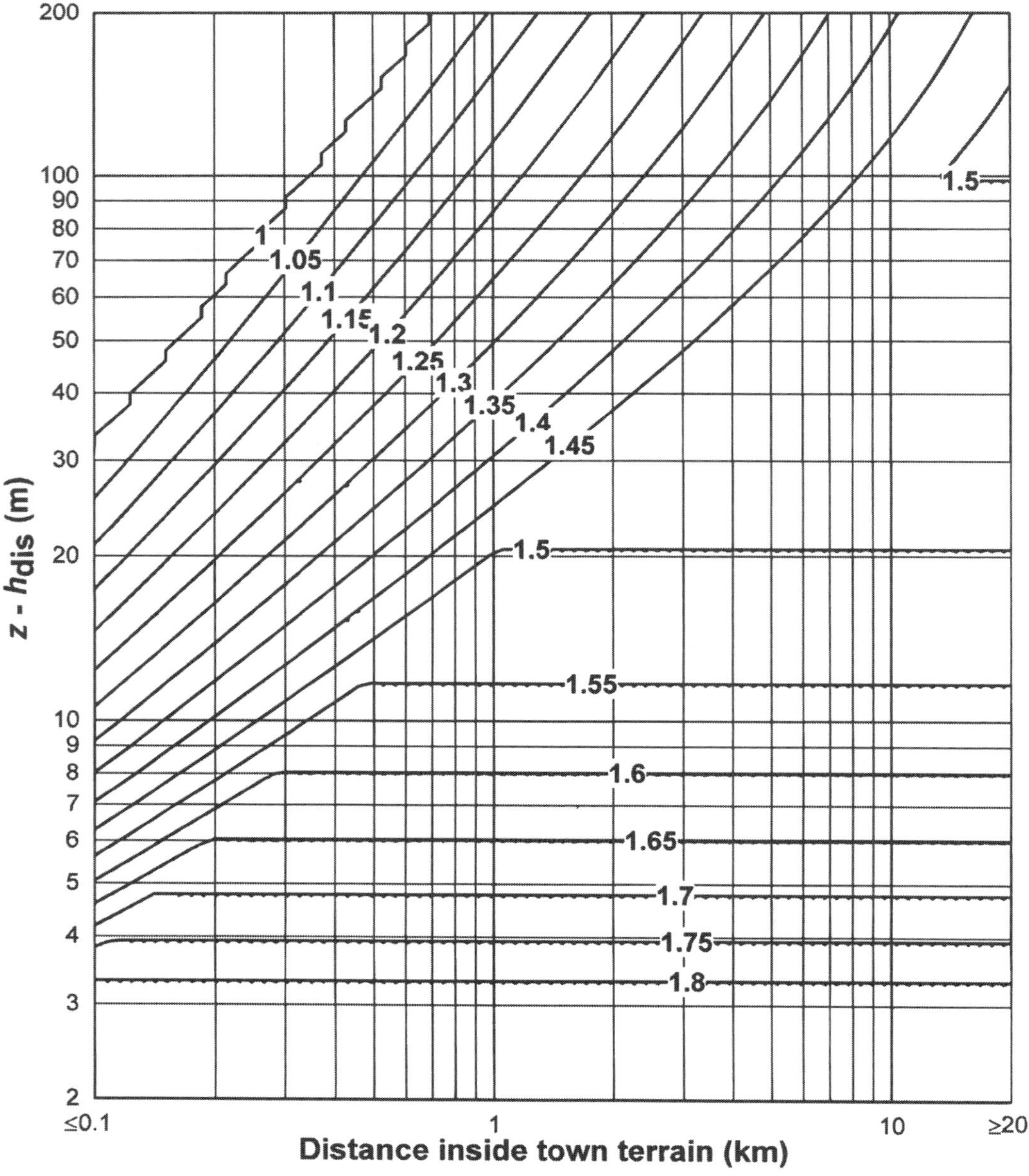

NOTE The height z is the height at which q_p is sought using Expression NA.4b).

Figure NA.6 – Values of turbulence correction factor $k_{I,T}$ for sites in Town terrain

4.5 Peak velocity pressure

(1) The peak velocity pressure $q_p(z)$ at height z, which includes mean and short-term velocity fluctuations, should be determined.

NOTE 1 The National Annex may give rules for the determination of $q_p(z)$. The recommended rule is given in expression (4.8).

$$q_p(z) = [1 + 7 \cdot I_v(z)] \cdot \frac{1}{2} \cdot \rho \cdot v_m^2(z) = c_e(z) \cdot q_b \tag{4.8}$$

where:

ρ is the air density, which depends on the altitude, temperature and barometric pressure to be expected in the region during wind storms

$c_e(z)$ is the exposure factor given in expression (4.9)

$$c_e(z) = \frac{q_p(z)}{q_b} \tag{4.9}$$

q_b is the basic velocity pressure given in expression (4.10)

$$q_b = \frac{1}{2} \cdot \rho \cdot v_b^2 \tag{4.10}$$

NOTE 2 The values for ρ may be given in the National Annex. The recommended value is 1,25 kg/m^3.

NOTE 3 The value 7 in expression (4.8) is based on a peak factor equal to 3,5 and is consistent with the values of the pressure and force coefficients in Section 7.

For flat terrain where $c_0(z)$ = 1,0 (see 4.3.3), the exposure factor $c_e(z)$ is illustrated in Figure 4.2 as a function of height above terrain and a function of terrain category as defined in Table 4.1.

In the UK NA ρ is taken as 1,226 kg/m^3.

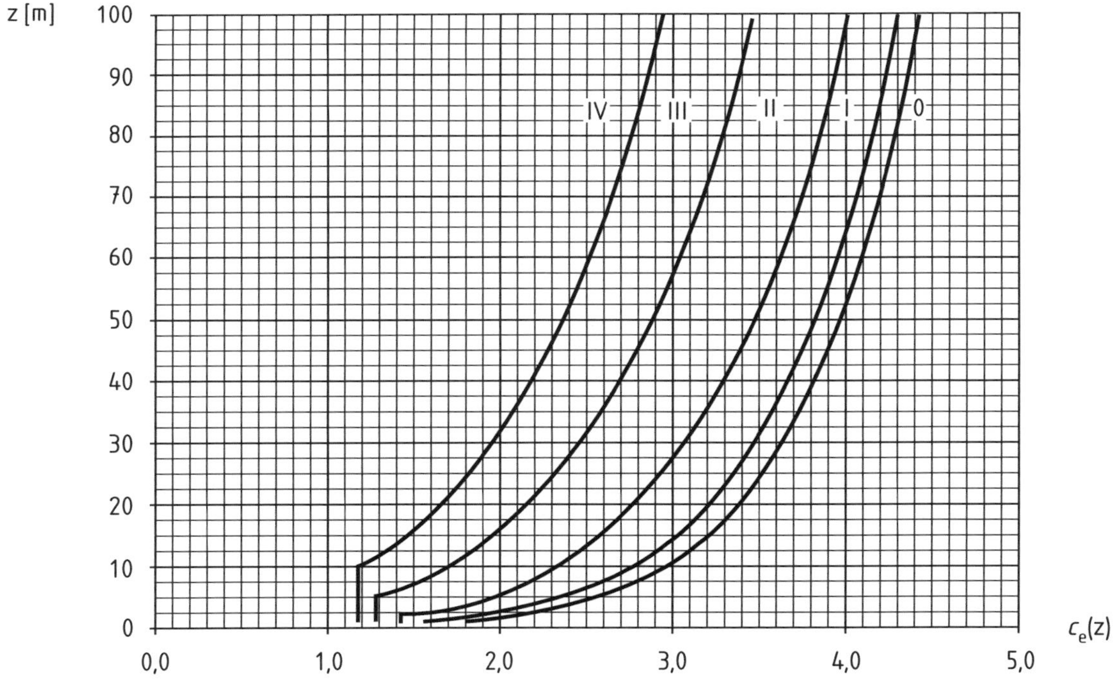

Figure 4.2 — Illustrations of the exposure factor $c_e(z)$ for c_0=1,0, k_I=1,0

NA.2.17 Determination of peak velocity pressure, $q_p(z)$

[BS EN 1991-1-4:2005, 4.5 (i) Note 1]

BS EN 1991-1-4:2005 Expression (4.8) does not apply.

When orography is not significant as defined by Figure NA.2 ($c_o = 1{,}0$):

$q_p(z) = c_e(z) q_b$ for sites in Country terrain; and (NA.3a))

$q_p(z) = c_e(z) \cdot c_{e,T} \cdot q_b$ for sites in Town terrain. (NA.3b))

The values of exposure factor $c_e(z)$ are given in Figure NA.7 and the values of exposure correction factor for Town terrain $c_{e,T}$ are given in Figure NA.8.

When orography is significant:

(NA.4a)) $q_p(z) = [q_p(z) \text{ from Equation NA.3a or NA.3b}] \cdot [(c_o(z) + 0.6)/1.6]^2$ for $z \leq 50$ m;

or

(NA.4b)) $q_p(z) = [1 + 3{,}0 \cdot I_v(z)]^2 \cdot 0.5 \cdot \rho \cdot v_m^2$ for $z > 50$ m.

Annex A to this National Annex shows flow diagrams for the determination of $q_p(z)$.

Where orography is significant see NA.2.17 of the UK NA.

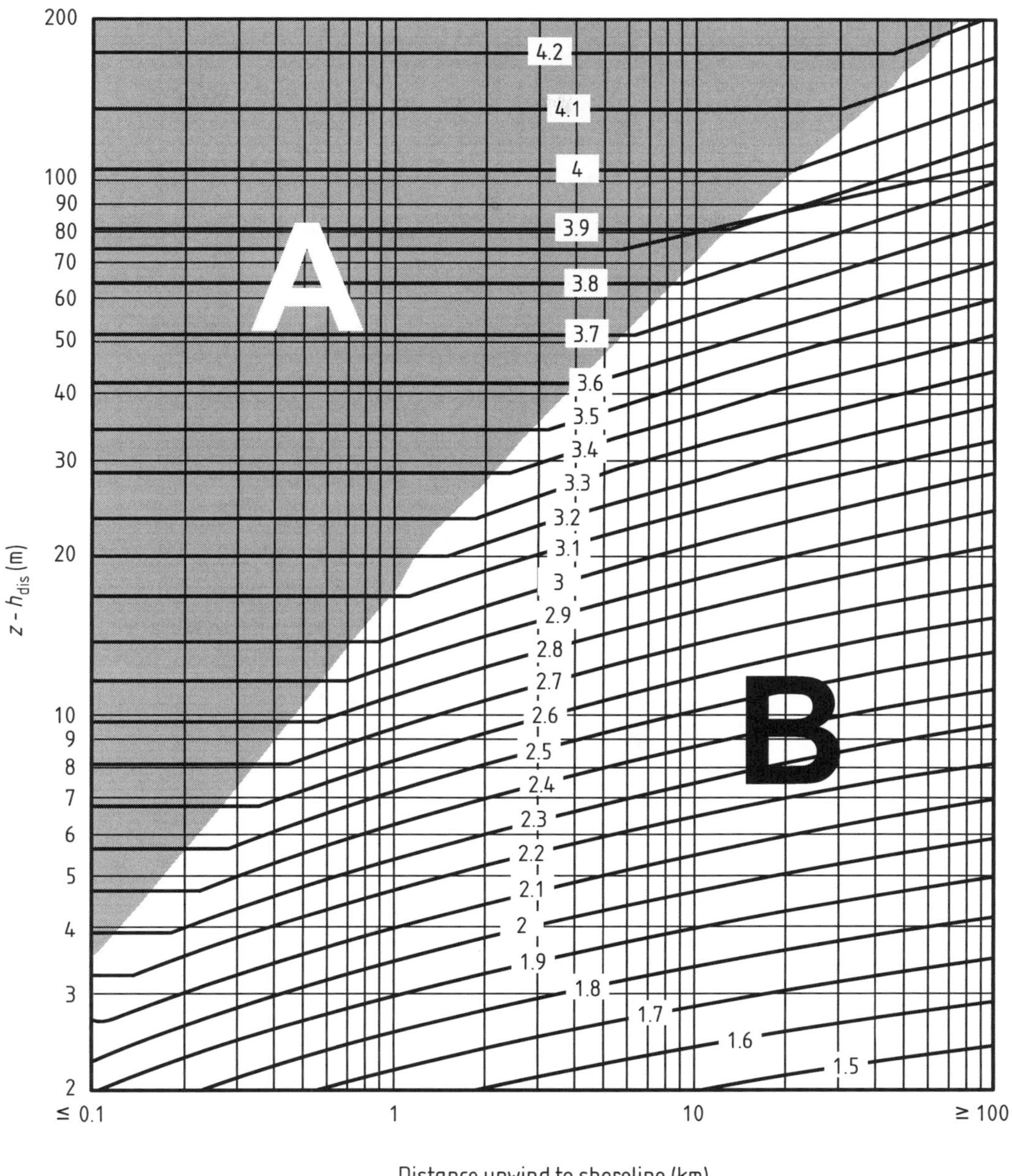

NOTE 1 The height z is the height at which q_p is sought using Equations NA.3a) or NA.3b).

NOTE 2 Zones A and B are indicated for use in Table NA.3.

Figure NA.7 — Values of $c_e(z)$

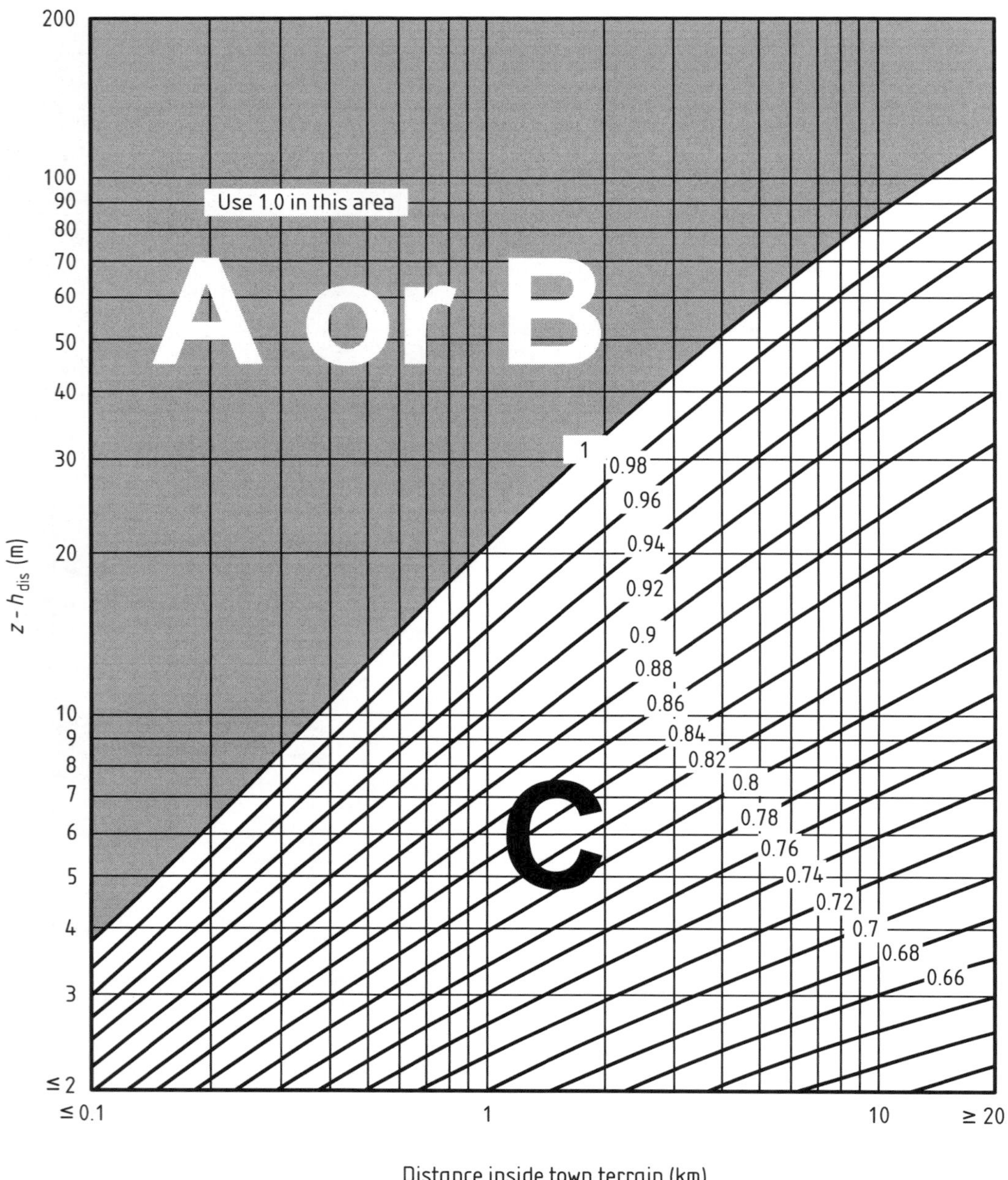

NOTE 1 The height z is the height at which q_p is sought using Equations NA.3a) or NA.3b).

NOTE 2 Zones A, B and C are indicated for use in Table NA.3.

Figure NA.8 — Values of exposure correction factor $c_{e,T}$ for sites in Town terrain

Table NA.3 — Size factor c_s for zones A, B and C indicated in Figure NA.7 and Figure NA.8

$b + h$	$z - h_{dis}$ = 6 m			$z - h_{dis}$ = 10 m			$z - h_{dis}$ = 30 m			$z - h_{dis}$ = 50 m			$z - h_{dis}$ = 200 m		
m	A	B	C	A	B	C	A	B	C	A	B	C	A	B	C
1	0.99	0.98	0.97	0.99	0.99	0.97	0.99	0.99	0.98	0.99	0.99	0.99	0.99	0.99	0.99
5	0.96	0.96	0.92	0.97	0.96	0.93	0.98	0.97	0.95	0.98	0.98	0.96	0.98	0.98	0.98
10	0.95	0.94	0.88	0.95	0.95	0.90	0.96	0.96	0.93	0.97	0.96	0.94	0.98	0.97	0.97
20	0.93	0.91	0.84	0.93	0.92	0.87	0.95	0.94	0.90	0.95	0.95	0.92	0.96	0.96	0.95
30	0.91	0.89	0.81	0.92	0.91	0.84	0.94	0.93	0.88	0.94	0.93	0.90	0.96	0.95	0.93
40	0.90	0.88	0.79	0.91	0.89	0.82	0.93	0.91	0.86	0.93	0.92	0.88	0.95	0.94	0.92
50	0.89	0.86	0.77	0.90	0.88	0.80	0.92	0.90	0.85	0.92	0.91	0.87	0.94	0.94	0.91
70	0.87	0.84	0.74	0.88	0.86	0.77	0.90	0.89	0.83	0.91	0.90	0.85	0.93	0.92	0.90
100	0.85	0.82	0.71	0.86	0.84	0.74	0.89	0.87	0.80	0.90	0.88	0.82	0.92	0.91	0.88
150	0.83	0.80	0.67	0.84	0.82	0.71	0.87	0.85	0.77	0.88	0.86	0.79	0.90	0.89	0.85
200	0.81	0.78	0.65	0.83	0.80	0.69	0.85	0.83	0.74	0.86	0.84	0.77	0.89	0.88	0.83
300	0.79	0.75	0.62	0.80	0.77	0.65	0.83	0.80	0.71	0.84	0.82	0.73	0.87	0.85	0.80

b = cross wind breadth of building or building part or width of element

h = height of building or building part or length of element

z = height of building or height to top of element (or height of building part, subject to BS EN 1991-1-4:2005 **7.2.2** (1))
interpolation may be used

The zone A, B or C to be used for a building can be determined as follows:

For sites in country, it is determined with respect to distance from shore and ($z - h_{dis}$) using Figure NA.7.

For sites in town, using the distance into town and ($z - h_{dis}$) in Figure NA.8 it is first determined whether zone C applies. If not, zone A or B will apply depending on the distance of the site from shore and ($z - h_{dis}$) as shown in Figure NA.7.

Section 5 Wind actions

5.1 General

(1)P Wind actions on structures and structural elements shall be determined taking account of both external and internal wind pressures.

NOTE A summary of recommended calculation procedures for the determination of wind actions is given in Table 5.1.

Table 5.1 — Calculation procedures for the determination of wind actions

Parameter	Subject Reference
Peak velocity pressure q_p	
basic wind velocity v_b	4.2 (2)P
reference height z_e	Section 7
terrain category	Table 4.1
characteristic peak velocity pressure q_p	4.5 (1)
turbulence intensity I_v	4.4
mean wind velocity v_m	4.3.1
orography coefficient $c_o(z)$	4.3.3
roughness coefficient $c_r(z)$	4.3.2
Wind pressures, e.g. for cladding, fixings and structural parts	
external pressure coefficient c_{pe}	Section 7
internal pressure coefficient c_{pi}	Section 7
net pressure coefficient $c_{p,net}$	Section 7
external wind pressure: $w_e=q_p\ c_{pe}$	5.2 (1)
internal wind pressure: $w_i=q_p\ c_{pi}$	5.2 (2)
Wind forces on structures, e.g. for overall wind effects	
structural factor: c_sc_d	6
wind force F_w calculated from force coefficients	5.3 (2)
wind force F_w calculated from pressure coefficients	5.3 (3)

5.2 Wind pressure on surfaces

(1) The wind pressure acting on the external surfaces, w_e, should be obtained from expression (5.1).

$$w_e = q_p(z_e) \cdot c_{pe} \tag{5.1}$$

where:

$q_p(z_e)$ is the peak velocity pressure

z_e is the reference height for the external pressure given in Section 7

c_{pe} is the pressure coefficient for the external pressure, see Section 7.

NOTE $q_p(z)$ is defined in 4.5.

(2) The wind pressure acting on the internal surfaces of a structure, w_i, should be obtained from expression (5.2)

$$w_i = q_p(z_i) \cdot c_{pi} \tag{5.2}$$

where:

$q_p(z_i)$ is the peak velocity pressure
z_i is the reference height for the internal pressure given in Section 7
c_{pi} is the pressure coefficient for the internal pressure given in Section 7.

NOTE $q_p(z)$ is defined in 4.5.

(3) The net pressure on a wall, roof or element is the difference between the pressures on the opposite surfaces taking due account of their signs. Pressure, directed towards the surface is taken as positive, and suction, directed away from the surface as negative. Examples are given in Figure 5.1.

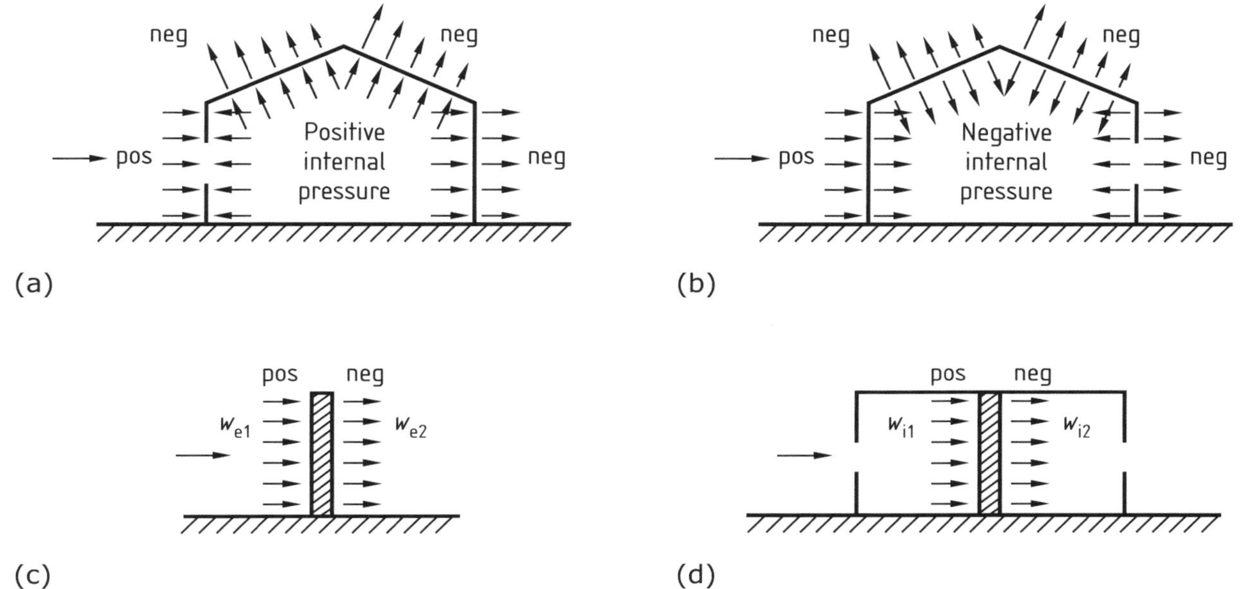

Figure 5.1 — Pressure on surfaces

5.3 Wind forces

(1) The wind forces for the whole structure or a structural component should be determined:

- by calculating forces using force coefficients (see (2)) or
- by calculating forces from surface pressures (see (3)).

This guide will only deal with calculating forces from surface pressures. For a detailed explanation for calculating forces from force coefficients (required for signboards, structural elements with rectangular sections, sharp edge sections, polygonal sections, circular cylinders, spheres, lattice structures and flags) see EN 1991-1-4, rest of 5.3(1), and Sections 7 and 8.

(3) The wind force F_w acting on a structure or a structural element may be determined by vectorial summation of the forces $F_{w,e}$, $F_{w,i}$ and F_{fr} calculated from the external and internal pressures using expressions (5.5) and (5.6) and the frictional forces resulting from the friction of the wind parallel to the external surfaces, calculated using expression (5.7).

external forces:

$$F_{w,e} = c_s c_d \cdot \sum_{surfaces} w_e \cdot A_{ref} \tag{5.5}$$

internal forces:

$$F_{w,i} = \sum_{surfaces} w_i \cdot A_{ref} \tag{5.6}$$

friction forces:

$$F_{fr} = c_{fr} \cdot q_p(z_e) \cdot A_{fr} \tag{5.7}$$

where:

c_sc_d is the structural factor as defined in Section 6
w_e is the external pressure on the individual surface at height z_e, given in expression (5.1)
w_i is the internal pressure on the individual surface at height z_i, given in expression (5.2)
A_{ref} is the reference area of the individual surface
c_{fr} is the friction coefficient derived from 7.5
A_{fr} is the area of external surface parallel to the wind, given in 7.5.

NOTE 1 For elements (e.g. walls, roofs), the wind force becomes equal to the difference between the external and internal resulting forces.

NOTE 2 Friction forces F_{fr} act in the direction of the wind components parallel to external surfaces.

(4) The effects of wind friction on the surface can be disregarded when the total area of all surfaces parallel with (or at a small angle to) the wind is equal to or less than 4 times the total area of all external surfaces perpendicular to the wind (windward and leeward).

Section 6 Structural factor c_sc_d

6.1 General

(1) The structural factor c_sc_d should take into account the effect on wind actions from the non-simultaneous occurrence of peak wind pressures on the surface (c_s) together with the effect of the vibrations of the structure due to turbulence (c_d).

NOTE The structural factor c_sc_d may be separated into a size factor c_s and a dynamic factor c_d, based on 6.3. Information on whether the structural factor c_sc_d should be separated or not may be given in the National Annex.

The National Annex for EN 1991-1-4 provides information on when and whether c_s and c_d should be separated. See NA.2.20.

6.2 Determination of c_sc_d

(1) c_sc_d should be determined as follows:

a) For buildings with a height less than 15 m the value of c_sc_d may be taken as 1.

b) For facade and roof elements having a natural frequency greater than 5 Hz, the value of c_sc_d may be taken as 1.

c) For framed buildings which have structural walls and which are less than 100 m high and whose height is less than 4 times the in-wind depth, the value of c_sc_d may be taken as 1.

d) For chimneys with circular cross-sections whose height is less than 60 m and 6,5 times the diameter, the value of c_sc_d may be taken as 1.

e) Alternatively, for cases a), b), c) and d) above, values of c_sc_d may be derived from 6.3.1.

f) For civil engineering works (other than bridges, which are considered in Section 8), and chimneys and buildings outside the limitations given in c) and d) above, c_sc_d should be derived from 6.3 or taken from Annex D.

NOTE 1 Natural frequencies of facade and roof elements may be calculated using Annex F (glazing spans smaller than 3 m usually lead to natural frequencies greater than 5 Hz).

NOTE 2 The figures in Annex D give values of c_sc_d for various types of structures. The figures give envelopes of safe values calculated from models complying with the requirements in 6.3.1.

For all other cases and detailed procedures for obtaining c_sc_d see EN 1991-1-4, 6.2, 6.3 and Annex B. See also NA.2.20 and Figure NA.9.

6.3.3 Wake buffeting

(1) For slender buildings ($h/d > 4$) and chimneys ($h/d > 6,5$) in tandem or grouped arrangement, the effect of increased turbulence in the wake of nearby structures (wake buffeting) should be taken into account.

(2) Wake buffeting effects may be assumed to be negligible if at least one of the following conditions applies:

- The distance between two buildings or chimneys is larger than 25 times the cross-wind dimension of the upstream building or chimney.
- The natural frequency of the downstream building or chimney is higher than 1 Hz.

NOTE If none of the conditions in 6.3.3 (2) is fulfilled wind tunnel tests or specialist advice is recommended.

a) vertical structures such as buildings etc.

b) parallel oscillator, i.e. horizontal structures such as beams etc.

c) pointlike structures such as signboards etc.

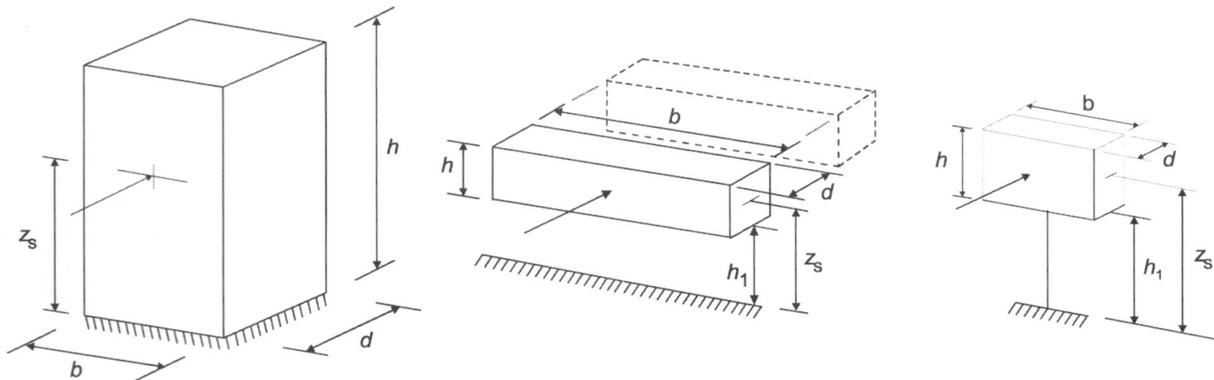

NOTE Limitations are also given in 1.1 (2)

$z_s = 0{,}6 \cdot h \geq z_{min}$

$z_s = h_1 + \frac{h}{2} \geq z_{min}$

$z_s = h_1 + \frac{h}{2} \geq z_{min}$

Figure 6.1 — General shapes of structures covered by the design procedure. The structural dimensions and the reference height used are also shown.

Section 7 Pressure and force coefficients

7.1 General

(1) This section should be used to determine the appropriate aerodynamic coefficients for structures. Depending on the structure the appropriate aerodynamic coefficient will be:

- Internal and external pressure coefficients, see 7.1.1 (1),
- Net pressure coefficients, see 7.1.1 (2),
- Friction coefficients, see 7.1.1 (3),
- Force coefficients, see 7.1.1 (4).

7.1.1 Choice of aerodynamic coefficient

This guide only gives pressure coefficients for buildings.

(1) The pressure coefficients should be determined for:

- Buildings, using 7.2 for both internal and external pressures, and for
- Circular cylinders, using 7.2.9 for the internal pressures and 7.9.1 for the external pressures.

NOTE 1 External pressure coefficients give the effect of the wind on the external surfaces of buildings; internal pressure coefficients give the effect of the wind on the internal surfaces of buildings.

NOTE 2 The external pressure coefficients are divided into overall coefficients and local coefficients. Local coefficients give the pressure coefficients for loaded areas of 1 m^2. They may be used for the design of small elements and fixings. Overall coefficients give the pressure coefficients for loaded areas of 10 m^2. They may be used for loaded areas larger than 10 m^2.

For the determination of pressure and force coefficients for other types of structures e.g.:

- canopy roofs;
- free-standing walls, parapets and fences;
- signboards;
- structural elements with rectangular cross section;
- structural elements with sharp edged section;
- structural elements with regular polygonal section;
- circular cylinders;
- spheres;
- lattice structures and scaffoldings;
- flags.

See Section 7 of EN 1991-1-4.

7.1.3 Effects of ice and snow

(1) If ice or snow alters the geometry of a structure so that it changes the reference area or shape, this should be taken into account.

NOTE Further information may be given in the National Annex.

7.2 Pressure coefficients for buildings

7.2.1 General

(1) The external pressure coefficients c_{pe} for buildings and parts of buildings depend on the size of the loaded area A, which is the area of the structure, that produces the wind action in the section to be calculated. The external pressure coefficients are given for loaded areas A of 1 m^2 and 10 m^2 in the tables for the appropriate building configurations as $c_{pe,1}$, for local coefficients, and $c_{pe,10}$, for overall coefficients, respectively.

NOTE 1 Values for $c_{pe,1}$ are intended for the design of small elements and fixings with an area per element of 1 m^2 or less such as cladding elements and roofing elements. Values for $c_{pe,10}$ may be used for the design of the overall load bearing structure of buildings.

NOTE 2 The National Annex may give a procedure for calculating external pressure coefficients for loaded areas above 1 m^2 based on external pressure coefficients $c_{pe,1}$ and $c_{pe,10}$. The recommended procedure for loaded areas up to 10 m^2 is given in Figure 7.2.

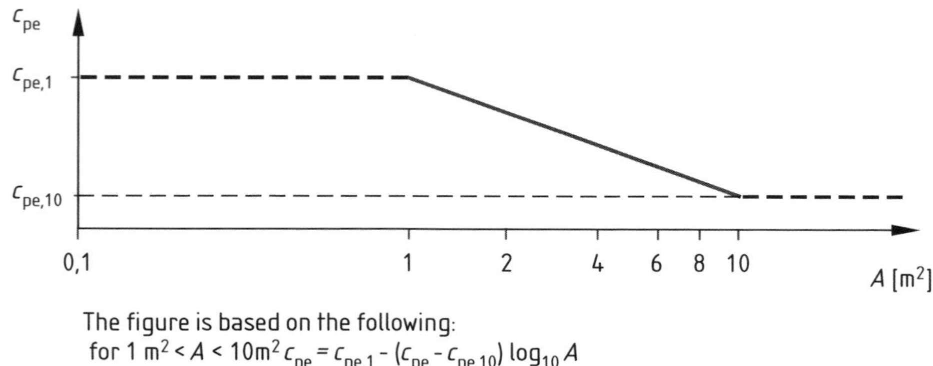

Figure 7.2 — Recommended procedure for determining the external pressure coefficient c_{pe} for buildings with a loaded area A between 1 m^2 and 10 m^2

(2) The values $c_{pe,10}$ and $c_{pe,1}$ in Tables 7.2 to 7.5 should be used for the orthogonal wind directions 0°, 90°, 180°. These values represent the most unfavourable values obtained in a range of wind directions $\theta = \pm 45°$ either side of the relevant orthogonal direction.

NA.2.25 Procedure for determining the external pressure coefficient for loaded areas between 1 m^2 and 10 m^2
[BS EN 1991-1-4:2005, 7.2.1 (1) Note 2]

BS EN 1991-1-4:2005 Figure 7.2 should not be used.

$c_{pe,1}$ values should be used for loaded areas 1 m^2 and $c_{pe,10}$ values should be used for loaded areas >1 m^2.

(3) For protruding roof corners the pressure on the underside of the roof overhang is equal to the pressure for the zone of the vertical wall directly connected to the protruding roof; the pressure at the top side of the roof overhang is equal to the pressure of the zone, defined for the roof.

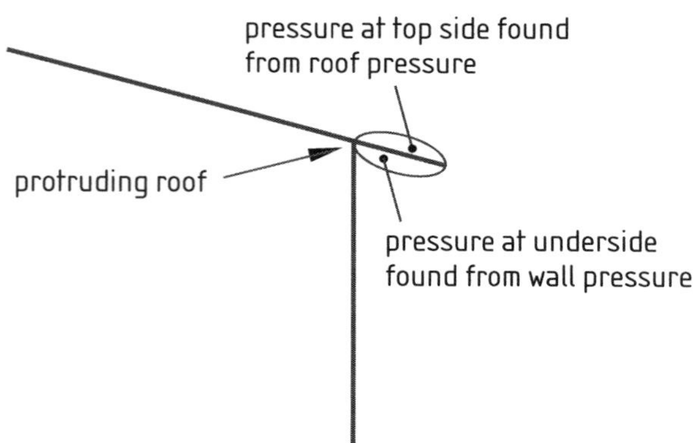

Figure 7.3 — Illustration of relevant pressures for protruding roofs

7.2.2 Vertical walls of rectangular plan buildings

(1) The reference heights, z_e, for walls of rectangular plan buildings (zone D, see Figure 7.5) depend on the aspect ratio *h/b* and are always the upper heights of the different parts of the walls. They are given in Figure 7.4 for the following three cases:

- A building, whose height *h* is less than *b* should be considered to be one part.
- A building, whose height *h* is greater than *b*, but less than 2*b*, may be considered to be two parts, comprising: a lower part extending upwards from the ground by a height equal to *b* and an upper part consisting of the remainder.
- A building, whose height *h* is greater than 2*b*, may be considered to be in multiple parts, comprising: a lower part extending upwards from the ground by a height equal to *b*; an upper part extending downwards from the top by a height equal to *b* and a middle region, between the upper and lower parts, which may be divided into horizontal strips with a height h_{strip} as shown in Figure 7.4.

NOTE The rules for the velocity pressure distribution for leeward wall and sidewalls (zones A, B, C and E, see Figure 7.5) may be given in the National Annex or be defined for the individual project. The recommended procedure is to take the reference height as the height of the building.

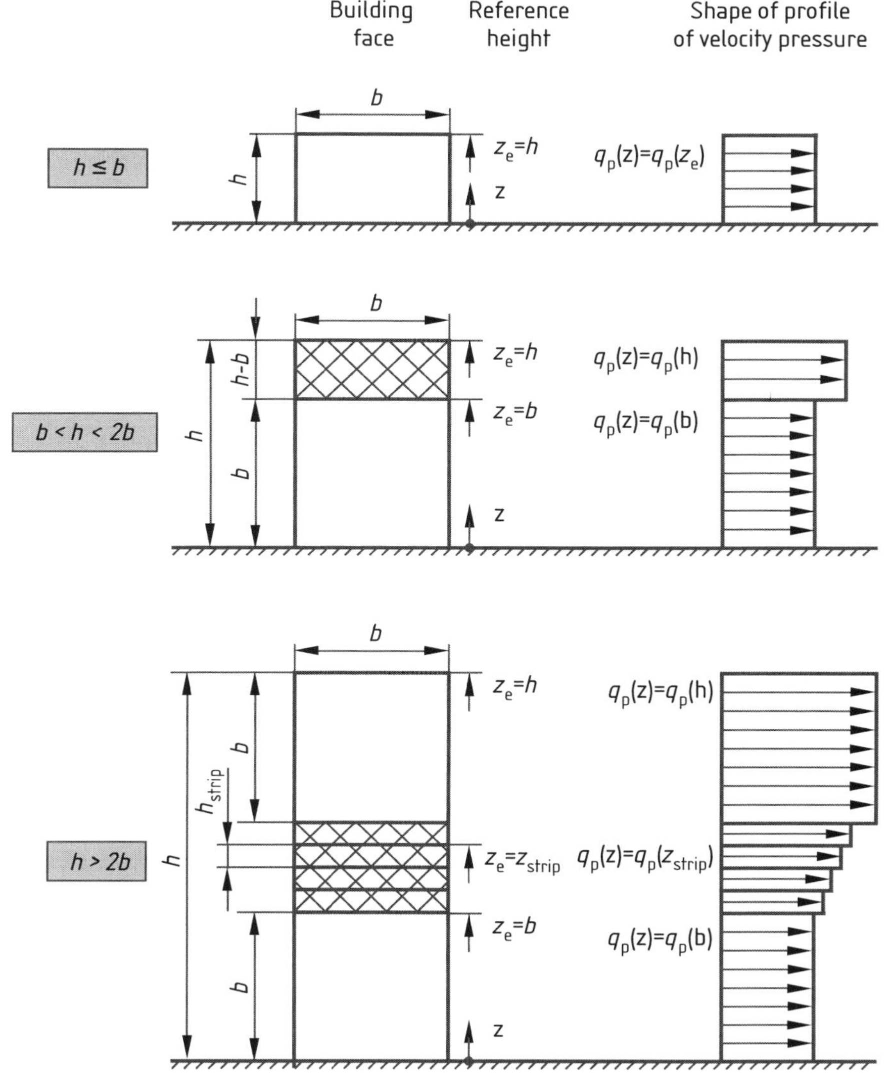

NOTE The velocity pressure should be assumed to be uniform over each horizontal strip considered.

Figure 7.4 — Reference height, z_e, depending on *h* and *b*, and corresponding velocity pressure profile

(2) The external pressure coefficients $c_{pe,10}$ and $c_{pe,1}$ for zones A, B, C, D and E are defined in Figure 7.5.

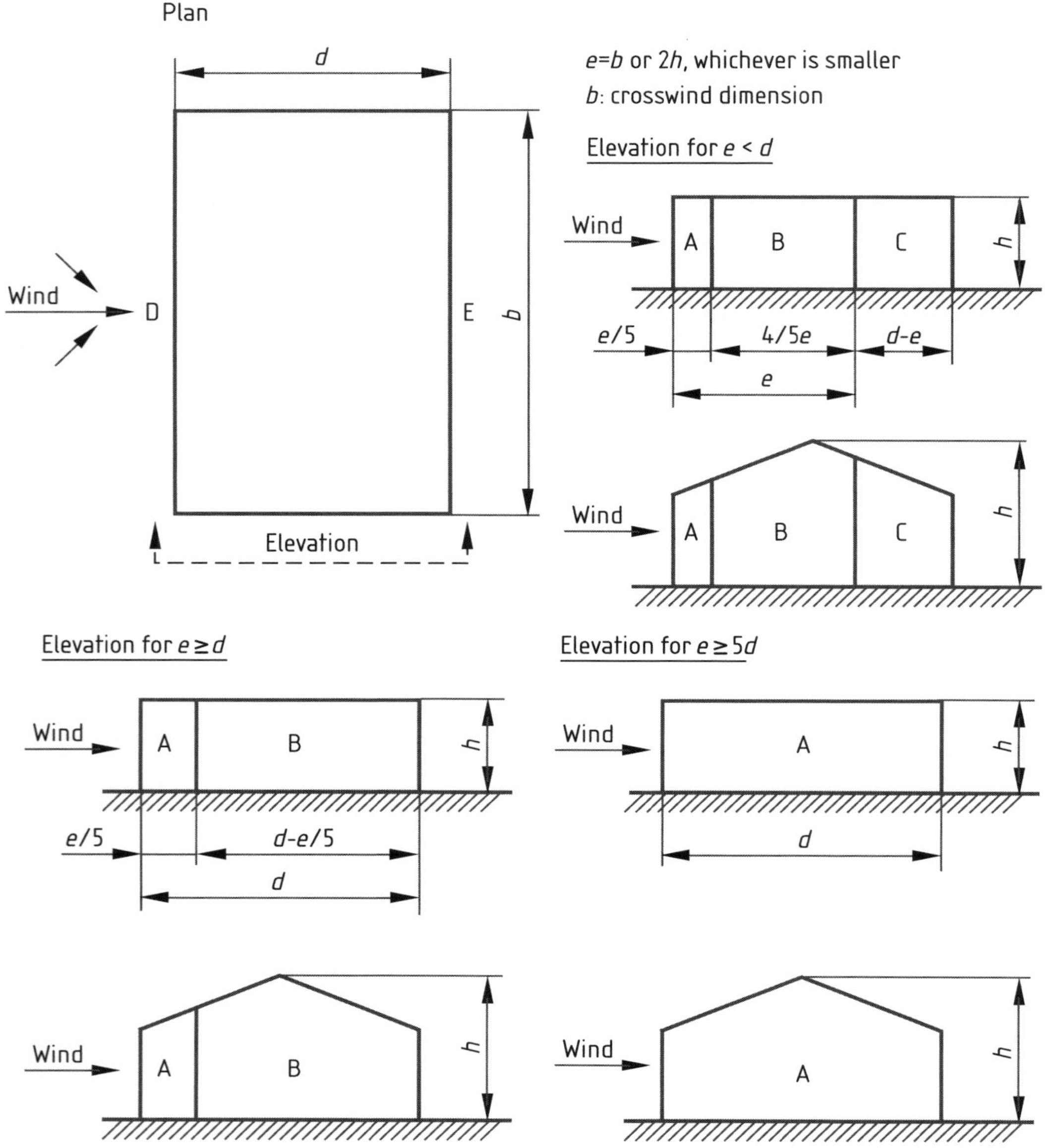

Figure 7.5 — Key for vertical walls

NOTE 1 The values of $c_{pe,10}$ and $c_{pe,1}$ may be given in the National Annex. The recommended values are given in Table 7.1, depending on the ratio h/d. For intermediate values of h/d, linear interpolation may be applied. The values of Table 7.1 also apply to walls of buildings with inclined roofs, such as duopitch and monopitch roofs.

Table 7.1 — Recommended values of external pressure coefficients for vertical walls of rectangular plan buildings

Zone	**A**		**B**		**C**		**D**		**E**	
h/d	$c_{pe,10}$	$c_{pe,1}$	$c_{pe,10}$	$c_{pe,1}$	$c_{pe,10}$	$c_{pe,1}$	$c_{pe,10}$	$c_{pe,1}$	$c_{pe,10}$	$c_{pe,1}$
5	-1,2	-1,4	-0,8	-1,1	-0,5		+0,8	+1,0	-0,7	
1	-1,2	-1,4	-0,8	-1,1	-0,5		+0,8	+1,0	-0,5	
≤ 0,25	-1,2	-1,4	-0,8	-1,1	-0,5		+0,7	+1,0	-0,3	

NOTE 2 For buildings with $h/d > 5$, the total wind loading may be based on the provisions given in Sections 7.6 to 7.8 and 7.9.2.

(3) In cases where the wind force on building structures is determined by application of the pressure coefficients c_{pe} on windward and leeward side (zones D and E) of the building simultaneously, the lack of correlation of wind pressures between the windward and leeward side may have to be taken into account.

NOTE The lack of correlation of wind pressures between the windward and leeward side may be considered as follows. For buildings with $h/d \geq 5$ the resulting force is multiplied by 1. For buildings with $h/d \leq 1$, the resulting force is multiplied by 0,85. For intermediate values of h/d, linear interpolation may be applied.

NA.2.27 Values of external pressure coefficients for vertical walls of rectangular-plan buildings [BS EN 1991-1-4:2005, 7.2.2 (2) Note 1]

BS EN 1991-1-4:2005 Table 7.1 may be used. For the determination of overall loads on buildings, the net pressure coefficients in Table NA.4 may be used instead of the sum of the pressure coefficients for zones D and E. Factor for accounting for lack of correlation between the front and rear faces may also be applied to the net pressure coefficients.

Table NA.4 — Net pressure coefficients for vertical walls of rectangular buildings

h/d	Net pressure coefficient $c_{pe,10}$
5	1.3
1.0	1.1
≥0.25	0.8

The following should be noted:

a) *In BS EN 1991-1-4:2005 Table 7.1, linear interpolation may be used for intermediate values of h/d.*

b) *The coefficients may be applied to non-vertical walls within ±15° of vertical.*

c) *For bridge piers, see* ***NA.2.52*** *relating to BS EN 1991-1-4:2005* ***8.4.2****.*

d) *Where the walls of two buildings face each other and the gap between them is less than e (smaller value of e in case of buildings with different e values), "funnelling" will accelerate the flow and make the pressure coefficients in zones A, B and C more negative than in the case where the building is "isolated", according to the following:*

   1) *where the gap between the buildings is < e/4 or > e, the coefficient for isolated case should be used;*

   2) *where the gap between the buildings is > e/4 and < e:*

   - *either use the funnelling values, conservatively, or*
   - *interpolate linearly according to the actual gap between the following values: the funnelling values to apply for a gap of e/2 and the isolated values to apply for a gap of e/4 and a gap of e;*

   3) *where the two buildings are sheltered by upwind buildings such that* $(h_r - h_{dis}) < 0.4h_r$ *for the lower of the two buildings, then funneling can be disregarded.*

e) *The external pressure coefficients for side faces affected by funneling should be taken as −1.6 for Zone A, − 0.9 for Zone B and − 0.9 for Zone C.*

NA.2.28 Pressure coefficients

The pressure coefficients given in BS EN 1991-1-4:2005, 7.2.3 to 7.2.6 are not given in a form that allows a National Choice; however, users of BS EN 1991-1-4 are recommended to follow the advisory note to this National Annex drafted in order to advise users on how to maintain the current levels of safety and economy of construction.

The Advisory note is reproduced at the end of this Section on page 1-96.

7.2.3 Flat roofs

(1) Flat roofs are defined as having a slope (α) of $-5° < \alpha < 5°$

(2) The roof should be divided into zones as shown in Figure 7.6.

(3) The reference height for flat roof and roofs with curved or mansard eaves should be taken as h. The reference height for flat roofs with parapets should be taken as $h + h_p$, see Figure 7.6.

(4) Pressure coefficients for each zone are given in Table 7.2.

(5) The resulting pressure coefficient on the parapet should be determined using 7.4.

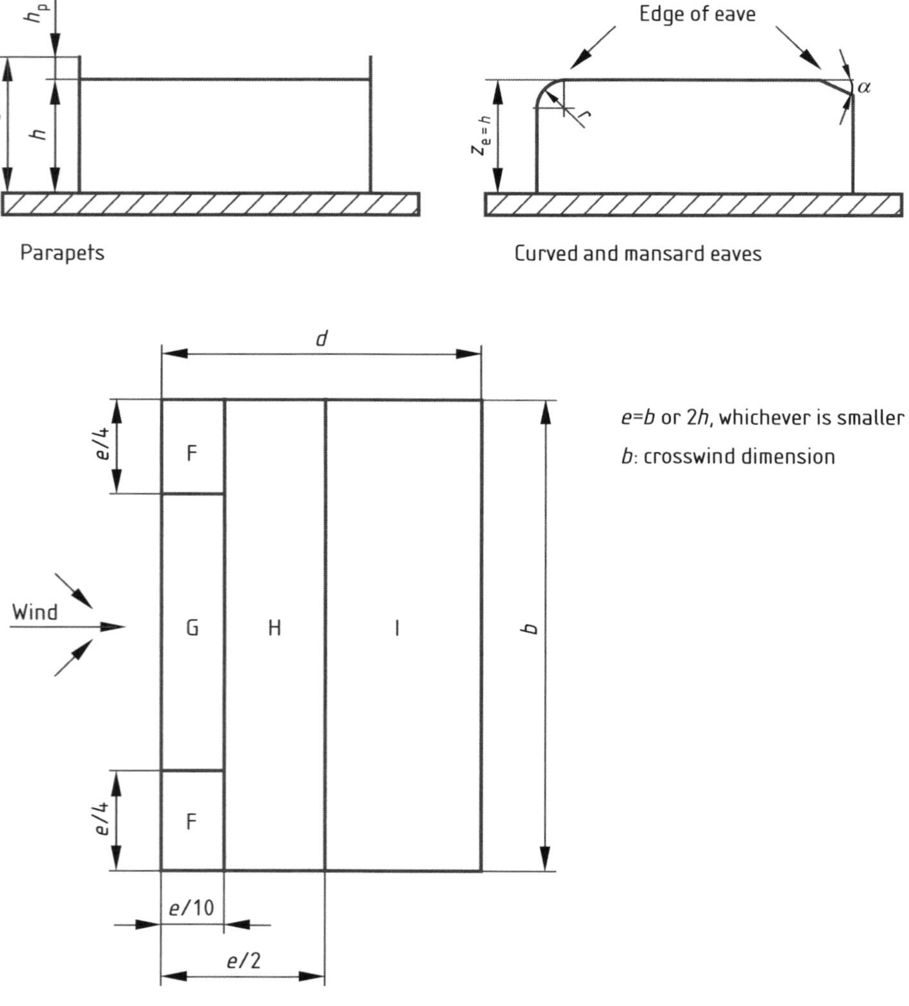

Figure 7.6 — Key for flat roofs

Table 7.2 — External pressure coefficients for flat roofs

Roof type		Zone F		Zone G		Zone H		Zone I	
		$c_{pe,10}$	$c_{pe,1}$	$c_{pe,10}$	$c_{pe,1}$	$c_{pe,10}$	$c_{pe,1}$	$c_{pe,10}$	$c_{pe,1}$
Sharp eaves		-1,8	-2,5	-1,2	-2,0	-0,7	-1,2	+0,2 -0,2	
With Parapets	h_p/h=0,025	-1,6	-2,2	-1,1	-1,8	-0,7	-1,2	+0,2 -0,2	
	h_p/h=0,05	-1,4	-2,0	-0,9	-1,6	-0,7	-1,2	+0,2 -0,2	
	h_p/h=0,10	-1,2	-1,8	-0,8	-1,4	-0,7	-1,2	+0,2 -0,2	
Curved Eaves	r/h = 0,05	-1,0	-1,5	-1,2	-1,8	-0,4		+0,2 -0,2	
	r/h = 0,10	-0,7	-1,2	-0,8	-1,4	-0,3		+0,2 -0,2	
	r/h = 0,20	-0,5	-0,8	-0,5	-0,8	-0,3		+0,2 -0,2	
Mansard Eaves	α = 30°	-1,0	-1,5	-1,0	-1,5	-0,3		+0,2 -0,2	
	α = 45°	-1,2	-1,8	-1,3	-1,9	-0,4		+0,2 -0,2	
	α = 60°	-1,3	-1,9	-1,3	-1,9	-0,5		+0,2 -0,2	

NOTE 1 For roofs with parapets or curved eaves, linear interpolation may be used for intermediate values of h_p/h and r/h.

NOTE 2 For roofs with mansard eaves, linear interpolation between α = 30°, 45° and α = 60° may be used. For α > 60° linear interpolation between the values for α = 60° and the values for flat roofs with sharp eaves may be used.

NOTE 3 In Zone I, where positive and negative values are given, both values shall be considered.

NOTE 4 For the mansard eave itself, the external pressure coefficients are given in Table 7.4 "External pressure coefficients for duopitch roofs: wind direction 0°", Zone F and G, depending on the pitch angle of the mansard eave.

NOTE 5 For the curved eave itself, the external pressure coefficients are given by linear interpolation along the curve, between values on the wall and on the roof.

7.2.4 Monopitch roofs

(1) The roof, including protruding parts, should be divided into zones as shown in Figure 7.7.
(2) The reference height z_e should be taken equal to h.
(3) The pressure coefficients for each zone that should be used are given in Table 7.3.

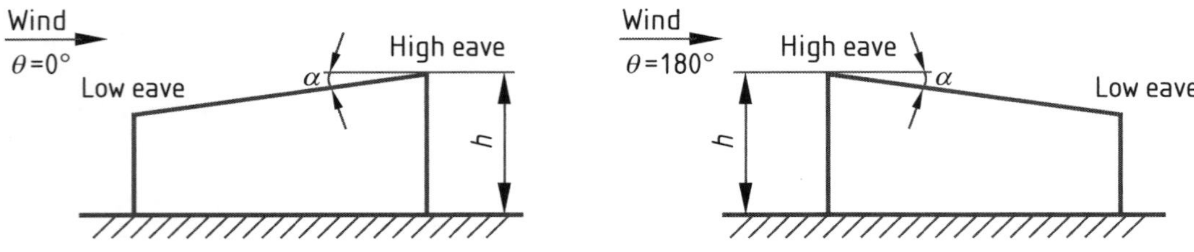

(a) general

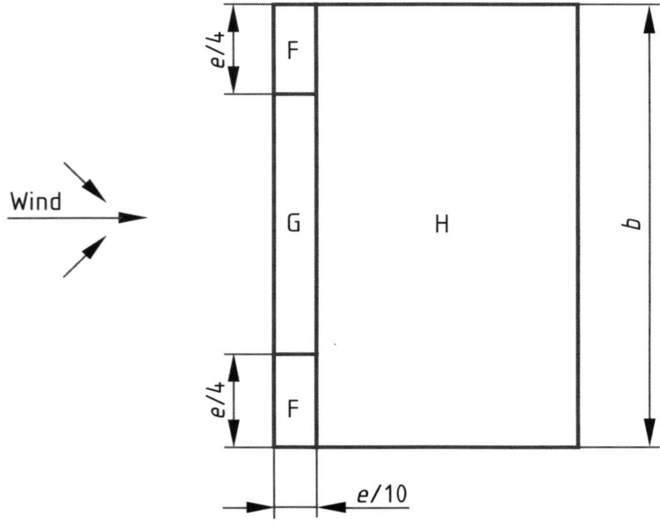

e=*b* or 2*h*, whichever is smaller

b: crosswind dimension

(b) wind directions θ = 0° and θ = 180°

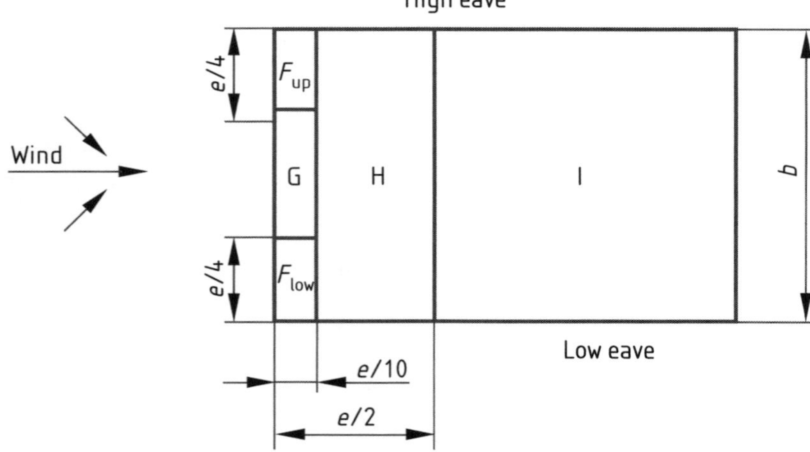

(c) wind directions θ = 90°

Figure 7.7 — Key for monopitch roofs

Table 7.3a — External pressure coefficients for monopitch roofs

Pitch Angle α	Zone for wind direction θ = 0°						Zone for wind direction θ = 180°					
	F		G		H		F		G		H	
	$c_{pe,10}$	$c_{pe,1}$	$c_{pe,10}$	$c_{pe,1}$	$c_{pe,10}$	$c_{pe,1}$	$c_{pe,10}$	$c_{pe,1}$	$c_{pe,10}$	$c_{pe,1}$	$c_{pe,10}$	$c_{pe,1}$
5°	-1,7	-2,5	-1,2	-2,0	-0,6	-1,2	-2,3	-2,5	-1,3	-2,0	-0,8	-1,2
	+0,0		+0,0		+0,0							
15°	-0,9	-2,0	-0,8	-1,5	-0,3		-2,5	-2,8	-1,3	-2,0	-0,9	-1,2
	+0,2		+0,2		+ 0,2							
30°	-0,5	-1,5	-0,5	-1,5	-0,2		-1,1	-2,3	-0,8	-1,5	-0,8	
	+0,7		+0,7		+0,4							
45°	-0,0		-0,0		-0,0		-0,6	-1,3	-0,5		-0,7	
	+0,7		+0,7		+0,6							
60°	+0,7		+0,7		+0,7		-0,5	-1,0	-0,5		-0,5	
75°	+0,8		+0,8		+0,8		-0,5	-1,0	-0,5		-0,5	

Table 7.3b — External pressure coefficients for monopitch roofs

Pitch Angle α	Zone for wind direction θ = 90°									
	F_{up}		F_{low}		G		H		I	
	$c_{pe,10}$	$c_{pe,1}$	$c_{pe,10}$	$c_{pe,1}$	$c_{pe,10}$	$c_{pe,1}$	$c_{pe,10}$	$c_{pe,1}$	$c_{pe,10}$	$c_{pe,1}$
5°	-2,1	-2,6	-2,1	-2,4	-1,8	-2,0	-0,6	-1,2	-0,5	
15°	-2,4	-2,9	-1,6	-2,4	-1,9	-2,5	-0,8	-1,2	-0,7	-1,2
30°	-2,1	-2,9	-1,3	-2,0	-1,5	-2,0	-1,0	-1,3	-0,8	-1,2
45°	-1,5	-2,4	-1,3	-2,0	-1,4	-2,0	-1,0	-1,3	-0,9	-1,2
60°	-1,2	-2,0	-1,2	-2,0	-1,2	-2,0	-1,0	-1,3	-0,7	-1,2
75°	-1,2	-2,0	-1,2	-2,0	-1,2	-2,0	-1,0	-1,3	-0,5	

NOTE 1 At θ = 0° (see Table a)) the pressure changes rapidly between positive and negative values around a pitch angle of α = +5° to +45°, so both positive and negative values are given. For those roofs, two cases should be considered: one with all positive values, and one with all negative values. No mixing of positive and negative values is allowed on the same face.

NOTE 2 Linear interpolation for intermediate pitch angles may be used between values of the same sign. The values equal to 0.0 are given for interpolation purposes.

7.2.5 Duopitch roofs

(1) The roof, including protruding parts, should be divided in zones as shown in Figure 7.8.
(2) The reference height z_e should be taken as h.
(3) The pressure coefficients for each zone that should be used are given in Table 7.4.

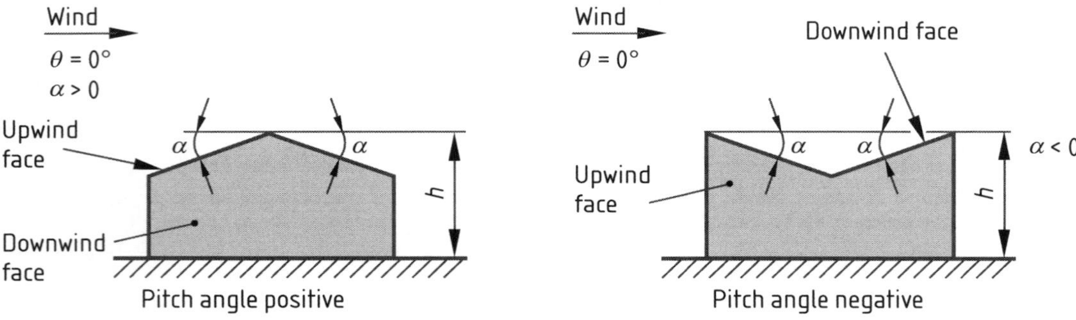

(a) general

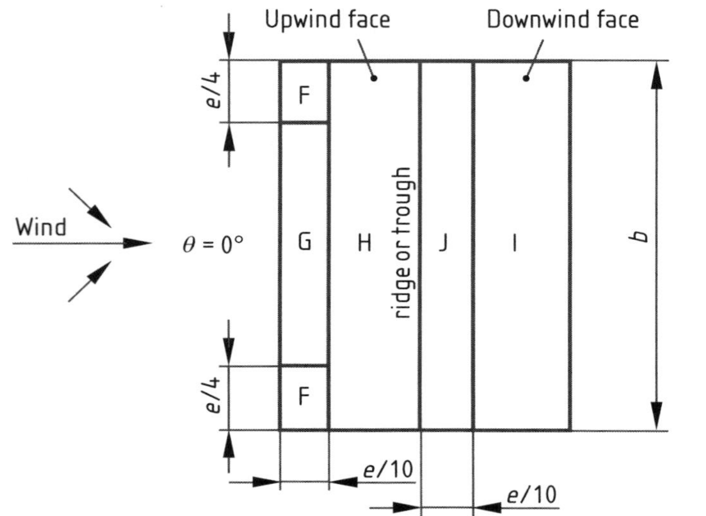

(b) wind directions $\theta = 0°$

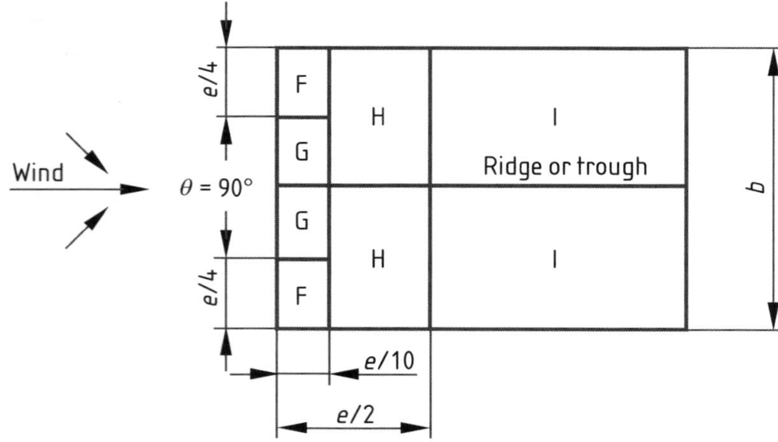

(c) wind directions $\theta = 90°$

Figure 7.8 — Key for duopitch roofs

Table 7.4a — External pressure coefficients for duopitch roofs

Pitch Angle α	Zone for wind direction θ = 0°									
	F		G		H		I		J	
	$c_{pe,10}$	$c_{pe,1}$	$c_{pe,10}$	$c_{pe,1}$	$c_{pe,10}$	$c_{pe,1}$	$c_{pe,10}$	$c_{pe,1}$	$c_{pe,10}$	$c_{pe,1}$
-45°	-0,6		-0,6		-0,8		-0,7		-1,0	-1,5
-30°	-1,1	-2,0	-0,8	-1,5	-0,8		-0,6		-0,8	-1,4
-15°	-2,5	-2,8	-1,3	-2,0	-0,9	-1,2	-0,5		-0,7	-1,2
-5°	-2,3	-2,5	-1,2	-2,0	-0,8	-1,2	+0,2		+0,2	
							-0,6		-0,6	
5°	-1,7	-2,5	-1,2	-2,0	-0,6	-1,2	-0,6		+0,2	
	+0,0		+0,0		+0,0				-0,6	
15°	-0,9	-2,0	-0,8	-1,5	-0,3		-0,4		-1,0	-1,5
	+0,2		+0,2		+0,2		+0,0		+0,0	+0,0
30°	-0,5	-1,5	-0,5	-1,5	-0,2		-0,4		-0,5	
	+0,7		+0,7		+0,4		+0,0		+0,0	
45°	-0,0		-0,0		-0,0		-0,2		-0,3	
	+0,7		+0,7		+0,6		+0,0		+0,0	
60°	+0,7		+0,7		+0,7		-0,2		-0,3	
75°	+0,8		+0,8		+0,8		-0,2		-0,3	

NOTE 1 At θ = 0° the pressure changes rapidly between positive and negative values on the windward face around a pitch angle of α = -5° to +45°, so both positive and negative values are given. For those roofs, four cases should be considered where the largest or smallest values of all areas F, G and H are combined with the largest or smallest values in areas I and J. No mixing of positive and negative values is allowed on the same face.

NOTE 2 Linear interpolation for intermediate pitch angles of the same sign may be used between values of the same sign. (Do not interpolate between α = +5° and α = -5°, but use the data for flat roofs in 7.2.3.) The values equal to 0,0 are given for interpolation purposes.

Table 7.4b — External pressure coefficients for duopitch roofs

Pitch angle α	Zone for wind direction θ = 90°							
	F		G		H		I	
	$c_{pe,10}$	$c_{pe,1}$	$c_{pe,10}$	$c_{pe,1}$	$c_{pe,10}$	$c_{pe,1}$	$c_{pe,10}$	$c_{pe,1}$
-45°	-1,4	-2,0	-1,2	-2,0	-1,0	-1,3	-0,9	-1,2
-30°	-1,5	-2,1	-1,2	-2,0	-1,0	-1,3	-0,9	-1,2
-15°	-1,9	-2,5	-1,2	-2,0	-0,8	-1,2	-0,8	-1,2
-5°	-1,8	-2,5	-1,2	-2,0	-0,7	-1,2	-0,6	-1,2
5°	-1,6	-2,2	-1,3	-2,0	-0,7	-1,2	-0,6	
15°	-1,3	-2,0	-1,3	-2,0	-0,6	-1,2	-0,5	
30°	-1,1	-1,5	-1,4	-2,0	-0,8	-1,2	-0,5	
45°	-1,1	-1,5	-1,4	-2,0	-0,9	-1,2	-0,5	
60°	-1,1	-1,5	-1,2	-2,0	-0,8	-1,0	-0,5	
75°	-1,1	-1,5	-1,2	-2,0	-0,8	-1,0	-0,5	

7.2.9 Internal pressure

(1)P Internal and external pressures shall be considered to act at the same time. The worst combination of external and internal pressures shall be considered for every combination of possible openings and other leakage paths.

(2) The internal pressure coefficient, c_{pi}, depends on the size and distribution of the openings in the building envelope. When in at least two sides of the buildings (facades or roof) the total area of openings in each side is more than 30 % of the area of that side, the actions on the structure should not be calculated from the rules given in this section but the rules of 7.3 and 7.4 should instead be used.

NOTE The openings of a building include small openings such as: open windows, ventilators, chimneys, etc. as well as background permeability such as air leakage around doors, windows, services and through the building envelope. The background permeability is typically in the range 0.01% to 0.1% of the face area. Additional information may be given in a National Annex.

(3) Where an external opening, such as a door or a window, would be dominant when open but is considered to be closed in the ultimate limit state, during severe windstorms, the condition with the door or window open should be considered as an accidental design situation in accordance with EN 1990.

NOTE Checking of the accidental design situation is important for tall internal walls (with high risk of hazard) when the wall has to carry the full external wind action because of openings in the building envelope.

(4) A face of a building should be regarded as dominant when the area of openings at that face is at least twice the area of openings and leakages in the remaining faces of the building considered.

NOTE This can also be applied to individual internal volumes within the building.

(5) For a building with a dominant face the internal pressure should be taken as a fraction of the external pressure at the openings of the dominant face. The values given by expressions (7.1) and (7.2) should be used.

When the area of the openings at the dominant face is twice the area of the openings in the remaining faces,

$$c_{pi} = 0,75 \cdot c_{pe} \tag{7.1}$$

When the area of the openings at the dominant face is at least 3 times the area of the openings in the remaining faces,

$$c_{pi} = 0,90 \cdot c_{pe} \tag{7.2}$$

where c_{pe} is the value for the external pressure coefficient at the openings in the dominant face. When these openings are located in zones with different values of external pressures an area weighted average value of c_{pe} should be used.

When the area of the openings at the dominant face is between 2 and 3 times the area of the openings in the remaining faces linear interpolation for calculating c_{pi} may be used.

(6) For buildings without a dominant face, the internal pressure coefficient c_{pi} should be determined from Figure 7.13, and is a function of the ratio of the height and the depth of the building, h/d, and the opening ratio μ for each wind direction θ, which should be determined from expression (7.3).

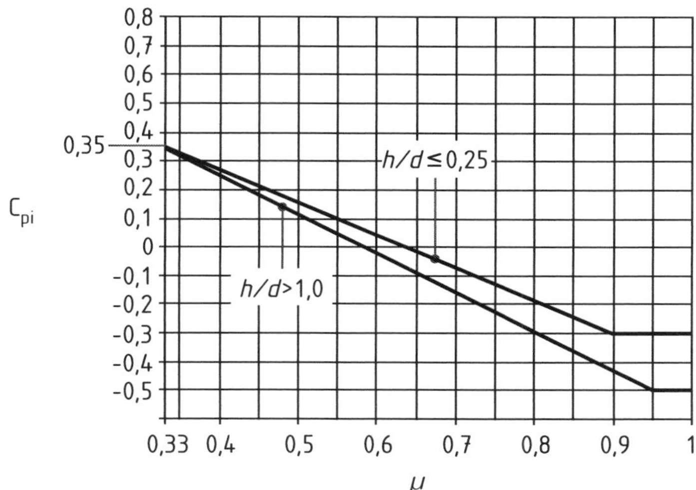

NOTE For values between h/d = 0,25 and h/d = 1,0 linear interpolation may be used.

Figure 7.13 — Internal pressure coefficients for uniformly distributed openings

$$\mu = \frac{\sum \text{area of openings where } c_{pe} \text{ is negative or } -0,0}{\sum \text{area of all openings}} \tag{7.3}$$

NOTE 1 This applies to façades and roof of buildings with and without internal partitions.

NOTE 2 Where it is not possible, or not considered justified, to estimate μ for a particular case then c_{pi} should be taken as the more onerous of +0,2 and -0,3.

(7) The reference height z_i for the internal pressures should be equal to the reference height z_e for the external pressures (see 5.1) on the faces which contribute by their openings to the creation of the internal pressure. If there are several openings the largest value of z_e should be used to determine z_i.

(8) The internal pressure coefficient of open silos and chimneys should be based on expression (7.4):

$$c_{pi} = -0,60 \tag{7.4}$$

The internal pressure coefficient of vented tanks with small openings should be based on expression (7.5):

$$c_{pi} = -0,40 \tag{7.5}$$

The reference height z_i is equal to the height of the structure.

Advisory note regarding BS EN 1991-1-4, 7.2.3 to 7.2.6

Calibration of BS EN 1991-1-4 against BS 6399-2 has shown that there are differences in the values of pressure coefficients and in some cases the EN values are significantly different to those currently used in the UK. National choice is not allowed for the external pressure coefficients. It is therefore recommended that the external pressure coefficients in BS 6399-2 continue to be used to maintain the current levels of safety and economy of construction. The tables affected together with the corresponding figures that define the zones are as follows.

Type of roof	Relevant tables and figures in BS EN 1991-1-4	Recommended tables and figures in BS 6399-2
1 Flat roofs	Table 7.2 and Figure 7.6	Table 8 and Figure 17
2 Mono pitch roofs	Tables 7.3a) and 7.3b) and Figure 7.7	Table 9 and Figure 19
3 Duo pitch roofs	Tables 7.4a) and 7.4b) and Figure 7.8	Table 10 and Figure 20
4 Hipped roofs	Table 7.5 and Figure 7.9	Table 11 and Figure 21

Attention is drawn to the requirement in the EN that fixings and small areas should be designed using $C_{pe,1}$ coefficients given in BS EN 1991-1-4. There is no equivalent coefficient in the BS for this.

Annex A (informative) Terrain effects

A.1 Illustrations of the upper roughness of each terrain category

Terrain category 0

Sea, coastal area exposed to the open sea

Terrain category I

Lakes or area with negligible vegetation and without obstacles

Terrain category II

Area with low vegetation such as grass and isolated obstacles (trees, buildings) with separations of at least 20 obstacle heights

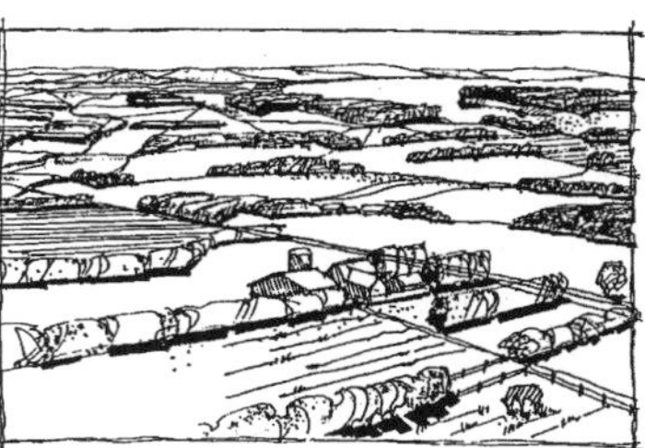

Terrain category III

Area with regular cover of vegetation or buildings or with isolated obstacles with separations of maximum 20 obstacle heights (such as villages, suburban terrain, permanent forest)

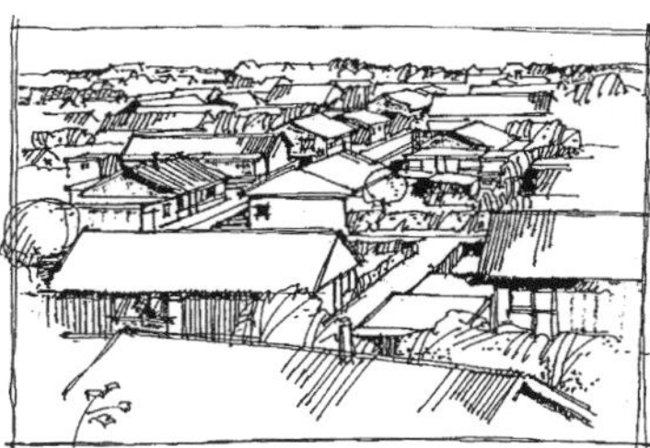

Terrain category IV

Area in which at least 15% of the surface is covered with buildings and their average height exceeds 15 m

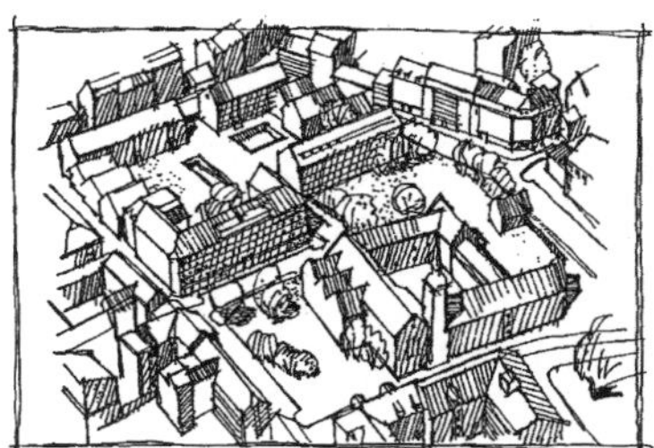

Terrain category 0 is sea terrain
I and II are country terrain
III and IV are town terrain.

Bibliography

ISO 2394 General principles on reliability for structures

[AC1) ISO 3898 Bases for design of structures — Notations — General symbols (AC1]

ISO 8930 General principles on reliability for structures — List of equivalent terms

[AC1) EN 12811-1 Temporary works equipment — Part 1: Scaffolds — Performance requirements and general design

ISO 12494 Atmospheric icing of structures (AC1]

Bibliography

Standards publications

For dated references, only the edition cited applies. For undated references, the latest edition of the referenced document (including any amendments) applies.

BS 5534, *Code of practice for slating and tiling (including shingles).*

BS EN 1991-2, *Eurocode 1: Actions on structures — Part 2: Traffic loads on bridges.*

BS EN 1993-3-1, *Eurocode 3 — Design of steel structures — Part 3-1: Towers, masts and chimneys.*

BS EN 12811-1, T*emporary works equipment — Scaffolds — Performance requirements and general design.*

BS EN 12899-1, *Fixed, vertical road traffic signs — Part 1: Fixed signs.*

PD 6688-1-4, *Background paper to National Annex to BS EN 1991-1-4.*

Other publications

[1] COOK, N.J. *The designer's guide to wind loading of building structures – Part 2: Static structures*. Butterworth-Heinemann Ltd, 1990.

[2] CERMAK, J.E., and N. Isyumov (editors). ASCE (American Society of Civil Engineers) manuals and reports on engineering practice. No 67. *Wind tunnel studies of buildings and structures*. ASCE, 1999.

[3] COOK, N.J. *Wind loading: a practical guide to BS 6399-2 wind loads on buildings*. Thomas Telford Ltd, 1999.

[4] BLACKMORE, P. BRE Digest SD5. *Wind loads on unclad structures*. BRE Press, 2004.

Useful references

[1] Cook N.J. *Designers' Guide to Eurocode 1: Part 1-4 Wind Actions*, Thomas Telford, London, 2009

Chapter 2 — Extracts from Eurocode 2: Design of concrete structures

The Eurocode extracts in this chapter are taken from EN 1992-1-1:2004 (incorporating corrigendum January 2008) *Eurocode 2: Design of concrete structures — Part 1.1: General rules and rules for buildings.*

The start and finish of text introduced or altered by corrigendum is indicated in the text by tags. Text altered by CEN corrigendum January 2008 is indicated in the text by [AC1⟩ ⟨AC1].

The National Annex extracts are taken from NA to BS EN 1992-1-1:2004 (incorporating National Amendment No 1), *UK National Annex to Eurocode 2: Design of concrete structures — Part 1-1: General rules and rules for buildings.*

The full list of the contents of EN 1992-1-1 follows, and is given for reference purposes. (Bold items are included in this chapter.)

2.4.2.4 Partial factors for materials
2.4.2.5 Partial factors for materials for foundations
2.4.3 Combinations of actions
2.4.4 Verification of static equilibrium - EQU
2.5 Design assisted by testing
2.6 Supplementary requirements for foundations
2.7 Requirements for fastenings
3 Materials
3.1 Concrete
3.1.1 General
3.1.2 Strength
3.1.3 Elastic deformation
3.1.4 Creep and shrinkage
3.1.5 Stress-strain relation for non-linear structural analysis
3.1.6 Design compressive and tensile strengths
3.1.7 Stress-strain relations for the design of sections
3.1.8 Flexural tensile strength
3.1.9 Confined concrete
3.2 Reinforcing steel
3.2.1 General
3.2.2 Properties
3.2.3 Strength
3.2.4 Ductility characteristics
3.2.5 Welding
3.2.6 Fatigue
3.2.7 Design assumptions
3.3 Prestressing steel
3.3.1 General
3.3.2 Properties
3.3.3 Strength
3.3.4 Ductility characteristics
3.3.5 Fatigue
3.3.6 Design assumptions
3.3.7 Prestressing tendons in sheaths
3.4 Prestressing devices
3.4.1 Anchorages and couplers
3.4.1.1 General
3.4.1.2 Mechanical properties
3.4.1.2.1 Anchored tendons
3.4.1.2.2 Anchored devices and anchorage zones
3.4.2 External non-bonded tendons
3.4.2.1 General
3.4.2.2 Anchorages
4 Durability and cover to reinforcement
4.1 General
4.2 Environmental conditions
4.3 Requirements for durability
4.4 Methods of verification
4.4.1 Concrete cover
4.4.1.1 General
4.4.1.2 Minimum cover, c_{min}
4.4.1.3 Allowance in design for tolerance
5 Structural analysis
5.1 General
5.1.1 General requirements
5.1.2 Special requirements for foundations
5.1.3 Load cases and combinations
5.1.4 Second order effects
5.2 Geometric imperfections

5.3 Idealisation of the structure
- **5.3.1 Structural models for overall analysis**
- **5.3.2 Geometric data**
  - **5.3.2.1 Effective width of flanges (all limit states)**
  - **5.3.2.2 Effective span of beams and slabs in buildings**

5.4 Linear elastic analysis

5.5 Linear analysis with limited redistribution

5.6 Plastic analysis
- 5.6.1 General
- 5.6.2 Plastic analysis for beams, frames and slabs
- 5.6.3 Rotation capacity
- 5.6.4 Analysis with struts and tie models

5.7 Non-linear analysis

5.8 Analysis of second order effects with axial load
- 5.8.1 Definitions
- **5.8.2 General**
- **5.8.3 Simplified criteria for second order effects**
  - **5.8.3.1 Slenderness criterion for isolated members**
  - **5.8.3.2 Slenderness and effective length of isolated members**
  - 5.8.3.3 Global second order effects in buildings
- **5.8.4 Creep**
- **5.8.5 Methods of analysis**
- 5.8.6 General method
- 5.8.7 Method based on nominal stiffness
  - 5.8.7.1 General
  - 5.8.7.2 Nominal stiffness
  - 5.8.7.3 Moment magnification factor
- **5.8.8 Method based on nominal curvature**
  - **5.8.8.1 General**
  - **5.8.8.2 Bending moments**
  - **5.8.8.3 Curvature**
- **5.8.9 Biaxial bending**

5.9 Lateral instability of slender beams

5.10 Prestressed members and structures
- **5.10.1 General**
- **5.10.2 Prestressing force during tensioning**
  - **5.10.2.1 Maximum stressing force**
  - **5.10.2.2 Limitation of concrete stress**
  - 5.10.2.3 Measurements
- **5.10.3 Prestress force**
- 5.10.4 Immediate losses of prestress for pre-tensioning
- 5.10.5 Immediate losses of prestress for post-tensioning
  - 5.10.5.1 Losses due to the instantaneous deformation of concrete
  - 5.10.5.2 Losses due to friction
  - 5.10.5.3 Losses at anchorage
- 5.10.6 Time dependent losses of prestress for pre- and post-tensioning
- 5.10.7 Consideration of prestress in analysis
- **5.10.8 Effects of prestressing at ultimate limit state**
- **5.10.9 Effects of prestressing at serviceability limit state and limit state of fatigue**

5.11 Analysis for some particular structural members

6 Ultimate limit states (ULS)

6.1 Bending with or without axial force

6.2 Shear
- **6.2.1 General verification procedure**
- **6.2.2 Members not requiring design shear reinforcement**
- **6.2.3 Members requiring design shear reinforcement**
- 6.2.4 Shear between web and flanges of T-sections
- 6.2.5 Shear at the interface between concretes cast at different times

6.3 Torsion
- **6.3.1 General**
- **6.3.2 Design procedure**
- **6.3.3 Warping torsion**

6.4 Punching
- **6.4.1 General**
- **6.4.2 Load distribution and basic control perimeter**
- **6.4.3 Punching shear calculation**
- **6.4.4 Punching shear resistance of slabs and column bases without shear reinforcement**
- 6.4.5 Punching shear resistance of slabs and column bases with shear reinforcement

6.5 Design with strut and tie models
- 6.5.1 General
- 6.5.2 Struts
- 6.5.3 Ties
- 6.5.4 Nodes

6.6 Anchorages and laps

6.7 Partially loaded areas

6.8 Fatigue
- 6.8.1 Verification conditions
- 6.8.2 Internal forces and stresses for fatigue verification
- 6.8.3 Combination of actions
- 6.8.4 Verification procedure for reinforcing and prestressing steel
- 6.8.5 Verification using damage equivalent stress range
- 6.8.6 Other verifications
- 6.8.7 Verification of concrete under compression or shear

7 Serviceability limit states (SLS)

7.1 General

7.2 Stress limitation

7.3 Crack control
- **7.3.1 General considerations**
- **7.3.2 Minimum reinforcement areas**
- **7.3.3 Control of cracking without direct calculation**
- 7.3.4 Calculation of crack widths

7.4 Deflection control
- **7.4.1 General considerations**
- **7.4.2 Cases where calculations may be omitted**
- 7.4.3 Checking deflections by calculation

8 Detailing of reinforcement and prestressing tendons - General

8.1 General

8.2 Spacing of bars

8.3 Permissible mandrel diameters for bent bars

8.4 Anchorage of longitudinal reinforcement
- **8.4.1 General**
- **8.4.2 Ultimate bond stress**
- **8.4.3 Basic anchorage length**
- **8.4.4 Design anchorage length**

8.5 Anchorage of links and shear reinforcement

8.6 Anchorage by welded bars

8.7 Laps and mechanical couplers
- 8.7.1 General
- **8.7.2 Laps**
- **8.7.3 Lap length**
- **8.7.4 Transverse reinforcement in the lap zone**
  - **8.7.4.1 Transverse reinforcement for bars in tension**
  - **8.7.4.2 Transverse reinforcement for bars permanently in compression**
- 8.7.5 Laps for welded mesh fabrics made of ribbed wires
  - 8.7.5.1 Laps of the main reinforcement
  - 8.7.5.2 Laps of secondary or distribution reinforcement

9.10 Tying systems
- 9.10.1 General
- 9.10.2 Proportioning of ties
  - 9.10.2.1 General
  - 9.10.2.2 Peripheral ties
  - 9.10.2.3 Internal ties
  - 9.10.2.4 Horizontal ties to columns and/or walls
  - 9.10.2.5 Vertical ties
- 9.10.3 Continuity and anchorage of ties

10 Additional rules for precast concrete elements and structures

10.1 General
- 10.1.1 Special terms used in this section

10.2 Basis of design, fundamental requirements

10.3 Materials
- 10.3.1 Concrete
  - 10.3.1.1 Strength
  - 10.3.1.2 Creep and shrinkage
- 10.3.2 Prestressing steel
  - 10.3.2.2 Technological properties of prestressing steel

10.5 Structural analysis
- 10.5.1 General
- 10.5.2 Losses of prestress

10.9 Particular rules for design and detailing
- 10.9.1 Restraining moments in slabs
- 10.9.2 Wall to floor connections
- 10.9.3 Floor systems
- 10.9.4 Connections and supports for precast elements
  - 10.9.4.1 Materials
  - 10.9.4.2 General rules for design and detailing of connections
  - 10.9.4.3 Connections transmitting compressive forces
  - 10.9.4.4 Connections transmitting shear forces
  - 10.9.4.5 Connections transmitting bending moments or tensile forces
  - 10.9.4.6 Half joints
  - 10.9.4.7 Anchorage of reinforcement at supports
- 10.9.5 Bearings
  - 10.9.5.1 General
  - 10.9.5.2 Bearings for connected (non-isolated) members
  - 10.9.5.3 Bearings for isolated members
- 10.9.6 Pocket foundations
  - 10.9.6.1 General
  - 10.9.6.2 Pockets with keyed surfaces
  - 10.9.6.3 Pockets with smooth surfaces
- 10.9.7 Tying systems

11 Lightweight aggregated concrete structures

11.1 General
- 11.1.1 Scope
- 11.1.2 Special symbols

11.2 Basis of design

11.3 Materials
- 11.3.1 Concrete
- 11.3.2 Elastic deformation
- 11.3.3 Creep and shrinkage
- 11.3.4 Stress-strain relations for structural analysis
- 11.3.5 Design compressive and tensile strengths
- 11.3.6 Stress-strain relations for the design of sections
- 11.3.7 Confined concrete

11.4 Durability and cover to reinforcement
- 11.4.1 Environmental conditions
- 11.4.2 Concrete cover and properties of concrete

Section 1 General

Approved Document A to the England and Wales Building Regulations cites the details and design approaches in BS 8110 as being one acceptable method to meet the requirement A3 of the Regulations in respect of disproportionate collapse. Some but not all the requirements also feature in BS EN 1992-1-1. In the absence of national choice given in the code, the missing material could not be introduced through the UK National Annex. Therefore these additional requirements have been incorporated in PD 6687 and a cross-reference has been made in NA.2 under clause 9.10.2.4 (2).

1.1 Scope

1.1.1 Scope of Eurocode 2

(1)P Eurocode 2 applies to the design of buildings and civil engineering works in plain, reinforced and prestressed concrete. It complies with the principles and requirements for the safety and serviceability of structures, the basis of their design and verification that are given in EN 1990: Basis of structural design.

(2)P Eurocode 2 deals only with the requirements for resistance, serviceability, durability and fire-resistance of concrete structures. Other requirements, e.g. concerning thermal or sound insulation, are not considered.

(3)P Eurocode 2 is intended to be used in conjunction with:

EN 1990:	*Basis of structural design*
EN 1991:	*Actions on structures*
hEN's	*Construction products relevant for concrete structures*
ENV 13670	*Execution of concrete structures*
EN 1997:	*Geotechnical design*
EN 1998:	*Design of structures for earthquake resistance, when concrete structures are built in seismic regions*

(4)P Eurocode 2 is subdivided into the following parts:

Part 1-1:	*General rules and rules for buildings*
Part 1-2:	*Structural fire design*
Part 2:	*Reinforced and prestressed concrete bridges*
Part 3:	*Liquid retaining and containing structures*

1.1.2 Scope of Part 1.1 of Eurocode 2

(1)P Part 1.1 of Eurocode 2 gives a general basis for the design of concrete structures in plain, reinforced and prestressed concrete made with normal and lightweight aggregates together with specific rules for buildings.

(2)P The following subjects are dealt with in Part 1.1:

Section 1:	**General**
Section 2:	**Basis of design**
Section 3:	**Materials**
Section 4:	**Durability and cover to reinforcement**
Section 5:	**Structural analysis**
Section 6:	**Ultimate limit states**
Section 7:	**Serviceability limit states**
Section 8:	**Detailing of reinforcement and prestressing tendons – General**
Section 9:	Detailing of members and particular rules
Section 10:	Additional rules for precast concrete elements and structures
Section 11:	Lightweight aggregate concrete structures
Section 12:	Plain and lightly reinforced concrete structures

Annexes A, B, C, D, E, F G, H, I, J

This guide contains selected material from the sections shown in bold above.

Nationally Determined Parameters (NDP's) Throughout the extracts from the Eurocode there are notes about NDP's of the form "NOTE The value of γ_ξ for use in a country may be found in its National Annex. The recommended value is 0,85." Where the value to be used in the UK differs from the recommended value in the Eurocode, this guide gives the recommended value for the UK either in a grey commentary box, or as a National Annex extract.

1.4 Distinction between principles and application rules

(1)P The rules given in EN 1990 apply.

1.5 Definitions

1.5.1 General

(1)P The terms and definitions given in EN 1990 apply.

1.5.2 Additional terms and definitions used in this standard

1.5.2.1
precast structures
structures characterised by structural elements manufactured elsewhere than in their final position in the structure. In the structure, elements are connected to ensure the required structural integrity

1.5.2.2
plain or lightly reinforced concrete members
structural concrete members having no reinforcement (plain concrete), or less reinforcement than the minimum amounts defined in Section 9

1.5.2.3
unbonded and external tendons
unbonded tendons for post-tensioned members having ducts which are permanently ungrouted, and tendons external to the concrete cross-section (which may be encased in concrete after stressing, or have a protective membrane)

1.5.2.4
prestress
the process of prestressing consists in applying forces to the concrete structure by stressing tendons relative to the concrete member. "Prestress" is used globally to name all the permanent effects of the prestressing process, which comprise internal forces in the sections, and deformations of the structure. Other means of prestressing are not considered in this standard

1.6 Symbols

For the purposes of this standard, the following symbols apply.

NOTE The notation used is based on ISO 3898:1987.

Latin upper case letters

A	Accidental action
A	Cross sectional area
A_c	Cross sectional area of concrete
A_p	Area of a prestressing tendon or tendons
A_s	Cross sectional area of reinforcement
$A_{s,min}$	Minimum cross sectional area of reinforcement
A_{sw}	Cross sectional area of shear reinforcement

D	Diameter of mandrel
D_{Ed}	Fatigue damage factor
E	Effect of action
E_c, $E_{c(28)}$	Tangent modulus of elasticity of normal weight concrete at a stress of $\sigma_c = 0$ and at 28 days
$E_{c,eff}$	Effective modulus of elasticity of concrete
E_{cd}	Design value of modulus of elasticity of concrete
E_{cm}	Secant modulus of elasticity of concrete
$E_c(t)$	Tangent modulus of elasticity of normal weight concrete at stress of $\sigma_c = 0$ and at time t
E_p	Design value of modulus of elasticity of prestressing steel
E_s	Design value of modulus of elasticity of reinforcing steel
EI	Bending stiffness
EQU	Static equilibrium
F	Action
F_d	Design value of an action
F_k	Characteristic value of an action
G_k	Characteristic permanent action
I	Second moment of area of concrete section
L	Length
M	Bending moment
M_{Ed}	Design value of the applied internal bending moment
N	Axial force
N_{Ed}	Design value of the applied axial force (tension or compression)
P	Prestressing force
P_0	Initial force at the active end of the tendon immediately after stressing
Q_k	Characteristic variable action
Q_{fat}	Characteristic fatigue load
R	Resistance
S	Internal forces and moments
S	First moment of area
SLS	Serviceability limit state
T	Torsional moment
T_{Ed}	Design value of the applied torsional moment
ULS	Ultimate limit state
V	Shear force
V_{Ed}	Design value of the applied shear force

Latin lower case letters

a	Distance
a	Geometrical data
Δa	Deviation for geometrical data
b	Overall width of a cross-section, or actual flange width in a T or L beam
b_w	Width of the web on T, I or L beams
d	Diameter; Depth
d	Effective depth of a cross-section
d_g	Largest nominal maximum aggregate size
e	Eccentricity
f_c	Compressive strength of concrete
f_{cd}	Design value of concrete compressive strength
f_{ck}	Characteristic compressive cylinder strength of concrete at 28 days
f_{cm}	Mean value of concrete cylinder compressive strength
f_{ctk}	Characteristic axial tensile strength of concrete
f_{ctm}	Mean value of axial tensile strength of concrete
f_p	Tensile strength of prestressing steel
f_{pk}	Characteristic tensile strength of prestressing steel
$f_{p0,1}$	0,1% proof-stress of prestressing steel
$f_{p0,1k}$	Characteristic 0,1% proof-stress of prestressing steel
$f_{p0,2k}$	Characteristic 0,2% proof-stress of reinforcement
f_t	Tensile strength of reinforcement

f_{tk}	Characteristic tensile strength of reinforcement
f_y	Yield strength of reinforcement
f_{yd}	Design yield of reinforcement
f_{yk}	Characteristic yield strength of reinforcement
f_{ywd}	Design yield strength of shear reinforcement
h	Height
h	Overall depth of a cross-section
i	Radius of gyration
k	Coefficient; Factor
l	(or l or L) Length; Span
m	Mass
r	Radius
$1/r$	Curvature at a particular section
t	Thickness
t	Time being considered
t_0	The age of concrete at the time of loading
u	Perimeter of concrete cross-section, having area A_c
u,v,w	Components of the displacement of a point
x	Neutral axis depth
x,y,z	Coordinates
z	Lever arm of internal forces

Greek lower case letters

α	Angle; ratio
β	Angle; ratio; coefficient
γ	Partial factor
γ_A	Partial factor for accidental actions A
γ_C	Partial factor for concrete
γ_F	Partial factor for actions, F
$\gamma_{F,fat}$	Partial factor for fatigue actions
$\gamma_{C,fat}$	Partial factor for fatigue of concrete
γ_G	Partial factor for permanent actions, G
γ_M	Partial factor for a material property, taking account of uncertainties in the material property itself, geometric deviation and the design model used
γ_P	Partial factor for actions associated with prestressing, P
γ_Q	Partial factor for variable actions, Q
γ_S	Partial factor for reinforcing or prestressing steel
$\gamma_{S,fat}$	Partial factor for reinforcing or prestressing steel under fatigue loading
γ_f	Partial factor for actions without taking account of model uncertainties
γ_g	Partial factor for permanent actions without taking account of model uncertainties
γ_m	Partial factor for a material property, taking account only of uncertainties in the material property
δ	Increment/redistribution ratio
ζ	Reduction factor/distribution coefficient
ε_c	Compressive strain in the concrete
ε_{c1}	Compressive strain in the concrete at the peak stress f_c
ε_{cu}	Ultimate compressive strain in the concrete
ε_u	Strain of reinforcement or prestressing steel at maximum load
ε_{uk}	Characteristic strain of reinforcement or prestressing steel at maximum load
θ	Angle
λ	Slenderness ratio
μ	Coefficient of friction between the tendons and their ducts
ν	Poisson's ratio
ν	Strength reduction factor for concrete cracked in shear
ξ	Ratio of bond strength of prestressing and reinforcing steel
ρ	Oven-dry density of concrete in kg/m^3
ρ_{1000}	Value of relaxation loss (in %), at 1000 hours after tensioning and at a mean temperature of 20°C
ρ_l	Reinforcement ratio for longitudinal reinforcement

ρ_w	Reinforcement ratio for shear reinforcement
σ_c	Compressive stress in the concrete
σ_{cp}	Compressive stress in the concrete from axial load or prestressing
σ_{cu}	Compressive stress in the concrete at the ultimate compressive strain ε_{cu}
τ	Torsional shear stress
ϕ	Diameter of a reinforcing bar or of a prestressing duct
ϕ_n	Equivalent diameter of a bundle of reinforcing bars
$\varphi(t,t_0)$	Creep coefficient, defining creep between times t and t_0, related to elastic deformation at 28 days
$\varphi(\infty,t_0)$	Final value of creep coefficient
ψ	Factors defining representative values of variable actions ψ_0 for combination values ψ_1 for frequent values ψ_2 for quasi-permanent values

Section 2 Basis of design

2.1 Requirements

2.1.1 Basic requirements

(1)P The design of concrete structures shall be in accordance with the general rules given in EN 1990.

(2)P The supplementary provisions for concrete structures given in this section shall also be applied.

(3) The basic requirements of EN 1990 Section 2 are deemed to be satisfied for concrete structures when the following are applied together:
- limit state design in conjunction with the partial factor method in accordance with EN 1990,
- actions in accordance with EN 1991,
- combination of actions in accordance with EN 1990 and
- resistances, durability and serviceability in accordance with this standard.

NOTE Requirements for fire resistance (see EN 1990 Section 5 and EN 1992-1-2) may dictate a greater size of member than that required for structural resistance at normal temperature.

2.3 Basic variables

2.3.1 Actions and environmental influences

2.3.1.1 General

(1) Actions to be used in design may be obtained from the relevant parts of EN 1991.

2.3.2 Material and product properties

2.3.2.1 General

(1) The rules for material and product properties are given in EN 1990 Section 4.

(2) Provisions for concrete, reinforcement and prestressing steel are given in Section 3 or the relevant Product Standard.

2.3.2.2 Shrinkage and creep

(1) Shrinkage and creep are time-dependent properties of concrete. Their effects should generally be taken into account for the verification of serviceability limit states.

(2) The effects of shrinkage and creep should be considered at ultimate limit states only where their effects are significant, for example in the verification of ultimate limit states of stability where second order effects are of importance. In other cases these effects need not be considered for ultimate limit states, provided that ductility and rotation capacity of the elements are sufficient.

(3) When creep is taken into account its design effects should be evaluated under the quasi-permanent combination of actions irrespective of the design situation considered, i.e. persistent, transient or accidental.

NOTE In most cases the effects of creep may be evaluated under permanent loads and the mean value of prestress.

2.3.3 Deformations of concrete

(1)P The consequences of deformation due to temperature, creep and shrinkage shall be considered in design.

(2) The influence of these effects is normally accommodated by complying with the application rules of this standard. Consideration should also be given to:

- minimising deformation and cracking due to early-age movement, creep and shrinkage through the composition of the concrete mix;
- minimising restraints to deformation by the provision of bearings or joints;
- if restraints are present, ensuring that their influence is taken into account in design.

(3) In building structures, temperature and shrinkage effects may be omitted in global analysis provided joints are incorporated at every distance d_{joint} to accommodate resulting deformations.

NOTE The value of d_{joint} is subject to a National Annex. The recommended value is 30 m. For precast concrete structures the value may be larger than that for cast in-situ structures, since part of the creep and shrinkage takes place before erection.

2.4 Verification by the partial factor method

2.4.1 General

(1) The rules for the partial factor method are given in EN 1990 Section 6.

2.4.2 Design values

2.4.2.1 Partial factor for shrinkage action

(1) Where consideration of shrinkage actions is required for ultimate limit state a partial factor, γ_{SH}, should be used.

NOTE The value of γ_{SH} for use in a country may be found in its National Annex. The recommended value is 1,0.

2.4.2.2 Partial factors for prestress

(1) Prestress in most situations is intended to be favourable and for the ultimate limit state verification the value of $\gamma_{P,fav}$ should be used. The design value of prestress may be based on the mean value of the prestressing force (see EN 1990 Section 4).

NOTE The value of $\gamma_{P,fav}$ for use in a Country may be found in its National Annex. The recommended value for persistent design situations is 1,0. This value may also be used for fatigue verification.

The value of $\gamma_{P,fav}$ for use in the UK for persistent and transient design situations is 0,9. This value may also be used for fatigue verification.

(2) In the verification of the limit state for stability with external prestress, where an increase of the value of prestress can be unfavourable, $\gamma_{P,unfav}$ should be used.

NOTE The value of $\gamma_{P,unfav}$ in the stability limit state for use in a Country may be found in its National Annex. The recommended value for global analysis is 1,3.

The value of $\gamma_{P,unfav}$ in the stability limit state for use in the UK is 1,1.

(3) In the verification of local effects $\gamma_{P,unfav}$ should also be used.

NOTE The value of $\gamma_{P,unfav}$ for local effects for use in a country may be found in its National Annex. The recommended value is 1,2. The local effects of the anchorage of pre-tensioned tendons are considered in 8.10.2.

2.4.2.3 Partial factor for fatigue loads

(1) The partial factor for fatigue loads is $\gamma_{F,fat}$.

NOTE The value of $\gamma_{F,fat}$ for use in a country may be found in its National Annex. The recommended value is 1,0.

2.4.2.4 Partial factors for materials

(1) Partial factors for materials for ultimate limit states, γ_C and γ_S should be used.

NOTE The values of γ_C and γ_S for use in a country may be found in its National Annex. The recommended values for "persistent & transient" and "accidental" design situations are given in Table 2.1N. These are not valid for fire design for which reference should be made to EN 1992-1-2.

For fatigue verification the partial factors for persistent design situations given in Table 2.1N are recommended for the values of $\gamma_{C,fat}$ and $\gamma_{S,fat}$.

Table 2.1N — Partial factors for materials for ultimate limit states

Design situations	γ_C for concrete	γ_S for reinforcing steel	γ_S for prestressing steel
Persistent & Transient	1,5	1,15	1,15
Accidental	1,2	1,0	1,0

(2) The values for partial factors for materials for serviceability limit state verification should be taken as those given in the particular clauses of this Eurocode.

NOTE The values of γ_c and γ_S in the serviceability limit state for use in a country may be found in its National Annex. The recommended value for situations not covered by particular clauses of this Eurocode is 1,0.

2.4.2.5 Partial factors for materials for foundations

(1) Design values of strength properties of the ground should be calculated in accordance with EN 1997.

(2) The partial factor for concrete γ_C given in 2.4.2.4 (1) should be multiplied by a factor, k_f, for calculation of design resistance of cast in place piles without permanent casing.

NOTE The value of k_f for use in a country may be found in its National Annex. The recommended value is 1,1.

2.4.3 Combinations of actions

(1) The general formats for combinations of actions for the ultimate and serviceability limit states are given in EN 1990, Section 6.

NOTE 1 Detailed expressions for combinations of actions are given in the normative annexes of EN 1990, i.e. Annex A1 for buildings, A2 for bridges, etc. with relevant recommended values for partial factors and representative values of actions given in the notes.

NOTE 2 Combination of actions for fatigue verification is given in 6.8.3.

(2) For each permanent action either the lower or the upper design value (whichever gives the more unfavourable effect) should be applied throughout the structure (e.g. self-weight in a structure).

NOTE There may be some exceptions to this rule (e.g. in the verification of static equilibrium, see EN 1990 Section 6). In such cases a different set of partial factors (Set A) may be used. An example valid for buildings is given in Annex A1 of EN 1990.

Section 3 Materials

3.1 Concrete

3.1.1 General

(1)P The following clauses give principles and rules for normal and high strength concrete.

3.1.2 Strength

(1)P The compressive strength of concrete is denoted by concrete strength classes which relate to the characteristic (5 %) cylinder strength f_{ck}, or the cube strength $f_{ck,cube}$, in accordance with EN 206-1.

(2)P The strength classes in this code are based on the characteristic cylinder strength f_{ck} determined at 28 days with a maximum value of C_{max}.

NOTE The value of C_{max} for use in a Country may be found in its National Annex. The recommended value is C90/105.

The value of C_{max} for use in the UK is C90/105. However, the shear strength of concrete classes higher than C50/60 should be determined by tests, unless there is evidence of satisfactory past performance of the particular mix including the type of aggregates used. Alternatively, shear strength of concrete strength classes higher than C50/60 may be limited to that of C50/60.

(3) The characteristic strengths for f_{ck} and the corresponding mechanical characteristics necessary for design are given in Table 3.1.

(4) In certain situations (e.g. prestressing) it may be appropriate to assess the compressive strength for concrete before or after 28 days, on the basis of test specimens stored under other conditions than prescribed in EN 12390.

If the concrete strength is determined at an age $t > 28$ days the values α_{cc} and α_{ct} defined in 3.1.6 (1)P and 3.1.6 (2)P should be reduced by a factor k_t.

NOTE The value of k_t for use in a Country may be found in its National Annex. The recommended value is 0,85.

The value of k_t for use in the UK is 1,0.

3.1.3 Elastic deformation

(1) The elastic deformations of concrete largely depend on its composition (especially the aggregates). The values given in this standard should be regarded as indicative for general applications. However, they should be specifically assessed if the structure is likely to be sensitive to deviations from these general values.

(2) The modulus of elasticity of a concrete is controlled by the moduli of elasticity of its components. Approximate values for the modulus of elasticity E_{cm} (secant value between $\sigma_c = 0$ and $0,4f_{cm}$), for concretes with quartzite aggregates, are given in Table 3.1. For limestone and sandstone aggregates the value should be reduced by 10 % and 30 % respectively. For basalt aggregates the value should be increased by 20 %.

NOTE A Country's National Annex may refer to non-contradictory complementary information.

Table 3.1 — Strength and deformation characteristics for concrete

<table>
<tr><th colspan="15">Strength classes for concrete</th><th>Analytical relation / Explanation</th></tr>
<tr><td>f_{ck} (MPa)</td><td>12</td><td>16</td><td>20</td><td>25</td><td>30</td><td>35</td><td>40</td><td>45</td><td>50</td><td>55</td><td>60</td><td>70</td><td>80</td><td>90</td><td></td></tr>
<tr><td>$f_{ck,cube}$ (MPa)</td><td>15</td><td>20</td><td>25</td><td>30</td><td>37</td><td>45</td><td>50</td><td>55</td><td>60</td><td>67</td><td>75</td><td>85</td><td>95</td><td>105</td><td></td></tr>
<tr><td>f_{cm} (MPa)</td><td>20</td><td>24</td><td>28</td><td>33</td><td>38</td><td>43</td><td>48</td><td>53</td><td>58</td><td>63</td><td>68</td><td>78</td><td>88</td><td>98</td><td>$f_{cm} = f_{ck} + 8$ (MPa)</td></tr>
<tr><td>f_{ctm} (MPa)</td><td>1,6</td><td>1,9</td><td>2,2</td><td>2,6</td><td>2,9</td><td>3,2</td><td>3,5</td><td>3,8</td><td>4,1</td><td>4,2</td><td>4,4</td><td>4,6</td><td>4,8</td><td>5,0</td><td>$f_{ctm} = 0{,}30 \times f_{ck}^{(2/3)} \leq$ C50/60
$f_{ctm} = 2{,}12 \cdot \ln(1 + (f_{cm}/10)) >$ C50/60</td></tr>
<tr><td>$f_{ctk,\,0,05}$ (MPa)</td><td>1,1</td><td>1,3</td><td>1,5</td><td>1,8</td><td>2,0</td><td>2,2</td><td>2,5</td><td>2,7</td><td>2,9</td><td>3,0</td><td>3,1</td><td>3,2</td><td>3,4</td><td>3,5</td><td>$f_{ctk,\,0,05} = 0{,}7 \times f_{ctm}$
5% fractile</td></tr>
<tr><td>$f_{clk,\,0,95}$ (MPa)</td><td>2,0</td><td>2,5</td><td>2,9</td><td>3,3</td><td>3,8</td><td>4,2</td><td>4,6</td><td>4,9</td><td>5,3</td><td>5,5</td><td>5,7</td><td>6,0</td><td>6,3</td><td>6,6</td><td>$f_{clk,\,0,95} = 1{,}3 \times f_{ctm}$
95% fractile</td></tr>
<tr><td>E_{cm} (GPa)</td><td>27</td><td>29</td><td>30</td><td>31</td><td>33</td><td>34</td><td>35</td><td>36</td><td>37</td><td>38</td><td>39</td><td>41</td><td>42</td><td>44</td><td>$E_{cm} = 22\,[(f_{cm})/10]^{0,3}$
(f_{cm} in MPa)</td></tr>
<tr><td>ε_{c1} (‰)</td><td>1,8</td><td>1,9</td><td>2,0</td><td>2,1</td><td>2,2</td><td>2,25</td><td>2,3</td><td>2,4</td><td>2,45</td><td>2,5</td><td>2,6</td><td>2,7</td><td>2,8</td><td>2,8</td><td>see Figure 3.2
ε_{c1} (‰) $= 0{,}7\, f_{cm}^{0,31} < 2{,}8$</td></tr>
<tr><td>ε_{cu1} (‰)</td><td colspan="9">3,5</td><td>3,2</td><td>3,0</td><td>2,8</td><td>2,8</td><td>2,8</td><td>see Figure 3.2
for $f_{ck} \geq 50$ Mpa
ε_{cu1} (‰) $= 2{,}8 + 27\,[(98 - f_{cm})/100]^4$</td></tr>
<tr><td>ε_{c2} (‰)</td><td colspan="9">2,0</td><td>2,2</td><td>2,3</td><td>2,4</td><td>2,5</td><td>2,6</td><td>see Figure 3.3
for $f_{ck} \geq 50$ Mpa
ε_{c2} (‰) $= 2{,}0 + 0{,}085\,(f_{ck} - 50)^{0,53}$</td></tr>
<tr><td>ε_{cu2} (‰)</td><td colspan="9">3,5</td><td>3,1</td><td>2,9</td><td>2,7</td><td>2,6</td><td>2,6</td><td>see Figure 3.3
for $f_{ck} \geq 50$ Mpa
ε_{cu2} (‰) $= 2{,}6 + 35\,[(90 - f_{cm})/100]^4$</td></tr>
<tr><td>n</td><td colspan="9">2,0</td><td>1,75</td><td>1,6</td><td>1,45</td><td>1,4</td><td>1,4</td><td>for $f_{ck} \geq 50$ Mpa
$n = 1{,}4 + 23{,}4\,[(90 - f_{cm})/100]^4$</td></tr>
<tr><td>ε_{c3} (‰)</td><td colspan="9">1,75</td><td>1,8</td><td>1,9</td><td>2,0</td><td>2,2</td><td>2,3</td><td>see Figure 3.4
for $f_{ck} \geq 50$ Mpa
ε_{c3} (‰) $= 1{,}75 + 0{,}55\,[(f_{ck} - 50)/40]$</td></tr>
<tr><td>ε_{cu3} (‰)</td><td colspan="9">3,5</td><td>3,1</td><td>2,9</td><td>2,7</td><td>2,6</td><td>2,6</td><td>see Figure 3.4
for $f_{ck} \geq 50$ Mpa
ε_{cu3} (‰) $= 2{,}6 + 35\,[(90 - f_{ck})/100]^4$</td></tr>
</table>

(4) Poisson's ratio may be taken equal to 0,2 for uncracked concrete and 0 for cracked concrete.

(5) Unless more accurate information is available, the linear coefficient of thermal expansion may be taken equal to $10 \cdot 10^{-6}$ K^{-1}.

3.1.4 Creep and shrinkage

(1)P Creep and shrinkage of the concrete depend on the ambient humidity, the dimensions of the element and the composition of the concrete. Creep is also influenced by the maturity of the concrete when the load is first applied and depends on the duration and magnitude of the loading.

(2) The creep coefficient, $\varphi(t,t_0)$ is related to E_c, the tangent modulus, which may be taken as 1,05 E_{cm}. Where great accuracy is not required, the value found from Figure 3.1 may be considered as the creep coefficient, provided that the concrete is not subjected to a compressive stress greater than $0,45f_{ck}(t_0)$ at an age t_0, the age of concrete at the time of loading.

NOTE For further information, including the development of creep with time, Annex B may be used.

(3) The creep deformation of concrete $\varepsilon_{cc}(\infty,t_0)$ at time $t = \infty$ for a constant compressive stress σ_c applied at the concrete age t_0, is given by:

$$\varepsilon_{cc}(\infty, t_0) = \varphi(\infty, t_0) \cdot (\sigma_c / E_c) \qquad (3.6)$$

(4) When the compressive stress of concrete at an age t_0 exceeds the value $0,45f_{ck}(t_0)$ then creep non-linearity should be considered. Such a high stress can occur as a result of pre-tensioning, e.g. in precast concrete members at tendon level. In such cases the non-linear notional creep coefficient should be obtained as follows:

AC1 $$\varphi_{nl}(\infty, t_0) = \varphi(\infty, t_0) \exp(1,5(k_\sigma - 0,45)) \qquad (3.7)$$

where:

$\varphi_{nl}(\infty,t_0)$ is the non-linear notional creep coefficient, which replaces $\varphi(\infty, t_0)$
k_σ is the stress-strength ratio $\sigma_c / f_{ck}(t_0)$, where σ_c is the compressive stress and $f_{ck}(t_0)$ is the characteristic concrete compressive strength at time of loading. AC1

(5) The values given in Figure 3.1 are valid for ambient temperatures between –40°C and +40°C and a mean relative humidity between RH = 40% and RH = 100%. The following symbols are used:

$\varphi(\infty,t_0)$ is the final creep coefficient
t_0 is the age of the concrete at time of loading in days
h_0 is the notional size = $2A_c / u$, where A_c is the concrete cross-sectional area and u is the perimeter of that part which is exposed to drying
S is Class S, according to 3.1.2 (6)
N is Class N, according to 3.1.2 (6)
R is Class R, according to 3.1.2 (6)

Class S includes CEM 32,5N.
Class N includes CEM 23,SR and 42,5N.
Class R includes CEM 42,5R, CEM 53,5N and CEM 53,5R.

Generally, Class R may be assumed. Where the ground granulated blastfurnace slag (ggbs) exceeds 35% of the cement combination or where fuel ash exceeds 20% of the cement combination, Class N may be assumed. Where ggbs exceeds 65% or fuel ash exceeds 35%, Class S may be assumed.

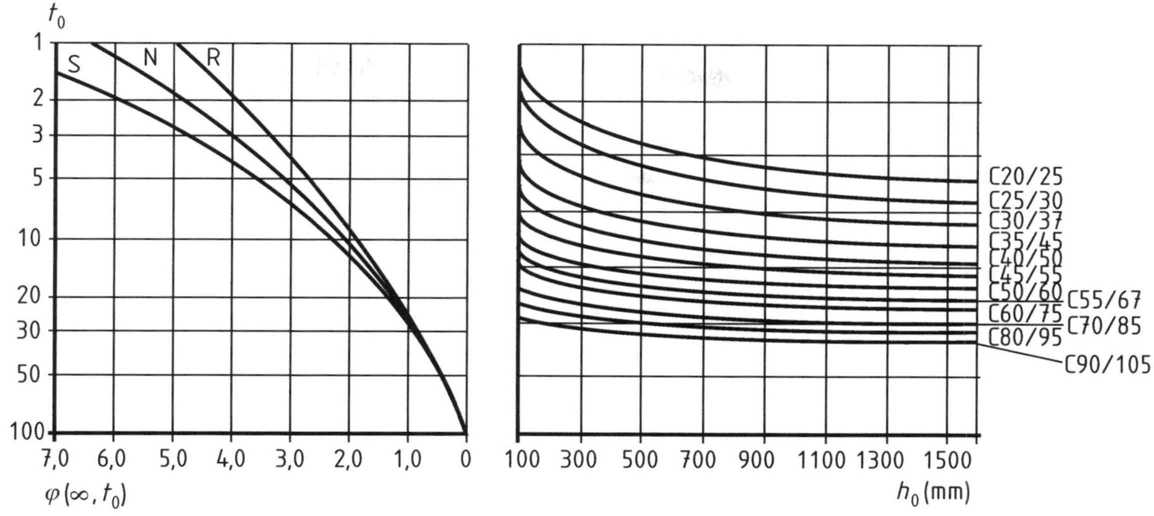

a) inside conditions, RH = 50 %

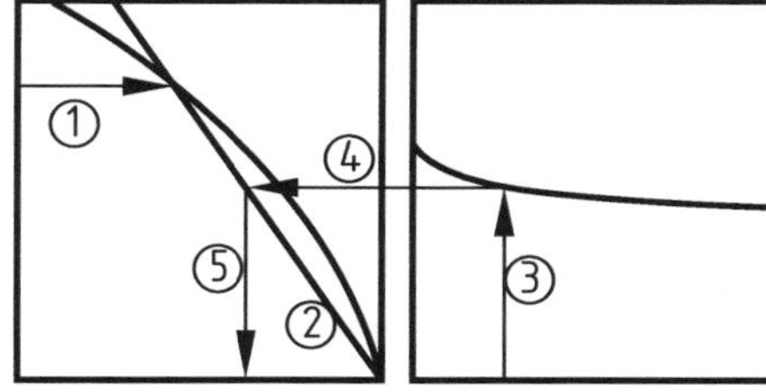

Note:
- intersection point between lines 4 and 5 can also be above point 1
- for t_0 > 100 it is sufficiently accurate to assume t_0 = 100 (and use the tangent line)

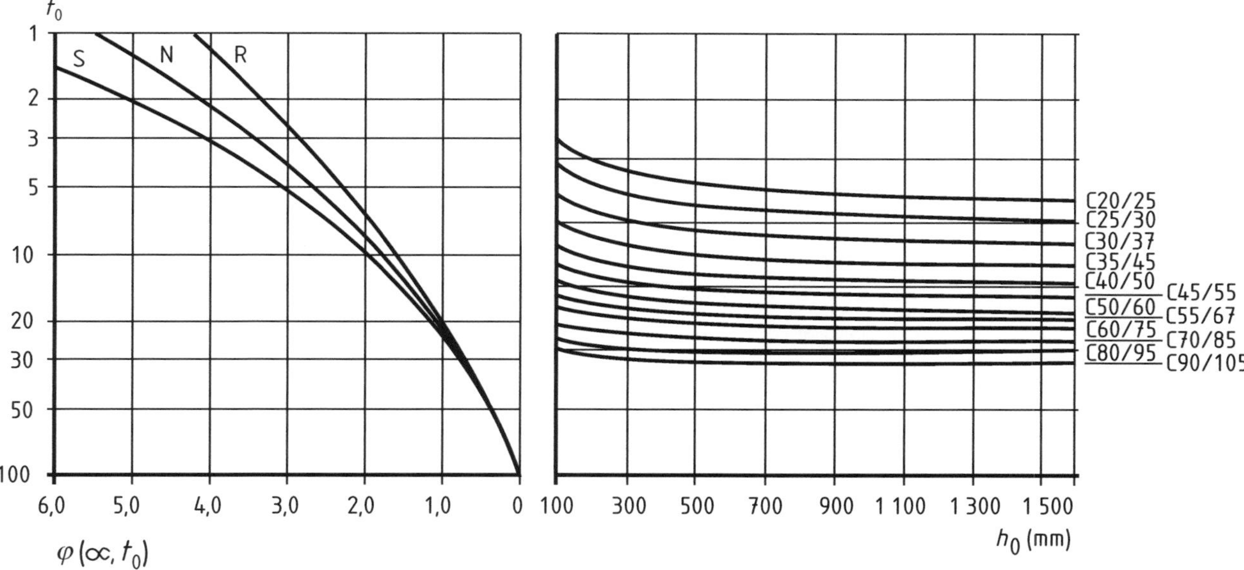

b) outside conditions, RH = 80 %

Figure 3.1 — Method for determining the creep coefficient $\varphi(\infty, t_0)$ for concrete under normal environmental conditions

(6) The total shrinkage strain is composed of two components, the drying shrinkage strain and the autogenous shrinkage strain. The drying shrinkage strain develops slowly, since it is a function of the migration of the water through the hardened concrete. The autogenous shrinkage strain develops during hardening of the concrete: the major part therefore develops in the early days after casting. Autogenous shrinkage is a linear function of the concrete strength. It should be considered specifically when new concrete is cast against hardened concrete. Hence the values of the total shrinkage strain ε_{cs} follow from

$$\varepsilon_{cs} = \varepsilon_{cd} + \varepsilon_{ca} \quad (3.8)$$

where:

ε_{cs} is the total shrinkage strain
ε_{cd} is the drying shrinkage strain
ε_{ca} is the autogenous shrinkage strain

The final value of the drying shrinkage strain, $\varepsilon_{cd,\infty}$ is equal to k_h. $\varepsilon_{cd,0}$, may be taken from Table 3.2 (expected mean values, with a coefficient of variation of about 30 %).

NOTE The formula for $\varepsilon_{cd,0}$ is given in EN 1992-1-1 Annex B.

Table 3.2 — Nominal unrestrained drying shrinkage values $\varepsilon_{cd,0}$ (in ‰) for concrete with cement CEM Class N

$f_{ck}/f_{ck,cube}$ (MPa)	Relative Humidity (in %)					
	20	40	60	80	90	100
20/25	0.62	0.58	0.49	0.30	0.17	0.00
40/50	0.48	0.46	0.38	0.24	0.13	0.00
60/75	0.38	0.36	0.30	0.19	0.10	0.00
80/95	0.30	0.28	0.24	0.15	0.08	0.00
90/105	0.27	0.25	0.21	0.13	0.07	0.00

The development of the drying shrinkage strain in time follows from:

$$\varepsilon_{cd}(t) = \beta_{ds}(t, t_s) \cdot k_h \cdot \varepsilon_{cd,0} \quad (3.9)$$

where

k_h is a coefficient depending on the notional size h_0 according to Table 3.3

Table 3.3 — Values for k_h in expression (3.9)

h_0	k_h
100	1,0
200	0,85
300	0,75
≥ 500	0,70

$$\beta_{ds}(t, t_s) = \frac{(t - t_s)}{(t - t_s) + 0{,}04\sqrt{h_0^3}} \quad (3.10)$$

where:

t is the age of the concrete at the moment considered, in days
t_s is the age of the concrete (days) at the beginning of drying shrinkage (or swelling). Normally this is at the end of curing
h_0 is the notional size (mm) of the cross-section
$= 2A_c/u$

where:

A_c is the concrete cross-sectional area
u is the perimeter of that part of the cross section which is exposed to drying

The autogenous shrinkage strain follows from:

$$\varepsilon_{ca}(t) = \beta_{as}(t)\,\varepsilon_{ca}(\infty) \qquad (3.11)$$

where:

$$\varepsilon_{ca}(\infty) = 2,5\,(f_{ck} - 10)\,10^{-6} \qquad (3.12)$$

and

$$\beta_{as}(t) = 1 - \exp\left(-0,2t^{0,5}\right) \qquad (3.13)$$

where t is given in days.

3.1.6 Design compressive and tensile strengths

(1)P The value of the design compressive strength is defined as

$$f_{cd} = \alpha_{cc}\, f_{ck} / \gamma_c \qquad (3.15)$$

where:

γ_c is the partial safety factor for concrete, see 2.4.2.4, and
α_{cc} is the coefficient taking account of long term effects on the compressive strength and of unfavourable effects resulting from the way the load is applied.

NOTE The value of α_{cc} for use in a Country should lie between 0,8 and 1,0 and may be found in its National Annex. The recommended value is 1.

The value of α_{cc} for use in the UK is 0,85 for compression in flexure and axial loading and 1,0 for other phenomena. However α_{cc} may be taken conservatively as 0,85 for all phenomena.

(2)P The value of the design tensile strength, f_{ctd}, is defined as

$$f_{ctd} = \alpha_{cc}\, f_{ctk,0,05} / \gamma_c \qquad (3.16)$$

where:

γ_c is the partial safety factor for concrete, see 2.4.2.4, and
α_{ct} is a coefficient taking account of long term effects on the tensile strength and of unfavourable effects, resulting from the way the load is applied.

NOTE The value of α_{ct} for use in a country may be found in its National Annex. The recommended value is 1,0.

3.1.7 Stress-strain relations for the design of cross-sections

(3) A rectangular stress distribution (as given in Figure 3.5) may be assumed. The factor λ, defining the effective height of the compression zone and the factor η, defining the effective strength, follow from:

$$\lambda = 0,8 \quad \text{for} \quad f_{ck} \leq 50 \text{ MPa} \tag{3.19}$$

$$\lambda = 0,8 - (f_{ck} - 50) / 400 \quad \text{for} \quad 50 < f_{ck} \leq 90 \text{ MPa} \tag{3.20}$$

and

$$\eta = 1,0 \quad \text{for} \quad f_{ck} \leq 50 \text{ MPa} \tag{3.21}$$

$$\eta = 1,0 - (f_{ck} - 50) / 200 \quad \text{for} \quad 50 < f_{ck} \leq 90 \text{ MPa} \tag{3.22}$$

NOTE If the width of the compression zone decreases in the direction of the extreme compression fibre, the value $\eta\, f_{cd}$ should be reduced by 10 %.

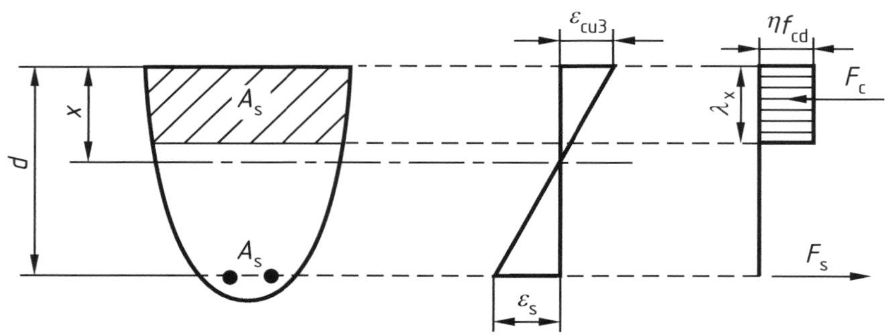

Figure 3.5 — Rectangular stress distribution

3.1.8 Flexural tensile strength

(1) The mean flexural tensile strength of reinforced concrete members depends on the mean axial tensile strength and the depth of the cross-section. The following relationship may be used:

$$f_{ctm,fl} = \max \{(1,6 - h/1000) f_{ctm} ; f_{ctm}\} \tag{3.23}$$

where:

h is the total member depth in mm
f_{ctm} is the mean axial tensile strength following from Table 3.1.

The relation given in expression (3.23) also applies for the characteristic tensile strength values.

3.2 Reinforcing steel

3.2.2 Properties

(3)P The application rules for design and detailing in this Eurocode are valid for a specified yield strength range, f_{yk} = 400 to 600 MPa.

NOTE The upper limit of f_{yk} within this range for use within a country may be found in its National Annex.

The properties of steel reinforcement in the UK for use with Eurocode 2 are given in BS 4449, *Steel for the reinforcement of concrete — Weldable reinforcing steel — Bar, coil and decoiled product — Specification.* A characteristic yield strength of 500 MPa has been adopted by the UK reinforcement industry.

3.2.7 Design assumptions

(1) Design should be based on the nominal cross-section area of the reinforcement and the design values derived from the characteristic values given in 3.2.2.

(2) For normal design, either of the following assumptions may be made (see Figure 3.8):

[AC1] a) an inclined top branch with a strain limit of ε_{ud} and a maximum stress of kf_{yk}/γ_s at ε_{uk}, [AC1] where $k = (f_t/f_y)_k$,
b) a horizontal top branch without the need to check the strain limit.

NOTE 1 The value of ε_{ud} for use in a country may be found in its National Annex. The recommended value is $0,9\varepsilon_{uk}$.

NOTE 2 The value of $(f_t/f_y)_k$ is given in Annex C.

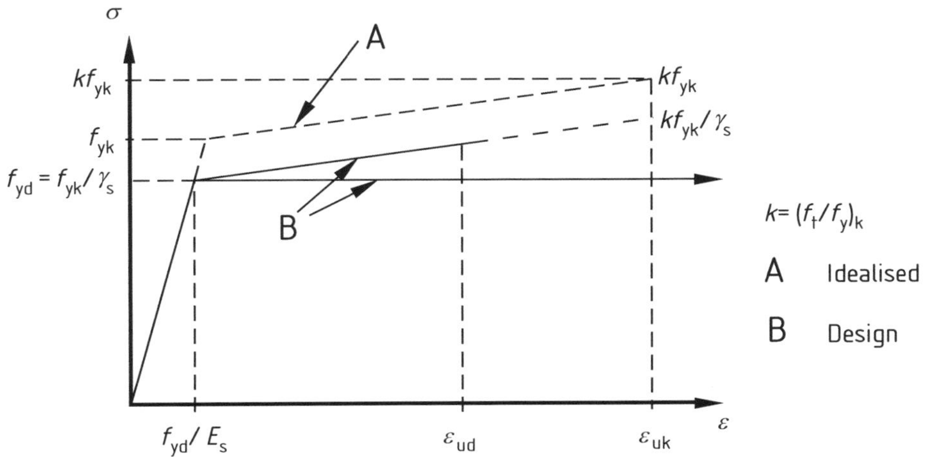

Figure 3.8 — Idealised and design stress-strain diagrams for reinforcing steel (for tension and compression)

(4) The design value of the modulus of elasticity, E_s, may be assumed to be 200 GPa.

3.3 Prestressing steel

3.3.2 Properties

(1)P The properties of prestressing steel are given in EN 10138, Parts 2 to 4 or European Technical Approval.

However, until this standard is published BS 5896, *Specification for high tensile steel wire and strand for the prestressing of concrete* (incorporating amendment no. 1) may be used in the UK.

3.3.6 Design assumptions

(1)P Structural analysis is performed on the basis of the nominal cross-section area of the prestressing steel and the characteristic values $f_{p0,1k}$, f_{pk} and ε_{uk}.

(2) The design value for the modulus of elasticity, E_p, may be assumed equal to 205 GPa for wires and bars. The actual value can range from 195 to 210 GPa, depending on the manufacturing process. Certificates accompanying the consignment should give the appropriate value.

(3) The design value for the modulus of elasticity, E_p, may be assumed equal to 195 GPa for strand. The actual value can range from 185 GPa to 205 GPa, depending on the manufacturing process. Certificates accompanying the consignment should give the appropriate value.

(6) The design value for the steel stress, f_{pd}, is taken as $f_{p0,1k}/\gamma_s$ (see Figure 3.10).

(7) For cross-section design, either of the following assumptions may be made (see Figure 3.10):

- an inclined branch, with a strain limit ε_{ud}. The design may also be based on the actual stress/strain relationship, if this is known, with stress above the elastic limit reduced analogously with Figure 3.10, or
- a horizontal top branch without strain limit.

NOTE The value of ε_{ud} for use in a country may be found in its National Annex. The recommended value is $0{,}9\varepsilon_{uk}$. If more accurate values are not known the recommended values are $\varepsilon_{ud} = 0{,}02$ and $f_{p0,1k}/f_{pk} = 0{,}9$.

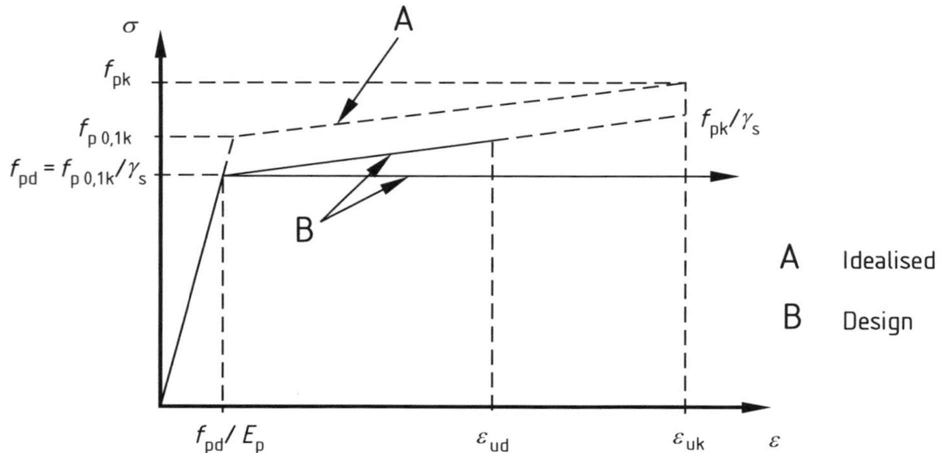

Figure 3.10 — Idealised and design stress-strain diagrams for prestressing steel (absolute values are shown for tensile stress and strain)

Section 4 Durability and cover to reinforcement

4.2 Environmental conditions

(2) Environmental conditions are classified according to Table 4.1, based on EN 206-1.

Table 4.1 — Exposure classes related to environmental conditions in accordance with EN 206-1

Class designation	Description of the environment	Informative examples where exposure classes may occur
1 No risk of corrosion or attack		
X0	For concrete without reinforcement or embedded metal: all exposures except where there is freeze/thaw, abrasion or chemical attack For concrete with reinforcement or embedded metal: very dry	Concrete inside buildings with very low air humidity
2 Corrosion induced by carbonation		
XC1	Dry or permanently wet	Concrete inside buildings with low air humidity Concrete permanently submerged in water
XC2	Wet, rarely dry	Concrete surfaces subject to long-term water contact Many foundations
XC3	Moderate humidity	Concrete inside buildings with moderate or high air humidity External concrete sheltered from rain
XC4	Cyclic wet and dry	Concrete surfaces subject to water contact, not within exposure class XC2
3 Corrosion induced by chlorides		
XD1	Moderate humidity	Concrete surfaces exposed to airborne chlorides
XD2	Wet, rarely dry	Swimming pools Concrete components exposed to industrial waters containing chlorides
XD3	Cyclic wet and dry	Parts of bridges exposed to spray containing chlorides Pavements Car park slabs
4 Corrosion induced by chlorides from sea water		
XS1	Exposed to airborne salt but not in direct contact with sea water	Structures near to or on the coast
XS2	Permanently submerged	Parts of marine structures
XS3	Tidal, splash and spray zones	Parts of marine structures

Class designation	Description of the environment	Informative examples where exposure classes may occur
5 Freeze/thaw attack		
XF1	Moderate water saturation, without de-icing agent	Vertical concrete surfaces exposed to rain and freezing
XF2	Moderate water saturation, with de-icing agent	Vertical concrete surfaces of road structures exposed to freezing and airborne de-icing agents
XF3	High water saturation, without de-icing agents	Horizontal concrete surfaces exposed to rain and freezing
XF4	High water saturation with de-icing agents or sea water	Road and bridge decks exposed to de-icing agents Concrete surfaces exposed to direct spray containing de-icing agents and freezing Splash zone of marine structures exposed to freezing
6 Chemical attack		
XA1	Slightly aggressive chemical environment according to EN 206-1, Table 2	Natural soils and ground water
XA2	Moderately aggressive chemical environment according to EN 206-1, Table 2	Natural soils and ground water
XA3	Highly aggressive chemical environment according to EN 206-1, Table 2	Natural soils and ground water

NOTE The composition of the concrete affects both the protection of the reinforcement and the resistance of the concrete to attack. Annex E gives indicative strength classes for the particular environmental exposure classes. This may lead to the choice of higher strength classes than required for the structural design. In such cases the value of f_{ctm} should be associated with the higher strength in the calculation of minimum reinforcement and crack width control (see 7.3.2–7.3.4).

In the UK, chemical attack is dealt with through the use of ACEC classes derived from BRE Special Digest 1. The XA classes are not used.

4.4 Methods of verification

4.4.1 Concrete cover

4.4.1.1 General

(1)P The concrete cover is the distance between the surface of the reinforcement closest to the nearest concrete surface (including links and stirrups and surface reinforcement where relevant) and the nearest concrete surface.

(2)P The nominal cover shall be specified on the drawings. It is defined as a minimum cover, c_{min} (see 4.4.1.2), plus an allowance in design for deviation, Δc_{dev} (see 4.4.1.3):

$$c_{nom} = c_{min} + \Delta c_{dev} \quad (4.1)$$

4.4.1.2 Minimum cover, c_{min}

(1)P Minimum concrete cover, c_{min}, shall be provided in order to ensure:
- the safe transmission of bond forces (see also Sections 7 and 8)
- the protection of the steel against corrosion (durability)
- an adequate fire resistance (see EN 1992-1-2)

(3) In order to transmit bond forces safely and to ensure adequate compaction of the concrete, the minimum cover should not be less than $c_{min,b}$ given in Table 4.2.

Table 4.2 — Minimum cover, $c_{min,b}$, requirements with regard to bond

Bond requirement	
Arrangment of bars	Minimum cover $c_{min,b}$*
Separated	Diameter of bar
Bundled	Equivalent diameter (ϕ_n) (see 8.9.1)
* If the nominal maximum aggregate size is greater than 32 mm, $c_{min,b}$ should be increased by 5 mm.	

NOTE The values of $c_{min.b}$ for post-tensioned circular and rectangular ducts for bonded tendons, and pre-tensioned tendons for use in a country may be found in its National Annex. The recommended values for post-tensioned ducts are:

- circular ducts: diameter
- rectangular ducts: greater of the smaller dimension or half the greater dimension.

There is no requirement for more than 80 mm for either circular or rectangular ducts.

The recommended values for pre-tensioned tendons are:

- 1,5 × diameter of strand or plain wire
- 2,5 × diameter of indented wire.

(5) The minimum cover values for reinforcement and prestresssing tendons in normal weight concrete taking account of the exposure classes and the structural classes is given by $c_{min,dur}$.

NOTE Structural classification and values of $c_{min,dur}$ for use in a country may be found in its National Annex.

The recommended Structural Class (design working life of 50 years) is S4 for the indicative concrete strengths given in Annex E and the recommended modifications to the structural class is given in Table 4.3N. The recommended minimum Structural Class is S1.

Values for the UK are in BS 8500, and table A.4 is included here.

The recommended values of $c_{min,dur}$ are given in Table 4.4N (reinforcing steel) and Table 4.5N (prestressing steel).

In the UK, BS 8500-1, *Concrete — Complementary British Standard to BS EN 206-1 — Method of specifying and guidance for the specifier* should be used.

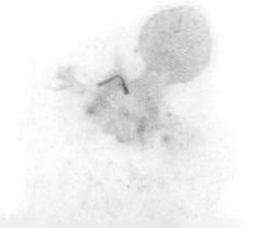

Table A.4 **Durability [A] recommendations for reinforced or prestressed elements with an intended working life of at least 50 years**

Nominal cover [B]	Compressive strength class where recommended, maximum water-cement ratio and minimum cement or combination content for normal-weight concrete [C] with 20 mm maximum aggregate size [D]							Cement/combination types
mm	**15 + Δc**	**20 + Δc**	**25 + Δc**	**30 + Δc**	**35 + Δc**	**40 + Δc**	**45 + Δc**	**50 + Δc**	
Corrosion induced by carbonation (XC exposure classes)									
XC1	C20/25 0.70 240	C20/25 0.70 240	C20/25 0.70 240	C20/25 0.70 240	C20/25 0.70 240	C20/25 0.70 240	C20/25 0.70 240	C20/25 0.70 240	All in Table A.6
XC2	—	—	C25/30 0.65 260	C25/30 0.65 260	C25/30 0.65 260	C25/30 0.65 260	C25/30 0.65 260	C25/30 0.65 260	All in Table A.6
XC3/4	—	C40/50 0.45 340	C30/37 0.55 300	C28/35 0.60 280	C25/30 0.65 260	C25/30 0.65 260	C25/30 0.65 260	C25/30 0.65 260	All in Table A.6 except IVB-V
	—	—	C40/50 0.45 340	C30/37 0.55 300	C28/35 0.60 280	C25/30 0.65 260	C25/30 0.65 260	C25/30 0.65 260	IVB-V
Corrosion induced by chlorides (XS from sea water, XD other than sea water) *Also adequate for any associated carbonation induced corrosion (XC)*									
XD1	—	—	C40/50 0.45 360	C32/40 0.55 320	C28/35 0.60 300	C28/35 0.60 300	C28/35 0.60 300	C28/35 0.60 300	All in Table A.6
XS1	—	—	—	C45/55 [E] 0.35 [F] 380	C35/45 [E] 0.45 360	C32/40 [E] 0.50 340	C32/40 [E] 0.50 340	C32/40 [E] 0.50 340	CEM I, IIA, IIB-S, SRPC
	—	—	—	C40/50 [E] 0.35 [F] 380	C32/40 [E] 0.45 360	C28/35 0.50 340	C25/30 0.55 320	C25/30 0.55 320	IIB-V, IIIA
	—	—	—	C32/40 [E] 0.40 380	C25/30 0.50 340	C25/30 0.50 340	C25/30 0.55 320	C25/30 0.55 320	IIIB
	—	—	—	C32/40 [E] 0.40 380	C28/35 0.50 340	C25/30 0.50 340	C25/30 0.55 320	C25/30 0.55 320	IVB-V
XD2 or XS2	—	—	—	C40/50 [E] 0.40 380	C32/40 [E] 0.50 340	C28/35 0.55 320	C28/35 0.55 320	C28/35 0.55 320	CEM I, IIA, IIB-S, SRPC
	—	—	—	C35/45 [E] 0.40 380	C28/35 0.50 340	C25/30 0.55 320	C25/30 0.55 320	C25/30 0.55 320	IIB-V, IIIA
	—	—	—	C32/40 [E] 0.40 380	C25/30 0.50 340	C20/25 0.55 320	C20/25 0.55 320	C20/25 0.55 320	IIIB, IVB-V

Table A.4 **Durability**[A] **recommendations for reinforced or prestressed elements with an intended working life of at least 50 years** (*continued*)

Nominal cover[B]	Compressive strength class where recommended, maximum water-cement ratio and minimum cement or combination content for normal-weight concrete[C] with 20 mm maximum aggregate size[D]								Cement/combination types
mm	**15 + Δc**	**20 + Δc**	**25 + Δc**	**30 + Δc**	**35 + Δc**	**40 + Δc**	**45 + Δc**	**50 + Δc**	
XD3	—	—	—	—	—	C45/55[E] 0.35[F] 380	C40/50[E] 0.40 380	C35/45[E] 0.45 360	CEM I, IIA, IIB-S, SRPC
	—	—	—	—	—	C35/45[E] 0.40 380	C32/40[E] 0.45 360	C28/35 0.50 340	IIB-V, IIIA
	—	—	—	—	—	C32/40[E] 0.40 380	C28/35 0.45 360	C25/30 0.50 340	IIIB, IVB-V
XS3	—	—	—	—	—	—	C45/55[E] 0.35[F] 380	C40/50[E] 0.40 380	CEM I, IIA, IIB-S, SRPC
	—	—	—	—	—	C35/45[E] 0.40 380	C32/40[E] 0.45 360	C28/35 0.50 340	IIB-V, IIIA
	—	—	—	—	—	C32/40[E] 0.40 380	C28/35 0.45 360	C25/30 0.50 340	IIIB, IVB-V

A dash (—) indicates that greater cover is recommended.

A) Where appropriate, account should be taken of the recommendations to resist freeze-thaw damage (see **A.4.3**, Table A.8), aggressive chemicals (see **A.4.4**, Table A.11) and abrasion (no guidance provided).

B) Expressed as the minimum cover to reinforcement plus an allowance in design for deviation, c, e.g. to allow for workmanship. Check the appropriate design code to see whether it is recommended that the minimum cover to prestressing steel is adjusted by a factor $\Delta c_{dur,\gamma}$.

C) Also applies to heavyweight concrete. For lightweight concrete the maximum w/c ratio and minimum cement or combination content applies, but the compressive strength class needs to be changed to a lightweight compressive strength class (see BS EN 206-1:2000, Table A.8 and **A.4.1**, Note 2) on the basis of equal cylinder strength if designing to BS EN 1992.

D) For adjustments to cement content for different maximum size of aggregate, see Table A.7.

E) If the concrete is specified as being air entrained in accordance with the XF2 or XF4 recommendations in Table A.8, the minimum compressive strength class for corrosion induced by chlorides may be reduced to C28/35.

F) In some parts of the UK it is not possible to produce a practical concrete with a maximum w/c ratio of 0.35.

4.4.1.3 Allowance in design for deviation

(1)P To calculate the nominal cover, c_{nom}, an addition to the minimum cover shall be made in design to allow for the deviation (Δc_{dev}). The required minimum cover shall be increased by the absolute value of the accepted negative deviation.

NOTE The value of Δc_{dev} for use in a country may be found in its National Annex. The recommended value is 10 mm.

(2) For buildings, ENV 13670-1 gives the acceptable deviation. This is normally also sufficient for other types of structures. It should be considered when choosing the value of nominal cover for design. The nominal value of cover for design should be used in the calculations and stated on the drawings, unless a value other than the nominal cover is specified (e.g. minimum value).

[AC1) (4) For concrete cast against uneven surfaces, the nominal cover should generally be (AC1] increased by allowing larger deviations in design. The increase should comply with the [AC1) difference caused by the unevenness, but the nominal cover should be at least k_1 mm for (AC1] concrete cast against prepared ground (including blinding) and k_2 mm for concrete cast directly against soil. The cover to the reinforcement for any surface feature, such as ribbed finishes or exposed aggregate, should also be increased to take account of the uneven surface (see 4.4.1.2 (11)).

NOTE The values of k_1 and k_2 for use in a Country may be found in its National Annex. The recommended values are 40 mm and 75 mm.

> The values of k_1 and k_2 for use in the UK are 40 mm and 65 mm.

Section 5 Structural analysis

5.1 General

5.1.1 General requirements

(1)P The purpose of structural analysis is to establish the distribution of either internal forces and moments, or stresses, strains and displacements, over the whole or part of a structure. Additional local analysis shall be carried out where necessary.

NOTE In most normal cases analysis will be used to establish the distribution of internal forces and moments, and the complete verification or demonstration of resistance of cross sections is based on these action effects; however, for certain particular elements, the methods of analysis used (e.g. finite element analysis) give stresses, strains and displacements rather than internal forces and moments. Special methods are required to use these results to obtain appropriate verification.

(2) Local analyses may be necessary where the assumption of linear strain distribution is not valid, e.g.:
- in the vicinity of supports
- local to concentrated loads
- in beam-column intersections
- in anchorage zones
- at changes in cross section.

5.1.3 Load cases and combinations

(1)P In considering the combinations of actions, see EN 1990 Section 6, the relevant cases shall be considered to enable the critical design conditions to be established at all sections, within the structure or part of the structure considered.

NOTE Where a simplification in the number of load arrangements for use in a country is required, reference is made to its National Annex. The following simplified load arrangements are recommended for buildings:

(a) alternate spans carrying the design variable and permanent loads ($\gamma_Q Q_k + \gamma_G G_k + P_m$), other spans carrying only the design permanent load, $\gamma_G G_k + P_m$ and
(b) any two adjacent spans carrying the design variable and permanent loads ($\gamma_Q Q_k + \gamma_G G_k + P_m$). All other spans carrying only the design permanent load, $\gamma_G G_k + P_m$.

In the UK a) and b) above, and the following two options are recommended for buildings:

1. all spans and alternate spans loaded;
   (a) all spans carrying the design variable and permanent load ($\gamma_Q Q_k + \gamma_G G_k + P_m$), and
   (b) alternate spans carrying the design variable and permanent load ($\gamma_Q Q_k + \gamma_G G_k + P_m$), other spans carrying only the design permanent load $\gamma_G G_k + P_m$.

In verification (b) the same value of γ_G should be used throughout the structure.

2. for slabs only:
   All spans loaded condition as above only if:
   a) in a one-way spanning slab the area of each bay exceeds 30 m^2;
   b) the ratio of the variable load Q_k to the permanent load G_k does not exceed 1,25;
   c) the variable load Q_k does not exceed 5 kN/m^2 excluding partitions.

Where analysis is carried out for the single load case of all spans loaded, the resulting support moments except those at the supports of cantilevers should be reduced by 20 %, with a consequential increase in the span moments.

In this context a bay means a strip across the full width of a structure bounded on the other two sides by lines of support.

The above simplifications are drafted using Expression 6.10 of EN 1990. They can also be applied in conjunction with Expressions 6.10a and 6.10b.

5.1.4 Second order effects

(1)P Second order effects (see EN 1990 Section 1) shall be taken into account where they are likely to affect the overall stability of a structure significantly and for the attainment of the ultimate limit state at critical sections.

(2) Second order effects should be taken into account according to 5.8.

5.2 Geometric imperfections

(1)P The unfavourable effects of possible deviations in the geometry of the structure and the position of loads shall be taken into account in the analysis of members and structures.

NOTE Deviations in cross section dimensions are normally taken into account in the material safety factors. These should not be included in structural analysis. A minimum eccentricity for cross-section design is given in 6.1 (4).

(2)P Imperfections shall be taken into account in ultimate limit states in persistent and accidental design situations.

(9) As a simplified alternative for walls and isolated columns in braced systems, an eccentricity $e_i = l_0/400$ may be used to cover imperfections related to normal execution deviations (see 5.2 (4)).

5.3 Idealisation of the structure

5.3.1 Structural models for overall analysis

(1)P The elements of a structure are classified, by consideration of their nature and function, as beams, columns, slabs, walls, plates, arches, shells etc. Rules are provided for the analysis of the commoner of these elements and of structures consisting of combinations of these elements.

5.3.2 Geometric data

5.3.2.1 Effective width of flanges (all limit states)

(1)P In T beams the effective flange width, over which uniform conditions of stress can be assumed, depends on the web and flange dimensions, the type of loading, the span, the support conditions and the transverse reinforcement.

(2) The effective width of flange should be based on the distance l_0 between points of zero moment, which may be obtained from Figure 5.2.

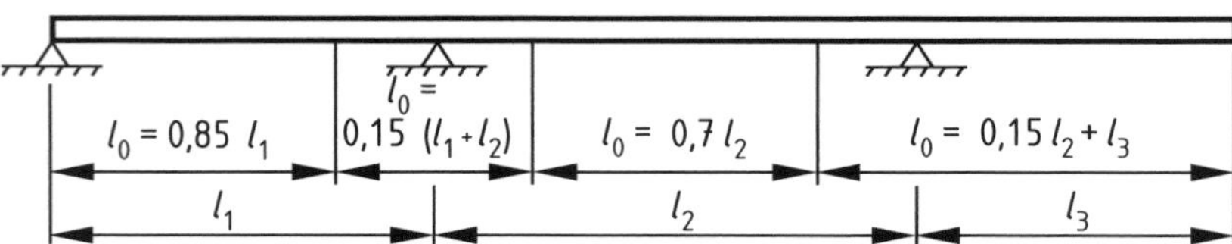

Figure 5.2 — Definition of l_0, for calculation of effective flange width

NOTE The length of the cantilever, l_3, should be less than half the adjacent span and the ratio of adjacent spans should lie between 2/3 and 1,5.

(3) The effective flange width b_{eff} for a T beam or L beam may be derived as:

$$b_{eff} = \sum b_{eff,i} + b_w \leq b \quad (5.7)$$

where

$$b_{eff,i} = 0,2b_i + 0,1l_0 \leq 0,2l_0 \quad (5.7a)$$

and

$$b_{eff,i} \leq b_i \quad (5.7b)$$

(for the notations see Figures 5.2 above and 5.3 below).

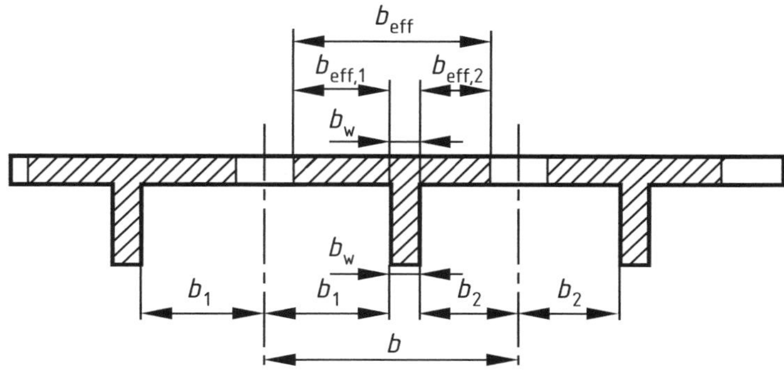

Figure 5.3 — Effective flange width parameters

(4) For structural analysis, where a great accuracy is not required, a constant width may be assumed over the whole span. The value applicable to the span section should be adopted.

5.3.2.2 Effective span of beams and slabs in buildings

NOTE The following provisions are provided mainly for member analysis. For frame analysis some of these simplifications may be used where appropriate.

(1) The effective span, l_{eff}, of a member should be calculated as follows:

$$l_{eff} = l_n + a_1 + a_2 \quad (5.8)$$

where:

l_n is the clear distance between the faces of the supports;
values for a_1 and a_2, at each end of the span, may be determined from the appropriate a_i values in Figure 5.4 where t is the width of the supporting element as shown.

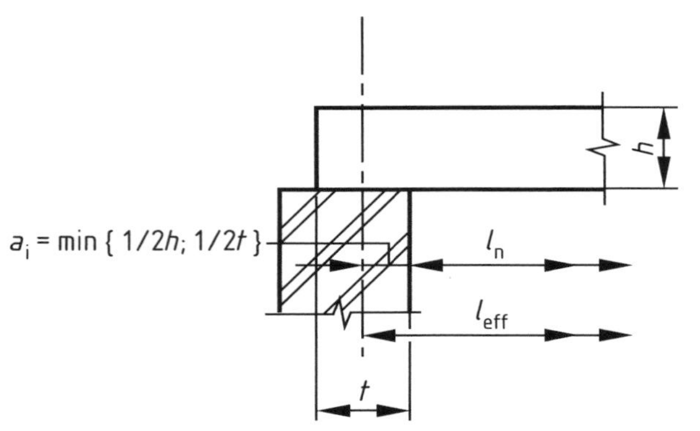

(a) Non-continuous members

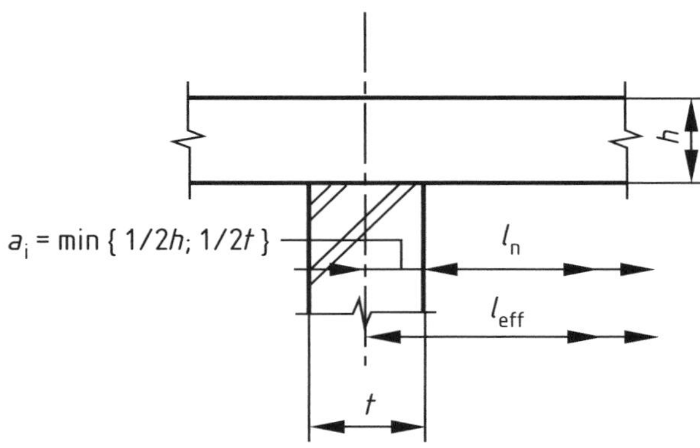

(b) Continuous members

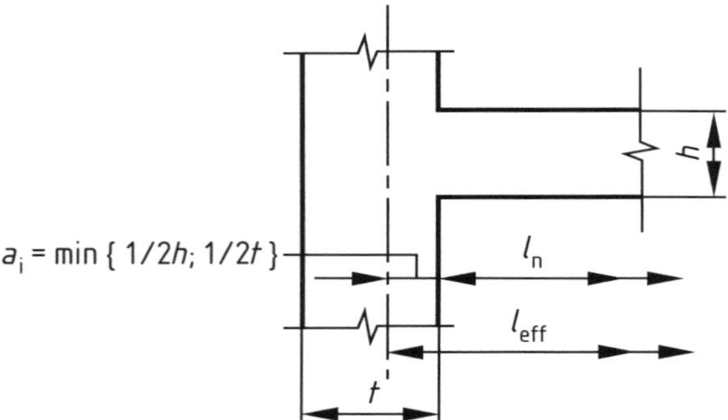

(c) Supports considered fully restrained

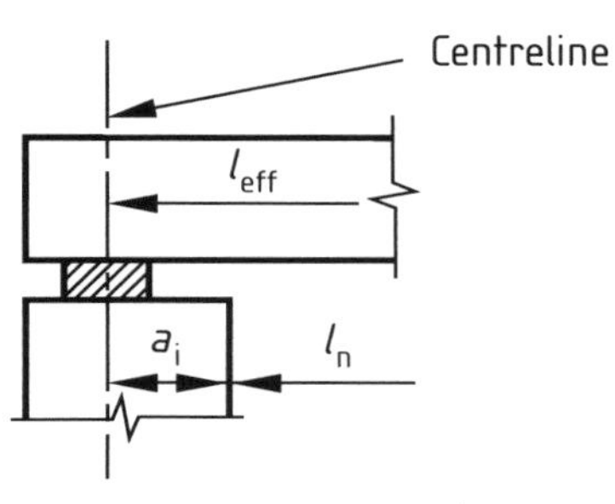

(d) Bearing provided

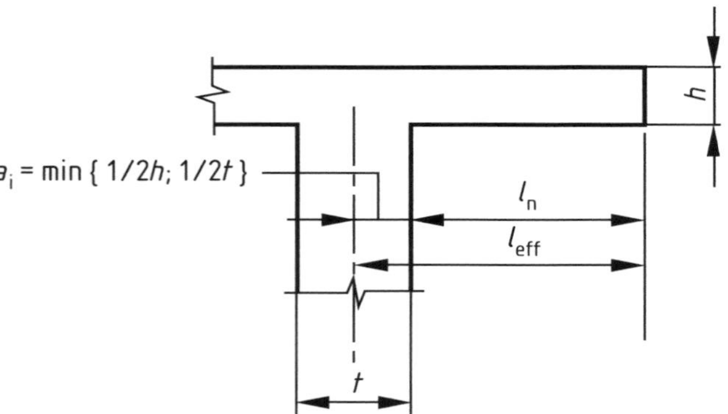

(e) Cantilever

Figure 5.4 — Effective span (l_{eff}) for different support conditions

(2) Continuous slabs and beams may generally be analysed on the assumption that the supports provide no rotational restraint.

(3) Where a beam or slab is monolithic with its supports, the critical design moment at the support should be taken as that at the face of the support. The design moment and reaction transferred to the supporting element (e.g. column, wall, etc.) should be taken as the greater of the elastic or redistributed values.

NOTE The moment at the face of the support should not be less than 0,65 that of the full fixed end moment.

(4) Regardless of the method of analysis used, where a beam or slab is continuous over a support which may be considered to provide no restraint to rotation (e.g. over walls), the design support moment, calculated on the basis of a span equal to the centre-to-centre distance between supports, may be reduced by an amount ΔM_{Ed} as follows:

$$\Delta M_{Ed} = F_{Ed,sup}\, t / 8 \qquad (5.9)$$

where:

$F_{Ed,sup}$ is the design support reaction
t is the breadth of the support (see Figure 5.4 b))

NOTE Where support bearings are used t should be taken as the bearing width.

5.4 Linear elastic analysis

(1) Linear analysis of elements based on the theory of elasticity may be used for both the serviceability and ultimate limit states.

(2) For the determination of the action effects, linear analysis may be carried out assuming:
i) uncracked cross sections,
ii) linear stress-strain relationships and
iii) mean value of the modulus of elasticity.

5.5 Linear elastic analysis with limited redistribution

(1)P The influence of any redistribution of the moments on all aspects of the design shall be considered.

(2) Linear analysis with limited redistribution may be applied to the analysis of structural members for the verification of ULS.

(3) The moments at ULS calculated using a linear elastic analysis may be redistributed, provided that the resulting distribution of moments remains in equilibrium with the applied loads.

(4) In continuous beams or slabs which:
a) are predominantly subject to flexure and
b) have the ratio of the lengths of adjacent spans in the range of 0,5 to 2,
redistribution of bending moments may be carried out without explicit check on the rotation capacity, provided that:

$$\delta \geq k_1 + k_2 x_u/d \quad \text{for } f_{ck} \leq 50\,\text{MPa} \qquad (5.10a)$$

$$\delta \geq k_3 + k_4 x_u/d \quad \text{for } f_{ck} \leq 50\,\text{MPa} \qquad (5.10b)$$

$\geq k_5$ where Class B and Class C reinforcement is used (see Annex C)

$\geq k_6$ where Class A reinforcement is used (see Annex C)

where:
δ is the ratio of the redistributed moment to the elastic bending moment
x_u is the depth of the neutral axis at the ultimate limit state after redistribution
d is the effective depth of the section.

NOTE The values of k_1, k_2, k_3, k_4, k_5 and k_6 for use in a Country may be found in its National Annex. The recommended value for k_1 is 0,44, for k_2 is 1,25(0,6+0,0014/ε_{cu2}), for k_3 = 0,54, for k_4 = 1,25(0,6+0,0014/ε_{cu2}), for k_5 = 0,7 and k_6 = 0,8. ε_{cu2} is the ultimate strain according to Table 3.1.

The values of k_1, k_2, k_3, k_4, k_5 and k_6 for use in the UK are $k_1 = k_3 = 0,4$, $k_2 = k_4 = 0,6 + (0,001\ 4/\varepsilon_{cu2})$, $k_5 = 0,7$ and $k_6 = 0,8$. ε_{cu2} is the ultimate strain according to Table 3.1.

(5) Redistribution should not be carried out in circumstances where the rotation capacity cannot be defined with confidence (e.g. in the comers of prestressed frames).

(6) For the design of columns the elastic moments from frame action should be used without any redistribution.

5.8 Analysis of second order effects with axial load

5.8.2 General

(1)P This clause deals with members and structures in which the structural behaviour is significantly influenced by second order effects (e.g. columns, walls, piles, arches and shells). Global second order effects are likely to occur in structures with a flexible bracing system.

(2)P Where second order effects are taken into account, see (6), equilibrium and resistance shall be verified in the deformed state. Deformations shall be calculated taking into account the relevant effects of cracking, non-linear material properties and creep.

NOTE In an analysis assuming linear material properties, this can be taken into account by means of reduced stiffness values, see 5.8.7.

(4)P The structural behaviour shall be considered in the direction in which deformations can occur, and biaxial bending shall be taken into account when necessary.

(5)P Uncertainties in geometry and position of axial loads shall be taken into account as additional first order effects based on geometric imperfections, see 5.2.

(6) Second order effects may be ignored if they are less than 10 % of the corresponding first order effects. Simplified criteria are given for isolated members in 5.8.3.1 and for structures in 5.8.3.3.

5.8.3 Simplified criteria for second order effects

5.8.3.1 Slenderness criterion for isolated members

(1) As an alternative to 5.8.2 (6), second order effects may be ignored if the slenderness λ is below a certain value λ_{lim}.

NOTE The value of λ_{lim} for use in a country may be found in its National Annex. The recommended value follows from:

$$\lambda_{lim} = 20 \cdot A \cdot B \cdot C / \sqrt{n} \qquad (5.13N)$$

where:

A	$= 1/(1+0{,}2\varphi_{ef})$	(if φ_{ef} is not known, A = 0,7 may be used)
B	$= \sqrt{1+2\omega}$	(if ω is not known, B = 1,1 may be used)
C	$= 1{,}7 - r_m$	(if r_m is not known, C = 0,7 may be used)
φ_{ef}	is the effective creep ratio; see 5.8.4	
ω	$= A_s f_{yd} / (A_c f_{cd})$; mechanical reinforcement ratio	
A_s	is the total area of longitudinal reinforcement	
n	$= N_{Ed} / (A_c f_{cd})$; relative normal force	
r_m	$= M_{01}/M_{02}$; moment ratio	
M_{01}, M_{02}	are the first order end moments, $\lvert M_{02}\rvert \geq \lvert M_{01}\rvert$	

If the end moments M_{01} and M_{02} give tension on the same side, r_m should be taken positive (i.e. $C \leq 1{,}7$), otherwise negative (i.e. $C > 1{,}7$).

In the following cases, r_m should be taken as 1,0 (i.e. $C = 0{,}7$):
- for braced members with first order moments only or predominantly due to imperfections or transverse loading
- for unbraced members in general.

For most braced members assuming $C = 0.7$ is unduly conservative and it is recommended that C is calculated.

(2) In cases with biaxial bending, the slenderness criterion may be checked separately for each direction. Depending on the outcome of this check, second order effects (a) may be ignored in both directions, (b) should be taken into account in one direction, or (c) should be taken into account in both directions.

5.8.3.2 Slenderness and effective length of isolated members

(1) The slenderness ratio is defined as follows:

$$\lambda = l_0 / i \tag{5.14}$$

where:

l_0 is the effective length, see 5.8.3.2 (2) to (7)

i is the radius of gyration of the uncracked concrete section

(2) For a general definition of the effective length, see 5.8.1. Examples of effective length for isolated members with constant cross section are given in Figure 5.7.

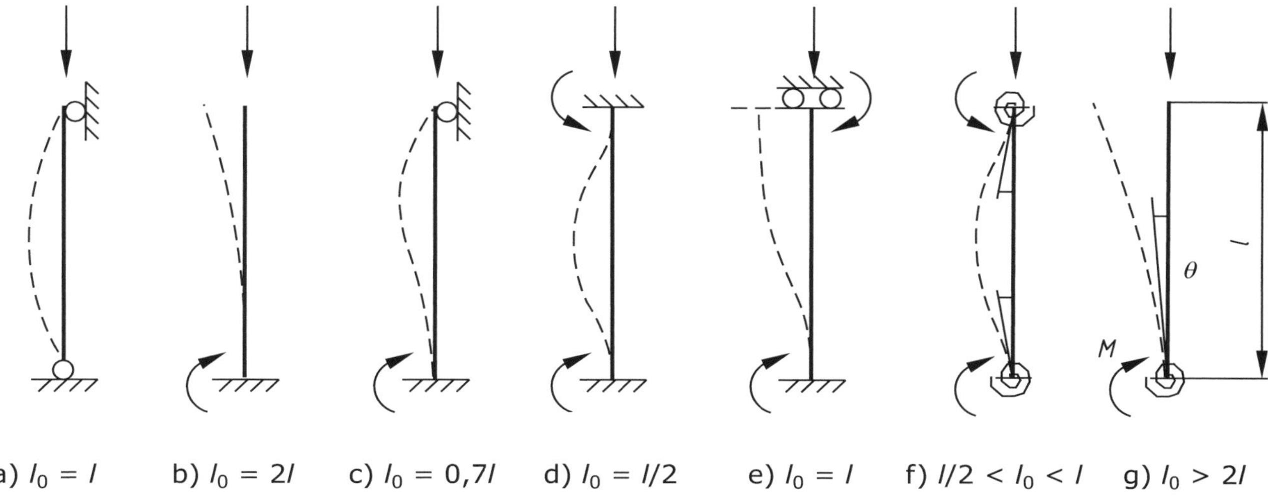

a) $l_0 = l$ b) $l_0 = 2l$ c) $l_0 = 0{,}7l$ d) $l_0 = l/2$ e) $l_0 = l$ f) $l/2 < l_0 < l$ g) $l_0 > 2l$

Figure 5.7 — Examples of different buckling modes and corresponding effective lengths for isolated members

(3) For compression members in regular frames, the slenderness criterion (see 5.8.3.1) should be checked with an effective length l_0 determined in the following way:

Braced members (see Figure 5.7 (f)):

$$l_0 = 0{,}5l \cdot \sqrt{\left(1 + \frac{k_1}{0{,}45 + k_1}\right) \cdot \left(1 + \frac{k_2}{0{,}45 + k_2}\right)} \tag{5.15}$$

Unbraced members (see Figure 5.7 (g)):

$$l_0 = l \cdot \max\left\{\sqrt{1 + 10 \cdot \frac{k_1 \cdot k_2}{k_1 + k_2}};\left(1 + \frac{k_1}{1 + k_1}\right) \cdot \left(1 + \frac{k_2}{1 + k_2}\right)\right\} \tag{5.16}$$

where:

k_1, k_2 are the relative flexibilities of rotational restraints at ends 1 and 2 respectively:

k $= (\theta / M) \cdot (EI / l)$

θ is the rotation of restraining members for bending moment M; see also Figure 5.7 (f) and (g)

EI is the bending stiffness of compression member, see also 5.8.3.2 (4) and (5)

l is the clear height of compression member between end restraints

NOTE $k = 0$ is the theoretical limit for rigid rotational restraint, and $k = \infty$ represents the limit for no restraint at all. Since fully rigid restraint is rare in practice, a minimum value of 0,1 is recommended for k_1 and k_2.

(4) If an adjacent compression member (column) in a node is likely to contribute to the rotation at buckling, then (EI/l) in the definition of k should be replaced by $[(EI/l)_a+(EI/l)_b]$, a and b representing the compression member (column) above and below the node.

(5) In the definition of effective lengths, the stiffness of restraining members should include the effect of cracking, unless they can be shown to be uncracked in ULS.

Alternatively PD 6687, *Background paper to the UK National Annexes to BS EN 1992-1* provides a simplification, based on the stiffness of the beams attached to either side of the column. This relative stiffness, k, can therefore be calculated as follows (provided the stiffness of adjacent columns does not vary by more than 15% of the higher stiffness):

$$k = \frac{EI_c}{l_c} \Big/ \sum \frac{2EI_b}{l_b} \geq 0.1$$

where

I_c, I_b are the column and beam uncracked second moments of area

l_c, l_b are the column and beam lengths

5.8.4 Creep

(1)P The effect of creep shall be taken into account in second order analysis, with due consideration of both the general conditions for creep (see 3.1.4) and the duration of different loads in the load combination considered.

(4) The effect of creep may be ignored, i.e. $\varphi_{ef} = 0$ may be assumed, if the following three conditions are met:

- $\varphi(\infty, t_0) \leq 2$
- $\lambda \leq 75$
- $M_{0Ed} / N_{Ed} \geq h$

Here M_{0Ed} is the first order moment and h is the cross-section depth in the corresponding direction.

NOTE If the conditions for neglecting second order effects according to 5.8.2 (6) or 5.8.3.3 are only just achieved, it may be too unconservative to neglect both second order effects and creep, unless the mechanical reinforcement ratio (ω, see 5.8.3.1 (1)) is at least 0,25.

5.8.5 Methods of analysis

(1) The methods of analysis include a general method, based on non-linear second order analysis, see 5.8.6 and the following two simplified methods:

(a) Method based on nominal stiffness, see 5.8.7
(b) Method based on nominal curvature, see 5.8.8.

NOTE 1 The selection of Simplified Method (a) and (b) to be used in a Country may be found in its National Annex.

NOTE 2 Nominal second order moments provided by the simplified methods (a) and (b) are sometimes greater than those corresponding to instability. This is to ensure that the total moment is compatible with the cross section resistance.

In the UK either Simplified Method (a) or (b) may be used.

5.8.8 Method based on nominal curvature

5.8.8.1 General

(1) This method is primarily suitable for isolated members with constant normal force and a defined effective length l_0 (see 5.8.3.2). The method gives a nominal second order moment based on a deflection, which in turn is based on the effective length and an estimated maximum AC1) curvature (see also 5.8.5 (3)). (AC1

(2) The resulting design moment is used for the design of cross sections with respect to bending moment and axial force according to 6.1.

5.8.8.2 Bending moments

(1) The design moment is:

$$M_{Ed} = M_{0Ed} + M_2 \qquad (5.31)$$

where:

M_{0Ed} is the first order moment, including the effect of imperfections, see also 5.8.8.2 (2)
M_2 is the nominal second order moment, see 5.8.8.2 (3).

The maximum value of M_{Ed} is given by the distributions of M_{0Ed} and M_2; the latter may be taken as parabolic or sinusoidal over the effective length.

NOTE For statically indeterminate members, M_{0Ed} is determined for the actual boundary conditions, whereas M_2 will depend on boundary conditions via the effective length, cf. 5.8.8.1 (1).

AC1) (2) For members without loads applied between their ends, differing first order end moments M_{01} and M_{02} may be replaced by an equivalent first order end moment M_{0e}: (AC1

$$M_{0e} = 0,6\,M_{02} + 0,4\,M_{01} \geq 0,4\,M_{02} \qquad (5.32)$$

M_{01} and M_{02} should have the same sign if they give tension on the same side, otherwise opposite signs. Furthermore, $|M_{02}| \geq |M_{01}|$

> M_{0e} is a moment at the mid-height of the column and may not give the maximum moment in the column.

(3) The nominal second order moment M_2 in expression (5.31) is

$$M_2 = N_{Ed}\,e_2 \qquad (5.33)$$

where:

N_{Ed} is the design value of axial force
e_2 is the deflection = $(1/r)\,{l_0}^2/c$
$1/r$ is the curvature, see 5.8.8.3
l_0 is the effective length, see 5.8.3.2
c is a factor depending on the curvature distribution, see 5.8.8.2 (4)

(4) For constant cross section, c = 10 ($\approx \pi^2$) is normally used. If the first order moment is constant, a lower value should be considered (8 is a lower limit, corresponding to constant total moment).

NOTE The value π^2 corresponds to a sinusoidal curvature distribution. The value for constant curvature is 8. Note that c depends on the distribution of the total curvature, whereas c_0 in 5.8.7.3 (2) depends on the curvature corresponding to the first order moment only.

5.8.8.3 Curvature

(1) For members with constant symmetrical cross-sections (incl. reinforcement), the following may be used:

$$1/r = K_r \cdot K_\varphi \cdot 1/r_0 \tag{5.34}$$

where:

K_r is a correction factor depending on axial load, see 5.8.8.3 (3)
K_φ is a factor for taking account of creep, see 5.8.8.3 (4)
$1/r_0$ $= \varepsilon_{yd} / (0{,}45d)$
ε_{yd} $= f_{yd} / E_s$
d is the effective depth; see also 5.8.8.3 (2)

(2) If all reinforcement is not concentrated on opposite sides, but part of it is distributed parallel to the plane of bending, d is defined as

$$d = (h/2) + i_s \tag{5.35}$$

where i_s is the radius of gyration of the total reinforcement area.

(3) K_r in expression (5.34) should be taken as:

$$K_r = (n_u - n) / (n_u - n_{bal}) \leq 1 \tag{5.36}$$

where:

n $= N_{Ed} / (A_c f_{cd})$, relative axial force
N_{Ed} is the design value of axial force
n_u $= 1 + \omega$
n_{bal} is the value of n at maximum moment resistance; the value 0,4 may be used
ω $= A_s f_{yd} / (A_c f_{cd})$
A_s is the total area of reinforcement
A_c is the area of concrete cross section

(4) The effect of creep should be taken into account by the following factor:

$$K_\varphi = 1 + \beta\varphi_{ef} \geq 1 \tag{5.37}$$

where:

φ_{ef} is the effective creep ratio, see 5.8.4
β $= 0{,}35 + f_{ck}/200 - \lambda/150$
λ is the slenderness ratio, see 5.8.3.1

5.8.9 Biaxial bending

(1) The general method described in 5.8.6 may also be used for biaxial bending. The following provisions apply when simplified methods are used. Special care should be taken to identify the section along the member with the critical combination of moments.

(2) Separate design in each principal direction, disregarding biaxial bending, may be made as a first step. Imperfections need to be taken into account only in the direction where they will have the most unfavourable effect.

(3) No further check is necessary if the slenderness ratios satisfy the following two conditions:

$$\lambda_y / \lambda_z \leq 2 \quad \text{and} \quad \lambda_z / \lambda_y \leq 2 \tag{5.38a}$$

[AC1) and if the relative eccentricities e_y/h_{eq} and e_z/b_{eq} (see Figure 5.8) satisfy one the following (AC1] conditions:

$$\frac{e_y / h_{eq}}{e_z / b_{eq}} \leq 0{,}2 \quad or \quad \frac{e_z / b_{eq}}{e_y / h_{eq}} \leq 0{,}2 \tag{5.38b}$$

where:

b, h	are the width and depth for section
b	$= i_y \cdot \sqrt{12}$ and $h = i_z \cdot \sqrt{12}$ for an arbitrary section
λ_y, λ_z	are the slenderness ratios i_0/i with respect to y- and z-axis respectively
i_y, i_z	are the radii of gyration with respect to y- and z-axis respectively
e_z	$= M_{Edy} / N_{Ed}$; eccentricity along z-axis
e_y	$= M_{Edz} / N_{Ed}$; eccentricity along y-axis
M_{Edy}	is the design moment about y-axis, including second order moment
M_{Edz}	is the design moment about z-axis, including second order moment
N_{Ed}	is the design value of axial load in the respective load combination

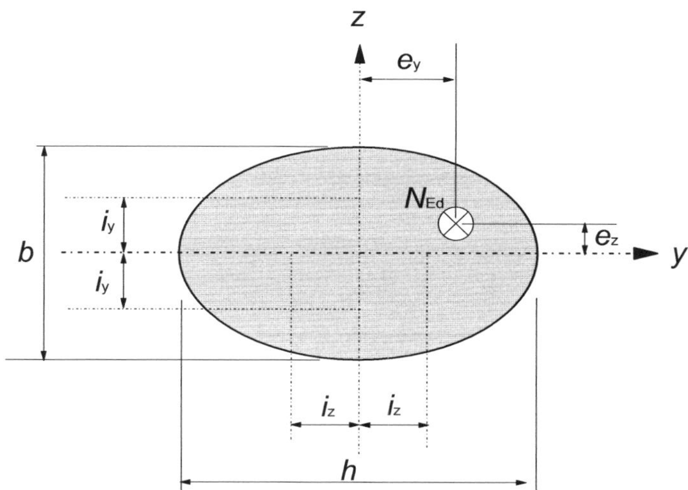

Figure 5.8 — Definition of eccentricities e_y and e_z

(4) If the condition of expression (5.38) is not fulfilled, biaxial bending should be taken into account including the second order effects in each direction (unless they may be ignored according to 5.8.2 (6) or 5.8.3). In the absence of an accurate cross-section design for biaxial bending, the following simplified criterion may be used:

$$\left(\frac{M_{Edz}}{M_{Rdz}}\right)^a + \left(\frac{M_{Edy}}{M_{Rdy}}\right)^a \leq 1{,}0 \qquad (5.39)$$

where:

$M_{Edz/y}$ is the design moment around the respective axis, including a second order moment

$M_{Rdz/y}$ is the moment resistance in the respective direction

a is the exponent

for circular and elliptical cross-sections: $a = 2$

for rectangular cross-sections, with linear interpolation for intermediate values:

N_{Ed}/N_{Rd}	0,1	0,7	1,0
$a =$	1,0	1,5	2,0

N_{Ed} is the design value of axial force

N_{Rd} $= A_c f_{cd} + A_s f_{yd}$, design axial resistance of section

where:

A_c is the gross area of the concrete section

A_s is the area of longitudinal reinforcement

5.9 Lateral instability of slender beams

(1)P Lateral instability of slender beams shall be taken into account where necessary, e.g. for precast beams during transport and erection, for beams without sufficient lateral bracing in the finished structure etc. Geometric imperfections shall be taken into account.

(2) A lateral deflection of l / 300 should be assumed as a geometric imperfection in the verification of beams in unbraced conditions, with l = total length of beam. In finished structures, bracing from connected members may be taken into account.

(3) Second order effects in connection with lateral instability may be ignored if the following conditions are fulfilled:

– persistent situations: $\frac{l_{0t}}{b} \leq \frac{50}{(h/b)^{1/3}}$ and $h/b \leq 2,5$ (5.40a)

– transient situations: $\frac{l_{0t}}{b} \leq \frac{70}{(h/b)^{1/3}}$ and $h/b \leq 3,5$ (5.40b)

where:
l_{0t} is the distance between torsional restraints
h is the total depth of beam in central part of l_{0t}
b is the width of compression flange

(4) Torsion associated with lateral instability should be taken into account in the design of supporting structures.

5.10 Prestressed members and structures

5.10.1 General

(1)P The prestress considered in this Standard is that applied to the concrete by stressed tendons.

(2) The effects of prestressing may be considered as an action or a resistance caused by prestrain and precurvature. The bearing capacity should be calculated accordingly.

(3) In general prestress is introduced in the action combinations defined in EN 1990 as part of the loading cases and its effects should be included in the applied internal moment and axial force.

(4) Following the assumptions of (3) above, the contribution of the prestressing tendons to the resistance of the section should be limited to their additional strength beyond prestressing. This may be calculated assuming that the origin of the stress/strain relationship of the tendons is displaced by the effects of prestressing.

Prestress losses including immediate losses, friction losses, losses at anchorages and the time-dependent losses due to creep should be considered in the design.

5.10.2 Prestressing force during tensioning

5.10.2.1 Maximum stressing force

(1)P The force applied to a tendon, P_{max} (i.e. the force at the active end during tensioning) shall not exceed the following value:

$$P_{max} = A_p \cdot \sigma_{p,max} \quad (5.41)$$

where:
A_p is the cross-sectional area of the tendon
$\sigma_{p,max}$ is the maximum stress applied to the tendon
$= \min\{k_1 \cdot f_{pk} ; k_2 \cdot f_{p0,1k}\}$

NOTE The values of k_1 and k_2 for use in a country may be found in its National Annex. The recommended values are k_1 = 0,8 and k_2 = 0,9.

5.10.2.2 Limitation of concrete stress

(5) The concrete compressive stress in the structure resulting from the prestressing force and other loads acting at the time of tensioning or release of prestress, should be limited to:

$$\sigma_c \leq 0,6\, f_{ck}(t) \quad (5.42)$$

where $f_{ck}(t)$ is the characteristic compressive strength of the concrete at time t when it is subjected to the prestressing force.

For pre-tensioned elements the stress at time of transfer of prestress may be increased to $k_6.f_{ck}(t)$, if it can be justified by tests or experience that longitudinal cracking is prevented.

NOTE The value of k_6 for use in a country may be found in its National Annex. The recommended value is 0,7.

If the compressive stress permanently exceeds 0,45 $f_{ck}(t)$ the non-linearity of creep should be taken into account.

5.10.3 Prestress force

(2) The value of the initial prestress force $P_{m0}(x)$ (at time $t = t_0$) applied to the concrete immediately after tensioning and anchoring (post-tensioning) or after transfer of prestressing (pre-tensioning), which is obtained by subtracting from the force at tensioning P_{max} the immediate losses $\Delta P_i(x)$, should not exceed the following value:

$$P_{m0}(x) = A_p \cdot \sigma_{pm0}(x) \tag{5.43}$$

where:

$\sigma_{pm0}(x)$ is the stress in the tendon immediately after tensioning or transfer $= \min\{k_7 \cdot f_{pk}\ ;\ k_8 \cdot f_{p0,1k}\}$

NOTE The values of k_7 and k_8 for use in a country may be found in its National Annex. The recommended value for k_7 is 0,75 and for k_8 is 0,85.

(4) The mean value of the prestress force $P_{m,t}(x)$ at the time $t > t_0$ should be determined with respect to the prestressing method. In addition to the immediate losses the time-dependent losses of prestress $\Delta P_{c+s+r}(x)$ (see 5.10.6) as a result of creep and shrinkage of the concrete and the long term relaxation of the prestressing steel should be considered and $P_{m,t}(x) = P_{m0}(x) - \Delta P_{c+s+r}(x)$.

5.10.8 Effects of prestressing at ultimate limit state

(1) In general, the design value of the prestressing force may be determined by $P_{d,t}(x) = \gamma_P \cdot P_{m,t}(x)$ (see 5.10.3 (4) for the definition of $P_{m,t}(x)$) and 2.4.2.2 for γ_P.

5.10.9 Effects of prestressing at serviceability limit state and limit state of fatigue

(1)P For serviceability and fatigue calculations allowance shall be made for possible variations in prestress. Two characteristic values of the prestressing force at the serviceability limit state are estimated from:

$$P_{k,sup} = r_{sup} P_{m,t}(x) \tag{5.47}$$

$$P_{k,inf} = r_{inf} P_{m,t}(x) \tag{5.48}$$

where:

$P_{k,sup}$ is the upper characteristic value
$P_{k,inf}$ is the lower characteristic value

NOTE The values of r_{sup} and r_{inf} for use in a Country may be found in its National Annex. The recommended values are:

- for pre-tensioning or unbonded tendons: $r_{sup} = 1{,}05$ and $r_{inf} = 0{,}95$
- for post-tensioning with bonded tendons: $r_{sup} = 1{,}10$ and $r_{inf} = 0{,}90$
- when appropriate measures (e.g. direct measurements of pretensioning) are taken: $r_{sup} = r_{inf} = 1{,}0$.

The value of r_{sup} and r_{inf} for use in the UK is 1,0.

Section 6 Ultimate Limit States (ULS)

6.1 Bending with or without axial force

(2)P When determining the ultimate moment resistance of reinforced or prestressed concrete cross-sections, the following assumptions are made:

- plane sections remain plane,
- the strain in bonded reinforcement or bonded prestressing tendons, whether in tension or in compression, is the same as that in the surrounding concrete,
- the tensile strength of the concrete is ignored,
- the stresses in the concrete in compression are derived from the design stress/strain relationship given in 3.1.7,
- the stresses in the reinforcing or prestressing steel are derived from the design curves in 3.2 (Figure 3.8) and 3.3 (Figure 3.10),
- the initial strain in prestressing tendons is taken into account when assessing the stresses in the tendons.

(3)P The compressive strain in the concrete shall be limited to ε_{cu2}, or ε_{cu3}, depending on the stress-strain diagram used, see 3.1.7 and Table 3.1. The strains in the reinforcing steel and the prestressing steel shall be limited to ε_{ud} (where applicable); see 3.2.7 (2) and 3.3.6 (7) respectively.

(4) For cross-sections with symmetrical reinforcement loaded by the compression force it is necessary to assume the minimum eccentricity, e_0 = h/30 but not less than 20 mm, where h is the depth of the section.

(6) The possible range of strain distributions is shown in Figure 6.1.

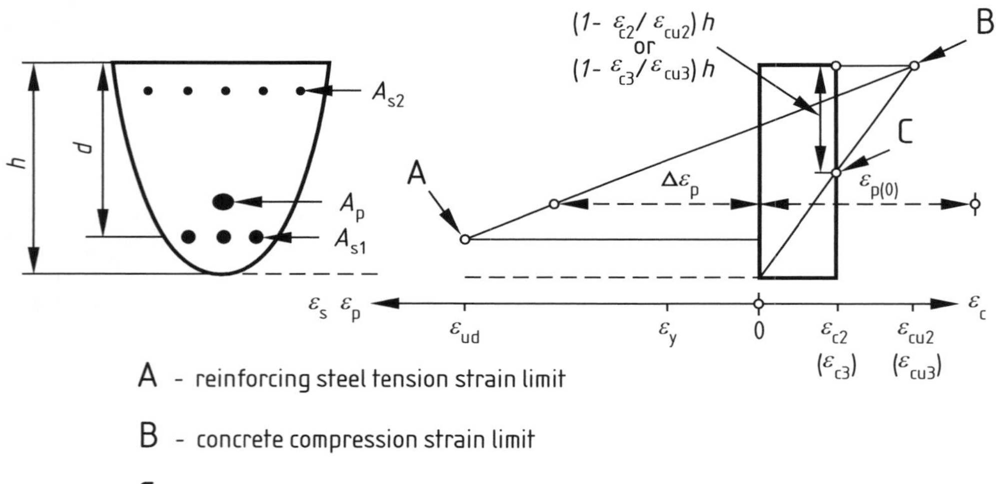

Figure 6.1 — Possible strain distributions in the ultimate limit state

6.2 Shear

6.2.1 General verification procedure

(1)P For the verification of the shear resistance the following symbols are defined:

$V_{Rd,c}$ is the design shear resistance of the member without shear reinforcement.
$V_{Rd,s}$ is the design value of the shear force which can be sustained by the yielding shear reinforcement.
$V_{Rd,max}$ is the design value of the maximum shear force which can be sustained by the member, limited by crushing of the compression struts.

In members with inclined chords the following additional values are defined (see Figure 6.2):

V_{ccd} is the design value of the shear component of the force in the compression area, in the case of an inclined compression chord.

V_{td} is the design value of the shear component of the force in the tensile reinforcement, in the case of an inclined tensile chord.

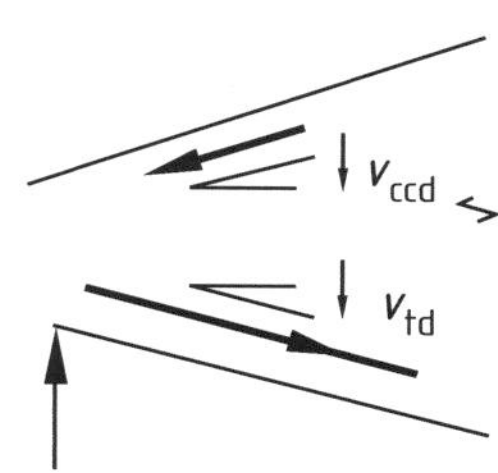

Figure 6.2 — Shear component for members with inclined chords

(2) The shear resistance of a member with shear reinforcement is equal to:

$$V_{Rd} = V_{Rd,s} + V_{ccd} + V_{td} \tag{6.1}$$

(3) In regions of the member where $V_{Ed} \leq V_{Rd,c}$ no calculated shear reinforcement is necessary. V_{Ed} is the design shear force in the section considered resulting from external loading and prestressing (bonded or unbonded).

(4) When, on the basis of the design shear calculation, no shear reinforcement is required, minimum shear reinforcement should nevertheless be provided according to 9.2.2. The minimum shear reinforcement may be omitted in members such as slabs (solid, ribbed or hollow core slabs) where transverse redistribution of loads is possible. Minimum reinforcement may also be omitted in members of minor importance (e.g. lintels with span ≤ 2 m) which do not contribute significantly to the overall resistance and stability of the structure.

(5) In regions where $V_{Ed} > V_{Rd,c}$ according to expression (6.2), sufficient shear reinforcement [AC1) should be provided in order that $V_{Ed} \leq V_{Rd}$ (see expression (6.1)). (AC1]

(6) The sum of the design shear force and the contributions of the flanges, $V_{Ed} - V_{ccd} - V_{td}$, should not exceed the permitted maximum value $V_{Rd,max}$ (see 6.2.3), anywhere in the member.

(7) The longitudinal tension reinforcement should be able to resist the additional tensile force caused by shear (see 6.2.3 (7)).

(8) For members subject to predominantly uniformly distributed loading the design shear force need not be checked at a distance less than d from the face of the support. Any shear reinforcement required should continue to the support. In addition it should be verified that the shear at the support does not exceed $V_{Rd,max}$ (see also 6.2.2 (6) and 6.2.3 (8)).

(9) Where a load is applied near the bottom of a section, sufficient vertical reinforcement to carry the load to the top of the section should be provided in addition to any reinforcement required to resist shear.

6.2.2 Members not requiring design shear reinforcement

(1) The design value for the shear resistance $V_{Rd,c}$ is given by:

$$V_{Rd,c} = \left[C_{Rd,c}\, k\, (100\rho_l\, f_{ck})^{1/3} + k_1\, \sigma_{cp}\right] b_w\, d \tag{6.2a}$$

with a minimum of

$$V_{Rd,c} = (v_{min} + k_1\, \sigma_{cp})\, b_w\, d \tag{6.2b}$$

where:

f_{ck} is in MPa

k $= 1 + \sqrt{\frac{200}{d}} \leq 2,0$ with d in mm

ρ_l $= \frac{A_{sl}}{b_w d} \leq 0,02$

A_{sl} is the area of the tensile reinforcement, which extends ≥ $(l_{bd} + d)$ beyond the section considered (see Figure 6.3)

b_w is the smallest width of the cross-section in the tensile area [mm]

σ_{cp} $= N_{Ed}/A_c < 0,2\ f_{cd}$ [MPa]

N_{Ed} is the axial force in the cross-section due to loading or prestressing [in N] ($N_{Ed} > 0$ for AC1 compression). The influence of imposed deformations on N_{Ed} may be ignored. AC1

A_c is the area of concrete cross section [mm²]

$V_{Rd,c}$ is [N]

NOTE The values of $C_{Rd,c}$, v_{min} and k_1 for use in a country may be found in its National Annex. The recommended value for $C_{Rd,c}$ is $0,18/\gamma_c$, that for v_{min} is given by expression (6.3N) and that for k_1 is 0,15.

For use in the UK see also 3.1.2(2)P for requirement for concrete class > C50/60.

$$v_{min} = 0,035\, k^{3/2} \cdot f_{ck}^{\ 1/2} \tag{6.3N}$$

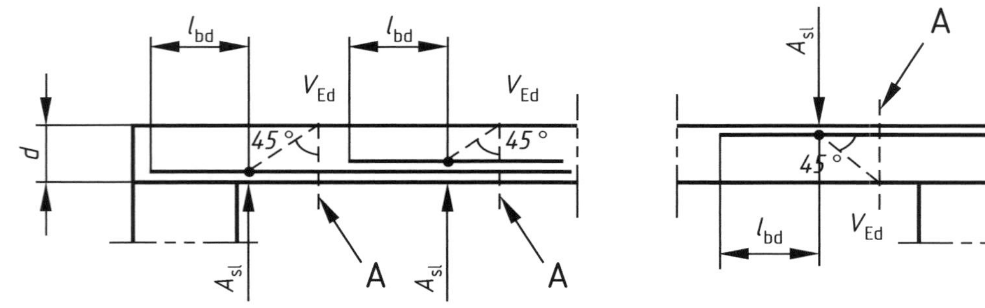

Figure 6.3 — Definition of A_{sl} in expression (6.2)

(2) In prestressed single span members without shear reinforcement, the shear resistance of the regions cracked in bending may be calculated using expression (6.2a). In regions uncracked in bending (where the flexural tensile stress is smaller than $f_{ctk,0,05}/\gamma_c$) the shear resistance should be limited by the tensile strength of the concrete. In these regions the shear resistance is given by:

$$V_{Rd,c} = \frac{I \cdot b_w}{S} \sqrt{(f_{ctd})^2 + \alpha_l \sigma_{cp} f_{ctd}} \tag{6.4}$$

where

I is the second moment of area

b_w is the width of the cross-section at the centroidal axis, allowing for the presence of ducts in accordance with expressions (6.16) and (6.17)

S is the first moment of area above and about the centroidal axis

α_l $= l_x / l_{pt2} \leq 1,0$ for pretensioned tendons
$= 1,0$ for other types of prestressing

l_x is the distance of section considered from the starting point of the transmission length

l_{pt2} is the upper bound value of the transmission length of the prestressing element according to expression (8.18)

σ_{cp} is the concrete compressive stress at the centroidal axis due to axial loading and/or prestressing ($\sigma_{cp} = N_{Ed}/A_c$ in MPa, $N_{Ed} > 0$ in compression).

For cross-sections where the width varies over the height, the maximum principal stress may occur on an axis other than the centroidal axis. In such a case the minimum value of the shear resistance should be found by calculating $V_{Rd,c}$ at various axes in the cross-section.

(3) The calculation of the shear resistance according to expression (6.4) is not required for cross-sections that are nearer to the support than the point which is the intersection of the elastic centroidal axis and a line inclined from the inner edge of the support at an angle of 45°.

(5) For the design of the longitudinal reinforcement, in the region cracked in flexure, the M_{Ed}-line should be shifted over a distance $a_l = d$ in the unfavourable direction (see 9.2.1.3 (2)).

(6) For members with loads applied on the upper side within a distance $0{,}5d \leq a_v \leq 2d$ from the edge of a support (or centre of bearing where flexible bearings are used), the contribution of this load to the shear force V_{Ed} may be reduced by multiplying by $\beta = a_v/2d$. This reduction may be applied for checking $V_{Rd,c}$ in expression (6.2a). This is only valid provided that the longitudinal reinforcement is fully anchored at the support. For $a_v \leq 0{,}5d$ the value $a_v = 0{,}5d$ should be used.

The shear force V_{Ed}, calculated without reduction by β, should however always satisfy the condition

$$V_{Ed} \leq 0{,}5\, b_w d \nu f_{cd} \qquad (6.5)$$

where ν is a strength reduction factor for concrete cracked in shear.

NOTE The value of ν for use in a country may be found in its National Annex. The recommended value follows from:

$$\nu = 0{,}6\left[1 - \frac{f_{ck}}{250}\right] \quad (f_{ck} \text{ in MPa}) \qquad (6.6N)$$

For use in the UK see also 3.1.2(2)P for requirement for concrete class > C50/60.

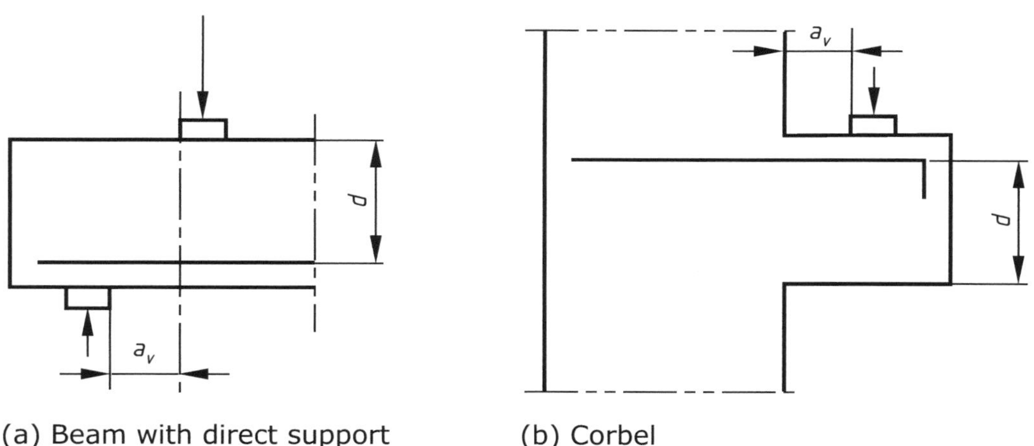

(a) Beam with direct support (b) Corbel

Figure 6.4 — Loads near supports

6.2.3 Members requiring design shear reinforcement

(1) The design of members with shear reinforcement is based on a truss model (Figure 6.5). Limiting values for the angle θ of the inclined struts in the web are given in 6.2.3 (2).

In Figure 6.5 the following notations are shown:

α is the angle between shear reinforcement and the beam axis perpendicular to the shear force (measured positive as shown in Figure 6.5)
θ is the angle between the concrete compression strut and the beam axis perpendicular to the shear force
F_{td} is the design value of the tensile force in the longitudinal reinforcement
F_{cd} is the design value of the concrete compression force in the direction of the longitudinal member axis

b_w is the minimum width between tension and compression chords
z is the inner lever arm, for a member with constant depth, corresponding to the bending moment in the element under consideration. In the shear analysis of reinforced concrete without axial force, the approximate value $z = 0,9d$ may normally be used.

In elements with inclined prestressing tendons, longitudinal reinforcement at the tensile chord [AC1) should be provided to carry the longitudinal tensile force due to shear defined in (7). (AC1]

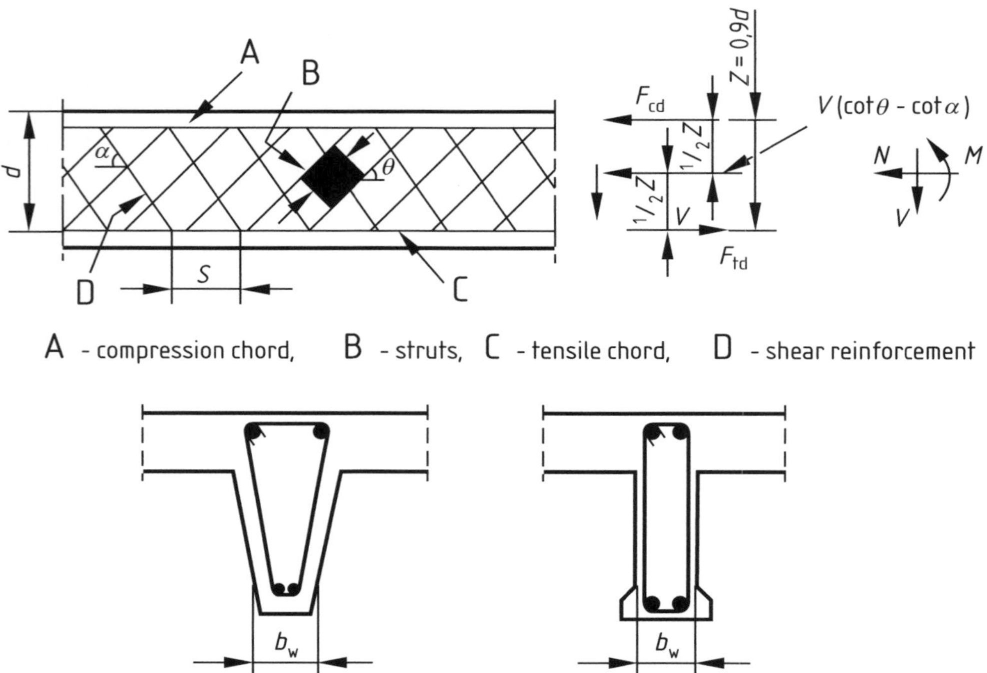

Figure 6.5 — Truss model and notation for shear reinforced members

(2) The angle θ should be limited.

NOTE The limiting values of $\cot\theta$ for use in a country may be found in its National Annex. The recommended limits are given in Expression (6.7N).

$$1 \leq \cot\theta \leq 2,5 \quad (6.7N)$$

The limiting values of $\cot\theta$ for use in the UK are the recommended limits given in expression (6.7N) except in elements in which shear co-exists with externally applied tension (i.e. tension caused by restraint is not considered here). In these elements, $\cot\theta$ should be taken as 1,0.

(3) For members with vertical shear reinforcement, the shear resistance, V_{Rd} is the smaller value of:

$$V_{Rd,s} = \frac{A_{sw}}{s} z f_{ywd} \cot\theta \quad (6.8)$$

NOTE If Expression (6.10) is used the value of f_{ywd} should be reduced to 0,8 f_{ywk} in expression (6.8)

and

$$V_{Rd,max} = \alpha_{cw} b_w z \nu_1 f_{cd} / (\cot\theta + \tan\theta) \quad (6.9)$$

where:
A_{sw} is the cross-sectional area of the shear reinforcement
s is the spacing of the stirrups
f_{ywd} is the design yield strength of the shear reinforcement
ν_1 is a strength reduction factor for concrete cracked in shear
α_{cw} is a coefficient taking account of the state of the stress in the compression chord

NOTE 1 The value of ν_1 and α_{cw} for use in a country may be found in its National Annex. The recommended value of ν_1 is ν (see expression (6.6N)).

The value of ν_1 and α_{cw} for use in the UK ν_1 is ν see expression (6.6N). The values of ν_1 and α_{cw} should not give rise to a value of $V_{Rd,max}$ greater than $200b_w^2$ at sections more than d from the edge of a support.

NOTE 2 If the design stress of the shear reinforcement is below 80% of the characteristic yield stress f_{yk}, ν_1 may be taken as:

$\nu_1 = 0,6$ for $f_{ck} \leq 60$ MPa (6.10.aN)
$\nu_1 = 0,9 - f_{ck}/200 > 0,5$ for $f_{ck} \geq 60$ MPa (6.10.bN)

However, if the design stress of the shear reinforcement is below 80% of the characteristic yield stress in the UK f_{yk}, ν_1 may be taken as:

$\nu_1 = 0,54\ (1 - 0,5 \cos \alpha)$ for $f_{ck} \leq 60$ MPa
$\nu_1 = (0,84 - f_{ck}/200)\ (1 - 0,5 \cos \alpha) > 0,5$ for $f_{ck} \geq 60$ MPa

NOTE 3 The recommended value of α_{cw} is as follows:

$1,0$ for non-prestressed structures
$(1 + \sigma_{cp}/f_{cd})$ for $0 < \sigma_{cp} \leq 0,25\ f_{cd}$ (6.11.aN)
$1,25$ for $0,25\ f_{cd} < \sigma_{cp} \leq 0,5\ f_{cd}$ (6.11.bN)
$2,5\ (1 - \sigma_{cp}/f_{cd})$ for $0,5\ f_{cd} < \sigma_{cp} < 1,0\ f_{cd}$ (6.11.cN)

where:
σ_{cp} is the mean compressive stress, measured positive, in the concrete due to the design axial force. This should be obtained by averaging it over the concrete section taking account of the reinforcement. The value of σ_{cp} need not be calculated at a distance less than $0,5d \cot \theta$ from the edge of the support.

NOTE 4 The maximum effective cross-sectional area of the shear reinforcement, $A_{sw,max}$, for $\cot \theta = 1$ is given by:

$$\frac{A_{sw,max} f_{ywd}}{b_w s} \leq \frac{1}{2} \alpha_{cw} \nu_1 f_{cd} \quad (6.12)$$

(5) In regions where there is no discontinuity of V_{Ed} [AC1) (e.g. for uniformly distributed loading applied at the top) shear reinforcement in any length increment $l = z(\cot \theta)$ may be (AC1] calculated using the smallest value of V_{Ed} in the increment.

(6) [AC1) Where the web contains grouted metal ducts (AC1] with a diameter $\phi > b_w/8$ the shear resistance $V_{Rd,max}$ should be calculated on the basis of a nominal web thickness given by:

$$b_{w,nom} = b_w - 0,5\Sigma\phi \quad (6.16)$$

where ϕ is the outer diameter of the duct and $\Sigma\phi$ is determined for the most unfavourable level.

For grouted metal ducts with $\phi \leq b_w/8$, $b_{w,nom} = b_w$.

For non-grouted ducts, grouted plastic ducts and unbonded tendons the nominal web thickness is:

$$b_{w,nom} = b_w - 1,2\Sigma\phi \qquad (6.17)$$

The value 1,2 in expression (6.17) is introduced to take account of splitting of the concrete struts due to transverse tension. If adequate transverse reinforcement is provided this value may be reduced to 1,0.

(7) The additional tensile force, ΔF_{td}, in the longitudinal reinforcement due to shear V_{Ed} may be calculated from:

$$\Delta F_{td} = 0,5\,V_{Ed}\,(\cot\theta - \cot\alpha) \qquad (6.18)$$

$(M_{Ed}/z) + \Delta F_{td}$ should be taken not greater than $M_{Ed,max}/z$, where $M_{Ed,max}$ is the maximum moment along the beam.

(8) For members with loads applied on the upper side within a distance $0,5d \leq a_v \leq 2,0d$ the contribution of this load to the shear force V_{Ed} may be reduced by multiplying by $\beta = a_v/2d$.

The shear force V_{Ed}, calculated in this way, should satisfy the condition

$$V_{Ed} \leq A_{sw} \cdot f_{ywd} \sin\alpha \qquad (6.19)$$

where $A_{sw} \cdot f_{ywd}$ is the resistance of the shear reinforcement crossing the inclined shear crack between the loaded areas (see Figure 6.6). Only the shear reinforcement within the central length $0,75a_v$ should be taken into account. The reduction by β should only be applied for calculating the shear reinforcement. It is only valid provided that the longitudinal reinforcement is fully anchored at the support.

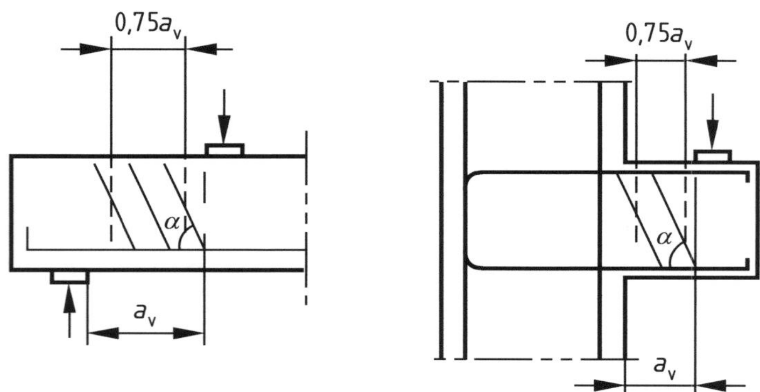

Figure 6.6 — Shear reinforcement in short shear spans with direct strut action

For $a_v \leq 0,5d$ the value $a_v = 0,5d$ should be used.

[AC1] The value V_{Ed}, calculated without reduction by β, should however always be less than $V_{Rd,max}$, see expression (6.9). [AC1]

6.3 Torsion

6.3.1 General

(1)P Where the static equilibrium of a structure depends on the torsional resistance of elements of the structure, a full torsional design covering both ultimate and serviceability limit states shall be made.

(2) Where, in statically indeterminate structures, torsion arises from consideration of compatibility only, and the structure is not dependent on the torsional resistance for its stability, then it will normally be unnecessary to consider torsion at the ultimate limit state. In such cases a minimum reinforcement, given in Sections 7.3 and 9.2, in the form of stirrups and longitudinal bars should be provided in order to prevent excessive cracking.

(3) The torsional resistance of a section may be calculated on the basis of a thin-walled closed section, in which equilibrium is satisfied by a closed shear flow. Solid sections may be modelled as equivalent thin-walled sections. Complex shapes, such as T-sections, may be divided into a series of sub-sections, each of which is modelled as an equivalent thin-walled section, and the total torsional resistance taken as the sum of the capacities of the individual elements.

(4) The distribution of the acting torsional moments over the sub-sections should be in proportion to their uncracked torsional stiffnesses. For non-solid sections the equivalent wall thickness should not exceed the actual wall thickness.

(5) Each sub-section may be designed separately.

6.3.2 Design procedure

(1) The shear stress in a wall of a section subject to a pure torsional moment may be calculated from:

$$\tau_{t,i}\, t_{ef,i} = \frac{T_{Ed}}{2A_k} \qquad (6.26)$$

The shear force $V_{Ed,i}$ in a wall i due to torsion is given by:

$$V_{Ed,i} = \tau_{t,i}\, t_{ef,i}\, z_i \qquad (6.27)$$

where

T_{Ed} is the applied design torsion (see Figure 6.11).

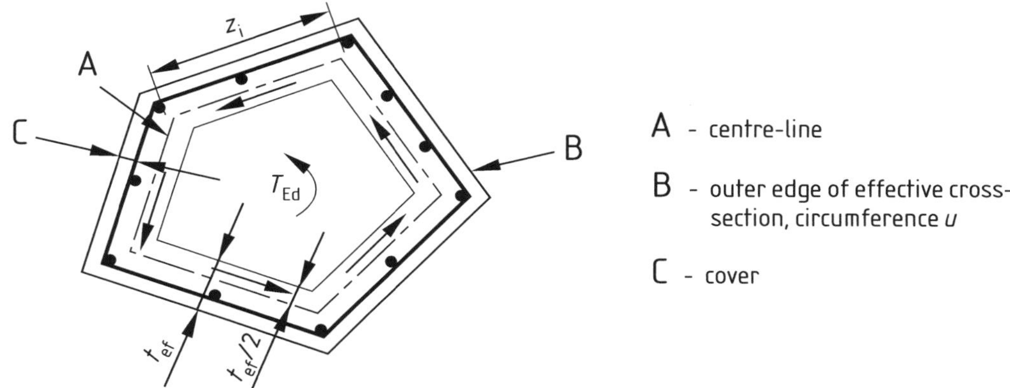

Figure 6.11 — Notations and definitions used in Section 6.3

- A_k is the area enclosed by the centre-lines of the connecting walls, including inner hollow areas
- $\tau_{t,i}$ is the torsional shear stress in wall i
- $t_{ef,i}$ is the effective wall thickness. It may be taken as A/u, but should not be taken as less than twice the distance between edge and centre of the longitudinal reinforcement. For hollow sections the real thickness is an upper limit
- A is the total area of the cross-section within the outer circumference, including inner hollow areas
- u is the outer circumference of the cross-section
- z_i is the side length of wall i defined by the distance between the intersection points with the adjacent walls.

(2) The effects of torsion and shear for both hollow and solid members may be superimposed, assuming the same value for the strut inclination θ . The limits for θ given in 6.2.3 (2) are also fully applicable for the case of combined shear and torsion.

The maximum bearing capacity of a member loaded in shear and torsion follows from 6.3.2 (4).

(3) The required cross-sectional area of the longitudinal reinforcement for torsion ΣA_{sl} may be calculated from expression (6.28):

$$\frac{\Sigma A_{sl} f_{yd}}{u_k} = \frac{T_{Ed}}{2A_k} \cot \theta \qquad (6.28)$$

where
u_k is the perimeter of the area A_k
f_{yd} is the design yield stress of the longitudinal reinforcement A_{sl}
θ is the angle of compression struts (see Figure 6.5).

In compressive chords, the longitudinal reinforcement may be reduced in proportion to the available compressive force. In tensile chords the longitudinal reinforcement for torsion should be added to the other reinforcement. The longitudinal reinforcement should generally be distributed over the length of side, z_i, but for smaller sections it may be concentrated at the ends of this length.

(4) The maximum resistance of a member subjected to torsion and shear is limited by the capacity of the concrete struts. In order not to exceed this resistance the following condition should be satisfied:

$$T_{Ed} / T_{Rd,max} + V_{Ed} / V_{Rd,max} \leq 1,0 \qquad (6.29)$$

where:
T_{Ed} is the design torsional moment
V_{Ed} is the design transverse force
$T_{Rd,max}$ is the design torsional resistance moment according to

$$T_{Rd,max} = 2\nu\, \alpha_{cw} f_{cd} A_k t_{ef,i} \sin \theta \cos \theta \qquad (6.30)$$

AC1 where ν follows from 6.2.2 (6) and α_{cw} from Expression (6.9). AC1

$V_{Rd,max}$ is the maximum design shear resistance according to expressions (6.9) or (6.14). In solid cross sections the full width of the web may be used to determine $V_{Rd,max}$.

(5) For approximately rectangular solid sections only minimum reinforcement is required (see 9.2.1.1) provided that the following condition is satisfied:

$$T_{Ed} / T_{Rd,c} + V_{Ed} / V_{Rd,c} \leq 1,0 \qquad (6.31)$$

where
$T_{Rd,c}$ is the torsional cracking moment, which may be determined by setting $\tau_{t,I} = f_{ctd}$
$V_{Rd,c}$ follows from expression (6.2).

6.3.3 Warping torsion

(1) For closed thin-walled sections and solid sections, warping torsion may normally be ignored.

6.4 Punching

6.4.1 General

(1)P The rules in this section complement those given in 6.2 and cover punching shear in solid slabs, waffle slabs with solid areas over columns, and foundations.

(2)P Punching shear can result from a concentrated load or reaction acting on a relatively small area, called the loaded area A_{load} of a slab or a foundation.

(3) An appropriate verification model for checking punching failure at the ultimate limit state is shown in Figure 6.12.

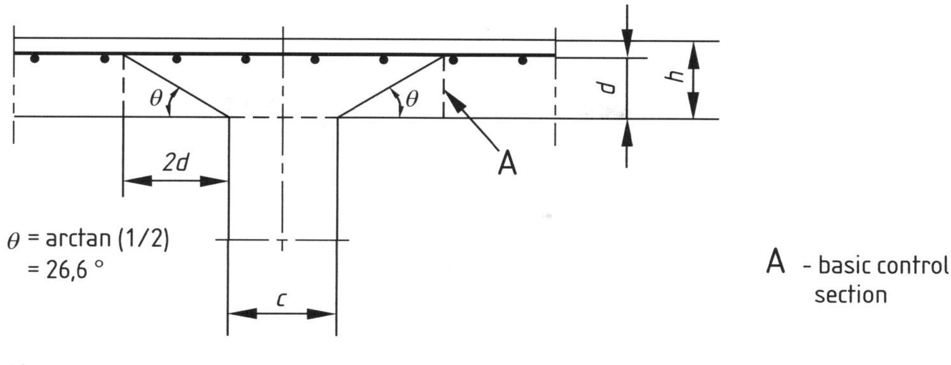

a) Section

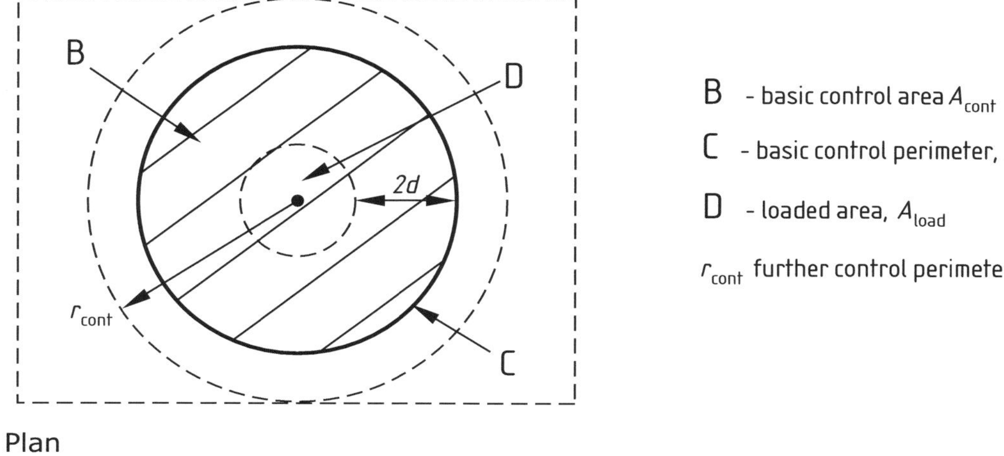

b) Plan

Figure 6.12 — Verification model for punching shear at the ultimate limit state

(4) The shear resistance should be checked at the face of the column and at the basic control perimeter u_1. If shear reinforcement is required a further perimeter $u_{out,ef}$ should be found where shear reinforcement is no longer required.

(5) The rules given in 6.4 are principally formulated for the case of uniformly distributed loading. In special cases, such as footings, the load within the control perimeter adds to the resistance of the structural system, and may be subtracted when determining the design punching shear stress.

6.4.2 Load distribution and basic control perimeter

(1) The basic control perimeter u_1 may normally be taken to be at a distance 2,0*d* from the loaded area and should be constructed so as to minimise its length (see Figure 6.13).

The effective depth of the slab is assumed constant and may normally be taken as:

$$d_{eff} = \frac{(d_y + d_z)}{2} \tag{6.32}$$

where d_y and d_z are the effective depths of the reinforcement in two orthogonal directions.

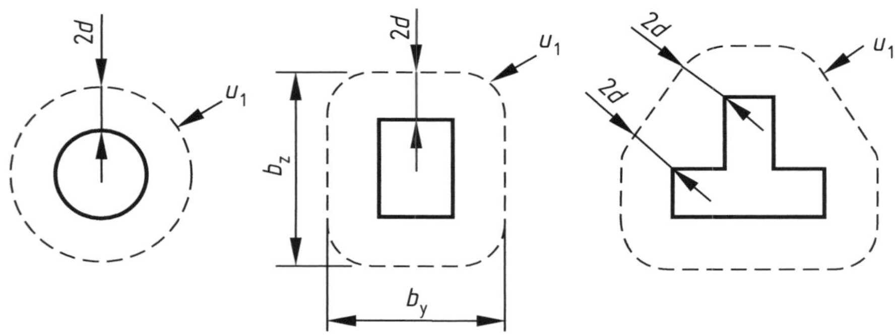

Figure 6.13 — Typical basic control perimeters around loaded areas

(2) Control perimeters at a distance less than 2*d* should be considered where the concentrated force is opposed by a high pressure (e.g. soil pressure on a base), or by the effects of a load or reaction within a distance 2*d* of the periphery of area of application of the force.

(3) For loaded areas situated near openings, if the shortest distance between the perimeter of the loaded area and the edge of the opening does not exceed 6*d*, that part of the control perimeter contained between two tangents drawn to the outline of the opening from the centre of the loaded area is considered to be ineffective (see Figure 6.14).

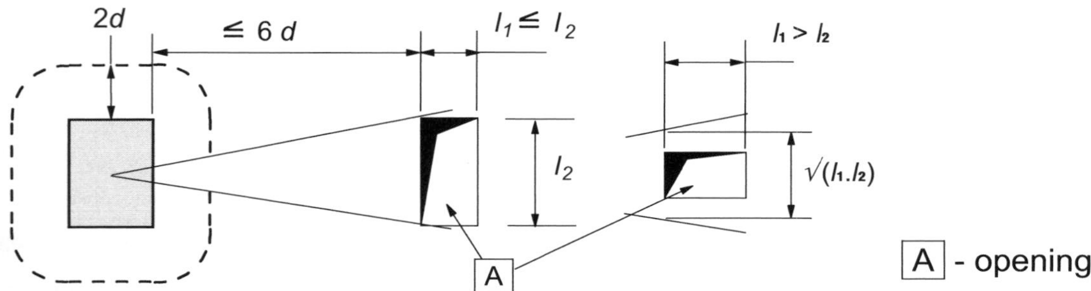

Figure 6.14 — Control perimeter near an opening

(6) The control section is that which follows the control perimeter and extends over the effective depth *d*. For slabs of constant depth, the control section is perpendicular to the middle plane of the slab. For slabs or footings of variable depth other than step footings, the effective depth may be assumed to be the depth at the perimeter of the loaded area as shown in Figure 6.16.

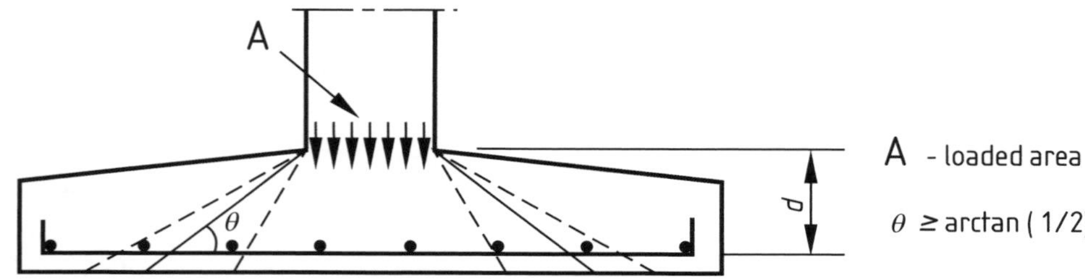

Figure 6.16 — Depth of control section in a footing with variable depth

6.4.3 Punching shear calculation

(1)P The design procedure for punching shear is based on checks at the face of the column and at the basic control perimeter, u_1. If shear reinforcement is required a further perimeter $u_{out,ef}$ (see Figure 6.22) should be found where shear reinforcement is no longer required. The following design shear stresses [MPa] along the control sections, are defined:

$v_{Rd,c}$ is the design value of the punching shear resistance of a slab without punching shear reinforcement along the control section considered,

$v_{Rd,cs}$ is the design value of the punching shear resistance of a slab with punching shear reinforcement along the control section considered,

$v_{Rd,max}$ is the design value of the maximum punching shear resistance along the control section considered.

(2) The following checks should be carried out:

(a) At the column perimeter, or the perimeter of the loaded area, the maximum punching shear stress should not be exceeded:

AC1⟩ $v_{Ed} \leq v_{Rd,\,max}$ ⟨AC1

(b) Punching shear reinforcement is not necessary if:

AC1⟩ $v_{Ed} \leq v_{Rd,\,c}$ ⟨AC1

(c) Where v_{Ed} exceeds the value $v_{Rd,c}$ for the control section considered, punching shear reinforcement should be provided according to 6.4.5.

(3) Where the support reaction is eccentric with regard to the control perimeter, the maximum shear stress should be taken as:

$$v = \beta \frac{V_{Ed}}{u_i \, d} \qquad (6.38)$$

where

d is the mean effective depth of the slab, which may be taken as $(d_y + d_z)/2$

where

d_y, d_z are the effective depths in the y- and z- directions of the control section

u_i is the length of the control perimeter being considered

β is given by:

$$\beta = 1 + k \frac{M_{Ed}}{V_{Ed}} - \frac{u_1}{W_1} \qquad (6.39)$$

where

u_1 is the length of the basic control perimeter

k is a coefficient dependent on the ratio between the column dimensions c_1 and c_2: its value is a function of the proportions of the unbalanced moment transmitted by uneven shear and by bending and torsion (see Table 6.1)

W_1 corresponds to a distribution of shear as illustrated in Figure 6.19 and is a function of the basic control perimeter u_1:

AC1⟩ $W_i = \int_0^{u_1} |e| \, dl$ ⟨AC1 (6.40)

dl is a length increment of the perimeter

e is the distance of dl from the axis about which the moment M_{ed} acts

(6) For structures where the lateral stability does not depend on frame action between the slabs and the columns, and where the adjacent spans do not differ in length by more than 25 %, approximate values for β may be used.

NOTE Values of β for use in a country may be found in its National Annex. Recommended values are given in Figure 6.21N.

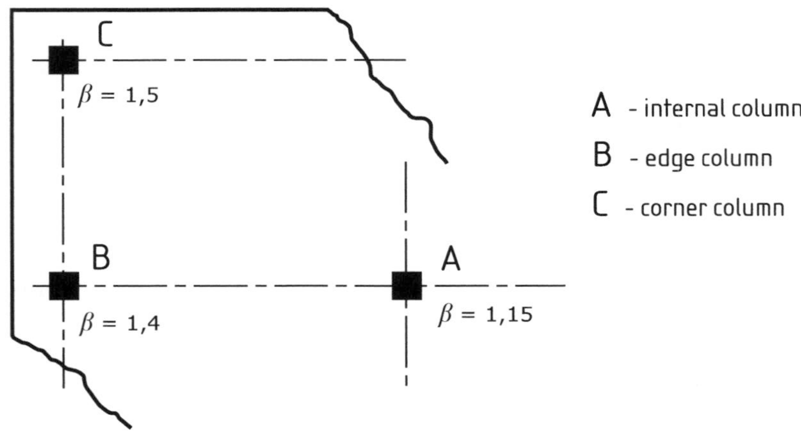

Figure 6.21N — Recommended values for β

(8) The punching shear force V_{Ed} in a foundation slab may be reduced due to the favourable action of the soil pressure.

(9) The vertical component V_{pd} resulting from inclined prestressing tendons crossing the control section may be taken into account as a favourable action where relevant.

6.4.4 Punching shear resistance of slabs and column bases without shear reinforcement

(1) The punching shear resistance of a slab should be assessed for the basic control section according to 6.4.2. The design punching shear resistance [MPa] may be calculated as follows:

$$v_{Rd,c} = C_{Rd,c}\, k\, (100\rho_l f_{ck})^{1/3} + k_1 \sigma_{cp} \geq (v_{min} + k_1 \sigma_{cp}) \qquad (6.47)$$

where:

f_{ck} is in MPa

k $= 1 + \sqrt{\frac{200}{d}} \leq 2,0$ d in mm

ρ_l $= \sqrt{\rho_{ly} \cdot \rho_{lz}} \leq 0,02$

ρ_{ly}, ρ_{lz} relate to the bonded tension steel in y- and z- directions respectively. The values ρ_{ly} and ρ_{lz} should be calculated as mean values taking into account a slab width equal to the column width plus 3d each side

σ_{cp} $= (\sigma_{c,y} + \sigma_{c,z}) / 2$

where

$\sigma_{c,y}$, $\sigma_{c,z}$ are the normal concrete stresses in the critical section in y- and z- directions (MPa, positive if compression):

$$\sigma_{c,y} = \frac{N_{Ed,y}}{A_{cy}} \text{ and } \sigma_{c,z} = \frac{N_{Ed,z}}{A_{cz}}$$

N_{Edy}, N_{Edz} are the longitudinal forces across the full bay for internal columns and the longitudinal force across the control section for edge columns. The force may be from a load or prestressing action.

A_c is the area of concrete according to the definition of N_{Ed}.

NOTE The values of $C_{Rd,c}$, v_{min} and k_1 for use in a country may be found in its National Annex. The recommended value for $C_{Rd,c}$ is $0,18/\gamma_c$, for v_{min} is given by expression (6.3N) and that for k_1 is 0,1.

See also 3.1.2(2)P for requirement for concrete class > C50/60 for UK.

(2) The punching resistance of column bases should be verified at control perimeters within $2d$ from the periphery of the column.

The lowest value of resistance found in this way should control the design.

For concentric loading the net applied force is

$$V_{Ed,red} = V_{Ed} - \Delta V_{Ed} \qquad (6.48)$$

where:
V_{Ed} is the applied shear force
ΔV_{Ed} is the net upward force within the control perimeter considered i.e. upward pressure from soil minus self weight of base.

$$v_{Ed} = V_{Ed,red} / ud \qquad (6.49)$$

[AC1) $$v_{Rd} = C_{Rd,c}\, k\, (100\rho\, f_{ck})^{1/3} \times 2d/a \geq v_{min} \times 2d/a \qquad (6.50)$$ (AC1]

where
a is the distance from the periphery of the column to the control perimeter considered
$C_{Rd,c}$ is defined in 6.4.4(1)
v_{min} is defined in 6.4.4(1
k is defined in 6.4.4(1)

For eccentric loading

$$v_{Ed} = \frac{V_{Ed,red}}{ud}\left[1 + k\frac{M_{Ed}\,u}{V_{Ed,red}\,W}\right] \qquad (6.51)$$

Where k is defined in 6.4.3 (3) or 6.4.3 (4) as appropriate and W is similar to W_1 but for perimeter u.

Section 7 Serviceability Limit States (SLS)

7.1 General

(1)P This section covers the common serviceability limit states. These are:

- stress limitation (see 7.2)
- crack control (see 7.3)
- deflection control (see 7.4).

Other limit states (such as vibration) may be of importance in particular structures but are not covered in this standard.

(2) In the calculation of stresses and deflections, cross-sections should be assumed to be uncracked provided that the flexural tensile stress does not exceed $f_{ct,eff}$. The value of $f_{ct.eff}$ may be taken as f_{ctm} or $f_{ctm,fl}$ provided that the calculation for minimum tension reinforcement is also based on the same value. For the purposes of calculating crack widths and tension stiffening f_{ctm} should be used.

7.2 Stress limitation

(1)P The compressive stress in the concrete shall be limited in order to avoid longitudinal cracks, micro-cracks or high levels of creep, where they could result in unacceptable effects on the function of the structure.

(2) Longitudinal cracks may occur if the stress level under the characteristic combination of loads exceeds a critical value. Such cracking may lead to a reduction of durability. In the absence of other measures, such as an increase in the cover to reinforcement in the compressive zone or confinement by transverse reinforcement, it may be appropriate to limit the compressive stress to a value k_1f_{ck} in areas exposed to environments of exposure classes XD, XF and XS (see Table 4.1).

NOTE The value of k_1 for use in a country may be found in its National Annex. The recommended value is 0,6.

(3) If the stress in the concrete under the quasi-permanent loads is less than k_2f_{ck}, linear creep may be assumed. If the stress in concrete exceeds k_2f_{ck}, non-linear creep should be considered (see 3.1.4)

NOTE The value of k_2 for use in a country may be found in its National Annex. The recommended value is 0,45.

(4)P Tensile stresses in the reinforcement shall be limited in order to avoid inelastic strain, unacceptable cracking or deformation.

(5) [AC1) For the appearance unacceptable cracking or deformation (AC1] may be assumed to be avoided if, under the characteristic combination of loads, the tensile stress in the reinforcement does not exceed k_3f_{yk}. Where the stress is caused by an imposed deformation, the tensile stress should not exceed k_4f_{yk}. The mean value of the stress in prestressing tendons should not exceed k_5f_{yk}.

NOTE The values of k_3, k_4 and k_5 for use in a country may be found in its National Annex. The recommended values are 0,8, 1,0 and 0,75 respectively.

7.3 Crack control

7.3.1 General considerations

(1)P Cracking shall be limited to an extent that will not impair the proper functioning or durability of the structure or cause its appearance to be unacceptable.

(2)P Cracking is normal in reinforced concrete structures subject to bending, shear, torsion, or tension resulting from either direct loading or restraint or imposed deformations.

(3) Cracks may also arise from other causes such as plastic shrinkage or expansive chemical reactions within the hardened concrete. Such cracks may be unacceptably large but their avoidance and control lie outside the scope of this section.

(4) Cracks may be permitted to form without any attempt to control their width, provided they do not impair the functioning of the structure.

(5) [AC1) A limiting value, w_{max}, for the calculated crack width, w_k, taking into account (AC1] the proposed function and nature of the structure and the costs of limiting cracking, should be established.

NOTE The value of w_{max} for use in a Country may be found in its National Annex. The recommended values for relevant exposure classes are given in Table 7.1N.

The values of w_{max} for use in the UK are given in Table NA.3.

Table NA.3 — Recommended values of w_{max} (mm) for use in the UK

<table>
<tr><th rowspan="2">Exposure Class</th><th>Reinforced members and prestressed members without bonded tendons</th><th>Prestressed members with bonded tendons</th></tr>
<tr><td>Quasi-permanent load combination</td><td>Frequent load combination</td></tr>
<tr><td>X0, XC1</td><td>0,3[1]</td><td>0,2</td></tr>
<tr><td>XC2, XC3, XC4</td><td rowspan="2">0,3</td><td>0,2[2]</td></tr>
<tr><td>XD1, XD2, XD3, XS1, XS2, XS3</td><td>Decompression[3]</td></tr>
<tr><td colspan="3">NOTE 1 For X0, XC1 exposure classes, crack width has no influence on durability and this limit is set to produce acceptable appearance. In the absence of specific requirements for appearance this limit may be relaxed.

NOTE 2 For these exposure classes, in addition, decompression should be checked under the quasi-permanent combination of loads.

NOTE 3 Consideration should be given to limiting crack widths outside the zone of decompression, where passive reinforcement is present or the cover is excessive that will result in aesthetically unacceptable crack widths. Appropriate limits in this table may be used.</td></tr>
</table>

In the absence of specific requirements (e.g. water-tightness), it may be assumed that limiting the calculated crack widths to the values of w_{max} given in Table NA.3, under the quasi-permanent combination of loads, will generally be satisfactory for reinforced concrete members in buildings with respect to appearance and durability.

The durability of prestressed members may be more critically affected by cracking. In the absence of more detailed requirements, it may be assumed that limiting the calculated crack widths to the values of w_{max} given in Table 7.1N, under the frequent combination of loads, will generally be satisfactory for prestressed concrete members. The decompression limit requires that all parts of the tendons or duct lie at least 25 mm within concrete in compression.

(6) For members with only unbonded tendons, the requirements for reinforced concrete elements apply. For members with a combination of bonded and unbonded tendons requirements for prestressed concrete members with bonded tendons apply.

(9) Crack widths may be calculated according to 7.3.4. A simplified alternative is to limit the bar size or spacing according to 7.3.3.

7.3.2 Minimum reinforcement areas

(1)P If crack control is required, a minimum amount of bonded reinforcement is required to control cracking in areas where tension is expected. The amount may be estimated from equilibrium between the tensile force in concrete just before cracking and the tensile force in reinforcement at yielding or at a lower stress if necessary to limit the crack width.

(2) Unless a more rigorous calculation shows lesser areas to be adequate, the required minimum areas of reinforcement may be calculated as follows. In profiled cross sections like T-beams and box girders, minimum reinforcement should be determined for the individual parts of the section (webs, flanges).

$$A_{s,min}\,\sigma_s = k_c\, k\, f_{ct,eff}\, A_{ct} \quad (7.1)$$

where:

$A_{s,min}$ is the minimum area of reinforcing steel within the tensile zone

A_{ct} is the area of concrete within the tensile zone. The tensile zone is that part of the section which is calculated to be in tension just before formation of the first crack

σ_s is the absolute value of the maximum stress permitted in the reinforcement immediately after formation of the crack. This may be taken as the yield strength of the reinforcement, f_{yk}. A lower value may, however, be needed to satisfy the crack width limits according to the maximum bar size or spacing (see 7.3.3(2))

$f_{ct,eff}$ is the mean value of the tensile strength of the concrete effective at the time when the cracks may first be expected to occur:
$f_{ct,eff} = f_{ctm}$ or lower, ($f_{ctm}(t)$), if cracking is expected earlier than 28 days

k is the coefficient which allows for the effect of non-uniform self-equilibrating stresses, which lead to a reduction of restraint forces
= 1,0 for webs with $h \leq 300$ mm or flanges with widths less than 300 mm
= 0,65 for webs with $h \geq 800$ mm or flanges with widths greater than 800 mm
intermediate values may be interpolated

k_c is a coefficient which takes account of the stress distribution within the section immediately prior to cracking and of the change of the lever arm:

For pure tension $k_c = 1,0$

For bending or bending combined with axial forces:

- For rectangular sections and webs of box sections and T -sections:

$$k_c = 0.4 \cdot \left[1 - \frac{\sigma_c}{k_1\,(h/h^*)\, f_{ct,eff}}\right] \leq 1 \quad (7.2)$$

- For flanges of box sections and T -sections:

$$k_c = 0,9 \cdot \frac{F_{cr}}{A_{ct}\, f_{ct,eff}} \geq 0,5 \quad (7.3)$$

where

σ_c is the mean stress of the concrete acting on the part of the section under consideration:

$$\sigma_c = \frac{N_{Ed}}{bh} \quad (7.4)$$

N_{Ed} is the axial force at the serviceability limit state acting on the part of the cross-section under consideration (compressive force positive). N_{Ed} should be determined considering the characteristic values of prestress and axial forces under the relevant combination of actions

h^* $h^* = h$ for $h < 1{,}0$ m
$h^* = 1{,}0$ m for $h \geq 1{,}0$ m

k_1 is a coefficient considering the effects of axial forces on the stress distribution:

$k_1 = 1{,}5$ if N_{Ed} is a compressive force

$k_1 = \frac{2h^*}{3h}$ if N_{Ed} is a tensile force

F_{cr} is the absolute value of the tensile force within the flange immediately prior to cracking due to the cracking moment calculated with $f_{ct,eff}$.

(3) Bonded tendons in the tension zone may be assumed to contribute to crack control within a distance ≤ 150 mm from the centre of the tendon. This may be taken into account by adding the term $\xi_1 A_p' \Delta\sigma_p$ to the left hand side of expression (7.1)

where

A_p' is the area of pre- or post-tensioned tendons within $A_{c,eff}$

$A_{c,eff}$ is the effective area of concrete in tension surrounding the reinforcement or prestressing tendons of depth, $h_{c,ef}$, where $h_{c,ef}$ is the lesser of 2,5(h-d), (h-x)/3 or h/2 (see Figure 7.1)

ξ_1 is the adjusted ratio of bond strength taking into account the different diameters of prestressing and reinforcing steel:

$$\xi_1 = \sqrt{\xi \cdot \frac{\phi_s}{\phi_p}} \qquad (7.5)$$

ξ is the ratio of bond strength of prestressing and reinforcing steel, according to Table 6.2 in 6.8.2.

ϕ_s is the largest bar diameter of reinforcing steel

ϕ_p is the equivalent diameter of prestressing steel according to 6.8.2

$\Delta\sigma_p$ is stress variation in prestressing tendons from the state of zero strain of the concrete at the same level.

Table 6.2 — Ratio of bond strength, ξ, between tendons and reinforcing steel

Prestressing steel	ξ		
	Pre-tensioned	Bonded, post-tensioned	
		≤ C50/60	≥ C70/85
Smooth bars and wires	Not applicable	0,3	0,15
Strands	0,6	0,5	0,25
Indented wires	0,7	0,6	0,30
Ribbed wires	0,8	0,7	0.35
NOTE For intermediate values between C50/60 and C70/85 interpolation may be used.			

(4) In prestressed members no minimum reinforcement is required in sections where, under the characteristic combination of loads and the characteristic value of prestress, the concrete is compressed or the absolute value of the tensile stress in the concrete is below $\sigma_{ct,p}$.

NOTE The value of $\sigma_{ct,p}$ for use in a country may be found in its National Annex. The recommended value is $f_{ct,eff}$ in accordance with 7.3.2 (2).

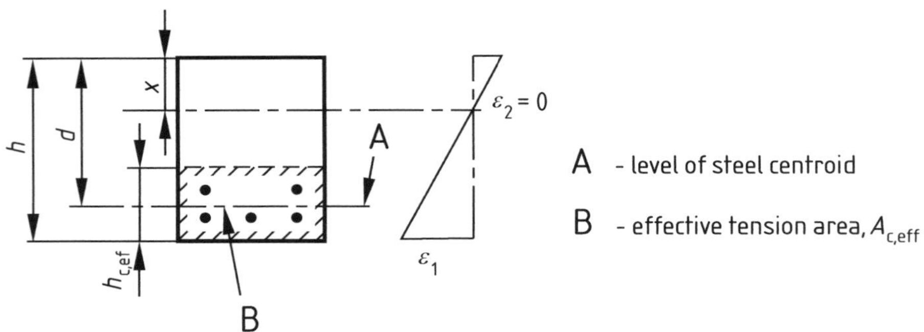

a) Beam

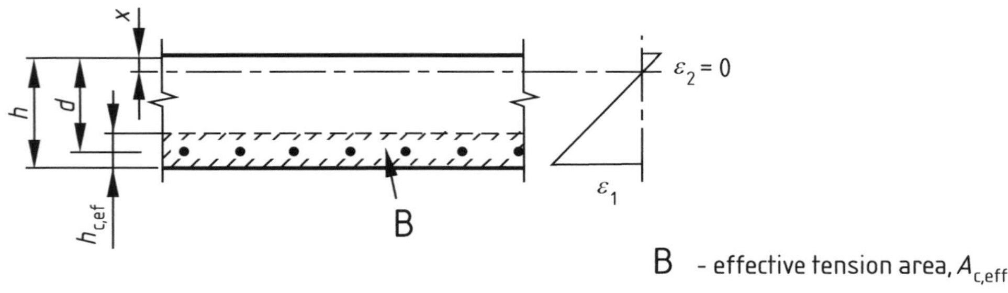

b) Slab

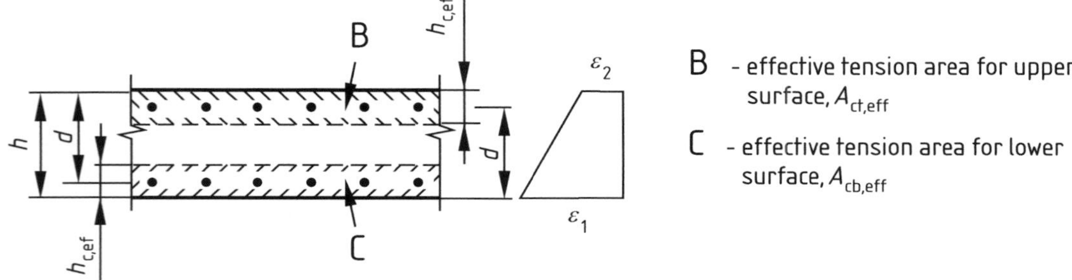

c) Member in tension

Figure 7.1 — Effective tension area (typical cases)

7.3.3 Control of cracking without direct calculation

(1) For reinforced or prestressed slabs in buildings subjected to bending without significant axial tension, specific measures to control cracking are not necessary where the overall depth does not exceed 200 mm and the provisions of 9.3 have been applied.

(2) The rules given in 7.3.4 may be presented in a tabular form by restricting the bar diameter or spacing as a simplification.

NOTE Where the minimum reinforcement given by 7.3.2 is provided, crack widths are unlikely to be excessive if:

- for cracking caused dominantly by restraint, the bar sizes given in Table 7.2 are not exceeded where the steel stress is the value obtained immediately after cracking (i.e. as σ_s in expression (7.1)).
- for cracks caused mainly by loading, either the provisions of Table 7.2N or the provisions of Table 7.3N are complied with. The steel stress should be calculated on the basis of a cracked section under the relevant combination of actions.

For pre-tensioned concrete, where crack control is mainly provided by tendons with direct bond, Tables 7.2N and 7.3N may be used with a stress equal to the total stress minus prestress. For post-tensioned concrete, where crack control is provided mainly by ordinary reinforcement, the tables may be used with the stress in this reinforcement calculated with the effect of prestressing forces included.

Table 7.2N — Maximum bar diameters ϕ^*_s for crack control[1]

Steel stress[2] [MPa]	Maximum bar size [mm]		
	w_k= 0,4 mm	w_k= 0,3 mm	w_k= 0,2 mm
160	40	32	25
200	32	25	16
240	20	16	12
280	16	12	8
320	12	10	6
360	10	8	5
400	8	6	4
450	6	5	–

NOTE 1 The values in the table are based on the following assumptions:
AC1⟩ c = 25mm; $f_{ct,eff}$ = 2,9MPa; h_{cr} = 0,5; $(h-d)$ = 0,1h; k_1 = 0,8; k_2 = 0,5; k_c = 0,4; k = 1,0; k_t = 0,4 and k_4 = 1,0. ⟨AC1

NOTE 2 Under the relevant combinations of actions.

Table 7.3N — Maximum bar spacing for crack control[1]

Steel stress[2] [MPa]	Maximum bar size [mm]		
	w_k= 0,4 mm	w_k= 0,3 mm	w_k= 0,2 mm
160	300	300	200
200	300	250	150
240	250	200	100
280	200	150	50
320	150	100	–
360	100	50	–

For NOTEs see Table 7.2N.

The maximum bar diameter should be modified as follows:

Bending (at least part of section in compression):

$$\phi_s = \phi^*_s (f_{ct,eff} / 2,9) \frac{k_c h_{cr}}{2(h-d)} \tag{7.6N}$$

Tension (uniform axial tension):

$$\phi_s = \phi^*_s (f_{ct,eff} / 2,9) h_{cr} / (8(h-d)) \tag{7.7N}$$

where:
ϕ_s is the adjusted maximum bar diameter
ϕ^*_s is the maximum bar size given in Table 7.2N
h is the overall depth of the section
h_{cr} is the depth of the tensile zone immediately prior to cracking, considering the characteristic values of prestress and axial forces under the quasi-permanent combination of actions
d is the effective depth to the centroid of the outer layer of reinforcement.

Where all the section is under tension $h - d$ is the minimum distance from the centroid of the layer of reinforcement to the face of the concrete (consider each face where the bar is not placed symmetrically).

(3) Beams with a total depth of 1000 mm or more, where the main reinforcement is concentrated in only a small proportion of the depth, should be provided with additional skin reinforcement to control cracking on the side faces of the beam. This reinforcement should be evenly distributed between the level of the tension steel and the neutral axis and should be located within the links. The area of the skin reinforcement should not be less than the amount obtained from 7.3.2 (2) taking k as 0,5 and σ_s as f_{yk}. The spacing and size of suitable bars may be obtained from 7.3.4 [AC1) or a suitable simplification assuming pure tension (AC1] and a steel stress of half the value assessed for the main tension reinforcement.

(4) It should be noted that there are particular risks of large cracks occurring in sections where there are sudden changes of stress, e.g.

- at changes of section
- near concentrated loads
- at positions where bars are curtailed
- in areas of high bond stress, particularly at the ends of laps.

Care should be taken at such areas to minimise the stress changes wherever possible. However, the rules for crack control given above will normally ensure adequate control at these points provided that the rules for detailing reinforcement given in Sections 8 and 9 are applied.

7.4 Deflection control

7.4.1 General considerations

(1)P The deformation of a member or structure shall not be such that it adversely affects its proper functioning or appearance.

(2) Appropriate limiting values of deflection taking into account the nature of the structure, of the finishes, partitions and fixings and upon the function of the structure should be established.

(3) Deformations should not exceed those that can be accommodated by other connected elements such as partitions, glazing, cladding, services or finishes. In some cases limitation may be required to ensure the proper functioning of machinery or apparatus supported by the structure, or to avoid ponding on flat roofs.

NOTE The limiting deflections given in (4) and (5) below are derived from ISO 4356 and should generally result in satisfactory performance of buildings such as dwellings, offices, public buildings or factories. Care should be taken to ensure that the limits are appropriate for the particular structure considered and that that there are no special requirements. Further information on deflections and limiting values may be obtained from ISO 4356.

(4) The appearance and general utility of the structure may be impaired when the calculated sag of a beam, slab or cantilever subjected to quasi-permanent loads exceeds span/250. The sag is assessed relative to the supports. Pre-camber may be used to compensate for some or all of the deflection but any upward deflection incorporated in the formwork should not generally exceed span/250.

(5) Deflections that could damage adjacent parts of the structure should be limited. For the deflection after construction, span/500 is normally an appropriate limit for quasi-permanent loads. Other limits may be considered, depending on the sensitivity of adjacent parts.

(6) The limit state of deformation may be checked by either:

- limiting the span/depth ratio, according to 7.4.2 or
- comparing a calculated deflection, according to 7.4.3, with a limit value.

NOTE The actual deformations may differ from the estimated values, particularly if the values of applied moments are close to the cracking moment. The differences will depend on the dispersion of the material properties, on the environmental conditions, on the load history, on the restraints at the supports, ground conditions, etc.

7.4.2 Cases where calculations may be omitted

(1)P Generally, it is not necessary to calculate the deflections explicitly as simple rules, for example limits to span/depth ratio may be formulated, which will be adequate for avoiding deflection problems in normal circumstances. More rigorous checks are necessary for members that lie outside such limits, or where deflection limits other than those implicit in simplified methods are appropriate.

(2) Provided that reinforced concrete beams or slabs in buildings are dimensioned so that they comply with the limits of span to depth ratio given in this clause, their deflections may be considered as not exceeding the limits set out in 7.4.1 (4) and (5). The limiting ratio of span to effective depth may be estimated using expressions (7.16a) and (7.16b) and multiplying this by correction factors to allow for the type of reinforcement used and other variables. No allowance has been made for any pre-camber in the derivation of these expressions.

$$\frac{l}{d} = K\left[11 + 1,5\sqrt{f_{ck}}\frac{\rho_0}{\rho} + 3,2\sqrt{f_{ck}}\left(\frac{\rho_0}{\rho} - 1\right)^{3/2}\right] \quad \text{if } \rho \le \rho_0 \qquad (7.16a)$$

$$\frac{l}{d} = K\left[11 + 1,5\sqrt{f_{ck}}\frac{\rho_0}{\rho - \rho'} + \frac{1}{12}\sqrt{f_{ck}}\sqrt{\frac{\rho'}{\rho_0}}\right] \quad \text{if } \rho > \rho_0 \qquad (7.16b)$$

where:

l/d is the limit of span/depth

K is the factor to take into account the different structural systems

[AC1] ρ_0 is the reference reinforcement ratio $= 10^{-3}\sqrt{f_{ck}}$ [AC1]

ρ is the required tension reinforcement ratio at mid-span to resist the moment due to the design loads (at support for cantilevers)

ρ' is the required compression reinforcement ratio at mid-span to resist the moment due to design loads (at support for cantilevers)

f_{ck} is in MPa units

Expressions (7.16a) and (7.16b) have been derived on the assumption that the steel stress, under the appropriate design load at SLS at a cracked section at the mid-span of a beam or slab or at the support of a cantilever, is 310 MPa (corresponding roughly to f_{yk} = 500 MPa).

Where other stress levels are used, the values obtained using expression (7.16) should be multiplied by 310 /σ_s. It will normally be conservative to assume that:

$$310 / \sigma_s = 500 / (f_{yk} A_{s,req} / A_{s,prov}) \quad (7.17)$$

where:

σ_s is the tensile steel stress at mid-span (at support for cantilevers) under the design load at SLS

$A_{s,prov}$ is the area of steel provided at this section

$A_{s,req}$ is the area of steel required at this section for ultimate limit state.

For flanged sections where the ratio of the flange breadth to the rib breadth exceeds 3, the values of *l/d* given by expression (7.16) should be multiplied by 0,8.

For beams and slabs, other than flat slabs, with spans exceeding 7 m, which support partitions liable to be damaged by excessive deflections, the values of *l/d* given by expression (7.16) should be multiplied by 7/ l_{eff} (l_{eff} in metres, see 5.3.2.2 (1)).

For flat slabs where the greater span exceeds 8,5 m, and which support partitions liable to be damaged by excessive deflections, the values of *l/d* given by expression (7.16) should be multiplied by 8,5 / l_{eff} (l_{eff} in metres).

NOTE Values of *K* for use in a Country may be found in its National Annex. Recommended values of *K* are given in Table 7.4N. Values obtained using Expression (7.16) for common cases (C30, σ_s = 310 MPa, different structural systems and reinforcement ratios ρ = 0,5 % and ρ = 1,5 %) are also given.

Values of *K* for use in the UK are given in Table NA.5. Values obtained using expression (7.16) for common cases (C30, σ_s = 310 MPa, different structural systems and reinforcement ratios ρ = 0,5 % and ρ = 1,5 %) are also given.

Table NA.5 — Basic ratios of span/effective depth for reinforced concrete members without axial compression

Structural system	K	Concrete highly stressed $\rho = 1,5$ %	Concrete lightly stressed $\rho = 0,5$ %
Simply supported beam, one- or two-way spanning simply supported slab	1,0	14	20
End span of continuous beam or one-way continuous slab or two-way spanning slab continuous over one long side	1,3	18	26
Interior span of beam or one-way or two-way spanning slab	1,5	20	30
Slab supported on columns without beams (flat slab) (based on longer span)	1,2	17	24
Cantilever	0,4	6	8

NOTE 1 The values given have been chosen to be generally conservative and calculation may frequently show that thinner members are possible.

NOTE 2 For two-way spanning slabs, the check should be carried out on the basis of the shorter span. For flat slabs the longer span should be taken.

NOTE 3 The limits given for flat slabs correspond to a less severe limitation than a mid-span deflection of span/250 relative to the columns. Experience has shown this to be satisfactory.

A1 NOTE 4 The values of k in the table may not be appropriate when the form-work is struck at an early age or when the construction loads exceed the design load. In these cases, the deflections may need to be calculated using advice in specialist literature, e.g. the Concrete Society's report on deflections in concrete slabs and beams and an article for the Magazine of Concrete Research entitled *Are existing span to depth rules conservative for flat slabs?*, both of which are referenced in NA.4.

NOTE 5 When the span/depth ratio obtained from NA.3 or Expressions (7.16a) or (7.16b) is adjusted using either $(310/\sigma_s)$ or $(500/f_{yk})(A_{s,prov}/A_{s,req})$, such adjustment should be limited to a maximum value of 1.5. σ_s should be calculated under characteristic combination of load at serviceability limit state.

NOTE 6 The absolute value of span/depth may not, in any case, exceed $40K$. A1

The values given by expression (7.16) and Table 7.4N have been derived from results of a parametric study made for a series of beams or slabs simply supported with rectangular cross section, using the general approach given in 7.4.3. Different values of concrete strength class and a 500 MPa characteristic yield strength reinforcement were considered. For a given area of tension reinforcement the ultimate moment was calculated and the quasi-permanent load was assumed as 50 % of the corresponding total design load. The span/effective depth limits obtained satisfy the limiting deflection given in 7.4.1(5).

Section 8 Detailing of reinforcement and prestressing tendons – General

8.1 General

(1)P The rules given in this section apply to ribbed reinforcement, mesh and prestressing tendons subjected predominantly to static loading. They are applicable for normal buildings and bridges. They may not be sufficient for:

- elements subjected to dynamic loading caused by seismic effects or machine vibration, impact loading and
- to elements incorporating specially painted, epoxy or zinc coated bars.

8.2 Spacing of bars

(2) The clear distance (horizontal and vertical) between individual parallel bars or horizontal layers of parallel bars should be not less than the maximum of k_1. bar diameter, (d_g + k_2 mm) or 20 mm where d_g is the maximum size of aggregate.

NOTE The values of k_1 and k_2 for use in a country may be found in its National Annex. The recommended values are 1 and 5 mm respectively.

8.4 Anchorage of longitudinal reinforcement

8.4.1 General

(2) Methods of anchorage are shown in Figure 8.1 (see also 8.8 (3)).

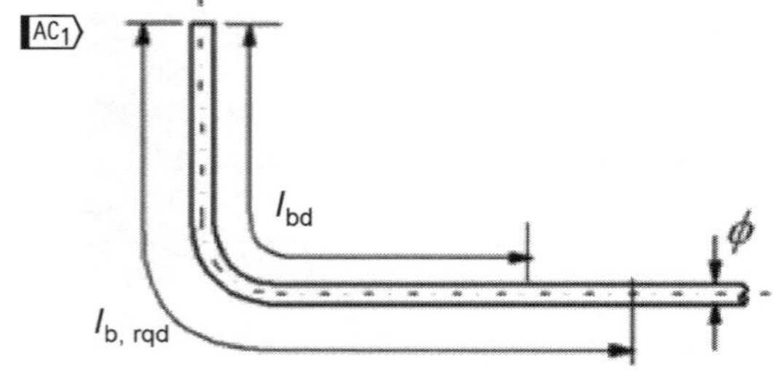

a) Basic tension anchorage length, $l_{b,rqd}$, for any shape measured along the centreline AC1

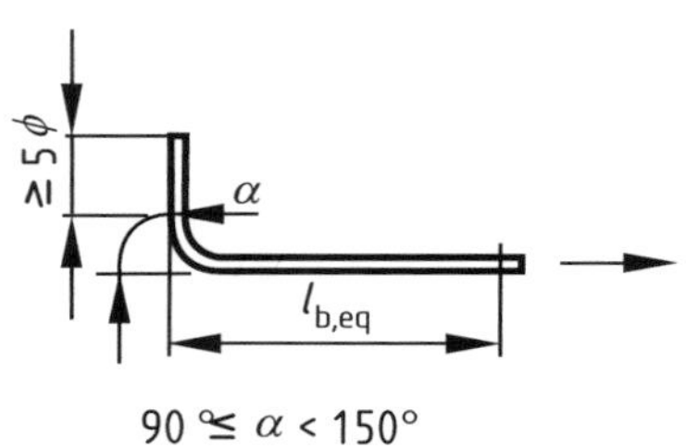

b) Equivalent anchorage length for standard bend

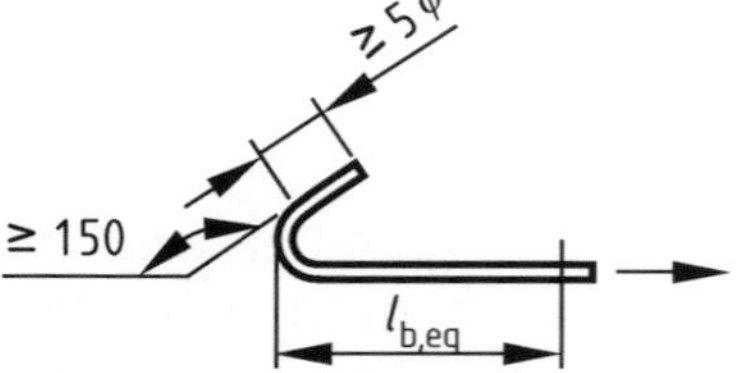

c) Equivalent anchorage length for standard hook

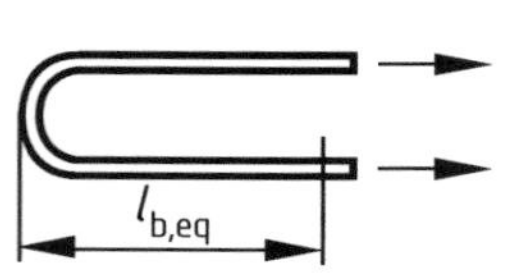

d) Equivalent anchorage length for standard loop

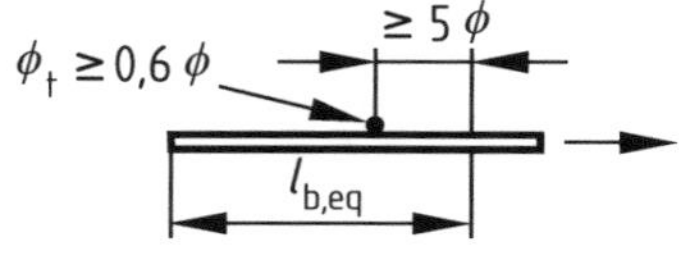

e) Equivalent anchorage length for welded transverse bar

Figure 8.1 — Methods of anchorage other than by a straight bar

(3) Bends and hooks do not contribute to compression anchorages.

8.4.2 Ultimate bond stress

(1)P The ultimate bond strength shall be sufficient to prevent bond failure.

(2) The design value of the ultimate bond stress, f_{bd}, for ribbed bars may be taken as:

$$f_{bd} = 2,25\, \eta_1\, \eta_2\, f_{ctd} \tag{8.2}$$

where:

f_{ctd} is the design value of concrete tensile strength according to 3.1.6 (2)P. Due to the increasing brittleness of higher strength concrete, $f_{ctk,0,05}$ should be limited here to the value for C60/75, unless it can be verified that the average bond strength increases above this limit

η_1 is a coefficient related to the quality of the bond condition and the position of the bar during concreting (see Figure 8.2):

η_1 = 1,0 when 'good' conditions are obtained and

η_1 = 0,7 for all other cases and for bars in structural elements built with slip-forms, unless it can be shown that 'good' bond conditions exist

η_2 is related to the bar diameter:

η_2 = 1,0 for $\phi \leq 32$ mm

η_2 = $(132 - \phi)/100$ for $\phi > 32$ mm.

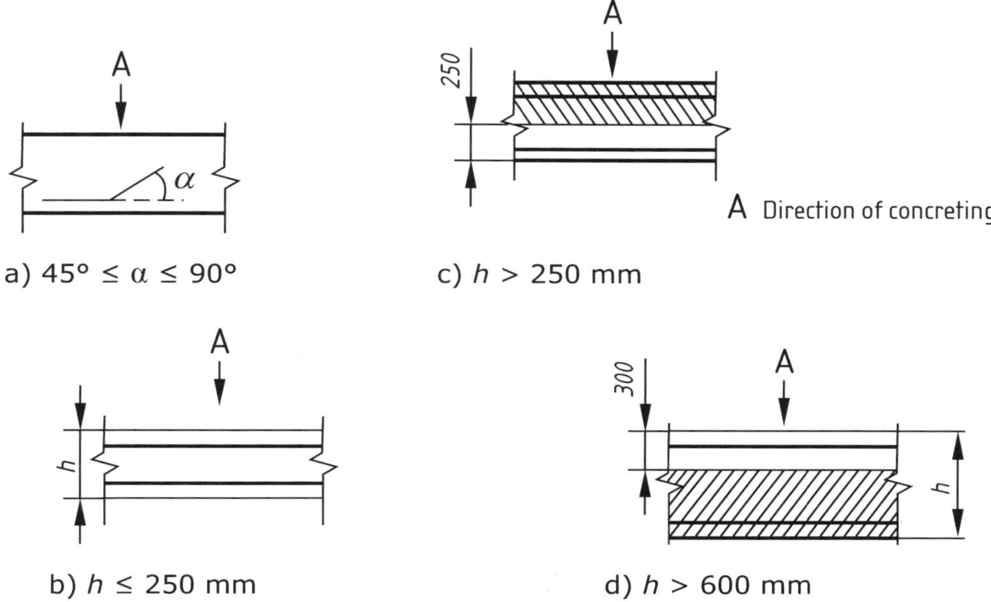

a) and b) 'Good' bond conditions for all bars

c) and d) Unhatched zone – 'good' bond conditions
Hatched zone – 'poor' bond conditions

Figure 8.2 — Description of bond conditions

8.4.3 Basic anchorage length

(2) The basic required anchorage length, $l_{b,rqd}$, for anchoring the force $A_s \cdot \sigma_{sd}$ in a straight bar assuming constant bond stress equal to f_{bd} follows from:

$$l_{b,rqd} = (\phi / 4)(\sigma_{sd} / f_{bd}) \tag{8.3}$$

where σ_{sd} is the design stress in the bar at the position from where the anchorage is measured from. Values for f_{bd} are given in 8.4.2.

[AC1) (3) For bent bars the basic required anchorage length, $l_{b,rqd}$, and the design length, l_{bd}, should be measured along the centre-line of the bar (see Figure 8.1a). (AC1]

8.4.4 Design anchorage length

(1) The design anchorage length, l_{bd}, is:

$$l_{bd} = \alpha_1 \alpha_2 \alpha_3 \alpha_4 \alpha_5 l_{b,rqd} \geq l_{b,min} \tag{8.4}$$

where α_1, α_2, α_3, α_4 and α_5 are coefficients given in Table 8.2:

α_1 is for the effect of the form of the bar assuming adequate cover (see Figure 8.1)
α_2 is for the effect of the concrete minimum cover c_d (see Figure 8.3).

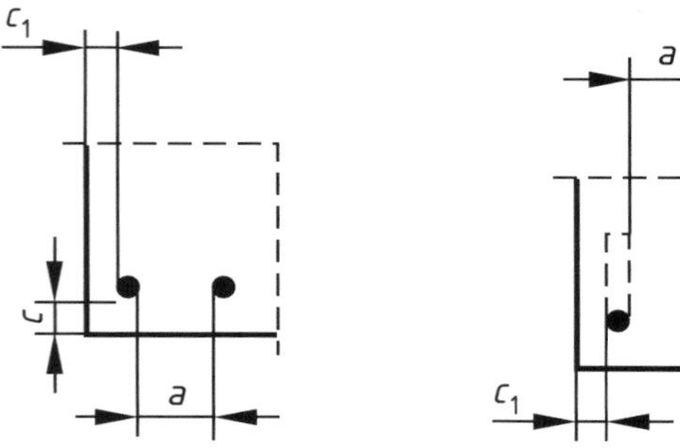

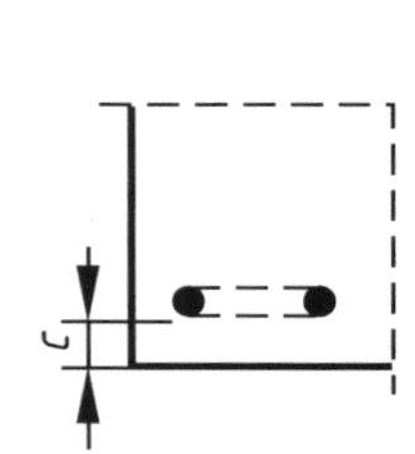

a) Straight bars $c_d = \min(a/2, c_1, c)$ b) Bent or hooked bars $c_d = \min(a/2, c_1)$ 3) Looped bars $c_d = c$

Figure 8.3 — Values of c_d for beams and slabs

α_3 is for the effect of confinement by transverse reinforcement
α_4 is for the influence of one or more welded transverse bars ($\phi_t > 0{,}6\phi$) along the design anchorage length l_{bd} (see also 8.6)
α_5 is for the effect of the pressure transverse to the plane of splitting along the design anchorage length.

The product $(\alpha_2\alpha_3\alpha_5) \geq 0{,}7$ (8.5)

$l_{b,rqd}$ is taken from expression (8.3)
$l_{b,min}$ is the minimum anchorage length if no other limitation is applied:
AC1) – for anchorages in tension: $l_{b,min} \geq \max\{0{,}3l_{b,rqd};\ 10\phi;\ 100\text{ mm}\}$ (8.6)
– for anchorages in compression: $l_{b,min} \geq \max\{0{,}6l_{b,rqd};\ 10\phi;\ 100\text{ mm}\}$ (8.7) (AC1

(2) As a simplified alternative to 8.4.4 (1) the tension anchorage of certain shapes shown in Figure 8.1 may be provided as an equivalent anchorage length, $l_{b,eq}$. $l_{b,eq}$ is defined in this figure and may be taken as:

- $\alpha_1 l_{b,rqd}$ for shapes shown in Figure 8.1b to 8.1d (see Table 8.2 for values of α_1)
- $\alpha_4 l_{b,rqd}$ for shapes shown in Figure 8.1e (see Table 8.2 for values of α_4)

where

α_1 and α_4 are defined in (1)

$l_{b,rqd}$ is calculated from expression (8.3).

Table 8.2 — Values of α_1, α_2, α_3, α_4 and α_5 coefficients

Influencing factor	Type of anchorage	Reinforcement bar	
		In tension	In compression
Shape of bars	Straight	$\alpha_1 = 1,0$	$\alpha_1 = 1,0$
	Other than straight (see Figure 8.1 (b), (c) and (d)	$\alpha_1 = 0,7$ if $c_d > 3\phi$ otherwise $\alpha_1 = 1,0$ (see Figure 8.3 for values of c_d)	$\alpha_1 = 1,0$
Concrete cover	Straight	$\alpha_2 = 1 - 0,15\ (c_d - \phi)/\phi$ $\geq 0,7$ $\leq 1,0$	$\alpha_2 = 1,0$
	Other than straight (see Figure 8.1 (b), (c) and (d)	$\alpha_2 = 1 - 0,15\ (c_d - 3\phi)/\phi$ $\geq 0,7$ $\leq 1,0$ (see Figure 8.3 for values of c_d)	$\alpha_2 = 1,0$
Confinement by transverse reinforcement not welded to main reinforcement	All types	$\alpha_3 = 1 - K\lambda$ $\geq 0,7$ $\leq 1,0$	$\alpha_3 = 1,0$
Confinement by welded transverse reinforcement*	All types, position and size as specified in Figure 8.1 (e)	$\alpha_4 = 0,7$	$\alpha_4 = 0,7$
Confinement by transverse pressure	All types	$\alpha_5 = 1 - 0,04p$ $\geq 0,7$ $\leq 1,0$	–

where:

λ $=(\Sigma A_{st} - \Sigma A_{st,min})/\ A_s$
ΣA_{st} cross-sectional area of the transverse reinforcement along the design anchorage length l_{bd}
$\Sigma A_{st,min}$ cross-sectional area of the minimum transverse reinforcement = 0,25 A_s for beams and 0 for slabs
A_s area of single anchored bar with maximum bar diameter
K values shown in Figure 8.4
p transverse pressure [MPa] at ultimate limit state along l_{bd}

* See also 8.6. For direct supports l_{bd} may be taken less than $l_{b,min}$ provided that there is at least one transverse wire welded with the support. This should be at least 15 mm from the face of the support.

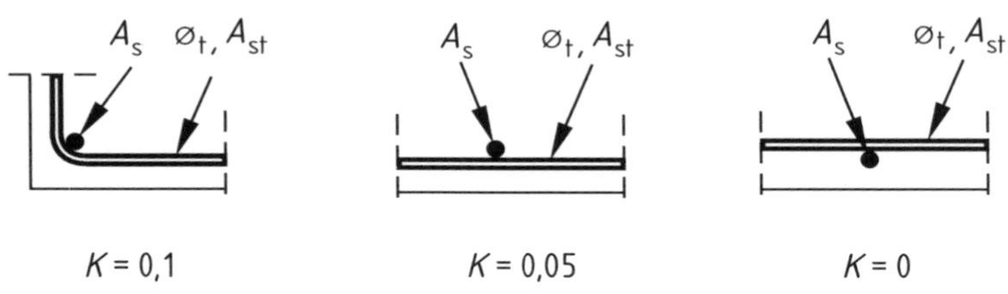

Figure 8.4 — Values of *K* for beams and slabs

8.7 Laps and mechanical couplers

8.7.2 Laps

(2) Laps:

- between bars should normally be staggered and not located in areas of high moments/forces (e.g. plastic hinges). Exceptions are given in (4) below;
- at any section should normally be arranged symmetrically.

(3) The arrangement of lapped bars should comply with Figure 8.7:

- the clear distance between two pairs of lapped bars should not be greater than 4ϕ or 50 mm, otherwise the lap length should be increased by a length equal to the clear space where it exceeds 4ϕ or 50 mm;
- the longitudinal distance between two adjacent laps should not be less than 0,3 times the lap length, l_0;
- in case of adjacent laps, the clear distance between adjacent bars should not be less than 2ϕ or 20 mm.

(4) When the provisions comply with (3) above, the permissible percentage of lapped bars in tension may be 100 % where the bars are all in one layer. Where the bars are in several layers the percentage should be reduced to 50 %.

All bars in compression and secondary (distribution) reinforcement may be lapped in one section.

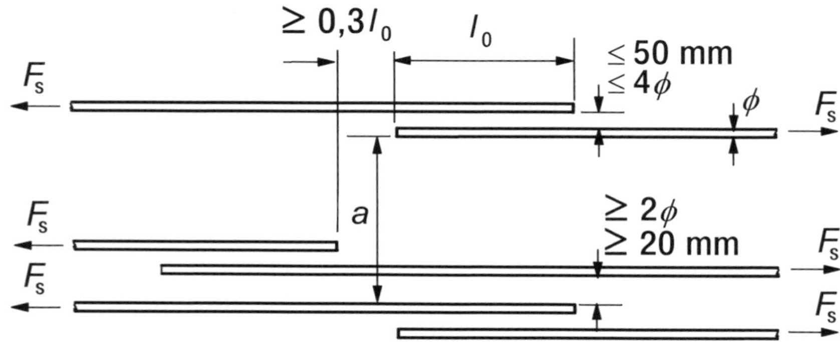

Figure 8.7 — Adjacent laps

8.7.3 Lap length

(1) The design lap length is:

$$l_0 = \alpha_1 \alpha_2 \alpha_3 \alpha_5 \alpha_6 \, l_{b,rqd} \geq l_{0,min} \tag{8.10}$$

where:

$l_{b,rqd}$ is calculated from expression (8.3)

AC1 $l_{0,min} \geq \max\{0,3\,\alpha_6\, l_{b,rqd}\,;15\phi\,;200\text{ mm}\}$ AC1 (8.11)

Values of α_1, α_2, α_3 and α_5 may be taken from Table 8.2; but, for the calculation of α_3, $\Sigma A_{st,min}$ should be taken as $1{,}0 A_s(\sigma_{sd}/f_{yd})$, with A_s = area of one lapped bar.

$\alpha_6 = (\rho_1/25)^{0,5}$ but not exceeding 1,5 nor less than 1,0, where ρ_1 is the percentage of reinforcement lapped within $0{,}65 l_0$ from the centre of the lap length considered (see Figure 8.8). Values of α_6 are given in Table 8.3.

Table 8.3 — Values of the coefficient α_6

Percentage of lapped bars relative to the total cross-section area	< 25 %	33 %	50 %	> 50 %
α_6	1	1,15	1,4	1,5
NOTE Intermediate values may be determined by interpolation.				

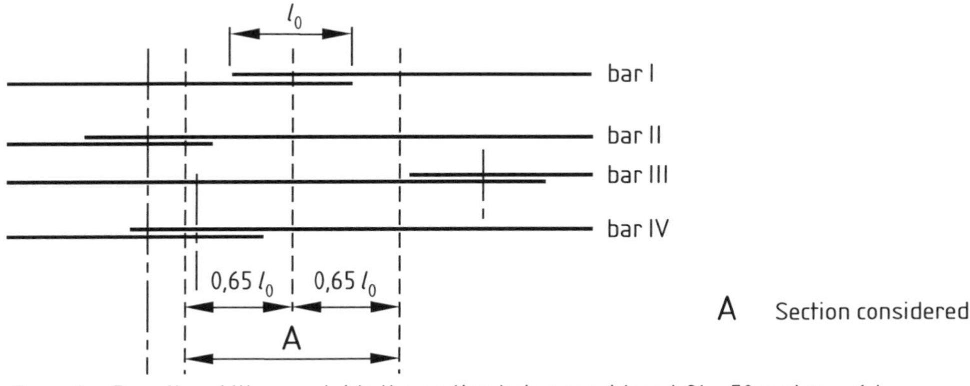

Figure 8.8 — Percentage of lapped bars in one lapped section

8.7.4 Transverse reinforcement in the lap zone

8.7.4.1 Transverse reinforcement for bars in tension

(1) Transverse reinforcement is required in the lap zone to resist transverse tension forces.

(2) Where the diameter, ϕ, of the lapped bars is less than 20 mm, or the percentage of lapped bars in any section is less than 25 %, then any transverse reinforcement or links necessary for other reasons may be assumed sufficient for the transverse tensile forces without further justification.

(3) Where the diameter, ϕ, of the lapped bars is greater than or equal to 20 mm, the transverse AC1 reinforcement should have a total area, ΣA_{st} (sum of all legs parallel to the layer of the spliced AC1 reinforcement) of not less than the area A_s of one lapped bar ($\Sigma A_{st} \geq A_s$). The transverse bar should be placed perpendicular to the direction of the lapped reinforcement and between that and the surface of the concrete.

If more than 50 % of the reinforcement is lapped at one point and the distance, a, between adjacent laps at a section is $\leq 10\phi$ (see Figure 8.7), transverse reinforcement should be formed by links or U bars anchored into the body of the section.

(4) The transverse reinforcement provided for (3) above should be positioned at the outer sections of the lap as shown in Figure 8.9(a).

8.7.4.2 Transverse reinforcement for bars permanently in compression

(1) In addition to the rules for bars in tension, one bar of the transverse reinforcement should be placed outside each end of the lap length and within 4ϕ of the ends of the lap length (Figure 8.9b).

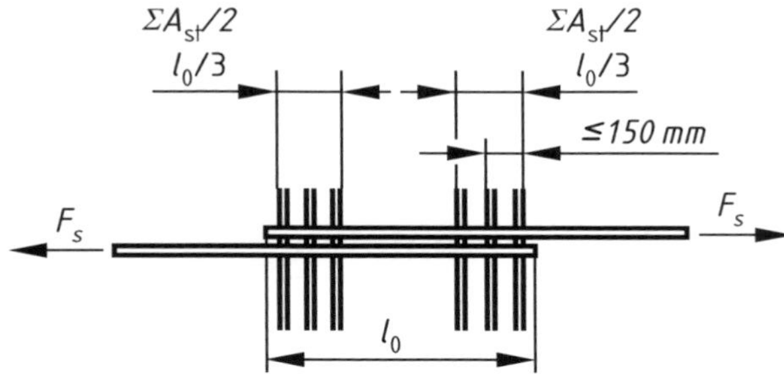

a) Bars in tension

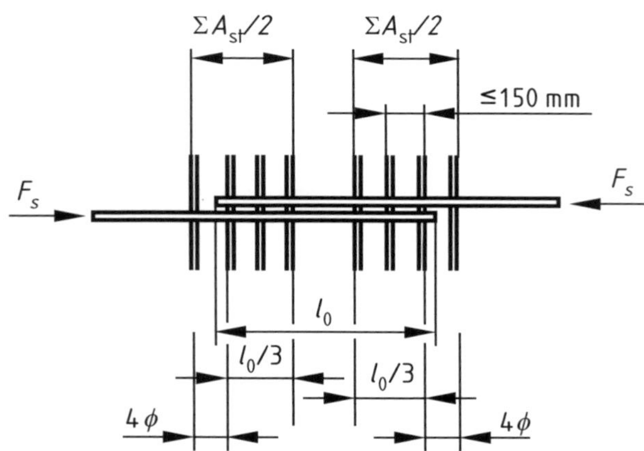

b) Bars in compression

Figure 8.9 — Transverse reinforcement for lapped splices

NA.4 References to non-contradictory complementary information

NA.4.1 General references

The following is a list of references that contain non-contradictory complementary information for use with BS EN 1992-1-1.

- PD 6687:2005, *Background paper to the UK National Annexes to BS EN 1992-1-1 and BS EN 1992-1-2*.
- *Guidance on the use of stainless steel reinforcement*, Technical Report 51, Concrete Society, 1998 [1].
- *Post-tensioned concrete floors — Design handbook*, Technical Report 43, The Concrete Society, 2005 [2].
- *Deflections in concrete slabs and beams*, Technical Report No. 58, Concrete Society, 2005 [3].
- VOLLUM, R.L. and T.R. HOSSAIN, *Are existing span to depth rules conservative for flat slabs?*, Magazine of Concrete Research, vol. 54, issue 6, 2002 [4].
- *Standard method of detailing structural concrete — A manual for best practice*, The Institution of Structural Engineers/Concrete Society, [5].

Bibliography

Standards publications

BS 8110 (all parts), *Structural use of concrete.*

BS 8500-1:2002, *Concrete — Complementary British Standard to BS EN 206-1 — Part 1: Method of specifying and guidance for the specifier.*

BS 8500-2:2002, *Concrete — Complementary British Standard to BS EN 206-1 — Part 2: Specification for constituent materials and concrete.*

BS 8666, *Scheduling, dimensioning, bending and cutting of steel reinforcement for concrete — Specification.*

BS EN 1990:2002, *Eurocode — Basis of structural design.*

BS EN 206-1:2000, *Concrete — Part 1: Specification, performance production and conformity.*

PD 6687:2006, *Background paper to the UK National Annexes to BS EN 1992-1-1 and BS EN 1992-1-2.*

[A1) PD 6687-2:2008, *Recommendations for the design of structures to BS EN 1992-2:2005.* (A1]

Other publications

[A1) [1] GREAT BRITAIN. The Building Regulations 2000. London: The Stationery Office.

[2] GREAT BRITAIN. The Building Regulations 2000 Approved Document A: Structure. London: The Stationery Office, 2004.

[3] GREAT BRITAIN. Building (Scotland) Regulations 2004, as amended: The Stationery Office.

[4] GREAT BRITAIN. The Scottish Building Standards Technical Handbook Domestic: The Stationery Office.

[5] GREAT BRITAIN. The Scottish Building Standards Technical Handbook Non-Domestic: The Stationery Office.

[6] GREAT BRITAIN. Building Regulations (Northern Ireland) 2000. Belfast: The Stationery Office. (A1]

Useful references

BS 4449:2005+A2:2009, *Steel for the reinforcement of concrete — Weldable reinforcing steel — Bar, coil and decoiled product — Specification*

BS 5896:1980 (Incorporating amendment no. 1), *Specification for high tensile steel wire and strand for the prestressing of concrete*

BS 8500-1:2006, *Concrete — Complementary British Standard to BS EN 206-1 — Method of specifying and guidance for the specifier*

PD 6687:2006, *Background paper to the UK National Annexes to BS EN 1992-1*

Chapter 3 — Extracts from Eurocode 3: Design of steel structures

The Eurocode extracts in this chapter are taken from EN 1993-1-1:2005 (incorporating corrigendum No 1, June 2006 and corrigendum No 2, April 2009), *Eurocode 3: Design of steel structures Part 1-1: General rules and rules for buildings* and EN 1993-1-8:2005 (incorporating corrigenda Nos 1 and 2), *Eurocode 3: Design of steel structures Part 1-8: Design of joints.*

Text in EN 1993-1-1 altered by June 2006 corrigendum is indicated by [AC1) (AC1]. Text altered by April 2009 corrigendum is indicated by [AC2) (AC2].

Text in EN 1993-1-8 altered by corrigenda 1 and 2 has not been tagged in this reproduction of the content.

The National Annex extracts are taken from NA to BS EN 1993-1-1:2005, *UK National Annex to Eurocode 3: Design of steel structures Part 1-1: General rules and rules for buildings* and NA to BS EN 1993-1-8:2005, *UK National Annex to Eurocode 3: Design of steel structures Part 1-8: Design of joints.*

The extracts included in this guide, and the accompanying commentary, have been selected to act as an introduction for students of steel design approaching the subject, and codification of design, for the first time. It is assumed that they will have a grounding in basic statics, strength of materials and structural analysis methods. They will be familiar with the concepts of limit state design and have an understanding of the material properties of structural steel.

Due to constraints of space, it has been assumed that a suitable 'lead-in' to steel design will be the design of individual members of basic rectangular frameworks of maximum three to four storeys. The resulting design forces within these members will have been obtained from statics, or as a result of more complex analysis, by hand or computer. The members will be composed of open cross-sections (universal beams (UB) or universal columns (UC)) or hollow sections with the beam/column connections being of traditional cleated or end-plated form using bolts and/or fillet welds. The extracts presented, and the corresponding commentary, are aimed at these areas within the document. The commentary also gives underlying reasons for some of the design rules where this is thought necessary or where the reasons are not immediately obvious. Although covered in EN 1993-1-1, bracing systems for such structures are not considered here. The overall stability of frameworks is a vital consideration, but is often provided for in these types of structures by the use of 'shear wall' infill panels and/or by stiff cores such as concrete lift shafts or stairwells. EN 1993-1-1 covers a wider range of issues than have been included in this guide. These include bracing systems, imperfections, a wide range of differing analysis methods, built-up members, the treatment of torsion and several other important design issues. As stated above, overall structural stability is an essential consideration in the design process for building frames and is not covered in this guide purely because the emphasis is on element design rather than the design of complete structures.

This chapter covers the use of EN 1993-1-1:2005 and EN 1993-1-8:2005, the full contents of which are shown below. (Bold items are included in this chapter.)

EN 1993-1-1:2005

2 Basis of design
2.1 Requirements
2.1.1 Basic requirements
2.1.2 Reliability management
2.1.3 Design working life, durability and robustness
2.2 Principles of limit state design
2.3 Basic variables
2.3.1 Actions and environmental influences
2.3.2 Material and product properties
2.4 Verification by the partial factor method
2.4.1 Design values of material properties
2.4.2 Design values of geometrical data
2.4.3 Design resistances
2.4.4 Verification of static equilibrium (EQU)
2.5 Design assisted by testing
3 Materials
3.1 General
3.2 Structural steel
3.2.1 Material properties
3.2.2 Ductility requirements
3.2.3 Fracture toughness
3.2.4 Through-thickness properties
3.2.5 Tolerances
3.2.6 Design values of material coefficients
3.3 Connecting devices
3.3.1 Fasteners
3.3.2 Welding consumables
3.4 Other prefabricated products in buildings
4 Durability
5 Structural analysis
5.1 Structural modelling for analysis
5.1.1 Structural modelling and basic assumptions
5.1.2 Joint modelling
5.1.3 Ground-structure interaction
5.2 Global analysis
5.2.1 Effects of deformed geometry of the structure
5.2.2 Structural stability of frames
5.3 Imperfections
5.3.1 Basis
5.3.2 Imperfections for global analysis of frames
5.3.3 Imperfection for analysis of bracing systems
5.3.4 Member imperfections
5.4 Methods of analysis considering material non-linearities
5.4.1 General
5.4.2 Elastic global analysis
5.4.3 Plastic global analysis
5.5 Classification of cross-sections
5.5.1 Basis
5.5.2 Classification
5.6 Cross-section requirements for plastic global analysis
6 Ultimate limit states
6.1 General
6.2 Resistance of cross-sections
6.2.1 General
6.2.2 Section properties
6.2.3 Tension
6.2.4 Compression
6.2.5 Bending moment
6.2.6 Shear
6.2.7 Torsion
6.2.8 Bending and shear

EN 1993-1-8:2005

1 Introduction
1.1 Scope
1.2 Normative references
1.3 Distinction between Principles and Application Rules
1.4 Terms and definitions
1.5 Symbols
2 Basis of design
2.1 Assumptions
2.2 General requirements
2.3 Applied forces and moments
2.4 Resistance of joints
2.5 Design assumptions
2.6 Joints loaded in shear subject to impact, vibration and/or load reversal
2.7 Eccentricity at intersections
3 Connections made with bolts, rivets or pins
3.1 Bolts, nuts and washers
3.1.1 General
3.1.2 Preloaded bolts
3.2 Rivets
3.3 Anchor bolts
3.4 Categories of bolted connections
3.4.1 Shear connections
3.4.2 Tension connections
3.5 Positioning of holes for bolts and rivets
3.6 Design resistance of individual fasteners
3.6.1 Bolts and rivets
3.6.2 Injection bolts
3.7 Group of fasteners
3.8 Long joints
3.9 Slip-resistant connections using 8.8 or 10.9 bolts
3.9.1 Design slip resistance
3.9.2 Combined tension and shear
3.9.3 Hybrid connections
3.10 Deductions for fastener holes
3.10.1 General
3.10.2 Design for block tearing
3.10.3 Angles connected by one leg and other unsymmetrically connected members in tension
3.10.4 Lug angles
3.11 Prying forces
3.12 Distribution of forces between fasteners at the ultimate limit state
3.13 Connections made with pins
3.13.1 General
3.13.2 Design of pins
4 Welded connections
4.1 General
4.2 Welding consumables
4.3 Geometry and dimensions
4.3.1 Type of weld
4.3.2 Fillet welds
4.3.3 Fillet welds all round
4.3.4 Butt welds
4.3.5 Plug welds
4.3.6 Flare groove welds
4.4 Welds with packings

7.3 Welds
- 7.3.1 Design resistance

7.4 Welded joints between CHS members
- 7.4.1 General
- 7.4.2 Uniplanar joints
- 7.4.3 Multiplanar joints

7.5 Welded joints between CHS or RHS brace members and RHS chord members
- 7.5.1 General
- 7.5.2 Uniplanar joints
- 7.5.3 Multiplanar joints

7.6 Welded joints between CHS or RHS brace members and I or H section chords

7.7 Welded joints between CHS or RHS brace members and channel section chord members

EN 1993-1-1:2005

Eurocode 3 Part 1-1 is a detailed document covering many design problems in depth, giving designers precise steps for checking certain design criteria, often giving a choice of methods – some are quicker and, by inference, conservative, whilst others are more precise, requiring more design input time. In other areas EN 1993-1-1 is lacking in precise detailed advice to designers (for example the treatment of effective lengths and particularly lateral torsional buckling), falling back on basic statements of principle. In these areas (noted in the commentary at appropriate points) designers will be obliged to look elsewhere to obtain guidance as to the rules to be applied in order to satisfy these principles. This is unlikely to be found in the National Annex as this is not the purpose of the document. At the time of writing there is no indication as to where this guidance will be obtained. The Steel Construction Institute (SCI), whose aim is to 'promote and develop the proper and effective use of steel in construction' is well aware of this shortage of detail in certain key areas. It is terming this information 'complementary information', and has started its own work on publications in this area. Already specific guidance for calculating elastic critical moment (M_{cr}) is available from http://www.steelbiz.org, where design charts and software are available to download.

The annexes include very useful guidance for the design of haunching systems in the plastic design of pitched-roof portal frames, a common form of construction in the UK.

EN 1993-1-8:2005

Eurocode 3 Part 1-8 gives UK designers, for effectively the first time, complete and comprehensive rules and guidance for the design of steel joints of all forms commonly used in building structures. Previous UK codes have given basic rules for fasteners and welding but not a great deal of advice concerning overall joint behaviour. This anomaly in UK joint design practice (partly due to a historic tradition of leaving the responsibility for joint design to the specialist fabricator) has been recognized over the last 10 years or so and has resulted in several notable design guides and textbooks aimed at increasing the database of knowledge of joint behaviour (see NA 2.7 in 5.2.1(2)).

Eurocode 3 Part 1-8 represents a 'quantum leap' in information and guidance for designers in the UK. This is particularly true for the design of joints between hollow section members (Section 7, but not dealt with in this guide) which has been codified for the first time, although there have been excellent design guides published by British Steel Tubes Division (now Corus) and by C.I.D.E.C.T. (Comité International pour le Developpement et l'Etude de la Construction Tubulaire).

Central to this new approach to the design of steelwork joints is the concept of classification of joints (either by stiffness or strength, see 5.2). In the past this classification in the UK has been qualitative, but now becomes numerically derived (see extracts from NA 2.7 contained in 5.2.1(2)).

The extracts and commentary presented in this book are brief, and of an introductory nature, in keeping with the aims of this guide and due to space restrictions. Eurocode 3 Part 1-8 justifies a far more in-depth study at a later stage. Attention is restricted to normal bolts (not pre-loaded) and fillet welding (not butt or plug welding) connecting open UB and UC sections, in keeping with the general scope adopted in this guide to Eurocode 3 Part 1-1.

Subclause 5.2 (dealing with the classification of joints) is included for reference and general interest, but will not be commented on at this stage. Similarly Section 6 and Table 6.1 are included as a valuable starting point for further study in the future.

Extracts from EN 1993-1-1

1. General

1.1 Scope

1.1.1 Scope of Eurocode 3

(1) Eurocode 3 applies to the design of buildings and civil engineering works in steel. It complies with the principles and requirements for the safety and serviceability of structures, the basis of their design and verification that are given in EN 1990 – Basis of structural design.

(2) Eurocode 3 is concerned only with requirements for resistance, serviceability, durability and fire resistance of steel structures. Other requirements, e.g. concerning thermal or sound insulation, are not covered.

(3) Eurocode 3 is intended to be used in conjunction with:

- EN 1990 "Basis of structural design"
- EN 1991 "Actions on structures"
- ENs, ETAGs and ETAs for construction products relevant for steel structures
- EN 1090 "Execution of steel structures – Technical requirements"
- EN 1992 to EN 1999 when steel structures or steel components are referred to.

(4) Eurocode 3 is subdivided in various parts:

EN 1993-1 Design of Steel Structures: General rules and rules for buildings
EN 1993-2 Design of Steel Structures: Steel bridges
EN 1993-3 Design of Steel Structures: Towers, masts and chimneys
EN 1993-4 Design of Steel Structures: Silos, tanks and pipelines
EN 1993-5 Design of Steel Structures: Piling
EN 1993-6 Design of Steel Structures: Crane supporting structures.

(5) EN 1993-2 to EN 1993-6 refer to the generic rules in EN 1993-1. The rules in parts EN 1993-2 to EN 1993-6 supplement the generic rules in EN 1993-1.

(6) EN 1993-1 "General rules and rules for buildings" comprises:

EN 1993-1-1	**Design of Steel Structures: General rules and rules for buildings**
EN 1993-1-2	Design of Steel Structures: Structural fire design
AC2 EN 1993-1-3	Design of Steel Structures: Cold-formed members and sheeting AC2
EN 1993-1-4	Design of Steel Structures: Stainless steels
EN 1993-1-5	Design of Steel Structures: Plated structural elements
EN 1993-1-6	Design of Steel Structures: Strength and stability of shell structures
EN 1993-1-7	Design of Steel Structures: Strength and stability of planar plated structures transversely loaded
EN 1993-1-8	**Design of Steel Structures: Design of joints**
EN 1993-1-9	Design of Steel Structures: Fatigue strength of steel structures
EN 1993-1-10	Design of Steel Structures: Selection of steel for fracture toughness and through-thickness properties
EN 1993-1-11	Design of Steel Structures: Design of structures with tension components made of steel.
EN 1993-1-12	Design of Steel Structures: Supplementary rules for high strength steel.

The parts of Eurocode 3 that are highlighted bold in 1.1.1(6) are covered in this chapter.

1.1.2 Scope of Part 1.1 of Eurocode 3

(1) EN 1993-1-1 gives basic design rules for steel structures with material thicknesses $t \geq 3$ mm. It also gives supplementary provisions for the structural design of steel buildings. These supplementary provisions are indicated by the letter "B" after the paragraph number, thus ( )B.

NOTE For cold formed [AC2) members and sheeting (AC2] see EN 1993-1-3.

(2) The following subjects are dealt with in EN 1993-1-1:

Section 1: General
Section 2: Basis of design
Section 3: Materials
Section 4: Durability
Section 5: Structural analysis
Section 6: Ultimate limit states
Section 7: Serviceability limit states.

(3) Sections 1 to 2 provide additional clauses to those given in EN 1990 "Basis of structural design".

(4) Section 3 deals with material properties of products made of low alloy structural steels.

(5) Section 4 gives general rules for durability.

(6) Section 5 refers to the structural analysis of structures, in which the members can be modelled with sufficient accuracy as line elements for global analysis.

(7) Section 6 gives detailed rules for the design of cross-sections and members.

(8) Section 7 gives rules for serviceability.

1.3 Assumptions

(1) In addition to the general assumptions of EN 1990 the following assumptions apply:

- fabrication and erection complies with EN 1090.

1.4 Distinction between principles and application rules

(1) The rules in EN 1990 clause 1.4 apply.

1.5 Terms and definitions

(1) The rules in EN 1990 clause 1.5 apply.

(2) The following terms and definitions are used in EN 1993-1-1 with the following meanings.

1.5.1
frame
the whole or a portion of a structure, comprising an assembly of directly connected structural elements, designed to act together to resist load; this term refers to both moment-resisting frames and triangulated frames; it covers both plane frames and three-dimensional frames

1.5.2
sub-frame
a frame that forms part of a larger frame, but is to be treated as an isolated frame in a structural analysis

1.5.3
type of framing
terms used to distinguish between frames that are either:

- **semi-continuous**, in which the structural properties of the members and joints need explicit consideration in the global analysis
- **continuous**, in which only the structural properties of the members need be considered in the global analysis
- **simple**, in which the joints are not required to resist moments

1.5.4
global analysis
the determination of a consistent set of internal forces and moments in a structure, which are in equilibrium with a particular set of actions on the structure

1.5.5
system length
distance in a given plane between two adjacent points at which a member is braced against lateral displacement in this plane, or between one such point and the end of the member

1.5.6
buckling length
system length of an otherwise similar member with pinned ends, which has the same [AC2⟩ critical buckling load ⟨AC2] as a given member or segment of member

1.5.7
shear lag effect
non-uniform stress distribution in wide flanges due to shear deformation; it is taken into account by using a reduced "effective" flange width in safety assessments

1.5.8
capacity design
design method for achieving the plastic deformation capacity of a member by providing additional strength in its connections and in other parts connected to it

1.5.9
uniform member
member with a constant cross-section along its whole length

1.6 Symbols

(1) For the purpose of this standard the following symbols apply.

(2) Additional symbols are defined where they first occur.

NOTE Symbols are ordered by appearance in EN 1993-1-1. Symbols may have various meanings.

Section 1

x-x	Axis along a member
y-y	Axis of a cross-section
z-z	Axis of a cross-section
u-u	Major principal axis (where this does not coincide with the y-y axis)
v-v	Minor principal axis (where this does not coincide with the z-z axis)
b	Width of a cross section
h	Depth of a cross section
d	Depth of straight portion of a web
t_w	Web thickness
t_f	Flange thickness
r	Radius of root fillet
r_1	Radius of root fillet
r_2	Toe radius
t	Thickness

Section 2

P_k	Nominal value of the effect of prestressing imposed during erection
G_k	Nominal value of the effect of permanent actions
[AC2⟩ X_k ⟨AC2]	Characteristic values of material property
X_n	Nominal values of material property
R_d	Design value of resistance
R_k	Characteristic value of resistance

γ_M General partial factor
γ_{Mi} Particular partial factor
γ_{Mf} Partial factor for fatigue
η Conversion factor
a_d Design value of geometrical data

Section 3

f_y Yield strength
f_u Ultimate strength
AC2) R_{eH} (AC2 Yield strength to product standards
R_m Ultimate strength to product standards
A_0 Original cross-section area
ε_y Yield strain
ε_u Ultimate strain
Z_{Ed} Required design Z-value resulting from the magnitude of strains from restrained metal shrinkage under the weld beads.
Z_{Rd} Available design Z-value
E Modulus of elasticity
G Shear modulus
ν Poisson's ratio in elastic stage
α Coefficient of linear thermal expansion

Section 5

α_{cr} Factor by which the design loads would have to be increased to cause elastic instability in a global mode
F_{Ed} Design loading on the structure
F_{cr} Elastic critical buckling load for global instability mode based on initial elastic stiffnesses
AC2) H_{Ed} Total design horizontal load, including equivalent forces transferred by the storey (storey shear) (AC2
AC2) V_{Ed} Total design vertical load on the frame transferred by the storey (storey thrust) (AC2
$\delta_{H,Ed}$ Horizontal displacement at the top of the storey, relative to the bottom of the storey
h Storey height
$\bar{\lambda}$ Non dimensional slenderness
N_{Ed} Design value of the axial force
ϕ Global initial sway imperfection
ϕ_0 Basic value for global initial sway imperfection
α_h Reduction factor for height h applicable to columns
h Height of the structure
α_m Reduction factor for the number of columns in a row
m Number of columns in a row
e_0 Maximum amplitude of a member imperfection
L Member length
η_{init} Amplitude of elastic critical buckling mode
η_{cr} Shape of elastic critical buckling mode
$e_{0,d}$ Design value of maximum amplitude of an imperfection
M_{Rk} Characteristic moment resistance of the critical cross section
N_{Rk} Characteristic resistance to normal force of the critical cross section
α Imperfection factor
$EI\,\eta_{cr}$ Bending moment due to η_{cr} at the critical cross section
χ Reduction factor for the relevant buckling curve
AC2) $\alpha_{ult,k}$ Minimum load amplifier of the design loads to reach the characteristic resistance of the most critical cross section of the structural component considering its in plane behaviour without taking lateral or lateral torsional buckling into account however accounting for all effects due to in plane geometrical deformation and imperfections, global and local, where relevant (AC2
α_{cr} Minimum force amplifier to reach the AC2) elastic critical buckling load (AC2
q Equivalent force per unit length
δ_q In-plane deflection of a bracing system
q_d Equivalent design force per unit length
M_{Ed} Design bending moment

k Factor for $e_{0,d}$

ε Strain

σ Stress

$\sigma_{com,Ed}$ Maximum design compressive stress in an element

ℓ Length

AC2⟩ ε Factor depending on f_y ⟨AC2

c Width or depth of a part of a cross section

α Portion of a part of a cross section in compression

ψ Stress or strain ratio

AC2⟩ k_σ Plate buckling factor ⟨AC2

d Outer diameter of circular tubular sections

Section 6

γ_{M0} Partial factor for resistance of cross-sections whatever the class is

γ_{M1} Partial factor for resistance of members to instability assessed by member checks

γ_{M2} Partial factor for resistance of cross-sections in tension to fracture

$\sigma_{x,Ed}$ Design value of the local longitudinal stress

$\sigma_{z,Ed}$ Design value of the local transverse stress

τ_{Ed} Design value of the local shear stress

N_{Ed} Design normal force

$M_{y,Ed}$ Design bending moment, y-y axis

$M_{z,Ed}$ Design bending moment, z-z axis

N_{Rd} Design values of the resistance to normal forces

$M_{y,Rd}$ Design values of the resistance to bending moments, y-y axis

$M_{z,Rd}$ Design values of the resistance to bending moments, z-z axis

s Staggered pitch, the spacing of the centres of two consecutive holes in the chain measured parallel to the member axis

p Spacing of the centres of the same two holes measured perpendicular to the member axis

n Number of holes extending in any diagonal or zig-zag line progressively across the member or part of the member

d_0 Diameter of hole

e_N Shift of the centroid of the effective area A_{eff} relative to the centre of gravity of the gross cross section

ΔM_{Ed} Additional moment from shift of the centroid of the effective area A_{eff} relative to the centre of gravity of the gross cross section

A_{eff} Effective area of a cross section

$N_{t,Rd}$ Design values of the resistance to tension forces

$N_{pl,Rd}$ Design plastic resistance to normal forces of the gross cross-section

$N_{u,Rd}$ Design ultimate resistance to normal forces of the net cross-section at holes for fasteners

A_{net} Net area of a cross section

$N_{net,Rd}$ Design plastic resistance to normal forces of the net cross-section

$N_{c,Rd}$ Design resistance to normal forces of the cross-section for uniform compression

$M_{c,Rd}$ Design resistance for bending about one principal axis of a cross-section

W_{pl} Plastic section modulus

$W_{el,min}$ Minimum elastic section modulus

$W_{eff,min}$ Minimum effective section modulus

A_f Area of the tension flange

$A_{f,net}$ Net area of the tension flange

V_{Ed} Design shear force

$V_{c,Rd}$ Design shear resistance

AC2⟩ $V_{pl,Rd}$ Design plastic shear resistance ⟨AC2

A_v Shear area

η Factor for shear area

S First moment of area

I Second moment of area

AC2⟩ A Cross-sectional area ⟨AC2

A_w Area of a web

A_f Area of one flange

T_{Ed} Design value of total torsional moments

T_{Rd} Design resistance to torsional moments

AC2⟩ $T_{t,Ed}$ Design value of internal St. Venant torsional moment ⟨AC2

AC2⟩ $T_{w,Ed}$ Design value of internal warping torsional moment ⟨AC2

$\tau_{t,Ed}$ Design shear stresses due to St. Venant torsion

$\tau_{w,Ed}$ Design shear stresses due to warping torsion

$\sigma_{w,Ed}$ Design direct stresses due to the bimoment B_{Ed}

AC2⟩ B_{Ed} Design value of the bimoment ⟨AC2

$V_{pl,T,Rd}$ Reduced design plastic shear resistance making allowance for the presence of a torsional moment

ρ Reduction factor to determine reduced design values of the resistance to bending moments making allowance for the presence of shear forces

$M_{V,,Rd}$ Reduced design values of the resistance to bending moments making allowance for the presence of shear forces

$M_{N,,Rd}$ Reduced design values of the resistance to bending moments making allowance for the presence of normal forces

n Ratio of design normal force to design plastic resistance to normal forces of the gross cross-section

a Ratio of web area to gross area

α Parameter introducing the effect of biaxial bending

β Parameter introducing the effect of biaxial bending

$e_{N,y}$ Shift of the centroid of the effective area A_{eff} relative to the centre of gravity of the gross cross section (y-y axis)

$e_{N,z}$ Shift of the centroid of the effective area A_{eff} relative to the centre of gravity of the gross cross section (z-z axis)

$W_{eff,min}$ Minimum effective section modulus

$N_{b,Rd}$ Design buckling resistance of a compression member

χ Reduction factor for relevant buckling mode

Φ Value to determine the reduction factor χ

a_0, a, b, c, d class indexes for buckling curves

N_{cr} Elastic critical force for the relevant buckling mode based on the gross cross sectional properties

i Radius of gyration about the relevant axis, determined using the properties of the gross cross-section

λ_1 Slenderness value to determine the relative slenderness

$\bar{\lambda}_T$ Relative slenderness for torsional or torsional-flexural buckling

$N_{cr,TF}$ Elastic torsional-flexural buckling force

$N_{cr,T}$ Elastic torsional buckling force

$M_{b,Rd}$ Design buckling resistance moment

χ_{LT} Reduction factor for lateral-torsional buckling

Φ_{LT} Value to determine the reduction factor χ_{LT}

α_{LT} Imperfection factor

$\bar{\lambda}_{LT}$ Non dimensional slenderness for lateral torsional buckling

M_{cr} Elastic critical moment for lateral-torsional buckling

AC2⟩ $\bar{\lambda}_{LT,0}$ Plateau length of the lateral torsional buckling curves for rolled and welded sections ⟨AC2

AC2⟩ β Correction factor for the lateral torsional buckling curves for rolled and welded sections ⟨AC2

$\chi_{LT,mod}$ Modified reduction factor for lateral-torsional buckling

f Modification factor for χ_{LT}

kc Correction factor for moment distribution

ψ Ratio of moments in segment

L_c Length between lateral restraints

$\bar{\lambda}_f$ Equivalent compression flange slenderness

$i_{f,z}$ Radius of gyration of compression flange about the minor axis of the section

$I_{eff,f}$ Effective second moment of area of compression flange about the minor axis of the section

$A_{eff,f}$ Effective area of compression flange

$A_{eff,w,c}$ Effective area of compressed part of web

$\bar{\lambda}_{c0}$ Slenderness parameter

$K_{f\ell}$ Modification factor

AC2⟩ $\Delta M_{y,Ed}$ Moments due to the shift of the centroidal y-y axis ⟨AC2

AC2⟩ $\Delta M_{z,Ed}$ Moments due to the shift of the centroidal z-z axis ⟨AC2

χ_y Reduction factor due to flexural buckling (y-y axis)

χ_z Reduction factor due to flexural buckling (z-z axis)

k_{yy} Interaction factor

k_{yz} Interaction factor
k_{zy} Interaction factor
k_{zz} Interaction factor
$\bar{\lambda}_{op}$ Global non dimensional slenderness of a structural component for out-of-plane buckling
χ_{op} Reduction factor for the non-dimensional slenderness $\bar{\lambda}_{op}$
$\alpha_{ult,k}$ Minimum load amplifier of the design loads to reach the characteristic resistance of the most critical cross section
AC2⟩ $\alpha_{cr,op}$ Minimum amplifier for the in plane design loads to reach the elastic critical buckling load with regard to lateral or lateral torsional buckling ⟨AC2
N_{Rk} Characteristic value of resistance to compression
$M_{y,Rk}$ Characteristic value of resistance to bending moments about y-y axis
$M_{z,Rk}$ Characteristic value of resistance to bending moments about z-z axis
Q_m Local force applied at each stabilized member at the plastic hinge locations
L_{stable} Stable length of segment
L_{ch} Buckling length of chord
h_0 Distance of centrelines of chords of a built-up column
a Distance between restraints of chords
α Angle between axes of chord and lacings
i_{min} Minimum radius of gyration of single angles
A_{ch} Area of one chord of a built-up column
$N_{ch,Ed}$ Design chord force in the middle of a built-up member
AC2⟩ M^{I}_{Ed} Design value of the maximum first order moment in the middle of the built-up member ⟨AC2
I_{eff} Effective second moment of area of the built-up member
S_v Shear stiffness of built-up member from the lacings or battened panel
AC2⟩ n Number of planes of lacings or battens ⟨AC2
A_d Area of one diagonal of a built-up column
d Length of a diagonal of a built-up column
A_V Area of one post (or transverse element) of a built-up column
I_{ch} In plane second moment of area of a chord
I_b In plane second moment of area of a batten
μ Efficiency factor
i_y Radius of gyration (y-y axis)

Annex A

C_{my} Equivalent uniform moment factor
C_{mz} Equivalent uniform moment factor
C_{mLT} Equivalent uniform moment factor
μ_y Factor
μ_z Factor
$N_{cr,y}$ Elastic flexural buckling force about the y-y axis
$N_{cr,z}$ Elastic flexural buckling force about the z-z axis
C_{yy} Factor
C_{yz} Factor
C_{zy} Factor
C_{zz} Factor
w_y Factor
w_z Factor
n_{pl} Factor
$\bar{\lambda}_{max}$ Maximum of $\bar{\lambda}_y$ and $\bar{\lambda}_z$
b_{LT} Factor
c_{LT} Factor
d_{LT} Factor
e_{LT} Factor
ψ_y Ratio of end moments (y-y axis)
$C_{my,0}$ Factor
$C_{mz,0}$ Factor
a_{LT} Factor
I_T St. Venant torsional constant
I_y Second moment of area about y-y axis
AC2⟩ C1 Ratio between the critical bending moment (largest value along the member) and the critical constant bending moment for a member with hinged supports ⟨AC2

$M_{i,Ed}(x)$ Maximum first order moment
$|\delta_x|$ Maximum member displacement along the member

Annex B

AC2⟩ α_s Factor s = sagging ⟨AC2
AC2⟩ α_h Factor h = hogging ⟨AC2
C_m Equivalent uniform moment factor

Annex AB

γ_G Partial factor for permanent loads
G_k Characteristic value of permanent loads
γ_Q Partial factor for variable loads
Q_k Characteristic value of variable loads

Annex BB

$\bar{\lambda}_{eff,v}$ Effective slenderness ratio for buckling about v-v axis
$\bar{\lambda}_{eff,y}$ Effective slenderness ratio for buckling about y-y axis
$\bar{\lambda}_{eff,z}$ Effective slenderness ratio for buckling about z-z axis
L System length
L_{cr} Buckling length
S Shear stiffness provided by sheeting
I_w Warping constant
$C_{\partial,k}$ Rotational stiffness provided by stabilizing continuum and connections
K_v Factor for considering the type of analysis
K_∂ Factor for considering the moment distribution and the type of restraint
$C_{\partial R,k}$ Rotational stiffness provided by the stabilizing continuum to the beam assuming a stiff connection to the member
$C_{\partial C,k}$ Rotational stiffness of the connection between the beam and the stabilizing continuum
$C_{\partial D,k}$ Rotational stiffness deduced from an analysis of the distorsional deformations of the beam cross sections
L_m Stable length between adjacent lateral restraints
L_k Stable length between adjacent torsional restraints
L_s Stable length between a plastic hinge location and an adjacent torsional restraint
C_1 Modification factor for moment distribution
Cm Modification factor for linear moment gradient
Cn Modification factor for non-linear moment gradient
a Distance between the centroid of the member with the plastic hinge and the centroid of the restraint members
B_0 Factor
B_1 Factor
B_2 Factor
AC2⟩ η Ratio of elastic critical values of axial forces ⟨AC2
i_s Radius of gyration related to centroid of restraining member
β_t Ratio of the algebraically smaller end moment to the larger end moment
R_1 Moment at a specific location of a member
R_2 Moment at a specific location of a member
R_3 Moment at a specific location of a member
R_4 Moment at a specific location of a member
R_5 Moment at a specific location of a member
R_E Maximum of R_1 or R_5
R_s Maximum value of bending moment anywhere in the length L_y
c Taper factor
h_h Additional depth of the haunch or taper
h_{max} Maximum depth of cross-section within the length L_y
h_{min} Minimum depth of cross-section within the length L_y
h_s Vertical depth of the un-haunched section
L_h Length of haunch within the length L_y
L_y Length between restraints

1.7 Conventions for member axes

(1) The convention for member axes is:

x-x – along the member
y-y – axis of the cross-section
z-z – axis of the cross-section.

(2) For steel members, the conventions used for cross-section axes are:

- generally:
  y-y – cross-section axis parallel to the flanges
  z-z – cross-section axis perpendicular to the flanges
- for angle sections:
  y-y – axis parallel to the smaller leg
  z-z – axis perpendicular to the smaller leg
- where necessary:
  u-u – major principal axis (where this does not coincide with the yy axis)
  v-v – minor principal axis (where this does not coincide with the zz axis)

(3) The symbols used for dimensions and axes of rolled steel sections are indicated in Figure 1.1.

(4) The convention used for subscripts that indicate axes for moments is: "Use the axis about which the moment acts."

NOTE All rules in this Eurocode relate to principal axis properties, which are generally defined by the axes y-y and z-z but for sections such as angles are defined by the axes u-u and v-v.

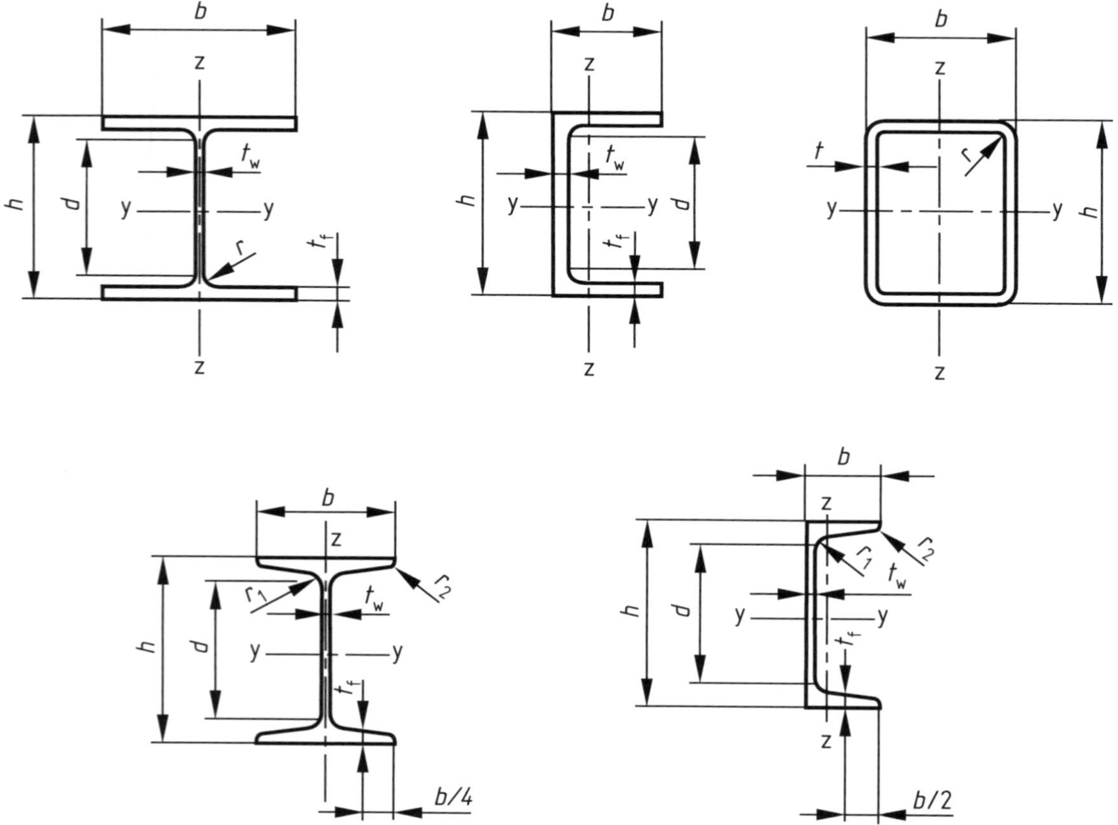

Figure 1.1 — Dimensions and axes of sections

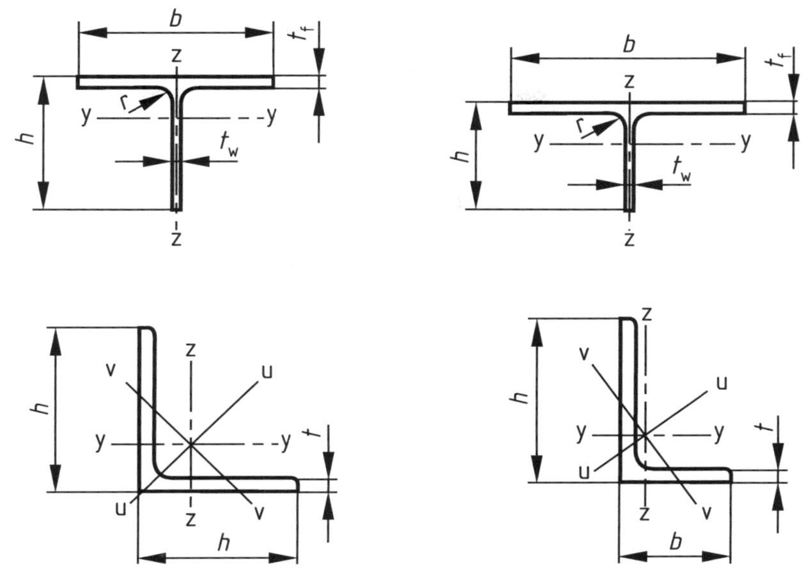

Figure 1.1 — Dimensions and axes of sections (*continued*)

Section 1 deals with the context and setting of the document. Notice should be taken of the definition of terms (1.5) and the conventions for member axes (1.7) (which are different in many cases from previous UK practice).

2 Basis of design

2.1 Requirements

2.1.1 Basic requirements

AC1 (1)P The design of steel structures shall be in accordance with the general rules given in EN 1990. AC1

(2) The supplementary provisions for steel structures given in this section shall also be applied.

(3) The basic requirements of EN 1990 section 2 shall be deemed to be satisfied where limit state design is used in conjunction with the partial factor method and the load combinations given in EN 1990 together with the actions given in EN 1991.

(4) The rules for resistances, serviceability and durability given in the various parts of EN 1993 should be applied.

2.2 Principles of limit state design

(1) The resistances of cross-sections and members specified in this Eurocode 3 for the ultimate limit states as defined in EN 1990, 3.3 are based on tests in which the material exhibited sufficient ductility to apply simplified design models.

(2) The resistances specified in this Eurocode Part may therefore be used where the conditions for materials in section 3 are met.

2.3 Basic variables

2.3.1 Actions and environmental influences

(1) Actions for the design of steel structures should be taken from EN 1991. For the combination of actions and partial factors of actions see Annex A to EN 1990.

NOTE 1 The National Annex may define actions for particular regional or climatic or accidental situations. The National Annex addresses actions for situations in NA.2.2.

NOTE 2B For proportional loading for incremental approach, see Annex AB.1.

NOTE 3B For simplified load arrangement, see Annex AB.2.

NA.2.2 There are no additional particular regional, climatic or accidental situations to consider.

2.4 Verification by the partial factor method

2.4.1 Design values of material properties

AC1 (1)P For the design of steel structures characteristic values X_k or nominal values X_n of material properties shall be used as indicated in this Eurocode. AC1

2.4.2 Design values of geometrical data

(1) Geometrical data for cross-sections and systems may be taken from product standards hEN or drawings for the execution to EN 1090 and treated as nominal values.

(2) Design values of geometrical imperfections specified in this standard are equivalent geometric imperfections that take into account the effects of:

- geometrical imperfections of members as governed by geometrical tolerances in product standards or the execution standard,
- structural imperfections due to fabrication and erection,
- residual stresses,
- variation of the yield strength.

2.4.3 Design resistances

(1) For steel structures equation (6.6c) or equation (6.6d) of EN 1990 applies:

$$R_d = \frac{R_k}{\gamma_M} = \frac{1}{\gamma_M} R_k \left(\eta_1 X_{k,1} ; \eta_i X_{k,i} ; a_d\right) \quad (2.1)$$

where

R_k is the characteristic value of the particular resistance determined with characteristic or nominal values for the material properties and dimensions

γ_M is the global partial factor for the particular resistance.

NOTE For the definitions of η_1, η_i, $X_{k,1}$, $X_{k,i}$ and a_d see EN 1990.

3 Materials

3.1 General

(1) The nominal values of material properties given in this section should be adopted as characteristic values in design calculations.

(2) This Part of EN 1993 covers the design of steel structures fabricated from steel material conforming to the steel grades listed in Table 3.1.

NOTE For other steel material and products see National Annex.

Other steel material and products are covered in NA.2.3.

NA 2.3 Clause 3.1(2) Other steel material and products

If other steels are used, due allowance should be made for variations in properties, including ductility and weldability. Further information on the ductility requirements for steel is given in BS EN 1993-1-1:2005, 3.2.2(1).

Steel castings and forgings may be used for components in bearings, junctions and other similar parts. Castings should conform to BS EN 10293 and forgings should conform to BS EN 10250-2.

Further guidance on steel castings is given in reference [1].

For higher strength steels see BS EN 1993-1-12.

3.2 Structural steel

3.2.1 Material properties

(1) The nominal values of the yield strength f_y and the ultimate strength f_u for structural steel should be obtained

a) either by adopting the values $f_y = R_{eH}$ and $f_u = R_m$ direct from the product standard
b) or by using the simplification given in Table 3.1.

NOTE The National Annex may give the choice.

NA 2.4 Clause 3.2.1(1) Material properties

The nominal values of the yield strength f_y and the ultimate strength f_u for structural steel should be those obtained from the product standard. The ultimate strength f_u should be taken as the lowest value of the range given for R_m in the product standard. Further information on the yield and ultimate strength for structural steel is also given in NA.4.

Table 3.1 — Nominal values of yield strength f_y and ultimate tensile strength f_u for hot rolled structural steel

Standard and steel grade	Nominal thickness of the element t [mm]			
	t ≤ 40 mm		40 mm < t ≤ 80 mm	
	f_y [N/mm²]	f_u [N/mm²]	f_y [N/mm²]	f_u [N/mm²]
EN 10025-2				
S 235	235	360	215	360
S 275	275	430	255	410
S 355	355	[AC2⟩ 490 ⟨AC2]	335	470
S 450	440	550	410	550
EN 10025-3				
S 275 N/NL	275	390	255	370
S 355 N/NL	355	490	335	470
S 420 N/NL	420	520	390	520
S 460 N/NL	460	540	430	540
EN 10025-4				
S 275 M/ML	275	370	255	360
S 355 M/ML	355	470	335	450
S 420 M/ML	420	520	390	500
S 460 M/ML	460	540	430	530
EN 10025-5				
S 235 W	235	360	215	340
S 355 W	355	[AC2⟩ 490 ⟨AC2]	335	490
EN 10025-6				
S 460 Q/QL/QL1	460	570	440	550

The grades of steel are those already used in UK. Note that thicker elements (>40 mm) have reduced f_y values. This is due to the manufacturing process where thinner sections have undergone more 'work hardening' by extra rolling. Using 3.2.1(1)a), i.e. taking the values directly from the standard, would also give decreasing design strength with increasing thickness but with more steps. In normal situations the flanges are both the critical and thickest element so it is reasonable that the yield strength is based on them. S235 steel is a basic grade commonly available in Europe, not generally available in UK, but the situation may change in the future.

Table 3.1 (continued) — Nominal values of yield strength f_y and ultimate tensile strength f_u for structural hollow sections

Standard and steel grade	Nominal thickness of the element t [mm]			
	t ≤ 40 mm		40 mm < t ≤ 65 mm	
	f_y [N/mm²]	f_u [N/mm²]	f_y [N/mm²]	f_u [N/mm²]
EN 10210-1				
S 235 H	235	360	215	340
S 275 H	275	430	255	410
S 355 H	355	510	335	490
S 275 NH/NLH	275	390	255	370
S 355 NH/NLH	355	490	335	470
[AC2⟩ S 420 NH/NLH ⟨AC2]	420	540	390	520
S 460 NH/NLH	460	560	430	550
EN 10219-1				
S 235 H	235	360		
S 275 H	275	430		
S 355 H	355	510		
S 275 NH/NLH	275	370		
S 355 NH/NLH	355	470		
S 460 NH/NLH	460	550		
S 275 MH/MLH	275	360		
S 355 MH/MLH	355	470		
S 420 MH/MLH	420	500		
S 460 MH/MLH	460	530		

3.2.6 Design values of material coefficients

(1) The material coefficients to be adopted in calculations for the structural steels covered by this Eurocode Part should be taken as follows:

- modulus of elasticity $E = 210\,000 \text{ N/mm}^2$
- shear modulus $G = \frac{E}{2(1+\nu)} \approx 81\,000 \text{ N/mm}^2$
- Poisson's ratio in elastic stage $\nu = 0,3$
- coefficient of linear thermal expansion $\alpha = 12 \times 10^{-6}$ per K (for $T \leq 100$ K)

NOTE For calculating the structural effects of unequal temperatures in composite concrete-steel structures to EN 1994 the coefficient of linear thermal expansion is taken as $\alpha = 10 \times 10^{-6}$ *per K.*

3.3 Connecting devices

3.3.1 Fasteners

(1) Requirements for fasteners are given in EN 1993-1-8.

3.3.2 Welding consumables

(1) Requirements for welding consumables are given in EN 1993-1-8.

5 Structural analysis

5.1 Structural modelling for analysis

5.1.1 Structural modelling and basic assumptions

AC1 (1)P Analysis shall be based upon calculation models of the structure that are appropriate for the limit state under consideration. AC1

(2) The calculation model and basic assumptions for the calculations shall reflect the structural behaviour at the relevant limit state with appropriate accuracy and reflect the anticipated type of behaviour of the cross-sections, members, joints and bearings.

AC1 (3)P The method used for the analysis shall be consistent with the design assumptions. AC1

(4)B For the structural modelling and basic assumptions for components of buildings see also EN 1993-1-5 and EN 1993-1-11.

Eurocode 3 Part 1-5 includes advice on finite element modelling of steelwork, and Eurocode 3 Part 1-11 includes advice on modelling cables.

5.1.2 Joint modelling

(1) The effects of the behaviour of the joints on the distribution of internal forces and moments within a structure, and on the overall deformations of the structure, may generally be neglected, but where such effects are significant (such as in the case of semi-continuous joints) they should be taken into account, see EN 1993-1-8.

(2) To identify whether the effects of joint behaviour on the analysis need be taken into account, a distinction may be made between three joint models as follows, see EN 1993-1-8, 5.1.1:

- simple, in which the joint may be assumed not to transmit bending moments;
- continuous, in which the behaviour of the joint may be assumed to have no effect on the analysis;
- semi-continuous, in which the behaviour of the joint needs to be taken into account in the analysis.

(3) The requirements of the various types of joints are given in EN 1993-1-8.

The modelling of joint behaviour is a very important initial aspect of the design process as it affects the structural analysis model to be adopted. 'Simple design' has been a widely used tool by UK designers in the past. In this approach all beams are considered simply supported and no moments are assumed to be transmitted directly to the supporting columns (except nominally as eccentrically-applied end reactions). The structure is then usually statically determinate and elements can be sized independently of the whole structure. Bracing of the overall structure then becomes an extremely important consideration, however. This method of simple design is no longer referred to in the UK National Annex.

Continuous behaviour is also a viable structural analysis model. The structure then usually becomes a rigid jointed statically indeterminate model suitable for standard computer analysis. However, the relative geometric properties of the constituent members then have an influence on the force distribution throughout the structure. As these are not known beforehand (at the initial design stage), some form of iteration will inevitably be required in the final design.

The important point to be emphasized is that initial design decisions concerning the member jointing methods need to be made by the designer and that these should be consistently followed and applied throughout the design and detailing process.

5.2 Global analysis

5.2.1 Effects of deformed geometry of the structure

(1) The internal forces and moments may generally be determined using either:

- first-order analysis, using the initial geometry of the structure or
- second-order analysis, taking into account the influence of the deformation of the structure.

(2) The effects of the deformed geometry (second-order effects) shall be considered if they increase the action effects significantly or modify significantly the structural behaviour.

(3) First-order analysis may be used for the structure, if the increase of the relevant internal forces or moments or any other change of structural behaviour caused by deformations can be neglected. This condition may be assumed to be fulfilled, if the following criterion is satisfied:

$$\alpha_{cr} = \frac{F_{cr}}{F_{Ed}} \geq 10 \quad \text{for elastic analysis}$$

$$\alpha_{cr} = \frac{F_{cr}}{F_{Ed}} \geq 15 \quad \text{for plastic analysis} \qquad (5.1)$$

where

α_{cr} is the factor by which the design loading would have to be increased to cause elastic instability in a global mode

F_{Ed} is the design loading on the structure

F_{cr} is the elastic critical buckling load for global instability mode based on initial elastic stiffnesses.

NOTE A greater limit for α_{cr} for plastic analysis is given in equation (5.1) because structural behaviour may be significantly influenced by non linear material properties in the ultimate limit state (e.g. where a frame forms plastic hinges with moment redistributions or where significant non linear deformations from semi-rigid joints occur). Where substantiated by more accurate approaches the National Annex may give a lower limit for α_{cr} for certain types of frames.

NA 2.9 Clause 5.2.1(3) Effects of deformed geometry of the structure

For plastic analysis of clad structures provided that the stiffening effects of masonry infill wall panels or diaphragms of profiled steel sheeting are not taken into account:

$\alpha_{cr} \geq 10$

For plastic analysis of portal frames subject to gravity loads only with frame imperfections:

$\alpha_{cr} \geq 5$

provided the following conditions are satisfied:

a) the span, L, does not exceed 5 times the mean height of the columns;
b) h_r satisfies the criterion:

$(h_r/s_a)^2 + (h_r/s_b)^2 \leq 0.5$

in which s_a and s_b are the horizontal distances from the apex to the columns.

NOTE For a symmetrical frame this expression simplifies to $h_r \leq 0,25L$.

5.4 Methods of analysis considering material non-linearities

5.4.1 General

(1) The internal forces and moments may be determined using either

a) elastic global analysis
b) plastic global analysis.

NOTE For finite element model (FEM) analysis see EN 1993-1-5.

(2) Elastic global analysis may be used in all cases.

(3) Plastic global analysis may be used only where the structure has sufficient rotation capacity at the actual location of the plastic hinge, whether this is in the members or in the joints. Where a plastic hinge occurs in a member, the member cross-sections should be double symmetric or single symmetric with a plane of symmetry in the same plane as the rotation of the plastic hinge and it should satisfy the requirements specified in 5.6. Where a plastic hinge occurs in a joint the joint should either have sufficient strength to ensure the hinge remains in the member or should be able to sustain the plastic resistance for a sufficient rotation, see EN 1993-1-8.

(4)B As a simplified method for a limited plastic redistribution of moments in continuous beams where following an elastic analysis some peak moments exceed the plastic bending resistance of 15 % maximum, the parts in excess of these peak moments may be redistributed in any member, provided that:

a) the internal forces and moments in the frame remain in equilibrium with the applied loads, and
b) all the members in which the moments are reduced have Class 1 or Class 2 cross-sections (see 5.5), and
c) lateral torsional buckling of the members is prevented.

5.4.2 Elastic global analysis

(1) Elastic global analysis shall be based on the assumption that the stress-strain behaviour of the material is linear, whatever the stress level is.

NOTE For the choice of a semi-continuous joint model see [AC2) 5.1.2 (AC2].

(2) Internal forces and moments may be calculated according to elastic global analysis even if the resistance of a cross section is based on its plastic resistance, see 6.2.

(3) Elastic global analysis may also be used for cross sections the resistances of which are limited by local buckling, see 6.2.

5.4.3 Plastic global analysis

(1) Plastic global analysis allows for the effects of material non-linearity in calculating the action effects of a structural system. The behaviour should be modelled by one of the following methods:

- by elastic-plastic analysis with plastified sections and/or joints as plastic hinges,
- by non-linear plastic analysis considering the partial plastification of members in plastic zones,
- by rigid plastic analysis neglecting the elastic behaviour between hinges.

(2) Plastic global analysis may be used where the members are capable of sufficient rotation capacity to enable the required redistributions of bending moments to develop, see 5.5 and 5.6.

(3) Plastic global analysis should only be used where the stability of members at plastic hinges can be assured, see 6.3.5.

(4) The bi-linear stress-strain relationship indicated in Figure 5.8 may be used for the grades of structural steel specified in section 3. Alternatively, a more precise relationship may be adopted, see EN 1993-1-5.

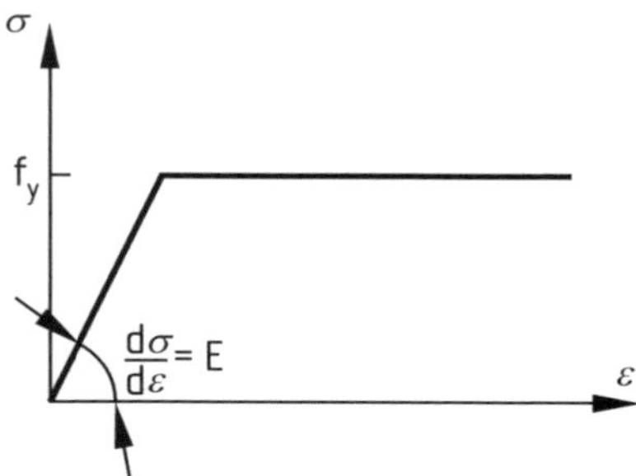

Figure 5.8 — Bi-linear stress-strain relationship

(5) Rigid plastic analysis may be applied if no effects of the deformed geometry (e.g. second-order effects) have to be considered. In this case joints are classified only by strength, see EN 1993-1-8.

(6) The effects of deformed geometry of the structure and the structural stability of the frame should be verified according to the principles in 5.2.

NOTE The maximum resistance of a frame with significantly deformed geometry may occur before all hinges of the first order collapse mechanism have formed.

5.5 Classification of cross sections

5.5.1 Basis

(1) The role of cross section classification is to identify the extent to which the resistance and rotation capacity of cross sections is limited by its local buckling resistance.

5.5.2 Classification

(1) Four classes of cross-sections are defined, as follows:

- Class 1 cross-sections are those which can form a plastic hinge with the rotation capacity required from plastic analysis without reduction of the resistance.
- Class 2 cross-sections are those which can develop their plastic moment resistance, but have limited rotation capacity because of local buckling.
- Class 3 cross-sections are those in which the stress in the extreme compression fibre of the steel member assuming an elastic distribution of stresses can reach the yield strength, but local buckling is liable to prevent development of the plastic moment resistance.
- Class 4 cross-sections are those in which local buckling will occur before the attainment of yield stress in one or more parts of the cross-section.

(2) In Class 4 cross-sections effective widths may be used to make the necessary allowances for reductions in resistance due to the effects of local buckling, see [AC2) EN 1993-1-5, 4.4 (AC2].

(3) The classification of a cross-section depends on the width to thickness ratio of the parts subject to compression.

(4) Compression parts include every part of a cross-section which is either totally or partially in compression under the load combination considered.

(5) The various compression parts in a cross-section (such as a web or flange) can, in general, be in different classes.

(6) A cross-section is classified according to the highest (least favourable) class of its compression parts. Exceptions are specified in 6.2.1(10) and 6.2.2.4(1).

(7) Alternatively the classification of a cross-section may be defined by quoting both the flange classification and the web classification.

(8) The limiting proportions for Class 1, 2, and 3 compression parts should be obtained from Table 5.2. A part which fails to satisfy the limits for Class 3 should be taken as Class 4.

(9) Except as given in (10) Class 4 sections may be treated as Class 3 sections if the width to thickness ratios are less than the limiting proportions for Class 3 obtained from Table 5.2 when ε is increased by

$$\sqrt{\frac{f_y / \gamma_{M0}}{\sigma_{com,Ed}}}$$

where $\sigma_{com,Ed}$ is the maximum design compressive stress in the part taken from first-order or where necessary second-order analysis.

(10) However, when verifying the design buckling resistance of a member using section 6.3, the limiting proportions for Class 3 should always be obtained from Table 5.2.

(11) Cross-sections with a Class 3 web and Class 1 or 2 flanges may be classified as class 2 cross-sections with an effective web in accordance with 6.2.2.4.

(12) Where the web is considered to resist shear forces only and is assumed not to contribute to the bending and normal force resistance of the cross-section, the cross-section may be designed as Class 2, 3 or 4 sections, depending only on the flange class.

NOTE For flange induced web buckling see EN 1993-1-5.

5.6 Cross-section requirements for plastic global analysis

(1) At plastic hinge locations, the cross-section of the member which contains the plastic hinge should have a rotation capacity of not less than the required at the plastic hinge location.

(2) In a uniform member sufficient rotation capacity may be assumed at a plastic hinge if both the following requirements are satisfied:

a) the member has Class 1 cross-sections at the plastic hinge location;
b) where a transverse force that exceeds 10 % of the shear resistance of the cross-section, see 6.2.6, is applied to the web at the plastic hinge location, web stiffeners should be provided within a distance along the member of h/2 from the plastic hinge location, [AC2⟩ where h is the height of the cross section. ⟨AC2]

Table 5.2 (sheet 1 of 3) — Maximum width-to-thickness ratios for compression parts

Internal compression parts

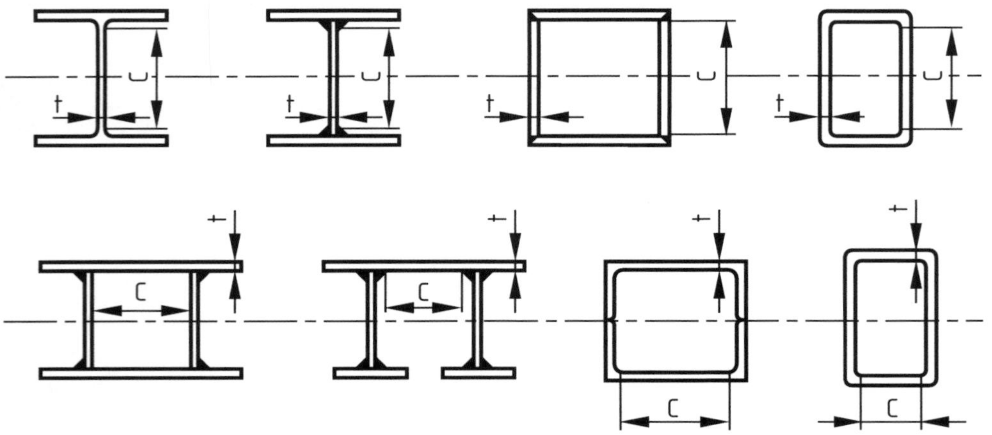

Axis of bending

Axis of bending

Class	Part subject to bending	Part subject to compression	Part subject to bending and compression
Stress distribution in parts (compression positive)	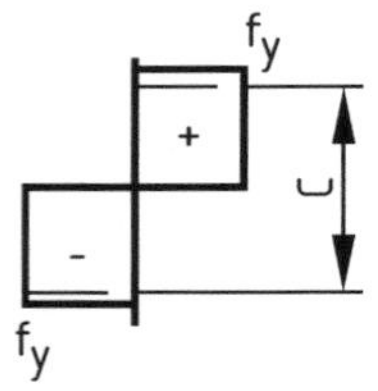	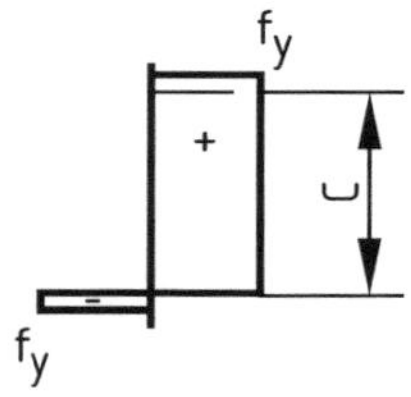	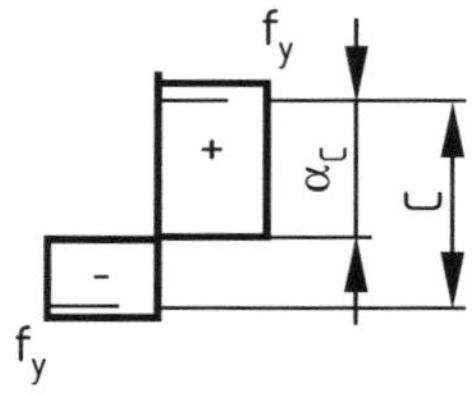
1	$c / t \leq 72\varepsilon$	$c / t \leq 33\varepsilon$	when $\alpha > 0,5: c/t \leq \dfrac{396\varepsilon}{13\alpha - 1}$ when $\alpha \leq 0,5: c/t \leq \dfrac{36\varepsilon}{\alpha}$
2	$c / t \leq 83\varepsilon$	$c / t \leq 38\varepsilon$	when $\alpha > 0,5: c/t \leq \dfrac{456\varepsilon}{13\alpha - 1}$ when $\alpha \leq 0,5: c/t \leq \dfrac{41,5\varepsilon}{\alpha}$
Stress distribution in parts (compression positive)	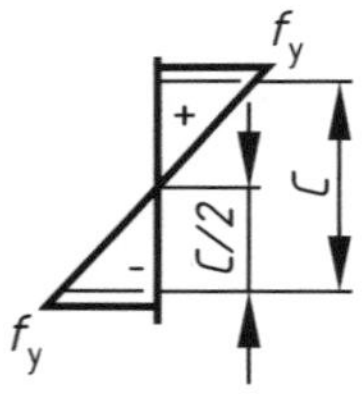	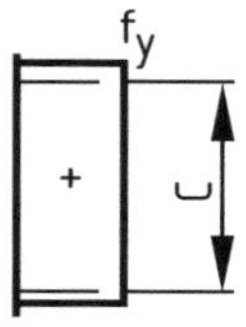	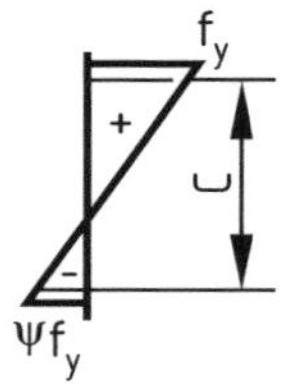
3	$c / t \leq 124\varepsilon$	$c / t \leq 42\varepsilon$	when $\psi > -1: c/t \leq \dfrac{42\varepsilon}{0,67 + 0,33\psi}$ when $\psi \leq -1: c/t \leq 62\varepsilon\,(1-\psi)\sqrt{(-\psi)}$

$\varepsilon = \sqrt{235 / f_y}$	f_y	235	275	355	420	460
	ε	1,00	0,92	0,81	0,75	0,71

*) $\psi \leq -1$ applies where either the compression stress $\sigma < f_y$ or the tensile strain $\varepsilon_y > f_y / E$.

Table 5.2 (sheet 2 of 3) — Maximum width-to-thickness ratios for compression parts

Outstand flanges

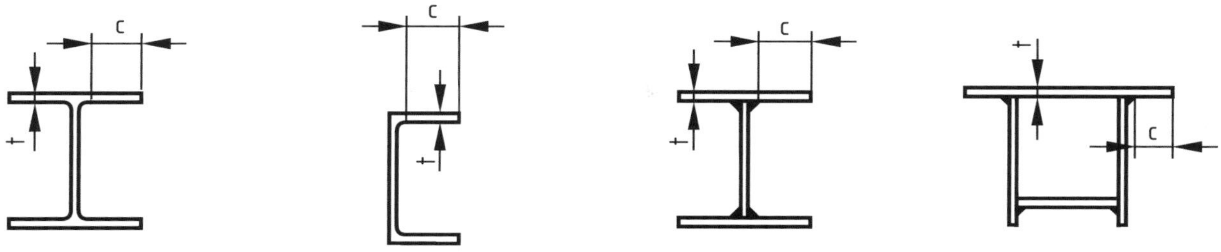

Rolled sections

Welded sections

Class	Part subject to compression	Part subject to bending and compression	
		Tip in compression	Tip in tension
Stress distribution in parts (compression positive)	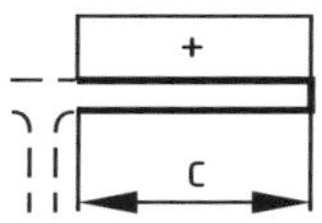	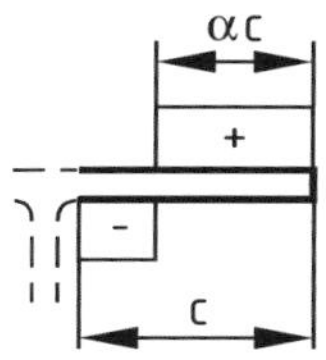	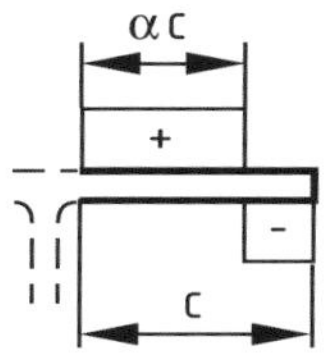
1	$c / t \leq 9\varepsilon$	$c / t \leq \frac{9\varepsilon}{\alpha}$	$c / t \leq \frac{9\varepsilon}{\alpha \sqrt{\alpha}}$
2	$c / t \leq 10\varepsilon$	$c / t \leq \frac{10\varepsilon}{\alpha}$	$c / t \leq \frac{10\varepsilon}{\alpha \sqrt{\alpha}}$
Stress distribution in parts (compression positive)	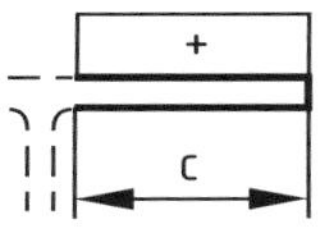	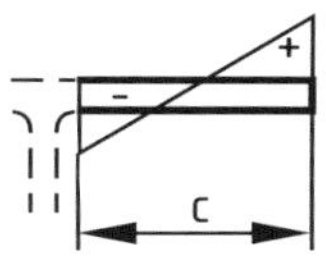	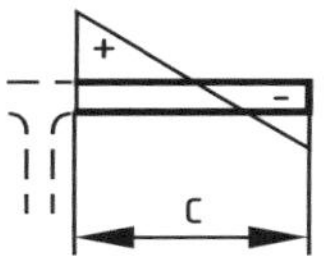
3	$c / t \leq 14\varepsilon$	$c / t \leq 21\varepsilon \sqrt{k_\sigma}$ For k_σ see EN 1993-1-5	

$\varepsilon = \sqrt{235 / f_y}$	f_y	235	275	355	420	460
	ε	1,00	0,92	0,81	0,75	0,71

Table 5.2 (sheet 3 of 3) — Maximum width-to-thickness ratios for compression parts

Angles						
Refer also to "Outstand flanges" (see sheet 2 of 3)	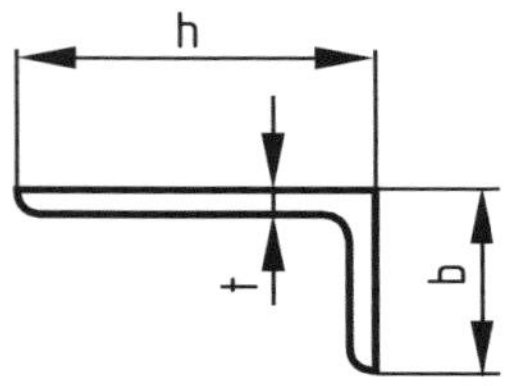 h, t, b	Does not apply to angles in continuous contact with other components				
Class	Section in compression					
Stress distribution across section (compression positive)	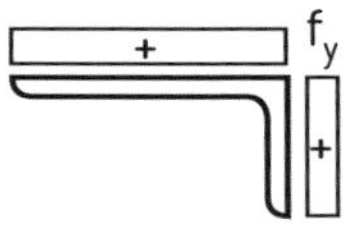 f_y + +					
3	$h/t \le 15\varepsilon : \frac{b+h}{2t} \le 11,5\varepsilon$					
Tubular sections						
	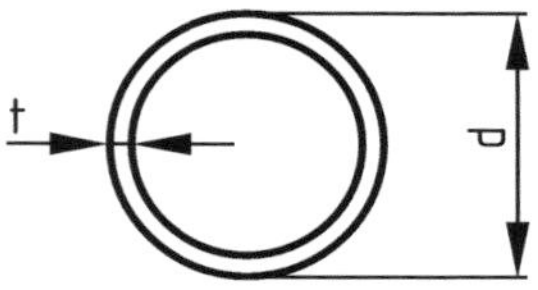 t, d					
Class	Section in bending and/or compression					
1	$d/t \le 50\varepsilon^2$					
2	$d/t \le 70\varepsilon^2$					
3	$d/t \le 90\varepsilon^2$ NOTE For $d/t \le 90\varepsilon^2$ see EN 1993-1-6.					
$\varepsilon = \sqrt{235/f_y}$	f_y	235	275	355	420	460
	ε	1,00	0,92	0,81	0,75	0,71
	ε^2	1,00	0,85	0,66	0,56	0,51

Section classification is a vital first step in checking the suitability of a trial section to sustain any given design actions. It is entirely concerned with the local buckling susceptibility of the chosen section and the resulting classification (into one of four classes defined) enters into many aspects of the ensuing checks on resistances to be made.

Local buckling should not be confused with overall buckling of a system length due to some aspect of compressive loading – these being checks applied subsequently (e.g. compression resistance, lateral torsional buckling, combined axial compression/bending etc.), and which involve the system length and end restraints. Local buckling is purely concerned with the behaviour of a short length of section when subjected to an action which involves some aspect of compressive loading. It is a function of:

- size, shape and slenderness of elements of the cross-section;
- type of compressive stress distribution applied;
- steel grade (the higher the grade the lower the limits of element slenderness).

Table 5.2 gives maximum width/thickness ratios for various cross-section shapes and stress distribution diagrams for Class 1, 2 and 3 (the inference being that if the Class 3 limits are not met, then the element is Class 4). Note that the material grade is reflected in the factor ε (defined at the bottom of Figure 5.2) which is always less than or equal to 1.0, so that slenderness limits for higher grade steels are lower for the various class of elements. A diagrammatic representation of the four classes of section is given in Figure A where a short length of section is subjected to an increasing major axis bending moment until failure.

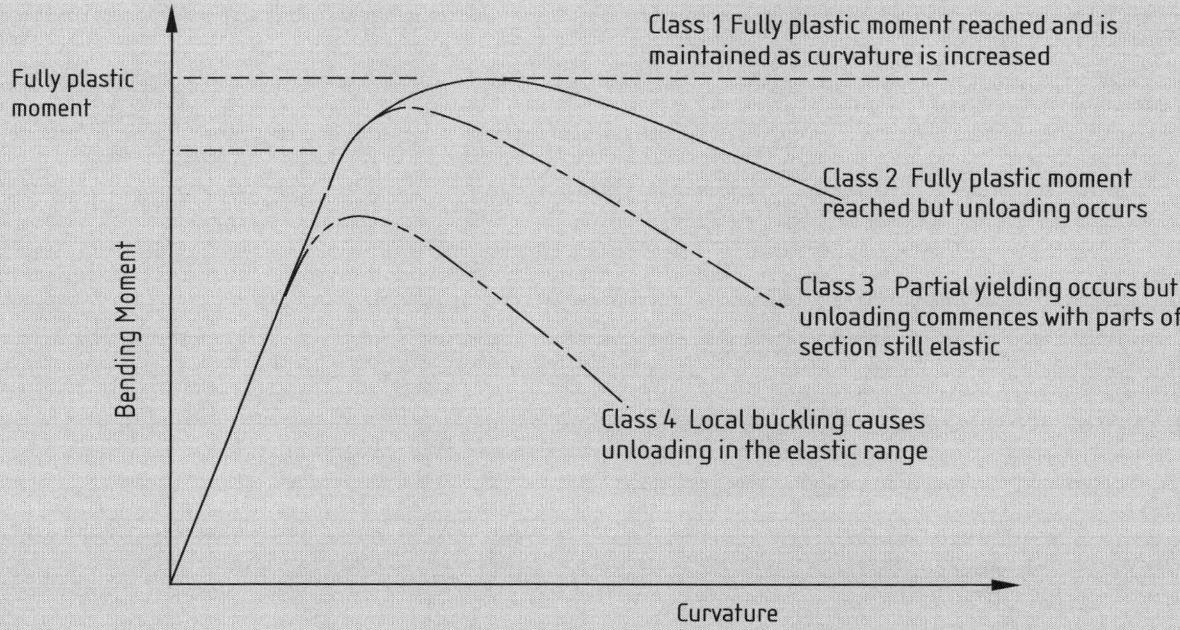

Figure A — Idealized moment curvature behaviour for four classes of cross-section

Note that in general only Class 1 sections can be used for plastic design (see 5.6(2)a)). The ability to rotate at a constant fully plastic moment (as in Class 1 sections) is a vital property in rigid plastic design. It is a requirement for plastic hinges forming at an early stage of loading to be able to rotate (and sustain full plastic moment) whilst other hinges form in the progression to a plastic collapse mechanism.

As a general guide the resistance in bending for Class 1 and 2 sections is based on the plastic modulus (W_{pl}), whilst Class 3 and 4 are based on the elastic modulus (W_{el}) (with added restrictions for Class 4).

Note 5.5.2(6) whereby the overall classification is based upon the least favourable (i.e. highest value) of its compressive elements.

Note also that any given section size is likely to have differing classifications depending upon the type of applied design loading (e.g. pure bending, axial compression or a combination of the two). Virtually all standard universal beams (UBs) in the UK are Class 1, or at least, Class 2 when used in major axis bending, whereas a significant number of these same sections are Class 3 or 4 when used in axial compression.

The method of treatment for Class 4 sections is not covered in this guide, but 5.5.2(2) refers to EN 1993-1-5. Essentially an 'effective section' approach is used whereby certain non-contributory parts of the section are removed and not considered when calculating the geometric properties of the cross-section.

A method of treating Class 4 sections as effectively Class 3 for local buckling classification (not overall buckling resistances, however) by modifying the definition of ε based upon the actual maximum stress in the element (calculated from analysis, first-order or second-order where necessary) is given in 5.5.2(9) and 5.5.2(10).

Worked example 1

Classify the section 457 × 152 UB74 in S275 steel for (1) major axis bending, and (2) axial compression.

Geometric properties of 457 × 152 UB74 (from steel tables)
Symbols (see Figure 1.1): b = 154,4 mm, h = 462,0 mm, d = 407,6 mm, t_f = 17,0 mm, t_w = 9,6 mm, r = 10,2 mm

(1) Major axis bending

Table 3.1 Max. thickness ≤ 40 mm, $f_y = 275\ \text{N/mm}^2$, $\varepsilon = \sqrt{235/275} = 0{,}924$

Table 5.2 Sheet 2: outstand flange $c/t_{actual} = (154{,}4/2 - 9{,}6/2 - 10{,}2)/17{,}0 = 3{,}66$

Limit for Class 1 $c/t \leq 9\varepsilon \leq 8{,}32$. Thus flange classification: Class 1

Table 5.2 Sheet 1: web part subjected to bending

$c/t_{actual} = 407{,}6/9{,}6 = 42{,}46$

Limit for Class 1 $c/t \leq 72\varepsilon \leq 66{,}53$. Thus web classification: Class 1

Overall classification of 457 × 152 UB74 in S275 steel for major axis bending: Class 1

(2) Axial compression

Table 5.2 Sheet 2: flange classification as before: Class 1

Web: Table 5.2 Sheet 1 $c/t_{actual} = 42{,}46$ as above

But limits for 'part subject to compression' (Table 5.2 Sheet 1):

Class 1 ≤ 33ε ≤ 30,5
Class 2 ≤ 38ε ≤ 35,1
Class 3 ≤ 42ε ≤ 38,8

Thus web classification: Class 4

Overall classification of 457 × 152 UB74 in S275 steel for axial compression: Class 4

NOTE As can be seen, classifying a section involves relatively routine calculations and it is anticipated that future steel properties tables will include classification classes of sections for various grades of steel and type of loading. Beware of using out-of-date steel property tables which may have been based on a different definition of the dimension 'c' for flanges of UBs and UCs, although such an error would usually be of a conservative nature.

6 Ultimate limit states

6.1 General

(1) The partial factors γ_M as defined in 2.4.3 should be applied to the various characteristic values of resistance in this section as follows:

- resistance of cross-sections whatever the class is: γ_{M0}
- resistance of members to instability assessed by member checks: γ_{M1}
- resistance of cross-sections in tension to fracture: γ_{M2}
- resistance of joints: see EN 1993-1-8

NOTE 1 For other recommended numerical values see EN 1993 Part 2 to Part 6. For structures not covered by EN 1993 Part 2 to Part 6 the National Annex may define the partial factors γ_{Mi}; it is recommended to take the partial factors γ_{Mi} from EN 1993-2.

NOTE 2 Partial factors γ_{Mi} for buildings may be defined in the National Annex. The following numerical values are recommended for buildings:

$\gamma_{M0} = 1,00$
$\gamma_{M1} = 1,00$
$\gamma_{M2} = 1,25$

NA.2.14 Clause 6.1(1) Partial factors for structures not covered by BS EN 1993 Part 2 to Part 6

For structures not covered by BS EN 1993: Parts 2 to 6, the partial factors should be appropriate for the structure and agreed with the client.

The National Annex defines partial factors for buildings in NA.2.15.

NA.2.15 Clause 6.1(1)B Partial safety factors for buildings

For buildings the following partial factors should be used:

$\gamma_{M0} = 1,00$
$\gamma_{M1} = 1,00$
$\gamma_{M2} = 1,10$

6.2 Resistance of cross-sections

6.2.1 General

[AC1) (1)P The design value of an action effect in each cross-section shall not exceed the corresponding design resistance and if several action effects act simultaneously the combined effect shall not exceed the resistance for that combination. (AC1]

(2) Shear lag effects and local buckling effects should be included by an effective width according to EN 1993-1-5. Shear buckling effects should also be considered according to EN 1993-1-5.

(3) The design values of resistance should depend on the classification of the cross-section.

(4) Elastic verification according to the elastic resistance may be carried out for all cross-sectional classes provided the effective cross-sectional properties are used for the verification of class 4 cross-sections.

(5) For the elastic verification the following yield criterion for a critical point of the cross section may be used unless other interaction formulae apply, see 6.2.8 to 6.2.10.

$$\left(\frac{\sigma_{x,Ed}}{f_y / \gamma_{M0}}\right)^2 + \left(\frac{\sigma_{z,Ed}}{f_y / \gamma_{M0}}\right)^2 - \left(\frac{\sigma_{x,Ed}}{f_y / \gamma_{M0}}\right)\left(\frac{\sigma_{z,Ed}}{f_y / \gamma_{M0}}\right) + 3\left(\frac{\tau_{Ed}}{f_y / \gamma_{M0}}\right)^2 \leq 1 \tag{6.1}$$

where

AC2⟩ $\sigma_{x,Ed}$ is the design value of the longitudinal stress at the point of consideration
$\sigma_{z,Ed}$ is the design value of the transverse stress at the point of consideration
τ_{Ed} is the design value of the shear stress at the point of consideration. ⟨AC2

NOTE The verification according to (5) can be conservative as it excludes partial plastic stress distribution, which is permitted in elastic design. Therefore it should only be performed where the interaction of on the basis of resistances N_{Rd}, M_{Rd}, V_{Rd} cannot be performed.

(6) The plastic resistance of cross sections should be verified by finding a stress distribution which is in equilibrium with the internal forces and moments without exceeding the yield strength. This stress distribution should be compatible with the associated plastic deformations.

(7) As a conservative approximation for all cross-section classes a linear summation of the utilisation ratios for each stress resultant may be used. For class 1, class 2 or class 3 cross-sections subjected to the combination of N_{Ed}, $M_{y,Ed}$ and $M_{z,Ed}$ this method may be applied by using the following criteria:

$$\frac{N_{Ed}}{N_{Rd}} + \frac{M_{y,Ed}}{M_{y,Rd}} + \frac{M_{z,Ed}}{M_{z,Rd}} \leq 1 \tag{6.2}$$

where N_{Rd}, $M_{y,Rd}$ and $M_{z,Rd}$ are the design values of the resistance depending on the cross sectional classification and including any reduction that may be caused by shear effects, see 6.2.8.

NOTE For class 4 cross sections see 6.2.9.3(2).

AC2⟩ (8) Where all the compression parts of a cross-section are Class 1 or Class 2, the cross-section may be taken as capable of developing its full plastic resistance in bending. ⟨AC2

(9) Where all the compression parts of a cross-section are Class 3, its resistance should be based on an elastic distribution of strains across the cross-section. Compressive stresses should be limited to the yield strength at the extreme fibres.

NOTE The extreme fibres may be assumed at the midplane of the flanges for ULS checks. For fatigue see EN 1993-1-9.

(10) Where yielding first occurs on the tension side of the cross-section, the plastic reserves of the tension zone may be utilised by accounting for partial plastification when determining the resistance of a Class 3 cross-section.

6.2.2 Section properties

6.2.2.1 Gross cross-section

(1) The properties of the gross cross-section shall be determined using the nominal dimensions. Holes for fasteners need not be deducted, but allowance shall be made for larger openings. Splice materials shall not be included.

6.2.2.2 Net area

(1) The net area of a cross-section shall be taken as its gross area less appropriate deductions for all holes and other openings.

(2) For calculating net section properties, the deduction for a single fastener hole should be the gross cross-sectional area of the hole in the plane of its axis. For countersunk holes, appropriate allowance should be made for the countersunk portion.

(3) Provided that the fastener holes are not staggered, the total area to be deducted for fastener holes should be the maximum sum of the sectional areas of the holes in any cross-section perpendicular to the member axis (see failure plane ② in Figure 6.1).

NOTE The maximum sum denotes the position of the critical fracture line.

Clause 6.1 defines the partial factors to be used in calculating various resistances of cross-sections. Note that such values can differ for differing types of structures i.e. buildings, bridges, silos etc.

Clause 6.2 is concerned purely with resistance (or strength) of a given cross-section subject to various actions, whereas 6.3 (see later commentary) is concerned with buckling resistances of members, and in general it is important that both aspects of behaviour are checked for conformity in any design. The only situation where overall buckling does not need to be considered is where the member is adequately or fully restrained.

Clause 6.2 states that if several actions occur simultaneously at a given cross-section, their combined effects need to be considered and the conservative linear interaction equation given in 6.2.1(7) is likely to be the most commonly used. Note that shear force is not directly quoted in this equation – its possible effect on moment design resistance is considered directly in the calculation of M_{Rd} (see 6.2.8(1),(2) and (3)). Note that a more effective way of dealing with the interaction of moment and axial force is given in 6.2.9.

Note also that 6.2.1(1) requires individual checks to be made on each action acting separately and this would be a logical first step prior to a 'combined' check.

The clauses related to net areas, which deal with deductions in section properties required for such things as holes drilled in the members for connection bolts etc., are not fully included in this guide. This is an important secondary consideration which would need to be checked in a final design process, but such detail would not likely be defined at an initial 'member sizing' stage, which is the emphasis given in this guide. Such considerations would normally not be critical as some local yielding at stress concentration points such as around bolt holes is expected and allowable.

6.2.3 Tension

AC1 (1)P The design value of the tension force N_{Ed} at each cross-section shall satisfy: AC1

$$\frac{N_{Ed}}{N_{t,Rd}} \leq 1,0 \tag{6.5}$$

(2) For sections with holes the design tension resistance $N_{t,Rd}$ should be taken as the smaller of:

a) the design plastic resistance of the gross cross-section

$$N_{pl,Rd} = \frac{Af_y}{\gamma_{M0}} \tag{6.6}$$

b) the design ultimate resistance of the net cross-section at holes for fasteners

$$N_{u,Rd} = \frac{0,9\, A_{net}\, f_u}{\gamma_{M2}} \tag{6.7}$$

(3) Where capacity design is requested, see EN 1998, the design plastic resistance $N_{pl,Rd}$ (as given in 6.2.3 (2) a)) should be less than the design ultimate resistance of the net section at fasteners holes $N_{u,Rd}$ (as given in 6.2.3(2) b)).

(4) In category C connections (see EN 1993-1-8, 3.4.1(1)), the design tension resistance $N_{t,Rd}$ in 6.2.3(1) of the net section at holes for fasteners should be taken as $N_{net,Rd}$, where:

$$N_{net,Rd} = \frac{A_{net} f_y}{\gamma_{M0}} \quad (6.8)$$

(5) For angles connected through one leg, see also EN 1993-1-8, 3.10.3. Similar consideration should also be given to other types of sections connected through outstands.

Tension is the easiest action to deal with involving no buckling characteristics. The only factors to note are reductions in cross-sectional areas due to holes, and possible unsymmetrical joint connections leading to a component of bending due to the eccentrically applied tensile action. Category C connections, which are designed to be no-slip at ultimate and thus no local yielding is permitted, are referred to in 6.2.3(4).

6.2.4 Compression

[AC1) (1)P The design value of the compression force N_{Ed} at each cross-section shall satisfy: (AC1]

$$\frac{N_{Ed}}{N_{c,Rd}} \leq 1,0 \quad (6.9)$$

(2) The design resistance of the cross-section for uniform compression $N_{c,Rd}$ shall be determined as follows:

$$N_{c,Rd} = \frac{A f_y}{\gamma_{M0}} \quad \text{for class 1, 2 or 3 cross-sections} \quad (6.10)$$

$$N_{c,Rd} = \frac{A_{eff} f_y}{\gamma_{M0}} \quad \text{for class 4 cross-sections} \quad (6.11)$$

(3) Fastener holes except for oversize and slotted holes as defined in EN 1090 need not be allowed for in compression members, provided that they are filled by fasteners.

(4) In the case of unsymmetrical Class 4 sections, the method given in 6.2.9.3 should be used to allow for the additional moment ΔM_{Ed} due to the eccentricity of the centroidal axis of the effective section, see 6.2.2.5(4).

6.2.5 Bending moment

[AC1) (1)P The design value of the bending moment M_{Ed} at each cross-section shall satisfy: (AC1]

$$\frac{M_{Ed}}{M_{c,Rd}} \leq 1,0 \quad (6.12)$$

where $M_{c,Rd}$ is determined considering fastener holes, see (4) to (6).

(2) The design resistance for bending about one principal axis of a cross-section is determined as follows:

$$M_{c,Rd} = M_{pl,Rd} = \frac{W_{pl} f_y}{\gamma_{M0}} \quad \text{for class 1 or 2 cross-sections} \quad (6.13)$$

$$M_{c,Rd} = M_{el,Rd} = \frac{W_{el,min} f_y}{\gamma_{M0}} \quad \text{for class 3 cross-sections} \quad (6.14)$$

$$M_{c,Rd} = \frac{W_{eff,min} f_y}{\gamma_{M0}} \quad \text{for class 4 cross-sections} \quad (6.15)$$

where $W_{el,min}$ and $W_{eff,min}$ correspond to the fibre with the maximum elastic stress.

(3) For bending about both axes, the methods given in 6.2.9 should be used.

(4) Fastener holes in the tension flange may be ignored provided that for the tension flange:

$$\frac{A_{f,net}\, 0,9\, f_u}{\gamma_{M2}} \geq \frac{A_f\, f_y}{\gamma_{M0}} \qquad (6.16)$$

where A_f is the area of the tension flange.

NOTE The criterion in (4) provides capacity design (see 1.5.8). AC2) deleted text (AC2

(5) Fastener holes in the tension zone of the web need not be allowed for, provided that the limit given in (4) is satisfied for the complete tension zone comprising the tension flange plus the tension zone of the web.

(6) Fastener holes except for oversize and slotted holes in the compression zone of the cross-section need not be allowed for, provided that they are filled by fasteners.

6.2.6 Shear

AC1) (1)P The design value of the shear force V_{Ed} at each cross-section shall satisfy: (AC1

$$\frac{V_{Ed}}{V_{c,Rd}} \leq 1,0 \qquad (6.17)$$

where $V_{c,Rd}$ is the design shear resistance. For plastic design $V_{c,Rd}$ is the design plastic shear resistance $V_{pl,Rd}$ as given in (2). For elastic design $V_{c,Rd}$ is the design elastic shear resistance calculated using (4) and (5).

(2) In the absence of torsion the design plastic shear resistance is given by:

$$V_{pl,Rd} = \frac{A_v\left(f_y / \sqrt{3}\right)}{\gamma_{M0}} \qquad (6.18)$$

where A_v is the shear area.

(3) The shear area A_v may be taken as follows:

a) rolled I and H sections, load parallel to web $A - 2bt_f + (t_w + 2r)\, t_f$ but not less than $\eta h_w\, t_w$

b) rolled channel sections, load parallel to web $A - 2bt_f + (t_w + r)\, t_f$

AC2) c) rolled T-section, load parallel to web – for rolled T-sections: $A_v = A - bt_f + (t_w + 2r)\frac{t_f}{2}$

– for welded T-sections: $A_v = t_w\left(h - \frac{t_f}{2}\right)$ (AC2

d) welded I, H and box sections, load parallel to web $\eta\Sigma\,(h_w\, t_w)$

e) welded I, H, channel and box sections, load parallel to flanges $A - \Sigma\,(h_w\, t_w)$

f) rolled rectangular hollow sections of uniform thickness:

load parallel to depth $Ah/(b+h)$

load parallel to width $Ab/(b+h)$

g) circular hollow sections and tubes of uniform thickness $2A/\pi$

where

A is the cross-sectional area;
b is the overall breadth;
h is the overall depth;
h_w is the depth of the web;
r is the root radius;
t_f is the flange thickness;
t_w is the web thickness (If the web thickness is not constant, t_w should be taken as the minimum thickness.);
η see EN 1993-1-5.

NOTE η may be conservatively taken to equal 1,0.

(4) For verifying the design elastic shear resistance $V_{c,Rd}$ the following criterion for a critical point of the cross-section may be used unless the buckling verification in section 5 of EN 1993-1-5 applies:

$$\frac{\tau_{Ed}}{f_y / (\sqrt{3}\,\gamma_{M0})} \leq 1,0 \qquad (6.19)$$

where τ_{Ed} may be obtained from: $\tau_{Ed} = \frac{V_{Ed}\,S}{I\,t}$ (6.20)

where

V_{Ed} is the design value of the shear force
S is the first moment of the area about the centroidal axis of that portion of the cross-section between the point at which the shear is required and the boundary of the cross-section
I is second moment of the area of the whole cross-section
t is the thickness at the examined point.

NOTE The verification according to (4) is conservative as it excludes partial plastic shear distribution, which is permitted in elastic design, see (5). Therefore it should only be carried out where the verification on the basis of $V_{c,Rd}$ according to equation (6.17) cannot be performed.

(5) For I- or H-sections the shear stress in the web may be taken as:

$$\tau_{Ed} = \frac{V_{Ed}}{A_w} \text{ if } A_f / A_w \geq 0,6 \qquad (6.21)$$

where

A_f is the area of one flange;
A_w is the area of the web: $A_w = h_w\, t_w$.

(6) In addition the shear buckling resistance for webs without intermediate stiffeners shall be according to section 5 of EN 1993-1-5, if

$$\frac{h_w}{t_w} > 72\,\frac{\varepsilon}{\eta} \qquad (6.22)$$

For η see section 5 of EN 1993-1-5.

NOTE η may be conservatively taken to equal 1,0.

(7) Fastener holes need not be allowed for in the shear verification except in verifying the design shear resistance at connection zones as given in EN 1993-1-8.

The shear area of a cross-section is defined in 6.2.6(3) and corresponds to that part of the section which theoretically resists shearing action, such as the web in an I-section beam. The value of A_v is likely to be tabulated in steel section property tables.

For normal design in buildings using rolled sections, unless the loading is very high over short spans or high point loads occur near support points, shear will not usually be found to be a problem, and rarely limits design. Furthermore the application of 6.2.8(3) (reduction in moment resistance due to shear) will rarely be invoked.

6.2.8 Bending and shear

(1) Where the shear force is present allowance shall be made for its effect on the moment resistance.

(2) Where the shear force is less than half the plastic shear resistance its effect on the moment resistance may be neglected except where shear buckling reduces the section resistance, see EN 1993-1-5.

(3) Otherwise the reduced moment resistance should be taken as the design resistance of the cross-section, calculated using a reduced strength

$(1-\rho) f_y$

for the shear area, (6.29)

where $\rho = \left(\frac{2 V_{Ed}}{V_{pl,Rd}}\right)^2$ and $V_{pl,Rd}$ is obtained from 6.2.6(2).

NOTE See also 6.2.10(3).

(5) The reduced design plastic resistance moment allowing for the shear force may alternatively be obtained for I-cross-sections with equal flanges and bending about the major axis as follows:

$$M_{y,V,Rd} = \frac{\left[W_{pl,y} - \frac{\rho A_w^2}{4t_w}\right] f_y}{\gamma_{M0}} \quad \text{but} \quad M_{y,V,Rd} \le M_{y,c,Rd} \qquad (6.30)$$

where $M_{y,c,Rd}$ is obtained from 6.2.5(2)
and $A_w = h_w t_w$

6.2.9 Bending and axial force

6.2.9.1 Class 1 and 2 cross-sections

(1) Where an axial force is present, allowance shall be made for its effect on the plastic moment resistance.

[AC1⟩ (2)P For class 1 and 2 cross-sections, the following criterion shall be satisfied: ⟨AC1]

$$M_{Ed} \le M_{N,Rd} \qquad (6.31)$$

where $M_{N,Rd}$ is the design plastic moment resistance reduced due to the axial force N_{Ed}.

(3) For a rectangular solid section without bolt holes $M_{N,Rd}$ should be taken as:

$$M_{N,Rd} = M_{pl,Rd}\left[1 - (N_{Ed} / N_{pl,Rd})^2\right] \qquad (6.32)$$

(4) For doubly symmetrical I- and H-sections or other flange sections, allowance need not be made for the effect of the axial force on the plastic resistance moment about the y-y axis when both the following criteria are satisfied:

$N_{Ed} \le 0,25\, N_{pl,Rd}$ and (6.33)

$$N_{Ed} \leq \frac{0,5\, h_w\, t_w\, f_y}{\gamma_{M0}} \tag{6.34}$$

For doubly symmetrical I- and H-sections, allowance need not be made for the effect of the axial force on the plastic resistance moment about the z-z axis when:

$$N_{Ed} \leq \frac{h_w\, t_w\, f_y}{\gamma_{M0}} \tag{6.35}$$

(5) For cross-sections where bolt holes are not to be accounted for, the following approximations may be used for standard rolled I or H sections and for welded I or H sections with equal flanges:

$$M_{N,y,Rd} = M_{pl,y,Rd}\,(1-n)\,/\,(1-0,5a) \text{ but } M_{N,y,Rd} \leq M_{pl,y,Rd} \tag{6.36}$$

$$\text{for } n \leq a\text{:}\; M_{N,z,Rd} = M_{pl,z,Rd} \tag{6.37}$$

$$\text{for } n > a\text{:}\; M_{N,z,Rd} = M_{pl,z,Rd}\left[1-\left(\frac{n-a}{1-a}\right)^2\right] \tag{6.38}$$

where $n = N_{Ed} / N_{pl.Rd}$

$a = (A - 2bt_f)/A$ but $a \leq 0,5$

For cross-sections where bolt holes are not to be accounted for, the following approximations may be used for rectangular structural hollow sections of uniform thickness and for welded box sections with equal flanges and equal webs:

$$M_{N,y,Rd} = M_{pl,y,Rd}\,(1-n)\,/\,(1-0,5a_w) \quad \text{but} \quad M_{N,y,Rd} \leq M_{pl,y,Rd} \tag{6.39}$$

$$M_{N,z,Rd} = M_{pl,z,Rd}\,(1-n)\,/\,(1-0,5a_f) \quad \text{but} \quad M_{N,z,Rd} \leq M_{pl,z,Rd} \tag{6.40}$$

where

$a_w = (A - 2bt)/A$ but $a_w \leq 0,5$ for hollow sections
$a_w = (A - 2bt_f)/A$ but $a_w \leq 0,5$ for welded box sections
$a_f = (A - 2ht)/A$ but $a_f \leq 0,5$ for hollow sections
$a_f = (A - 2ht_w)/A$ but $a_f \leq 0,5$ for welded box sections

(6) For bi-axial bending the following criterion may be used:

$$\left[\frac{M_{y,Ed}}{M_{N,y,Rd}}\right]^{\alpha} + \left[\frac{M_{z,Ed}}{M_{N,z,Rd}}\right]^{\beta} \leq 1 \tag{6.41}$$

in which α and β are constants, which may conservatively be taken as unity, otherwise as follows:

– I and H sections:

$\alpha = 2$; $\beta = 5n$ but $\beta \geq 1$

– circular hollow sections:

$\alpha = 2$; $\beta = 2$

AC2) $M_{N,y,Rd} = M_{N,z,Rd} = M_{pl,Rd}\,(1 - n^{1,7})$ (AC2

– rectangular hollow sections:

$$\alpha = \beta = \frac{1,66}{1-1,13n^2} \quad \text{but } \alpha = \beta \leq 6$$

where $n = N_{Ed} / N_{pl,Rd}$.

6.2.9.2 Class 3 cross-sections

AC1 (1)P In the absence of shear force, for Class 3 cross-sections the maximum longitudinal stress shall satisfy the criterion: AC1

$$\sigma_{x,Ed} \leq \frac{f_y}{\gamma_{M0}} \qquad (6.42)$$

where $\sigma_{x,Ed}$ is the design value of the local longitudinal stress due to moment and axial force taking account of fastener holes where relevant, see 6.2.3, 6.2.4 and 6.2.5.

6.2.10 Bending, shear and axial force

(1) Where shear and axial force are present, allowance should be made for the effect of both shear force and axial force on the resistance moment.

(2) Provided that the design value of the shear force V_{Ed} does not exceed 50% of the design plastic shear resistance $V_{pl.Rd}$ no reduction of the resistances defined for bending and axial force in 6.2.9 need be made, except where shear buckling reduces the section resistance, see EN 1993-1-5.

(3) Where V_{Ed} exceeds 50% of $V_{pl.Rd}$ the design resistance of the cross-section to combinations of moment and axial force should be calculated using a reduced yield strength

$$(1-\rho)\,f_y \qquad (6.45)$$

for the shear area

where $\rho = (2V_{Ed} / V_{pl.Rd} - 1)^2$ and $V_{pl,Rd}$ is obtained from 6.2.6(2).

NOTE Instead of reducing the yield strength, the plate thickness of the relevant part of the cross-section may also be reduced.

6.3 Buckling resistance of members

6.3.1 Uniform members in compression

6.3.1.1 Buckling resistance

(1) A compression member shall be verified against buckling as follows:

$$\frac{N_{Ed}}{N_{b,Rd}} \leq 1{,}0 \qquad (6.46)$$

where

N_{Ed} is the design value of the compression force
$N_{b,Rd}$ is the design buckling resistance of the compression member.

(3) The design buckling resistance of a compression member should be taken as:

$$N_{b,Rd} = \frac{\chi A f_y}{\gamma_{M1}} \quad \text{for Class 1, 2 and 3 cross-sections} \qquad (6.47)$$

$$N_{b,Rd} = \frac{\chi A_{eff} f_y}{\gamma_{M1}} \quad \text{for Class 4 cross-sections} \qquad (6.48)$$

where χ is the reduction factor for the relevant buckling mode.

NOTE For determining the buckling resistance of members with tapered sections along the member or for non-uniform distribution of the compression force second-order analysis according to 5.3.4(2) may be performed. For out-of-plane buckling see also 6.3.4.

(4) In determining A and A_{eff} holes for fasteners at the column ends need not to be taken into account.

6.3.1.2 Buckling curves

(1) For axial compression in members the value of χ for the appropriate non-dimensional slenderness $\bar{\lambda}$ should be determined from the relevant buckling curve according to:

$$\chi = \frac{1}{\Phi + \sqrt{\Phi^2 - \bar{\lambda}^2}} \text{ but } \chi \leq 1,0 \qquad (6.49)$$

where $\Phi = 0,5\left[1 + \alpha\left(\bar{\lambda} - 0,2\right) + \bar{\lambda}^2\right]$

$\bar{\lambda} = \sqrt{\frac{A\, f_y}{N_{cr}}}$ for Class 1, 2 and 3 cross–sections

$\bar{\lambda} = \sqrt{\frac{A_{eff}\, f_y}{N_{cr}}}$ for Class 4 cross–sections

α is an imperfection factor

N_{cr} is the elastic critical force for the relevant buckling mode based on the gross cross sectional properties.

(2) The imperfection factor α corresponding to the appropriate buckling curve should be obtained from Table 6.1 and Table 6.2.

Table 6.1 — Imperfection factors for buckling curves

Buckling curve	a_0	a	b	c	d
Imperfection factor α	0,13	0,21	0,34	0,49	0,76

(3) Values of the reduction factor χ for the appropriate non-dimensional slenderness $\bar{\lambda}$ may be obtained from Figure 6.4.

(4) For slenderness $\bar{\lambda} \leq 0,2$ or for $\frac{N_{Ed}}{N_{cr}} \leq 0,04$ the buckling effects may be ignored and only cross-sectional checks apply.

Table 6.2 — Selection of buckling curve for a cross-section

Cross section	Limits		Buckling about axis	Buckling curve: S 235, S 275, S 355, S 420	Buckling curve: S 460
Rolled sections	$h/b > 1,2$	$t_f \leq 40$ mm	y – y z – z	a b	a_0 a_0
Rolled sections	$h/b > 1,2$	40 mm < $t_f \leq 100$	y – y z – z	b c	a a
Rolled sections	$h/b \leq 1,2$	$t_f \leq 100$ mm	y – y z – z	b c	a a
Rolled sections	$h/b \leq 1,2$	$t_f > 100$ mm	y – y z – z	d d	c c
Welded I sections	$t_f \leq 40$ mm		y – y z – z	b c	b c
Welded I sections	$t_f > 40$ mm		y – y z – z	c d	c d
Hollow sections	hot finished		any	a	a_0
Hollow sections	cold formed		any	c	c
Welded box sections	generally (except as below)		any	b	b
Welded box sections	thick welds: $a > 0,5t_f$ $b/t_f < 30$ $h/t_w < 30$		any	c	c
U, T and solid sections			any	c	c
L sections			any	b	b

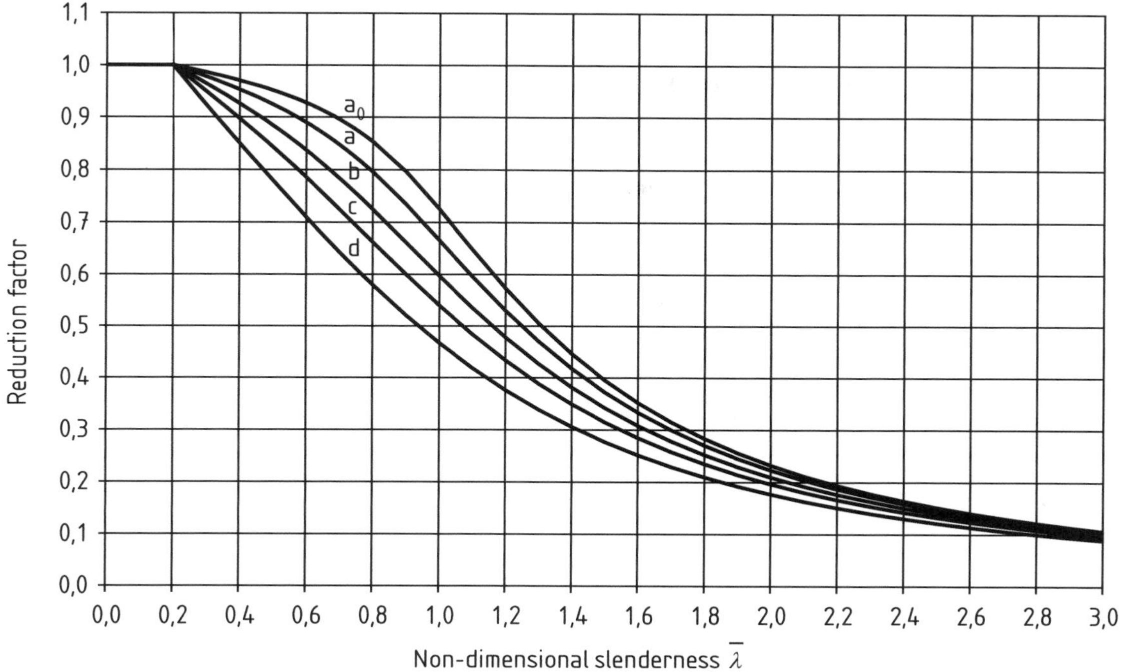

Figure 6.4 — Buckling curves

6.3.1.3 Slenderness for flexural buckling

(1) The non-dimensional slenderness $\overline{\lambda}$ is given by:

$$\overline{\lambda} = \sqrt{\frac{A\,f_y}{N_{cr}}} = \frac{L_{cr}}{i}\frac{1}{\lambda_1} \qquad \text{for Class 1, 2 and 3 cross-sections} \qquad (6.50)$$

$$\overline{\lambda} = \sqrt{\frac{A_{eff}\,f_y}{N_{cr}}} = \frac{L_{cr}}{i}\frac{\sqrt{\frac{A_{eff}}{A}}}{\lambda_1} \qquad \text{for Class 4 cross-sections} \qquad (6.51)$$

where

L_{cr} is the buckling length in the buckling plane considered

i is the radius of gyration about the relevant axis, determined using the properties of the gross cross-section

$$\lambda_1 = \pi\sqrt{\frac{E}{f_y}} = 93,9\varepsilon$$

$$\varepsilon = \sqrt{\frac{235}{f_y}} \quad (f_y \text{ in N/mm}^2)$$

NOTE B For elastic buckling of components of building structures see Annex BB.

(2) For flexural buckling the appropriate buckling curve should be determined from Table 6.2.

(1) Buckling curves

A total of five buckling curves are defined (although the top curve, a_0, is only used for high grade S460 steel). Specific curves are specified for various types of cross-section and buckling axis due to the manufacturing process involved in forming the sections. Due to differential cooling rates a series of 'locked-in' (residual) stresses are produced. These are in internal equilibrium in the unloaded sections but the compressive component of them influences the buckling behaviour of the member with varying severity. Sufficient research, both experimental and theoretical, has been carried out so that it is now possible to allocate each type of section and buckling axis to a series of categories reflected in these five curves. Note that welded made-up sections and cold formed sections are allocated a lower curve to reflect the relatively high residual stresses induced by these forming processes.

(2) A note on slenderness

UK designers are familiar with the term slenderness (or slenderness ratio) being defined as L_e/i where L_e is an 'effective length' which relates the buckling resistance of the member under consideration to the length of a pin-ended column with the same resistance. L_e is conveniently rendered dimensionless by dividing by the appropriate radius of gyration, i, for the axis being considered. EN 1993-1-1 uses the term λ for this slenderness, but introduces another slenderness parameter $\bar{\lambda}$, a so-called 'normalized' slenderness. This is defined as being the square root of the yield, or squash, load divided by the elastic critical load, N_{cr}. An analogous normalized slenderness term ($\bar{\lambda}_{LT}$) is used when considering bending moment (lateral torsional buckling) in 6.3.2.

The normalized slenderness $\bar{\lambda}$ can also be thought of as the ratio of the actual slenderness of the member in question (λ) divided by the slenderness of a notional pin-ended column of a length such that the elastic (Euler) critical stress is equal to the material strength, f_y, as the following argument demonstrates.

If this (Euler) column has a slenderness say λ_{Ey} and length L_{Ey} and a buckling resistance of N_{Ey} then:

$$N_{Ey} = f_y A = \frac{\pi^2 EI}{L_{Ey}{}^2} = \frac{\pi^2 EAi^2}{L_{Ey}{}^2}, \text{ and } \lambda_{Ey} = \frac{L_{Ey}}{i}$$

From which $\lambda_{Ey} = \pi \sqrt{\dfrac{E}{f_y}} \quad (= 93,9\varepsilon)$

Now $\bar{\lambda} = \dfrac{\lambda}{\lambda_{Ey}}$ and $\lambda = \dfrac{L}{i}$, $N_{cr} = \dfrac{\pi^2 EI}{L^2}$

Then $\lambda = \pi \sqrt{\dfrac{EA}{N_{cr}}}$

and $\bar{\lambda} = \sqrt{\dfrac{A f_y}{N_{cr}}}$ which is the form used in 6.3.1.2 (1).

One of the reasons that a normalized slenderness $\bar{\lambda}$ has been introduced is to remove f_y as a variable in Figure 6.4 so that it can be used for all steel grades.

(3) Summary of procedure for obtaining $N_{b.Rd}$

For each axis of buckling (y-y and z-z):

(a) Assess buckling (effective) length L_E – this will be a function of the actual (system) length modified by a factor possibly to be obtained by reference to the UK National Annex depending on the degree of restraint offered at the ends of the system length. Calculate λ (= L_E / i_y or L_E / i_z).

(b) Calculate $\bar{\lambda}$ from 6.3.1.2

$$\bar{\lambda} = \sqrt{\frac{A\,f_y}{N_{cr}}} \quad \text{for class 1, 2 or 3 sections}$$

$$= \frac{\lambda}{\pi\sqrt{\frac{E}{f_y}}} \quad \text{as shown in (2) above}$$

Note also that $\pi\sqrt{\frac{E}{f_y}} = 93{,}9\varepsilon$

(c) Calculate $\chi = \dfrac{1}{\phi + \sqrt{\phi^2 - \bar{\lambda}^2}}$ where $\phi = 0.5\left[1 + \alpha\left(\bar{\lambda} - 0{,}2\right) + \bar{\lambda}^2\right]$

where α is obtained from Table 6.1 depending on the buckling curve selected from Table 6.2

(d) Hence obtain $N_{b,Rd} = \dfrac{\chi\,A\,f_y}{\gamma_m}$ for class 1, 2 and 3

(Same procedure for Class 4 sections with the replacement of A with effective area A_{eff}.)

(e) $N_{b.Rd}$ is the lowest value obtained from (d) for y-y or z-z axes.

Worked example 2 – buckling resistance

Assess the buckling resistance of a 203 × 203 UC52 in grade S275 steel with the following system lengths. For buckling about the y-y axis the system length is 6 m whilst a buckling length due to end restraints has been assessed by the designer as 5,1 m (i.e. L_{Ey} = 0,85L). For minor axis buckling the member is restrained by secondary beams at mid height and the half length assessed to be pin ended (i.e. L_{Ez} = 3 m). (The results of this calculation will be used in worked example 4.)

Properties of 203 × 203 UC52
$A = 6630\ mm^2$, $i_y = 89{,}1\ mm$, $i_z = 51{,}8\ mm$

Section classification
It is left to the reader to confirm that the following apply:
Classification in bending: Class 1
Classification in axial compression: Class 1

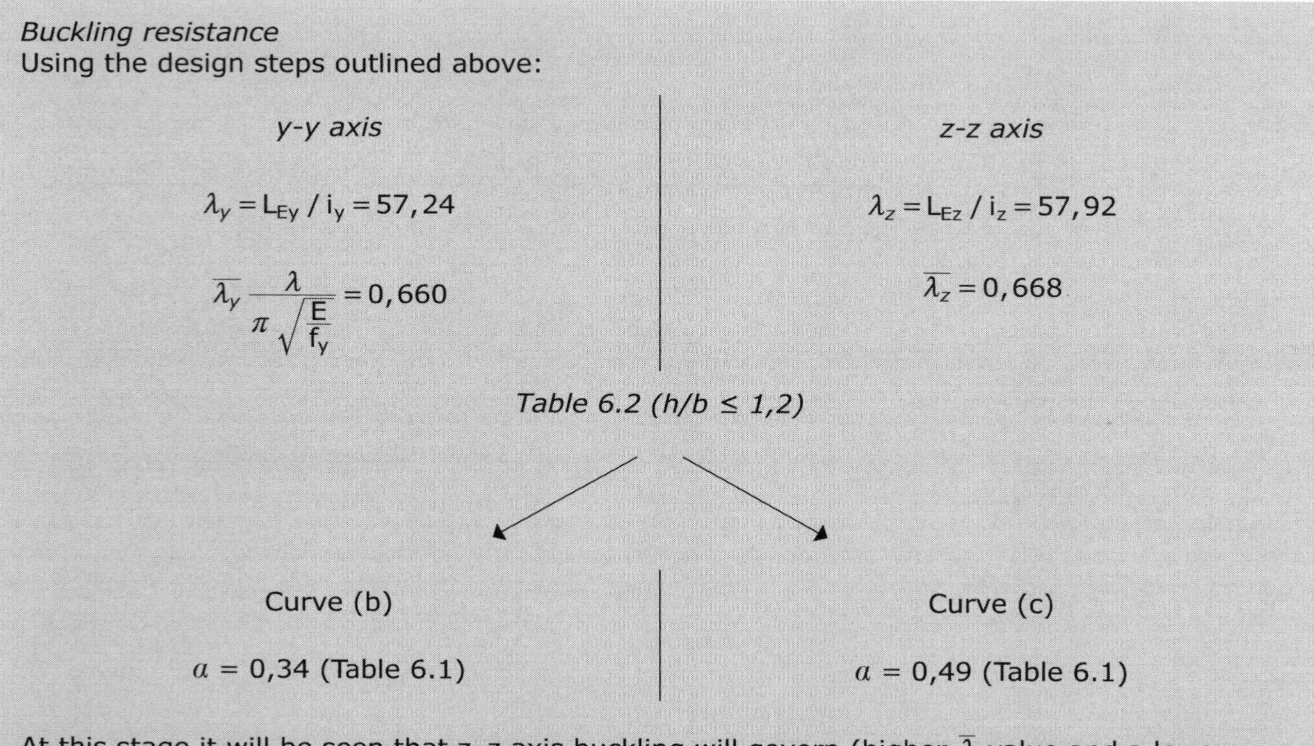

At this stage it will be seen that z–z axis buckling will govern (higher $\bar{\lambda}$ value and a lower design curve (c)) but for completeness calculations for both axes will continue (results needed in worked example 4)

$$\phi = 0.5\left(1 + \alpha\left(\bar{\lambda} - 0,2\right) + \bar{\lambda}^2\right)$$

$$\chi = \frac{1}{\phi + \sqrt{\left(\phi^2 - \bar{\lambda}^2\right)}}$$

y-y axis	z-z axis
$\phi = 0,796$	$\phi = 0,838$
$\chi = 0,806$	$\chi = 0,744$
$N_{y,b,Rd} = \chi \dfrac{A\,f_y}{\gamma_{MI}} = 1469\ \text{kN}$	$N_{z,b,Rd} = 1356\ \text{kN}$

$\therefore$ use the lower value of $N_{b,Rd} = 1356\ \text{kN}$

6.3.2 Uniform members in bending

6.3.2.1 Buckling resistance

(1) A laterally unrestrained beam subject to major axis bending shall be verified against lateral-torsional buckling as follows:

$$\frac{M_{Ed}}{M_{b,Rd}} \leq 1,0 \qquad (6.54)$$

where

M_{Ed} is the design value of the moment
$M_{b,Rd}$ is the design buckling resistance moment.

(2) Beams with sufficient restraint to the compression flange are not susceptible to lateral-torsional buckling. In addition, beams with certain types of cross-sections, such as square or circular hollow sections, fabricated circular tubes or square box sections are not susceptible to lateral-torsional buckling.

(3) The design buckling resistance moment of a laterally unrestrained beam should be taken as:

$$M_{b,Rd} = \chi_{LT} W_y \frac{f_y}{\gamma_{MI}} \quad (6.55)$$

where

W_y is the appropriate section modulus as follows:
- $W_y = W_{pl,y}$ for Class 1 or 2 cross-sections
- $W_y = W_{el,y}$ for Class 3 cross-sections
- $W_y = W_{eff,y}$ for Class 4 cross-sections

χ_{LT} is the reduction factor for lateral-torsional buckling.

NOTE 1 For determining the buckling resistance of beams with tapered sections second-order analysis according to 5.3.4(3) may be performed. For out-of-plane buckling see also 6.3.4.

NOTE 2B For buckling of components of building structures see also Annex BB.

(4) In determining W_y holes for fasteners at the beam end need not to be taken into account.

6.3.2.2 Lateral torsional buckling curves – general case

(1) Unless otherwise specified, see 6.3.2.3, for bending members of constant cross-section, the value of χ_{LT} for the appropriate non-dimensional slenderness $\bar{\lambda}_{LT}$ should be determined from:

$$\chi_{LT} = \frac{1}{\Phi_{LT} + \sqrt{\Phi_{LT}^2 - \bar{\lambda}_{LT}^2}} \quad \text{but} \quad \chi_{LT} \leq 1,0 \quad (6.56)$$

where $\Phi_{LT} = 0,5\left[1 + \alpha_{LT}\left(\bar{\lambda}_{LT} - 0,2\right) + \bar{\lambda}_{LT}^2\right]$

α_{LT} is an imperfection factor

$$\bar{\lambda}_{LT} = \sqrt{\frac{W_y f_y}{M_{cr}}}$$

M_{cr} is the elastic critical moment for lateral-torsional buckling

(2) M_{cr} is based on gross cross-sectional properties and takes into account the loading conditions, the real moment distribution and the lateral restraints.

NOTE The imperfection factor α_{LT} corresponding to the appropriate buckling curve may be obtained from the National Annex. The recommended values of α_{LT} are given in Table 6.3.

The National Annex defines the recommended values for α_{LT} in NA.2.16.

NA.2.16 Clause 6.3.2.2(2) Imperfection factors for lateral torsional buckling

The recommended values given in BS EN 1993-1-1:2005, Table 6.3 and Table 6.4 should be used.

Table 6.3 — Imperfection factors for lateral torsional buckling curves

Buckling curve	a	b	c	d
Imperfection factor α_{LT}	0,21	0,34	0,49	0,76

The recommendations for buckling curves are given in Table 6.4.

Table 6.4 — Lateral torsional buckling curve for cross-sections using equation (6.56)

Cross-section	Limits	Buckling curve
Rolled I sections	h/b ≤ 2 h/b > 2	**a** **b**
Welded I sections	h/b ≤ 2 h/b > 2	**c** **d**
Other cross-sections	–	**d**

(3) Values of the reduction factor χ_{LT} for the appropriate non-dimensional slenderness $\bar{\lambda}_{LT}$ may be obtained from Figure 6.4.

(4) For slendernesses $\bar{\lambda}_{LT} \leq \bar{\lambda}_{LT,0}$ (see 6.3.2.3) or for $\frac{M_{Ed}}{M_{cr}} \leq \bar{\lambda}_{LT,0}{}^2$ (see 6.3.2.3) lateral torsional buckling effects may be ignored and only cross-sectional checks apply.

6.3.2.3 Lateral torsional buckling curves for rolled sections or equivalent welded sections

(1) For rolled or equivalent welded sections in bending the values of χ_{LT} for the appropriate non-dimensional slenderness may be determined from

$$\chi_{LT} = \frac{1}{\Phi_{LT} + \sqrt{\Phi_{LT}^2 - \beta\bar{\lambda}_{LT}^2}} \quad \text{but} \begin{cases} \chi_{LT} \leq 1,0 \\ \chi_{LT} \leq \dfrac{1}{\bar{\lambda}_{LT}^2} \end{cases} \qquad (6.57)$$

$$\Phi_{LT} = 0,5\left[1 + \alpha_{LT}\left(\bar{\lambda}_{LT} - \bar{\lambda}_{LT,0}\right) + \beta\bar{\lambda}_{LT}^2\right]$$

NOTE The parameters $\bar{\lambda}_{LT,0}$ and β and any limitation of validity concerning the beam depth or h/b ratio may be given in the National Annex. The following values are recommended for rolled sections:

$\bar{\lambda}_{LT,0} = 0,4$ (maximum value)

$\beta = 0,75$ (minimum value)

The recommendations for buckling curves are given in Table 6.5.

The National Annex does not define the parameters or place any limitations.

Table 6.5 — Recommendation for the selection of lateral torsional buckling curve for cross-sections using equation (6.57)

Cross-section	**Limits**	**Buckling curve**
Rolled I-sections	h/b ≤ 2 h/b > 2	b c
Welded I-sections	h/b ≤ 2 h/b > 2	c d

NA.2.17 Clause 6.3.2.3(1) Lateral torsional buckling for rolled sections or equivalent welded sections

For buildings and bridges the following values of $\lambda_{LT,0}$ and ß should be used:

a. For rolled sections and hot-finished and cold-formed hollow sections

$\lambda_{LT,0} = 0.4$

ß = 0.75

b. For welded sections

$\lambda_{LT,0} = 0.2$

ß = 1.00

BS EN 1993-1-1:2005, Table 6.5 should be replaced with the following table:

Cross-section	Limits	Buckling curve
Rolled doubly symmetric I and H sections and hot-finished hollow sections	$h/b \leq 2$ $2.0 < h/b \leq 3.1$ $h/b > 3.1$	b c d
Angles (for moments in the major principal plane)		d
All other hot-rolled sections		d
Welded doubly symmetric sections and cold-formed hollow sections	$h/b \leq 2$ $2.0 \leq h/b < 3.1$	c d

(2) For taking into account the moment distribution between the lateral restraints of members the reduction factor χ_{LT} may be modified as follows:

$$\chi_{LT,mod} = \frac{\chi_{LT}}{f} \quad \text{but} \quad \text{AC2} \begin{cases} \chi_{LT,mod} \leq 1 \\ \chi_{LT,mod} \leq \dfrac{1}{\bar{\lambda}_{LT}^{2}} \end{cases} \text{AC2} \qquad (6.58)$$

NOTE The values of f may be defined in the National Annex. The following minimum values are recommended:

$$f = 1 - 0,5(1 - k_c)\left[1 - 2,0\left(\bar{\lambda}_{LT} - 0,8\right)^2\right] \quad \text{but } f \leq 1,0$$

k_c is a correction factor according to Table 6.6.

The National Annex defines f in NA.2.18.

NA.2.18 Clause 6.3.2.3(2) Modification factor, f

The recommended expression for f should be used in which k_c is given by:

$$k_c = \frac{1}{\sqrt{C_1}}$$

where:

$$C_1 = \frac{M_{cr} \text{ for the actual bending moment diagram}}{M_{cr} \text{ for a uniform bending moment diagram}}$$

Values of C_1 are given in the references list in NA.4.

Values of C_1 are given in the reference "A list of Non-contradictory, complementary information to be used with Eurocode 3: Design of Steel Structures: Part 1.1 General rules and rules for buildings", found at www.steel-ncci.co.uk.

Table 6.6 — Correction factors k_c

Moment distribution	k_c
 $\psi = 1$	1,0
 $-1 \leq \psi \leq 1$	$\frac{1}{1,33 - 0,33\psi}$
	0,94
	0,90
	0,91
	0,86
	0,77
	0,82

6.3.2.4 Simplified assessment methods for beams with restraints in buildings

(1)B Members with discrete lateral restraint to the compression flange are not susceptible to lateral-torsional buckling if the length L_c between restraints or the resulting equivalent compression flange slenderness $\bar{\lambda}_f$ satisfies:

$$\bar{\lambda}_f - \frac{k_c L_c}{i_{f,z}\lambda_1} \leq \bar{\lambda}_{c0}\frac{M_{c,Rd}}{M_{y,Ed}} \qquad (6.59)$$

where

$M_{y,Ed}$ is the maximum design value of the bending moment within the restraint spacing

$M_{c,Rd} = W_y \frac{f_y}{\gamma_{MI}}$

W_y is the appropriate section modulus corresponding to the compression flange
k_c is a slenderness correction factor for moment distribution between restraints, see Table 6.6
$i_{f,z}$ is the radius of gyration of the compression flange including 1/3 of the compressed part of the web area, about the minor axis of the section
$\bar{\lambda}_{c,0}$ is the slenderness limit of the equivalent compression flange defined above

$$\lambda_1 = \pi\sqrt{\frac{E}{f_y}} = 93,9\varepsilon$$

$$\varepsilon = \sqrt{\frac{235}{f_y}} \qquad (f_y \text{ in N/mm}^2)$$

NOTE 1B For Class 4 cross-sections $i_{f,z}$ may be taken as

$$i_{f,z} = \sqrt{\frac{I_{eff,f}}{A_{eff,f} + \frac{1}{3} A_{eff,w,c}}}$$

where

$I_{eff,f}$ is the effective second moment of area of the compression flange about the minor axis of the section
$A_{eff,f}$ is the effective area of the compression flange
$A_{eff,w,c}$ is the effective area of the compressed part of the web

NOTE 2B The slenderness limit $\overline{\lambda}_{c0}$ may be given in the National Annex. A limit value $\overline{\lambda}_{c0} = \overline{\lambda}_{LT,0} + 0,1$ is recommended, see 6.3.2.3.

The National Annex defines the slenderness limit in NA.2.19.

NA.2.19 Clause 6.3.2.4(1)B The slenderness limit $\overline{\lambda}_{c0}$

For I, H, channel and box sections used in buildings the value of $\overline{\lambda}_{c0}$ should be taken as 0,4

(2)B If the slenderness of the compression flange $\overline{\lambda}_f$ exceeds the limit given in (1)B, the design buckling resistance moment may be taken as:

$$M_{b,Rd} = k_{f\ell}\, \chi\, M_{c,Rd} \quad \text{but} \quad M_{b,Rd} \leq M_{c,Rd} \tag{6.60}$$

where

χ is the reduction factor of the equivalent compression flange determined with $\overline{\lambda}_f$
$k_{f\ell}$ is the modification factor accounting for the conservatism of the equivalent compression flange method.

NOTE B The modification factor may be given in the National Annex. A value $k_{f\ell} = 1,10$ is recommended.

The National Annex defines the modification factor in NA.2.19.

NA.2.20 Clause 6.3.2.4(2)B Modification factor, k_{fl}

The value of the modification factor $k_{f\ell}$ should be taken as:

$k_{f\ell} = 1,0$ for hot rolled I – sections
$k_{f\ell} = 1,0$ for welded I – sections with $h/b \leq 2$
$k_{f\ell} = 0,9$ for other sections

(3)B The buckling curves to be used in (2)B should be taken as follows:

curve d for welded sections provided that: $\frac{h}{t_f} \leq 44\varepsilon$

curve c for all other sections

where

h is the overall depth of the cross-section
t is the thickness of the compression flange.

NOTE B For lateral torsional buckling of components of building structures with restraints see also Annex BB.3.

Lateral torsional buckling (buckling resistance in bending) occurs in unrestrained, or inadequately restrained, beams bent about the major axis (whose minor axis inertia is significantly less than the major axis inertia as is the case for most beam sections). This causes the compression flange to buckle and deflect sideways, thus inducing twisting of the section. It is a complex form of behaviour and a realistic treatment of it in design is necessarily involved. The approach used in 6.3 is analogous to column (axial) buckling and the same buckling curves are used in 6.3 as in 6.2 (column buckling), with the exception of curve a_0. One of the main added complexities, however, concerns the variation in bending moment along the length being checked. It is this which is causing the compression in part of the section and hence inducing lateral torsional buckling (LTB), but unlike columns where the axial destabilizing force is constant, the bending moment can vary between restraint points.

Note that throughout 6.3.2 all slenderness values are based on minor axis radii of gyration (i_z) i.e. LTB is a minor axis buckling phenomena, although the applied design moments are about the major axis (y-y).

Values of slenderness below which LTB can be ignored are given in 6.3.2.2(4) and equation (6.59) i.e. the compression flange is sufficiently restrained or robust that this form of instability is not possible.

Note also that in Table 6.6 the parameter ϕ is the ratio of the end moments for a linear variation of bending moment (the larger value the denominator), moment reversal being reflected in the negative sign.

A general method for the treatment of LTB is given in 6.3.2.2, a method applicable to rolled sections in 6.3.2.3, and a simplified method for beams in buildings in 6.3.2.4. Both 6.3.2.2 and 6.3.2.3 introduce the term M_{cr}, the elastic critical moment, the term analogous to the Euler critical load for a column N_{cr}. Subclause 6.3.2.2(2) furthermore defines M_{cr} as being based on "gross cross-sectional properties and takes into account the loading conditions, the real moment distribution and the lateral restraints". It is thus within this term that all of the complex variables referred to above are contained, and no further guidance as to the evaluation of M_{cr} is given anywhere in the document (including Annex BB). At the time of writing this guide it should therefore be assumed that either the designer is intended to derive M_{cr} from first principles (in the view of the author this is difficult – in some cases of loading, a theoretical solution for M_{cr} does not exist, and various empirical or approximate formulae have been suggested e.g. Trahair, N.S. and Bradford, M.A., *The behaviour and design of steel structure*, London and New York: Chapman and Hall, 1988, Chapter 6.), or much more detailed guidance will be given in documents to be published in the member countries subsequent to the publication of EN 1993-1-1 (for example, see guidance for calculating elastic critical moment (M_{cr}) available from the Steel Construction Institute at http://www.steelbiz.org, where design charts and software are available to download).

Equation (6.58) in 6.3.2.3(2) could also present some confusion as it seems to imply that the factor "f" takes account of moment variation, which seems to conflict with the definition of M_{cr} which has already allowed for this. Further clarification of this clause should be awaited before it is used in its present form.

Worked example 3 – LTB

Check the suitability of a 457 × 152 UB74 in S275 steel used as a simply supported beam over an 8 m span subject to uniform end moments of 150 kNm (already appropriately factored to be the design loading). Assume that the ends of the beam are supported in such a way that lateral deflection and twist are prevented, while the flange ends are free to warp. In this somewhat contrived situation (see previous commentary) it can be shown that the elastic critical moment M_{cr} is given by:

$$M_{cr} = \frac{\pi\sqrt{(EI_z GI_t)}}{L}\sqrt{\left(1+\frac{\pi^2 EI_w}{GI_t L^2}\right)}$$ where previously undefined terms are:

I_w = warping constant (from tables)
I_t = torsion section constant (from tables)

This further reduces to the following (applicable to I sections)

$$M_{cr} \cong \frac{0.9\,Ah}{\left(\frac{L}{i_z}\right)^2}\sqrt{\left[1+\tfrac{1}{20}\left(\frac{Lt_f}{i_z h}\right)^2\right]} \quad \text{kN m}$$

(Refer to *Worked example 1*) Section classification in bending: Class 1 (already derived).
f_y = 275 N/mm^2
Geometric properties of 457 × 152 UB74 (from steel tables)
Symbols (see Figure 1.1): b = 154,4 mm, h= 462,0 mm, d= 407,6 mm, t_f = 17,0 mm, t_w = 9,6 mm, root radius, r = 10,2 mm, A = 9450 mm^2, i_z = 33,3 mm, $W_{pl.y}$ = 1,627,000 mm^3, I_w = 0,518 dm^6, I_t = 65,9 cm^2, I_z = 1047 cm^4

Although buckling resistance is, by inspection, the controlling factor in this beam, for completeness the bending resistance $M_{c.Rd}$ will also be calculated.

Bending resistance

Constant bending moment, therefore zero shear force – thus no reduction in $M_{c.Rd}$ due to shear.

Equation (6.13) $M_{c,Rd} = M_{pl,Rd} = \frac{W_{pl} f_y}{\gamma_{M0}}$ for Class 1 cross-sections

$= 447{,}43$ kNm

Buckling resistance

Buckling length = system length = L = 8 m

Above formulae give M_{cr} = 150,79 kNm (approximate formula) or M_{cr} = 154,17 kNm (more exact).

Taking M_{cr} = 150,79 kNm

Using 6.3.2.2 $\bar{\lambda}_{LT} = \sqrt{\frac{W_y f_y}{M_{cr}}} = 1{,}722$,

where $W_y = W_{pl,y}$ for Class 1 or 2 cross-sections

$\phi_{LT} = 0{,}5\left[1 + \alpha_{LT}(\bar{\lambda}_{LT} - \bar{\lambda}_{LT.0}) + \beta\bar{\lambda}_{LT}^2\right]$ (equation 6.57) where $\bar{\lambda}_{LT.0} = 0{,}4$, $\beta = 0{,}75$

and from Table 6.5 (h/b > 2) curve c: hence α_{LT} = 0.49 (Table 6.3).

$\therefore \phi_{LT} = 1{,}934$ and:

$\chi_{LT} = \frac{1}{\phi_{LT} + \sqrt{\phi^2_{LT} - \beta\bar{\lambda}^2_{LT}}}$ but $\chi_{LT} \leq 1{,}0$ and $\leq \frac{1}{\bar{\lambda}^2_{LT}}$

= 0,316 which is ≤ 1,0 and ≤ 0,337.

Equation (6.55) $M_{b,Rd} = \chi_{LT} W_y \frac{f_y}{\gamma_{M1}}$ and as before $W_y = W_{pl,y}$ for Class 1 section and γ_{M1} = 1,00 (6.1(1))

This gives $M_{b.Rd}$ = 141,4 kNm.

Thus the selected beam fails in LTB as 141,4 < 150,0 kNm.

6.3.3 Uniform members in bending and axial compression

(1) Unless second-order analysis is carried out using the imperfections as given in 5.3.2, the stability of uniform members with double symmetric cross-sections for sections not susceptible to distortional deformations should be checked as given in the following clauses, where a distinction is made for:

- members that are not susceptible to torsional deformations, e.g. circular hollow sections or sections restraint from torsion
- members that are susceptible to torsional deformations, e.g. members with open cross-sections and not restraint from torsion.

(2) In addition, the resistance of the cross-sections at each end of the member should satisfy the requirements given in 6.2.

NOTE 1 The interaction formulae are based on the modelling of simply supported single span members with end fork conditions and with or without continuous lateral restraints, which are subjected to compression forces, end moments and/or transverse loads.

NOTE 2 In case the conditions of application expressed in (1) and (2) are not fulfilled, see 6.3.4.

(3) For members of structural systems the resistance check may be carried out on the basis of the individual single span members regarded as cut out of the system. Second-order effects of the sway system (P-Δ effects) have to be taken into account, either by the end moments of the member or by means of appropriate buckling lengths respectively, see 5.2.2(3)c and 5.2.2(8).

(4) Members which are subjected to combined bending and axial compression should satisfy:

$$\frac{N_{Ed}}{\dfrac{\chi_y N_{Rk}}{\gamma_{MI}}} + k_{yy}\frac{M_{y,Ed} + \Delta M_{y,Ed}}{\chi_{LT}\dfrac{M_{y,Rk}}{\gamma_{MI}}} + k_{yz}\frac{M_{z,Ed} + \Delta M_{z,Ed}}{\dfrac{M_{z,Rk}}{\gamma_{MI}}} \le 1 \qquad (6.61)$$

$$\frac{N_{Ed}}{\dfrac{\chi_z N_{Rk}}{\gamma_{MI}}} + k_{zy}\frac{M_{y,Ed} + \Delta M_{y,Ed}}{\chi_{LT}\dfrac{M_{y,Rk}}{\gamma_{MI}}} + k_{zz}\frac{M_{z,Ed} + \Delta M_{z,Ed}}{\dfrac{M_{z,Rk}}{\gamma_{MI}}} \le 1 \qquad (6.62)$$

where

N_{Ed}, $M_{y,Ed}$ and $M_{z,Ed}$ are the design values of the compression force and the maximum moments about the y–y and z–z axis along the member, respectively

$\Delta M_{y,Ed}$, $\Delta M_{z,Ed}$ are the moments due to the shift of the centroidal axis according to 6.2.9.3 for class 4 sections, see Table 6.7

χ_y and χ_z are the reduction factors due to flexural buckling from 6.3.1

χ_{LT} is the reduction factor due to lateral torsional buckling from 6.3.2

k_{yy}, k_{yz}, k_{zy}, k_{zz} are the interaction factors.

Table 6.7 — Values for $N_{Rk} = f_y A_i$, $M_{i,Rk} = f_y W_i$ and $\Delta M_{i,Ed}$

Class	1	2	3	4
A_I	A	A	A	A_{eff}
W_y	$W_{pl,y}$	$W_{pl,y}$	$W_{el,y}$	$W_{eff,y}$
W_z	$W_{pl,z}$	$W_{pl,z}$	$W_{el,z}$	$W_{eff,z}$
$\Delta M_{y,Ed}$	0	0	0	$e_{N,y}\,N_{Ed}$
$\Delta M_{z,Ed}$	0	0	0	$e_{N,z}\,N_{Ed}$

NOTE For members not susceptible to torsional deformation χ_{LT} would be $\chi_{LT} = 1{,}0$.

(5) The interaction factors k_{yy}, k_{yz}, k_{zy}, k_{zz} depend on the method which is chosen.

NOTE 1 The interaction factors k_{yy}, k_{yz}, k_{zy} and k_{zz} have been derived from two alternative approaches. Values of these factors may be obtained from Annex A (alternative method 1) or from Annex B (alternative method 2).

NOTE 2 The National Annex may give a choice from alternative method 1 or alternative method 2.

The National Annex refers to this choice in NA 2.21.

NA. 2.21 Clause 6.3.3(5) Interactions factors k_{yy}, k_{yz}, k_{zy} and k_{zz}

The interaction factors k_{yy}, k_{yz}, k_{zy}, k_{zz} for doubly symmetric sections may be determined using either alternative Method 1 (given in Annex A) or alternative Method 2 (given in Annex B). Alternative Method 2 (given in Annex B) may also be used for sections that are not doubly symmetric when modified in accordance with NA 3.2.

NOTE 3 For simplicity verifications may be performed in the elastic range only.

Bending and axial effects on members are dealt with in 6.3.3 and is essentially a combination of 6.3.1 (for buckling resistance in compression) and 6.3.2 (buckling resistance in bending, i.e. lateral torsional buckling) given in the form of the interaction equations (6.61) and (6.62). These equations are linear summations of "utilization" ratios (the total not to exceed 100 % or 1.0). In each ratio the numerator is the applied design action, and the denominator the corresponding resistance to that action acting separately. The first term in the equations concerns axial compression effects, the second and third bending effects about the major and minor axes respectively. Note that lateral torsional buckling cannot occur for bending about the minor axis (z–z) and thus there is no χ_{LT} reduction factor in the third term of each equation.

While not immediately obvious, and also not explained, the following possible failure modes are all covered in equations (6.61) and (6.62):

(a) buckling about both axes due to axial compression;
(b) "amplification" of in-plane buckling effects due to applied moments increasing lateral deflections and possible in-plane buckling due to this amplification effect;
(c) lateral torsional buckling due to major axis moment;
(d) for Class 4 sections only, the increase in bending moment is due to eccentric action of axial force caused by removal of part of the cross-section when assessing cross sectional properties, thus turning an actual symmetric section into an idealised unsymmetric one when non-contributory parts of the web and/or flange are removed (the ΔM terms in the second and third ratios).

Many of the above four points are reflected in the "k" interaction factors to which reference is made in Annex A or B – two alternative approaches are defined for evaluating these factors.

The uncertainty regarding lateral torsional buckling (M_{cr} and $\bar{\lambda}_{LT}$) mentioned earlier also remains a problem for the designer in this clause.

Worked example 4 – combined axial/bending

The same 203 × 203 UC52 in S275 steel, and with the same system and buckling lengths, used in worked example 2, is subjected to the following design actions: axial force of 400 kN and major axis bending moments of 50 kNm at each end (causing constant bending moment along its length, no transverse loading applied), zero minor axis moment.

The equations to be satisfied are equations (6.61) and (6.62), given below:

$$\frac{N_{Ed}}{\frac{\chi_y N_{Rk}}{\gamma_{MI}}} + k_{yy}\frac{M_{y,Ed} + \Delta M_{y,Ed}}{\chi_{LT}\frac{M_{y,Rk}}{\gamma_{MI}}} + k_{yz}\frac{M_{z,Ed} + \Delta M_{z,Ed}}{\frac{M_{z,Rk}}{\gamma_{MI}}} \le 1$$

$$\frac{N_{Ed}}{\frac{\chi_z N_{Rk}}{\gamma_{MI}}} + k_{zy}\frac{M_{y,Ed} + \Delta M_{y,Ed}}{\chi_{LT}\frac{M_{y,Rk}}{\gamma_{MI}}} + k_{zz}\frac{M_{z,Ed} + \Delta M_{z,Ed}}{\frac{M_{z,Rk}}{\gamma_{MI}}} \le 1$$

In this case:

(a) minor axis moment $M_{z.Ed}$ is zero;
(b) Class 1 section (already classified) ∴ no ΔM moments;
(c) also electing method 2 for evaluation of k factors (no guidance available at time of writing as regards method 1 (Annex A) or method 2 (Annex B).

Footnote to Table B.1 gives $k_{zy} = 0$.

Thus in this example, the above equations reduce to:

$$\frac{N_{Ed}}{\frac{\chi_y N_{Rk}}{\gamma_{MI}}} + k_{yy}\frac{M_{y,Ed}}{\chi_{LT}\frac{M_{y,Rk}}{\gamma_{MI}}} \le 1.0 \text{ and}$$

$$\frac{N_{Ed}}{\frac{\chi_z N_{Rk}}{\gamma_{MI}}} \le 1.0$$

Taking the second condition first, the denominator has already been effectively determined in worked example 2:

$$\frac{N_{Ed}}{\frac{\chi_z N_{Rk}}{\gamma_{MI}}} = \frac{400}{1356} = 0.295 < 1,0 \therefore \text{ Equation (6.62) condition satisfied}$$

First condition
First term has again been determined from the previous example

$$\frac{N_{Ed}}{\frac{\chi_y N_{Rk}}{\gamma_{MI}}} = \frac{400}{1469} = 0,272$$

Concentrating on the major axis bending term $k_{yy}\frac{M_{y,Ed}}{\chi_{LT}\frac{M_{y,Rk}}{\gamma_{MI}}}$

(1) To obtain χ_{LT} using the same principles as worked example 3:

Calculate M_{cr} using the approximate equation given earlier for constant bending moment

$M_{cr} \cong \frac{0.9\,Ah}{\left(\frac{L}{i_z}\right)^2}\sqrt{\left[1 + \frac{1}{20}\left(\frac{Lt_f}{i_z h}\right)^2\right]}$ kN m. gives a value of 211,72 kN m (the more exact formula gives 235 kN m)

$$\bar{\lambda}_{LT} = \sqrt{\frac{W_y f_y}{M_{cr}}} = 0,858$$

Curve (b) Table 6.5 (h/b ≤ 2) α_{LT} = 0,34 gives ϕ_{LT} = 0.854 and $\chi_{LT} = 0.784 \left(\leq 1 \text{ and} \leq \frac{1}{\bar{\lambda}_{LT}^2} \right)$ leading to

$$\chi_{LT} \frac{M_{y,Rk}}{\gamma_{MI}} = \chi_{LT} \frac{W_{y,pl} f_y}{1.0} = 122,25 \, \text{kN m}$$

(2) To determine k_{yy}, as previously stated, method 2 (Annex B) has been selected. Referring to Table B.1:

$$k_{yy} = \begin{array}{l} C_{my}\left(1 + \left(\bar{\lambda}_y - 0,2\right) \dfrac{N_{Ed}}{\chi_y N_{Rk} / \gamma_{MI}}\right) \\ \leq C_{my}\left(1 + 0,8 \dfrac{N_{Ed}}{\chi_y N_{Rk} / \gamma_{MI}}\right) \end{array}$$

C_{my} from Table B.3 with ψ = 1 (constant bending moment) gives k_{yy} = 1,125 (note $\bar{\lambda}_y$ = 0.66 from worked example 2) and ≤ 1,2176 ∴ k_{yy} = 1.125.

The major axis moment ratio $k_{yy} \dfrac{M_{y,Ed}}{\chi_{LT} \dfrac{M_{y,Rk}}{\gamma_{MI}}}$ thus becomes 1,125 × 50/122,5 = 0,459

$$\therefore \frac{N_{Ed}}{\dfrac{\chi_y N_{Rk}}{\gamma_{MI}}} + k_{yy} \frac{M_{y,Ed}}{\chi_{LT} \dfrac{M_{y,Rk}}{\gamma_{MI}}} = 0,272 + 0,459 = 0,731 \therefore \text{Equation (6.61) satisfied.}$$

7 Serviceability limit states

7.2 Serviceability limit states for buildings

7.2.1 Vertical deflections

(1)B With reference to EN 1990 – Annex A1.4 limits for vertical deflections according to Figure A1.1 should be specified for each project and agreed with the client.

NOTE B The National Annex may specify limits.

7.2.2 Horizontal deflections

(1)B With reference to EN 1990 – Annex A1.4 limits for horizontal deflections according to Figure A1.2 should be specified for each project and agreed with the client.

NOTE B The National Annex may specify limits.

7.2.3 Dynamic effects

(1)B With reference to EN 1990 – Annex A1.4.4 the vibrations of structures on which the public can walk should be limited to avoid significant discomfort to users, and limits should be specified for each project and agreed with the client.

NOTE B The National Annex may specify limits for vibration floors.

NA. 2.23 Clause 7.2.1(1)B Vertical deflections

The following table gives suggested limits for calculated vertical deflections of certain members under the characteristic load combination due to variable loads and should not include permanent loads. Circumstances may arise where greater or lesser values would be more appropriate. Other members may also need deflection limits.

On low pitch and flat roofs the possibility of ponding should be investigated.

Vertical deflections	
Cantilevers	Length/180
Beams carrying plaster or other brittle finish	Span/360
Other beams (except purlins and sheeting rails)	Span/200
Purlins and sheeting rails	To suit the characteristics of particular cladding.

NA. 2.24 Clause 7.2.2(1)B Horizontal deflections

The following table gives suggested limits for calculated horizontal deflections of certain members under the characteristic load combination due to variable load. Circumstances may arise where greater or lesser values would be more appropriate. Other members may also need deflection limits.

Horizontal deflections	
Tops of columns in single-storey buildings except portal frames	Height/300
Columns in portal frame buildings, not supporting crane runways	To suit the characteristics of the particular cladding
In each storey of a building with more than one storey	Height of that storey/300

NA. 2.25 Clause 7.2.3(1)B Dynamic effects

Reference should be made to specialist literature as appropriate. For floor vibrations see NA.4.

Annex B [informative] Method 2: Interaction factors k_{ij} for interaction formula in 6.3.3 (4)

Table B.1 — Interaction factors k_{ij} for members not susceptible to torsional deformations

<table>
<tr><th rowspan="2">Interaction factors</th><th rowspan="2">Type of sections</th><th colspan="2">Design assumption</th></tr>
<tr><th>elastic cross-sectional properties class 3, class 4</th><th>plastic cross-sectional properties class 1, class 2</th></tr>
<tr><td>k_{yy}</td><td>I sections
RHS sections</td><td>$C_{my}\left(1+0,6\,\bar{\lambda}_y\frac{N_{Ed}}{\chi_y N_{Rk}/\gamma_{M1}}\right)$
$\leq C_{my}\left(1+0,6\frac{N_{Ed}}{\chi_y N_{Rk}/\gamma_{M1}}\right)$</td><td>$C_{my}\left(1+(\bar{\lambda}_y-0,2)\frac{N_{Ed}}{\chi_y N_{Rk}/\gamma_{M1}}\right)$
$\leq C_{my}\left(1+0,8\frac{N_{Ed}}{\chi_y N_{Rk}/\gamma_{M1}}\right)$</td></tr>
<tr><td>k_{yz}</td><td>I sections
RHS sections</td><td>k_{zz}</td><td>$0,6k_{zz}$</td></tr>
<tr><td>k_{zy}</td><td>I sections
RHS sections</td><td>$0,8k_{yy}$</td><td>$0,6k_{yy}$</td></tr>
<tr><td rowspan="2">k_{zz}</td><td>I sections</td><td rowspan="2">$C_{mz}\left(1+0,6\,\bar{\lambda}_z\frac{N_{Ed}}{\chi_z N_{Rk}/\gamma_{M1}}\right)$
$\leq C_{mz}\left(1+0,6\frac{N_{Ed}}{\chi_z N_{Rk}/\gamma_{M1}}\right)$</td><td>$C_{mz}\left(1+(2\bar{\lambda}_z-0,6)\frac{N_{Ed}}{\chi_z N_{Rk}/\gamma_{M1}}\right)$
$\leq C_{mz}\left(1+1,4\frac{N_{Ed}}{\chi_z N_{Rk}/\gamma_{M1}}\right)$</td></tr>
<tr><td>RHS sections</td><td>$C_{mz}\left(1+(\bar{\lambda}_z-0,2)\frac{N_{Ed}}{\chi_z N_{Rk}/\gamma_{M1}}\right)$
$\leq C_{mz}\left(1+0,8\frac{N_{Ed}}{\chi_z N_{Rk}/\gamma_{M1}}\right)$</td></tr>
<tr><td colspan="4">For I and H sections and rectangular hollow sections under axial compression and uniaxial bending $M_{y,Ed}$ the coefficient k_{zy} may be k_{zy} = 0.</td></tr>
</table>

Table B.2 — Interaction factors k_{ij} for members susceptible to torsional deformations

Interaction factors	Design assumptions	
	elastic cross-sectional properties class 3, class 4	plastic cross-sectional properties class 1, class 2
k_{yy}	k_{yy} from Table B.1	k_{yy} from Table B.1
k_{yz}	k_{yz} from Table B.1	k_{yz} from Table B.1
k_{zy}	$\left[1-\frac{0,05\bar{\lambda}_z}{(C_{mLT}-0,25)}\frac{N_{Ed}}{\chi_z N_{Rk}/\gamma_{M1}}\right]$ $\geq\left[1-\frac{0,05}{(C_{mLT}-0,25)}\frac{N_{Ed}}{\chi_z N_{Rk}/\gamma_{M1}}\right]$	$\left[1-\frac{0,1\bar{\lambda}_z}{(C_{mLT}-0,25)}\frac{N_{Ed}}{\chi_z N_{Rk}/\gamma_{M1}}\right]$ $\geq\left[1-\frac{0,1}{(C_{mLT}-0,25)}\frac{N_{Ed}}{\chi_z N_{Rk}/\gamma_{M1}}\right]$ for $\bar{\lambda}_z<0,4$: $k_{zy}=0,6+\bar{\lambda}_z\leq 1-\frac{0,1\bar{\lambda}_z}{(C_{mLT}-0,25)}\frac{N_{Ed}}{\chi_z N_{Rk}/\gamma_{M1}}$
k_{zz}	k_{zz} from Table B.1	k_{zz} from Table B.1

Table B.3 — Equivalent uniform moment factors C_m in Tables B.1 and B.2

Moment diagram	Range		C_{my} and C_{mz} and C_{mLT}	
			uniform loading	concentrated load
M, ψ M	$-1 \leq \psi \leq 1$		$0,6 + 0,4\psi \geq 0,4$	
M_h, M_s, ψM_h, $\alpha_s = M_s/M_h$	$0 \leq \alpha_s \leq 1$	$-1 \leq \psi \leq 1$	$0,2 + 0,8\alpha_s \geq 0,4$	$0,2 + 0,8\alpha_s \geq 0,4$
	$-1 \leq \alpha_s < 0$	$0 \leq \psi \leq 1$	$0,1 - 0,8\alpha_s \geq 0,4$	$-0,8\alpha_s \geq 0,4$
		$-1 \leq \psi < 0$	$0,1(1-\psi) - 0,8\alpha_s \geq 0,4$	$0,2(-\psi) - 0,8\alpha_s \geq 0,4$
M_h, M_s, ψM_h, $\alpha_h = M_h/M_s$	$0 \leq \alpha_h \leq 1$	$-1 \leq \psi \leq 1$	$0,95 + 0,05\alpha_h$	$0,90 + 0,10\alpha_h$
	$-1 \leq \alpha_h < 0$	$0 \leq \psi \leq 1$	$0,95 + 0,05\alpha_h$	$0,90 + 0,10\alpha_h$
		$-1 \leq \psi < 0$	$0,95 + 0,05\alpha_h(1+2\psi)$	AC2⟩ $0,90 + 0,10\alpha_h(1+2\psi)$ ⟨AC2

AC2⟩ For members with sway buckling mode the equivalent uniform moment factor should be taken C_{my} = 0,9 or C_{mz} = 0,9 respectively. ⟨AC2

C_{my}, C_{mz} and C_{mLT} shall be obtained according to the bending moment diagram between the relevant braced points as follows:

Moment factor	Bending axis	Points braced in direction
C_{my}	y-y	z-z
C_{mz}	z-z	y-y
C_{mLT}	y-y	y-y

Bibliography

Standards publications

For dated references, only the edition cited applies. For undated references, the latest edition of the referenced document (including any amendments) applies.

NA to BS EN 1991-1-5, *UK National Annex to Eurocode 3: Design of steel structures – Part 1-5: Plated structural elements*

BS EN 1993 (Parts 2 to 6), *Eurocode 3 – Design of steel structures*

NA to BS EN 1993-1-10, *UK National Annex to Eurocode 3: Design of steel structures – Part 1-10: Material toughness and through-thickness properties*

BS EN 1993-1-12, *Eurocode 3: Design of steel structures – Part 1-12: Supplementary rules for high strength steels*

BS EN 10025-2:2004, *Hot rolled products of structural steels – Part 2: Technical delivery conditions for non-alloy structural steels*

BS EN 10250-2, *Open steel die forgings for general engineering purposes – Part 2: Non-alloy quality and special steels*

BS EN 10293, *Steel castings for general engineering uses*

Other publications

[1] Castings in steel construction, SCI publication P 172, The Steel Construction Institute, Silwood Park, Ascot, Berkshire SL5 7QN.

EN 1993-1-8

1.1 Scope

(1) This part of EN 1993 gives design methods for the design of joints subject to predominantly static loading using steel grades S235, S275, S355, S420, S450 and S460.

1.3 Distinction between Principles and Application Rules

(1) The rules in EN 1990 clause 1.4 apply.

1.4 Terms and definitions

(1) The following terms and definitions apply:

1.4.1

basic component (of a joint)

part of a joint that makes a contribution to one or more of its structural properties

1.4.2

connection

location at which two or more elements meet. For design purposes it is the assembly of the basic components required to represent the behaviour during the transfer of the relevant internal forces and moments at the connection

1.4.3

connected member

any member that is joined to a supporting member or element

1.4.4

joint

zone where two or more members are interconnected. For design purposes it is the assembly of all the basic components required to represent the behaviour during the transfer of the relevant internal forces and moments between the connected members. A beam-to-column joint consists of a web panel and either one connection (single sided joint configuration) or two connections (double sided joint configuration), see Figure 1.1

1.4.5

joint configuration

type or layout of the joint or joints in a zone within which the axes of two or more inter-connected members intersect, see Figure 1.2

1.4.6

rotational capacity

the angle through which the joint can rotate without failing

1.4.7

rotational stiffness

the moment required to produce unit rotation in a joint

1.4.8

structural properties (of a joint)

resistance to internal forces and moments in the connected members, rotational stiffness and rotation capacity

1.4.9

uniplanar joint

in a lattice structure a uniplanar joint connects members that are situated in a single plane

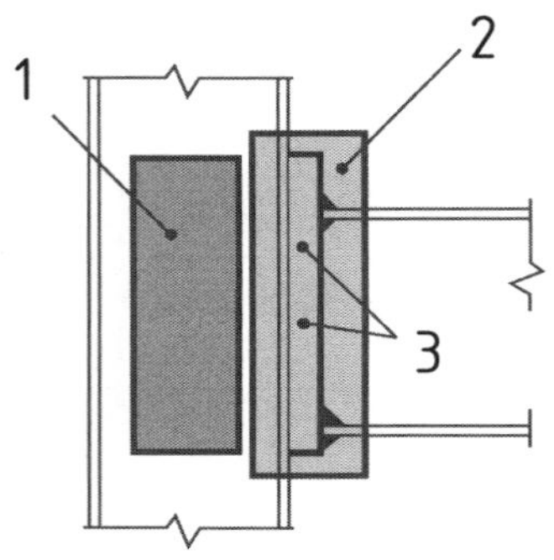

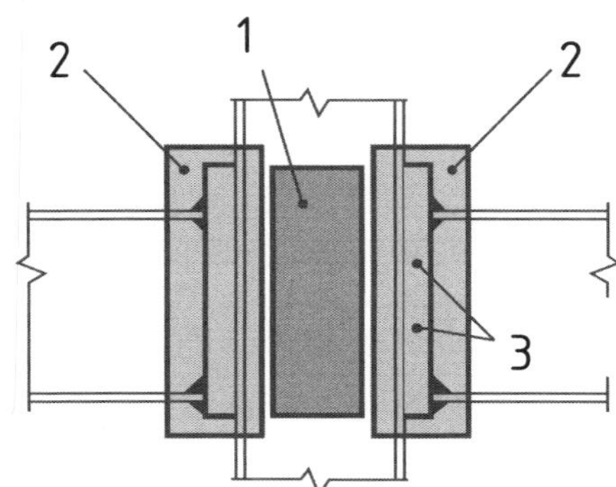

Joint = web panel in shear + connection

Left joint = web panel in shear + left connection

Right joint = web panel in shear + right connection

a) Single-sided joint configuration

b) Double-sided joint configuration

1 web panel in shear
2 connection
3 components (e.g. bolts, endplate)

Figure 1.1 — Parts of a beam-to-column joint configuration

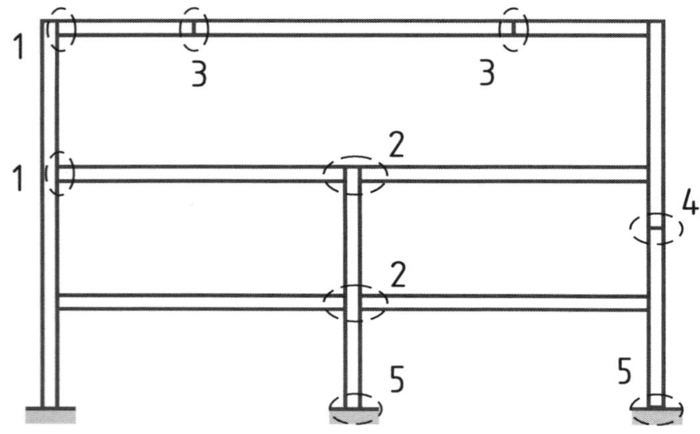

1 Single-sided beam-to-column joint configuration;

2 Double-sided beam-to-column joint configuration;

3 Beam splice;

4 Column splice;

5 Column base.

a) Major-axis joint configurations

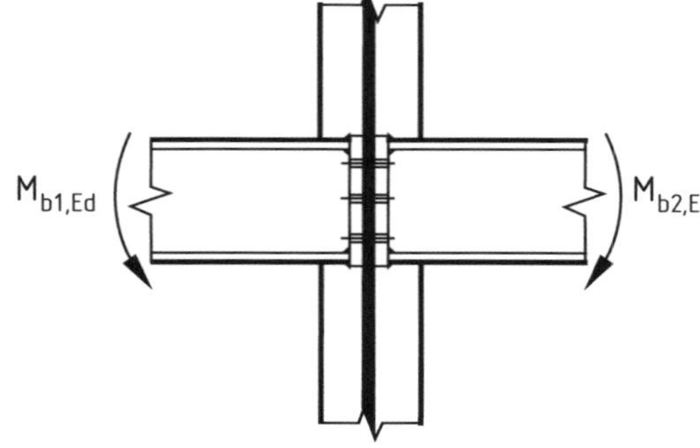

Double-sided beam-to-column joint configuration

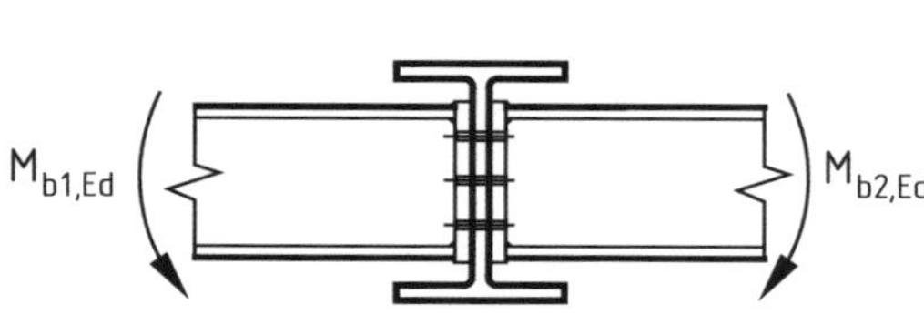

Double-sided beam-to-beam joint configuration

b) Minor-axis joint configurations (to be used only for balanced moments $M_{b1,Ed} = M_{b2,Ed}$)

Figure 1.2 — Joint configurations

1.5 Symbols

(1) The following symbols are used in this Standard:

d Nominal bolt diameter, the diameter of the pin or the diameter of the fastener
d_0 Hole diameter for a bolt, a rivet or a pin
$d_{o,t}$ Hole size for the tension face, generally the hole diameter, but for horizontally slotted holes the slot length should be used
$d_{o,v}$ Hole size for the shear face, generally the hole diameter, but for vertically slotted holes the slot length should be used
d_c Clear depth of the column web
d_m Mean of the across points and across flats dimensions of the bolt head or the nut, whichever is smaller
$f_{H,Rd}$ Design value of the Hertz pressure
f_{ur} Specified ultimate tensile strength of the rivet
e_1 End distance from the centre of a fastener hole to the adjacent end of any part, measured in the direction of load transfer, see Figure 3.1
e_2 Edge distance from the centre of a fastener hole to the adjacent edge of any part, measured at right angles to the direction of load transfer, see Figure 3.1
e_3 Distance from the axis of a slotted hole to the adjacent end or edge of any part, see Figure 3.1
e_4 Distance from the centre of the end radius of a slotted hole to the adjacent end or edge of any part, see Figure 3.1
l_{eff} Effective length of fillet weld
n Number of the friction surfaces or the number of fastener holes on the shear face
p_1 Spacing between centres of fasteners in a line in the direction of load transfer, see Figure 3.1
$p_{1,0}$ Spacing between centres of fasteners in an outer line in the direction of load transfer, see Figure 3.1
$p_{1,i}$ Spacing between centres of fasteners in an inner line in the direction of load transfer, see Figure 3.1
p_2 Spacing measured perpendicular to the load transfer direction between adjacent lines of fasteners, see Figure 3.1
r Bolt row number

NOTE In a bolted connection with more than one bolt-row in tension, the bolt-rows are numbered starting from the bolt-row furthest from the centre of compression.

s_s Length of stiff bearing
t_a Thickness of the angle cleat
t_{fc} Thickness of the column flange
t_p Thickness of the plate under the bolt or the nut
t_w Thickness of the web or bracket
t_{wc} Thickness of the column web
A Gross cross-section area of bolt
A_0 Area of the rivet hole
A_{vc} Shear area of the column, see EN 1993-1-1
A_s Tensile stress area of the bolt or of the anchor bolt
$A_{v,eff}$ Effective shear area
$B_{p,Rd}$ Design punching shear resistance of the bolt head and the nut
E Elastic modulus
$F_{p,Cd}$ Design preload force
$F_{t,Ed}$ Design tensile force per bolt for the ultimate limit state
$F_{t,Rd}$ Design tension resistance per bolt
$F_{T,Rd}$ Tension resistance of an equivalent T-stub flange
$F_{v,Rd}$ Design shear resistance per bolt
$F_{b,Rd}$ Design bearing resistance per bolt
$F_{s,Rd,ser}$ Design slip resistance per bolt at the serviceability limit state
$F_{s,Rd}$ Design slip resistance per bolt at the ultimate limit state
$F_{v,Ed,ser}$ Design shear force per bolt for the serviceability limit state
$F_{v,Ed}$ Design shear force per bolt for the ultimate limit state
$M_{j,Rd}$ Design moment resistance of a joint

S_{j}	Rotational stiffness of a joint
$S_{j,ini}$	Initial rotational stiffness of a joint
$V_{wp,Rd}$	Plastic shear resistance of a column web panel
z	Lever arm
μ	Slip factor
ϕ	Rotation of a joint

2 Basis of design

2.1 Assumptions

(1) The design methods given in this part of EN 1993 assume that the standard of construction is as specified in the execution standards given in 1.2 and that the construction materials and products used are those specified in EN 1993 or in the relevant material and product specifications.

2.2 General requirements

(1)P All joints shall have a design resistance such that the structure is capable of satisfying all the basic design requirements given in this Standard and in EN 1993-1-1.

(2) The partial safety factors γ_M for joints are given in Table 2.1.

Table 2.1 — Partial safety factors for joints

Resistance of members and cross-sections	γ_{M0} , γ_{M1} and γ_{M2} see EN 1993-1-1
Resistance of bolts Resistance of rivets Resistance of pins Resistance of welds Resistance of plates in bearing	γ_{M2}
Slip resistance – for hybrid connections or connections under fatigue loading – for other design situations	γ_{M3} $\gamma_{M3, ser}$
Bearing resistance of an injection bolt	γ_{M4}
Resistance of joints in hollow section lattice girder	γ_{M5}
Resistance of pins at serviceability limit state	$\gamma_{M6,ser}$
Preload of high strength bolts	γ_{M7}
Resistance of concrete	γ_c see EN 1992

NOTE Numerical values for γ_M may be defined in the National Annex. Recommended values are as follows: γ_{M2} = 1,25 ; γ_{M3} = 1,25 for hybrid connections or connections under fatigue loading and $\gamma_{M3, ser}$ = 1,1 for other design situations; γ_{M4} = 1,0 ; γ_{M5} = 1,0 ; $\gamma_{M6,ser}$ = 1,0 ; γ_{M7} = 1,1 .

(3)P Joints subject to fatigue shall also satisfy the principles given in EN 1993-1-9.

NA 2.3 Clause 2.2(2) Partial safety factors, γ_M, for joints

The partial factors given in Table NA.1 should be used.

Table NA.1 – Partial safety factors, γ_M, for joints

Resistance of members and cross-section	Partial factor	Value
Resistance of bolts	γ_{M2}	1.25
Resistance of rivets	γ_{M2}	1.25
Resistance of pins	γ_{M2}	1.25
Resistance of welds	γ_{M2}	1.25
Resistance of plates in bearing[A)]	γ_{M2}	1.25
Slip resistance: • At ultimate limit state (Category C) • At serviceability limit state (Category B)	 γ_{M3} $\gamma_{M3,ser}$	 1.25 1.10
Bearing resistance of an injection bolt	γ_{M4}	1.00
Resistance of joints in hollow section lattice girder	γ_{M5}	1.00
Resistance of pins at serviceability limit state	$\gamma_{M6,ser}$	1.00
Preload of high strength bolts • For bolts conforming to BS EN 14399-4 and BS EN 14399-8 • Others	 γ_{M7} γ_{M7}	 1.10 1.00
A) In certain circumstances deformation at serviceability may control and a γ_{M2} = 1.50 might be more appropriate. The option for deformation control applies where it is important to avoid deformation of the bolt holes (i.e. when a_b = 1.0). Deformation control need only be applied to the component of the bolt force acting in the direction in which avoiding deformation is important.		

2.3 Applied forces and moments

(1)P The forces and moments applied to joints at the ultimate limit state shall be determined according to the principles in EN 1993-1-1.

2.4 Resistance of joints

(1) The resistance of a joint shall be determined on the basis of the resistances of its basic components.

(2) Linear-elastic or elastic-plastic analysis may be used in the design of joints.

(3) Where fasteners with different stiffenesses are used to carry a shear load the fasteners with the highest stiffness should be designed to carry the design load. An exception to this design method is given in 3.9.3.

2.5 Design assumptions

(1)P Joints shall be designed on the basis of a realistic assumption of the distribution of internal forces and moments. The following assumptions shall be used to determine the distribution of forces:

(a) the internal forces and moments assumed in the analysis are in equilibrium with the forces and moments applied to the joints,
(b) each element in the joint is capable of resisting the internal forces and moments,

(c) the deformations implied by this distribution do not exceed the deformation capacity of the fasteners or welds and the connected parts,
(d) the assumed distribution of internal forces shall be realistic with regard to relative stiffnesses within the joint,
(e) the deformations assumed in any design model based on elastic-plastic analysis are based on rigid body rotations and/or in-plane deformations which are physically possible, and
(f) any model used is in compliance with the evaluation of test results (see EN 1990).

(2) The application rules given in this part satisfy 2.5(1).

Clause 2.5(1) effectively states that the designer should identify the 'load path' through a joint and satisfy themselves that all 'links in the chain' are recognized and checked. The load path identified should be consistent with the assumptions made in the structural model adopted for the structure in both strength and deformation characteristics.

3 Connections made with bolts, rivets or pins

3.1 Bolts, nuts and washers

3.1.1 General

(1) All bolts, nuts and washers should comply with 1.2.4 Reference Standards: Group 4.

(2) The rules in this Standard are valid for the bolt classes given in Table 3.1.

(3) The yield strength f_{yb} and the ultimate tensile strength f_{ub} for bolt classes 4.6, 5.6, 6.8, 8.8 and 10.9 are given in Table 3.1. These values should be adopted as characteristic values in design calculations.

Table 3.1 — Nominal values of the yield strength f_{yb} and the ultimate tensile strength f_{ub} for bolts

Bolt class	4.6	5.6	6.8	8.8	10.9
f_{yb} (N/mm^2)	240	300	480	640	900
f_{ub} (N/mm^2)	400	500	600	800	1000

NOTE The National Annex may exclude certain bolt classes.

NA.2.4 Type of bolt class [BS EN 1993-1-8:2005, 3.1.1(3)]

Bolts of classes 5.8 and 6.8 should be excluded. Bolt class 4.8 may be used provided they are manufactured in accordance with BS EN ISO 898-1 and suitable procedures to avoid hydrogen embrittlement are employed in the manufacturing process.

3.1.2 Preloaded bolts

(1) Only bolt assemblies of classes 8.8 and 10.9 conforming to the requirements given in 1.2.4 Reference Standards: Group 4 for High Strength Structural Bolting with controlled tightening in accordance with the requirements in 1.2.7 Reference Standards: Group 7 may be used as preloaded bolts.

NA.2.5 Clause 3.4.2(1) Level of preload

If the preload is not explicitly used in the design calculations then no specific level of preload is required.

3.4 Categories of bolted connections

3.4.1 Shear connections

(1) Bolted connections loaded in shear should be designed as one of the following:

a) **Category A: Bearing type**
In this category bolts from class 4.6 up to and including class 10.9 should be used. No preloading and special provisions for contact surfaces are required. The design ultimate shear load should not exceed the design shear resistance, obtained from 3.6, nor the design bearing resistance, obtained from 3.6 and 3.7.

b) **Category B: Slip-resistant at serviceability limit state**
In this category preloaded bolts in accordance with 3.1.2(1) should be used. Slip should not occur at the serviceability limit state. The design serviceability shear load should not exceed the design

slip resistance, obtained from 3.9. The design ultimate shear load should not exceed the design shear resistance, obtained from 3.6, nor the design bearing resistance, obtained from 3.6 and 3.7.

c) **Category C: Slip-resistant at ultimate limit state**
In this category preloaded bolts in accordance with 3.1.2(1) should be used. Slip should not occur at the ultimate limit state. The design ultimate shear load should not exceed the design slip resistance, obtained from 3.9, nor the design bearing resistance, obtained from 3.6 and 3.7. In addition for a connection in tension, the design plastic resistance of the net cross-section at bolt holes $N_{net,Rd}$, (see 6.2 of EN 1993-1-1) should be checked, at the ultimate limit state.

The design checks for these connections are summarised in Table 3.2.

3.4.2 Tension connections

(1) Bolted connection loaded in tension should be designed as one of the following:

a) **Category D: non-preloaded**
In this category bolts from class 4.6 up to and including class 10.9 should be used. No preloading is required. This category should not be used where the connections are frequently subjected to variations of tensile loading. However, they may be used in connections designed to resist normal wind loads.

b) **Category E: preloaded**
In this category preloaded 8.8 and 10.9 bolts with controlled tightening in conformity with 1.2.7 Reference Standards: Group 7 should be used.

The design checks for these connections are summarized in Table 3.2.

Table 3.2 — Categories of bolted connections

Category	Criteria	Remarks
	Shear connections	
A bearing type	$F_{v,Ed} \leq F_{v,Rd}$ $F_{v,Ed} \leq F_{b,Rd}$	No preloading required. Bolt classes from 4.6 to 10.9 may be used.
B slip-resistant at serviceability	$F_{v,Ed.ser} \leq F_{s,Rd,ser}$ $F_{v,Ed} \leq F_{v,Rd}$ $F_{v,Ed} \leq F_{b,Rd}$	Preloaded 8.8 or 10.9 bolts should be used. For slip resistance at serviceability see 3.9.
C slip-resistant at ultimate	$F_{v,Ed} \leq F_{s,Rd}$ $F_{v,Ed} \leq F_{b,Rd}$ $\Sigma F_{v,Ed} \leq N_{net,Rd}$	Preloaded 8.8 or 10.9 bolts should be used. For slip resistance at ultimate see 3.9. $N_{net,Rd}$ see EN 1993-1-1
	Tension connections	
D non-preloaded	$F_{t,Ed} \leq F_{t,Rd}$ $F_{t,Ed} \leq B_{p,Rd}$	No preloading required. Bolt classes from 4.6 to 10.9 may be used. $B_{p,Rd}$ see Table 3.4.
E preloaded	$F_{t,Ed} \leq F_{t,Rd}$ $F_{t,Ed} \leq B_{p,Rd}$	Preloaded 8.8 or 10.9 bolts should be used. $B_{p,Rd}$ see Table 3.4.
The design tensile force $F_{t,Ed}$ should include any force due to prying action, see 3.11. Bolts subjected to both shear force and tensile force should also satisfy the criteria given in Table 3.4.		

NOTE When the preload is not explicitly used in the design calculations for slip resistances but is required for execution purposes or as a quality measure (e.g. for durability) then the level of preload can be specified in the National Annex.

The preload is covered in NA.2.5.

This identifies the fact that bolts loaded in shear can be considered as Bearing type (i.e. the parts need to slip into bearing to resist load) or two types of slip resistant situations, depending on the limit state desired to be satisfied. Table 3.2 gives a useful summary of the situation.

3.5 Positioning of holes for bolts and rivets

(1) Minimum and maximum spacing, end and edge distances for bolts and rivets are given in Table 3.3.

(2) Minimum and maximum spacing, end and edge distances for structures subjected to fatigue, see EN 1993-1-9.

Table 3.3 — Minimum and maximum spacing, end and edge distances

Distances and spacings, see Figure 3.1	Minimum	Maximum[1) 2) 3)]		
		Structures made from steels conforming to EN 10025 except steels conforming to EN 10025-5		Structures made from steels conforming to EN 10025-5
		Steel exposed to the weather or other corrosive influences	Steel not exposed to the weather or other corrosive influences	Steel used unprotected
End distance e_1	$1,2d_0$	$4t + 40$ mm		The larger of $8t$ or 125 mm
Edge distance e_2	$1,2d_0$	$4t + 40$ mm		The larger of $8t$ or 125 mm
Distance e_3 in slotted holes	$1,5d_0$ [4)]			
Distance e_4 in slotted holes	$1,5d_0$ [4)]			
Spacing p_1	$2,2d_0$	The smaller of $14t$ or 200 mm	The smaller of $14t$ or 200 mm	The smaller of $14t_{min}$ or 175 mm
Spacing $p_{1,0}$		The smaller of $14t$ or 200 mm		
Spacing $p_{1,i}$		The smaller of $28t$ or 400 mm		
Spacing p_2 [5)]	$2,4d_0$	The smaller of $14t$ or 200 mm	The smaller of $14t$ or 200 mm	The smaller of $14t_{min}$ or 175 mm

1) Maximum values for spacings, edge and end distances are unlimited, except in the following cases:
- for compression members in order to avoid local buckling and to prevent corrosion in exposed members (the limiting values are given in the table) and;
- for exposed tension members to prevent corrosion (the limiting values are given in the table).

2) The local buckling resistance of the plate in compression between the fasteners should be calculated according to EN 1993-1-1 using $0,6p_1$ as buckling length. Local buckling between the fasteners need not be checked if p_1/t is smaller than 9ε. The edge distance should not exceed the local buckling requirements for an outstand element in the compression members, see EN 1993-1-1. The end distance is not affected by this requirement.

3) t is the thickness of the thinner outer connected part.

4) The dimensional limits for slotted holes are given in 2.8. Reference Standards: Group 7.

5) For staggered rows of fasteners a minimum line spacing of $p_2 = 1,2d_0$ may be used, provided that the minimum distance, L, between any two fasteners is greater than or equal to $2,4d_0$ (see Figure 3.1b).

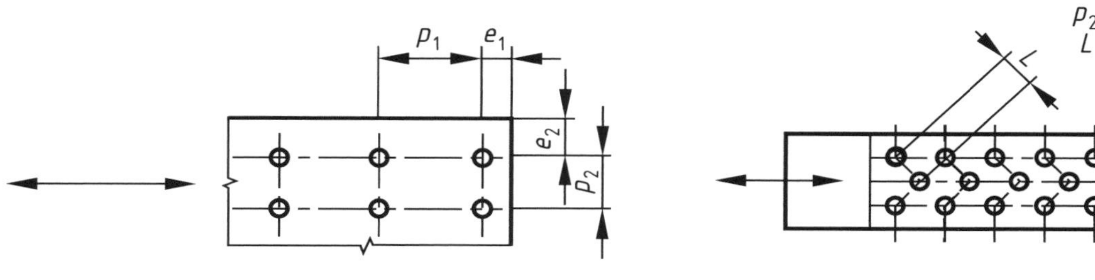

a) Symbols for spacing of fasteners

b) Symbols for staggered spacing

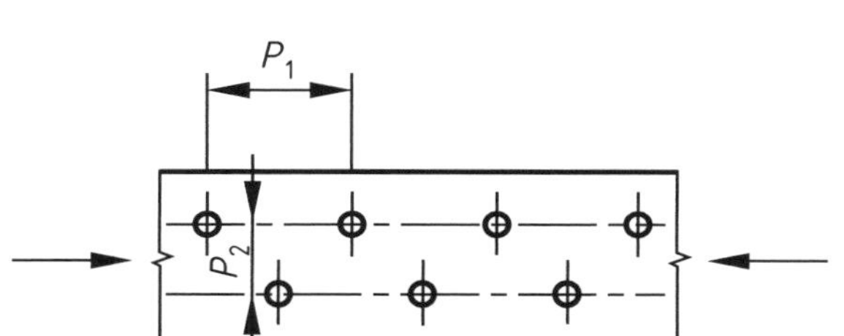

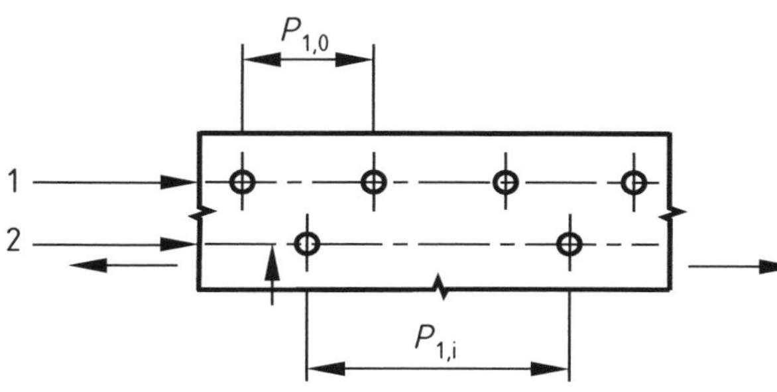

$p_1 \leq 14t$ and ≤ 200 mm

$p_2 \leq 14t$ and ≤ 200 mm

c) Staggered spacing – compression

$p_{1,0} \leq 14t$ and ≤ 200 mm

1 outer row

$p_{1,i} \leq 28t$ and ≤ 400 mm

2 inner row

d) Spacing in tension members

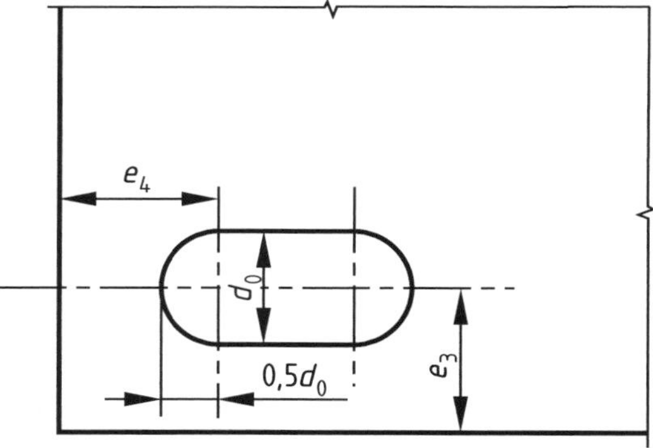

e) End and edge distances for slotted holes

Figure 3.1 — Symbols for end and edge distances and spacing of fasteners

3.6 Design resistance of individual fasteners

3.6.1 Bolts and rivets

(1) The design resistance for an individual fastener subjected to shear and/or tension is given in Table 3.4.

(2) For preloaded bolts in accordance with 3.1.2(1) the design preload, $F_{p,Cd}$, to be used in design calculations should be taken as:

$$F_{p,Cd} = 0,7\, f_{ub}\, A_s \,/\, \gamma_{M7} \qquad (3.1)$$

NOTE Where the preload is not used in design calculations see note to Table 3.2.

(3) The design resistances for tension and for shear through the threaded portion of a bolt given in Table 3.4 should only be used for bolts manufactured in conformity with 1.2.4 Reference Standard: Group 4. For bolts with cut threads, such as anchor bolts or tie rods fabricated from round steel bars where the threads comply with EN 1090, the relevant values from Table 3.4 should be multiplied by a factor of 0,85. For bolts with cut threads where the threads do not comply with EN1090 the relevant values from Table 3.4 should be multiplied by a factor of 0,85.

(4) The design shear resistance $F_{v,Rd}$ given in Table 3.4 should only be used where the bolts are used in holes with nominal clearances not exceeding those for normal holes as specified in 2.8 Reference Standards: Group 7.

(5) M12 and M14 bolts may also be used in 2 mm clearance holes provided that the design resistance of the bolt group based on bearing is less than or equal to the design resistance of the bolt group based on bolt shear. In addition for class 4.8, 5.8, 6.8, 8.8 and 10.9 bolts the design shear resistance $F_{v,Rd}$ should be taken as 0,85 times the value given in Table 3.4.

(6) Fit bolts should be designed using the method for bolts in normal holes.

(7) The thread of a fit bolt should not be included in the shear plane.

(8) The length of the threaded portion of a fit bolt included in the bearing length should not exceed 1/3 of the thickness of the plate, see Figure 3.2.

(9) The hole tolerance used for fit bolts should be in accordance with 2.8 Reference Standards: Group 7.

(10) In single lap joints with only one bolt row, see Figure 3.3, the bolts should be provided with washers under both the head and the nut. The design bearing resistance $F_{b,Rd}$ for each bolt should be limited to:

$$F_{b,Rd} \leq 1,5\, f_u\, d\, t \,/\, \gamma_{M2} \qquad (3.2)$$

NOTE Single rivets should not be used in single lap joints.

(11) In the case of class 8.8 or 10.9 bolts, hardened washers should be used for single lap joints with only one bolt or one row of bolts.

(12) Where bolts or rivets transmitting load in shear and bearing pass through packing of total thickness t_p greater than one-third of the nominal diameter d, see Figure 3.4, the design shear resistance $F_{v,Rd}$ calculated as specified in Table 3.4, should be multiplied by a reduction factor β_p given by:

$$\beta_p = \frac{9d}{8d + 3t_p} \quad \text{but } \beta_p \leq 1 \qquad (3.3)$$

(13) For double shear connections with packing on both sides of the splice, t_p should be taken as the thickness of the thicker packing.

(14) Riveted connections should be designed to transfer shear forces. If tension is present the design tensile force $F_{t,Ed}$ should not exceed the design tension resistance $F_{t,Rd}$ given in Table 3.4.

(15) For grade S 235 steel the "as driven" value of f_{ur} may be taken as 400 N/mm^2.

(16) As a general rule, the grip length of a rivet should not exceed 4,5d for hammer riveting and 6,5d for press riveting.

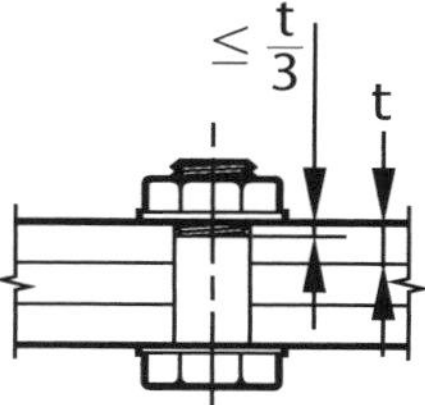

Figure 3.2 — Threaded portion of the shank in the bearing length for fit bolts

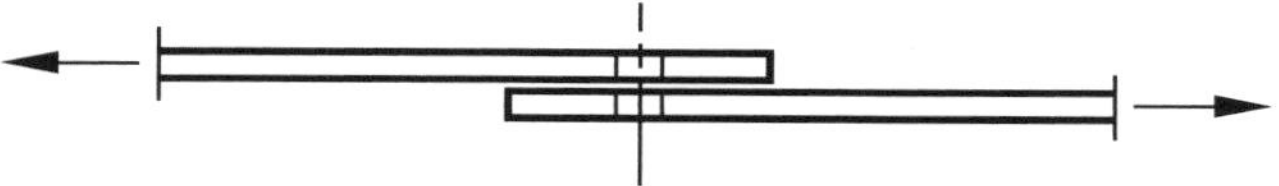

Figure 3.3 — Single lap joint with one row of bolts

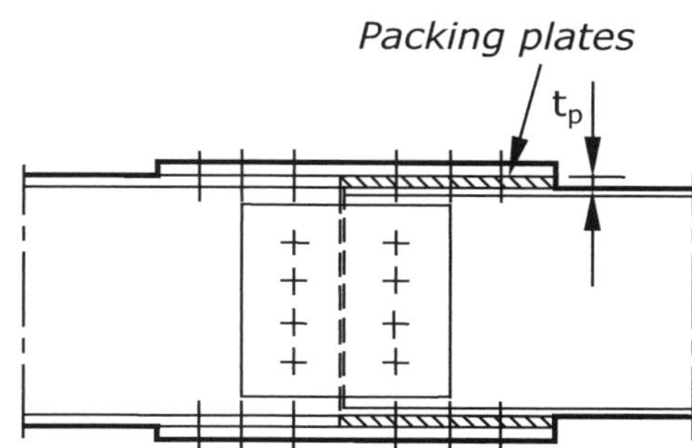

Figure 3.4 — Fasteners through packings

Table 3.4 — Design resistance for individual fasteners subjected to shear and/or tension

Failure mode	Bolts	Rivets
Shear resistance per shear plane	$F_{v,Rd} = \dfrac{\alpha_v f_{ub} A}{\gamma_{M2}}$ – where the shear plane passes through the threaded portion of the bolt (A is the tensile stress area of the bolt A_s): – for classes 4.6, 5.6 and 8.8: $\alpha_v = 0,6$ – for classes 4.8, 5.8, 6.8 and 10.9: $\alpha_v = 0,5$ – where the shear plane passes through the unthreaded portion of the bolt (A is the gross cross-section of the bolt): $\alpha_v = 0,6$	$F_{v,Rd} = \dfrac{0,6 f_{ur} A_0}{\gamma_{M2}}$
Bearing resistance [1), 2), 3)]	$F_{b,Rd} = \dfrac{k_1 \alpha_b f_u d t}{\gamma_{M2}}$ where α_b is the smallest of α_d ; $\dfrac{f_{ub}}{f_u}$ or 1,0; in the direction of load transfer: – for end bolts: $\alpha_d = \dfrac{e_1}{3d_0}$; for inner bolts: $\alpha_d = \dfrac{p_1}{3d_0} - \dfrac{1}{4}$ perpendicular to the direction of load transfer: – for edge bolts: k_1 is the smallest of $2,8\dfrac{e_2}{d_0} - 1,7$, $1,4\dfrac{p_2}{d_0} - 1,7$ and $2,5$ – for inner bolts: k_1 is the smallest of $1,4\dfrac{p_2}{d_0} - 1,7$ or $2,5$	
Tension resistance [2)]	$F_{t,Rd} = \dfrac{k_2 f_{ub} A_s}{\gamma_{M2}}$ where $k_2 = 0,63$ for countersunk bolt, otherwise $k_2 = 0,9$	$F_{t,Rd} = \dfrac{0,6 f_{ur} A_0}{\gamma_{M2}}$
Punching shear resistance	$B_{p,Rd} = 0,6 \pi d_m t_p f_u / \gamma_{M2}$	No check needed
Combined shear and tension	$\dfrac{F_{v,Ed}}{F_{v,Rd}} + \dfrac{F_{t,Ed}}{1,4 F_{t,Rd}} \leq 1,0$	

1) The bearing resistance $F_{b,Rd}$ for bolts
- in oversized holes is 0,8 times the bearing resistance for bolts in normal holes.
- in slotted holes, where the longitudinal axis of the slotted hole is perpendicular to the direction of the force transfer, is 0,6 times the bearing resistance for bolts in round, normal holes.

2) For countersunk bolt:
- the bearing resistance $F_{b,Rd}$ should be based on a plate thickness t equal to the thickness of the connected plate minus half the depth of the countersinking.
- For the determination of the tension resistance $F_{t,Rd}$ the angle and depth of countersinking should conform with 2.8 Reference Standards: Group 4, otherwise the tension resistance $F_{t,Rd}$ should be adjusted accordingly.

3) When the load on a bolt is not parallel to the edge, the bearing resistance may be verified separately for the bolt load components parallel and normal to the end.

3.7 Group of fasteners

(1) The design resistance of a group of fasteners may be taken as the sum of the design bearing resistances $F_{b,Rd}$ of the individual fasteners provided that the design shear resistance $F_{v,Rd}$ of each individual fastener is greater than or equal to the design bearing resistance $F_{b,Rd}$. Otherwise the design resistance of a group of fasteners should be taken as the number of fasteners multiplied by the smallest design resistance of any of the individual fasteners.

3.8 Long joints

(1) Where the distance L_j between the centres of the end fasteners in a joint, measured in the direction of force transfer (see Figure 3.7), is more than $15d$, the design shear resistance $F_{v,Rd}$ of all the fasteners calculated according to Table 3.4 should be reduced by multiplying it by a reduction factor β_{Lf}, given by:

$$\beta_{Lf} = 1 - \frac{L_j - 15d}{200d} \qquad (3.5)$$

but $\beta_{Lf} \leq 1{,}0$ and $\beta_{Lf} \geq 0{,}75$

(2) The provision in 3.8(1) does not apply where there is a uniform distribution of force transfer over the length of the joint, e.g. the transfer of shear force between the web and the flange of a section.

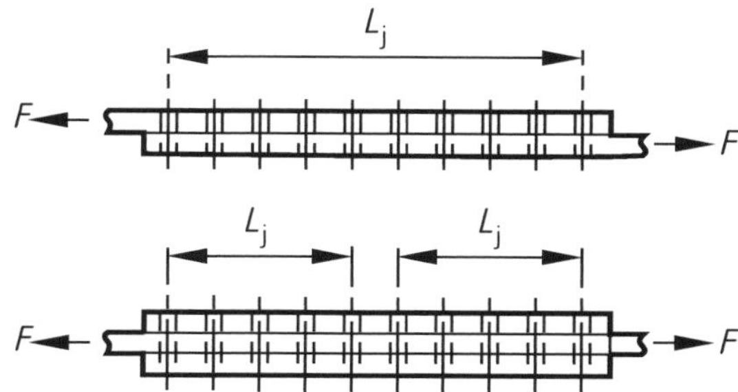

Figure 3.7 — Long joints

> Clause 3.8 recognizes that in a long group of fasteners, the outer ones carry more load than the inner ones, and an appropriate reduction in shear resistance of the assemblage needs to be applied.

3.9 Slip-resistant connections using 8.8 or 10.9 bolts

3.9.1 Design slip resistance

(1) The design slip resistance of a preloaded class 8.8 or 10.9 bolt should be taken as:

$$F_{s,Rd} = \frac{k_s\, n\, \mu}{\gamma_{M3}} F_{p,C} \qquad (3.6a)$$

$$F_{s,Rd,ser} = \frac{k_s\, n\, \mu}{\gamma_{M3,ser}} F_{p,C} \qquad (3.6b)$$

where:

k_s is given in Table 3.6

n is the number of the friction planes

μ is the slip factor obtained either by specific tests for the friction surface in accordance with 2.8 Reference Standards: Group 7 or when relevant as given in Table 3.7.

(2) For class 8.8 and 10.9 bolts conforming with 2.8 Reference Standards: Group 4, with controlled tightening in conformity with 2.8 Reference Standards: Group 7, the preloading force $F_{p,C}$ to be used in equation (3.6) should be taken as:

$$F_{p,C} = 0,7\, f_{ub}\, A_s \tag{3.7}$$

Table 3.6 — Values of k_s

Description	k_s
Bolts in normal holes.	1,0
Bolts in either oversized holes or short slotted holes with the axis of the slot perpendicular to the direction of load transfer.	0,85
Bolts in long slotted holes with the axis of the slot perpendicular to the direction of load transfer.	0,7
Bolts in short slotted holes with the axis of the slot parallel to the direction of load transfer.	0,76
Bolts in long slotted holes with the axis of the slot parallel to the direction of load transfer.	0,63

Table 3.7 — Slip factor, μ, for pre-loaded bolts

Class of friction surfaces (see 2.8 Reference Standard: Group 7)	Slip factor μ
A	0,5
B	0,4
C	0,3
D	0,2

NOTE 1 The requirements for testing and inspection are given in 2.8 Reference Standards: Group 7.
NOTE 2 The classification of any other surface treatment should be based on test specimens representative of the surfaces used in the structure using the procedure set out in 2.8 Reference Standards: Group 7.
NOTE 3 The definitions of the class of friction surface are given in 2.8 Reference Standards: Group 7.
NOTE 4 With painted surface treatments account should made for any loss of pre-load which occur over time.

3.9.2 Combined tension and shear

(1) If a slip-resistant connection is subjected to an applied tensile force, $F_{t,Ed}$ or $F_{t,Ed,ser}$, in addition to the shear force, $F_{v,Ed}$ or $F_{v,Ed,ser}$, tending to produce slip, the design slip resistance per bolt should be taken as follows:

for a category B connection: $$F_{s,Rd,ser} = \frac{k_s\, n\, \mu\,(F_{p,C} - 0,8\, F_{t,Ed,ser})}{\gamma_{M3,ser}} \tag{3.8a}$$

for a category C connection: $$F_{s,Rd} = \frac{k_s\, n\, \mu\,(F_{p,C} - 0,8\, F_{t,Ed})}{\gamma_{M3}} \tag{3.8b}$$

(2) If, in a moment connection, a contact force on the compression side counterbalances the applied tensile force no reduction in slip resistance is required.

3.9.3 Hybrid connections

(1) As an exception to 2.4 (3), preloaded class 8.8 and 10.9 bolts in connections designed as slip-resistant at the ultimate limit state (Category C in 3.4) may be assumed to share load with welds, provided that the final tightening of the bolts is carried out after the welding is complete.

3.10 Deductions for fastener holes

3.10.1 General

(1) Deduction for holes in the member design should be made according to EN 1993-1-1.

3.10.2 Design for block tearing

(1) Block tearing consists of failure in shear at the row of bolts along the shear face of the hole group accompanied by tensile rupture along the line of bolt holes on the tension face of the bolt group. Figure 3.8 shows block tearing.

(2) For a symmetric bolt group subject to concentric loading the design block tearing resistance, $V_{eff,1,Rd}$ is given by:

$$V_{eff,1,Rd} = f_u A_{nt} / \gamma_{M2} + (1/\sqrt{3}) f_y A_{nv} / \gamma_{M0} \qquad (3.9)$$

where:

A_{nt} is net area subjected to tension;
A_{nv} is net area subjected to shear.

(3) For a bolt group subject to eccentric loading the design block shear tearing resistance $V_{eff,2,Rd}$ is given by:

$$V_{eff,2,Rd} = 0,5 f_u A_{nt} / \gamma_{M2} + (1/\sqrt{3}) f_y A_{nv} / \gamma_{M0} \qquad (3.10)$$

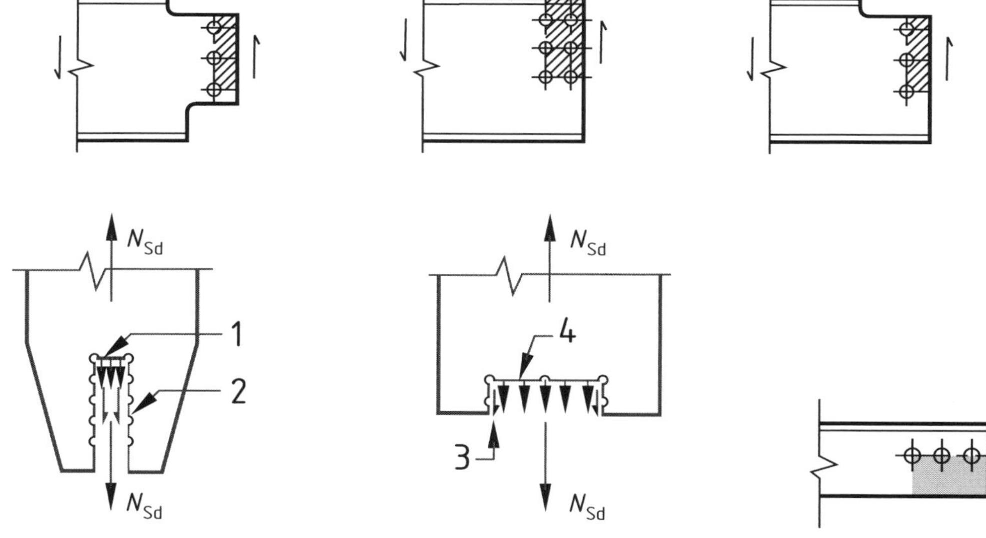

1 small tension force
2 large shear force
3 small shear force
4 large tension force

Figure 3.8 — Block tearing

3.10.3 Angles connected by one leg and other unsymmetrically connected members in tension

(1) The eccentricity in joints, see 2.7(1), and the effects of the spacing and edge distances of the bolts, shall be taken into account in determining the design resistance of:

- unsymmetrical members;
- symmetrical members that are connected unsymmetrically, such as angles connected by one leg.

(2) A single angle in tension connected by a single row of bolts in one leg, see Figure 3.9, may be treated as concentrically loaded over an effective net section for which the design ultimate resistance should be determined as follows:

with 1 bolt: $$N_{u,Rd} = \frac{2,0\,(e_2 - 0,5d_0)\,t\,f_u}{\gamma_{M2}} \qquad (3.11)$$

with 2 bolts: $$N_{u,Rd} = \frac{\beta_2\,A_{net}\,f_u}{\gamma_{M2}} \qquad (3.12)$$

with 3 or more bolts: $$N_{u,Rd} = \frac{\beta_3\,A_{net}\,f_u}{\gamma_{M2}} \qquad (3.13)$$

where:

β_2 and β_3 are reduction factors dependent on the pitch p_1 as given in Table 3.8. For intermediate values of p_1 the value of β may be determined by linear interpolation;

A_{net} is the net area of the angle. For an unequal-leg angle connected by its smaller leg, A_{net} should be taken as equal to the net section area of an equivalent equal-leg angle of leg size equal to that of the smaller leg.

Table 3.8 — Reduction factors β_2 and β_3

Pitch	p_1	$\leq 2,5\ d_o$	$\geq 5,0\ d_o$
2 bolts	β_2	0,4	0,7
3 bolts or more	β_3	0,5	0,7

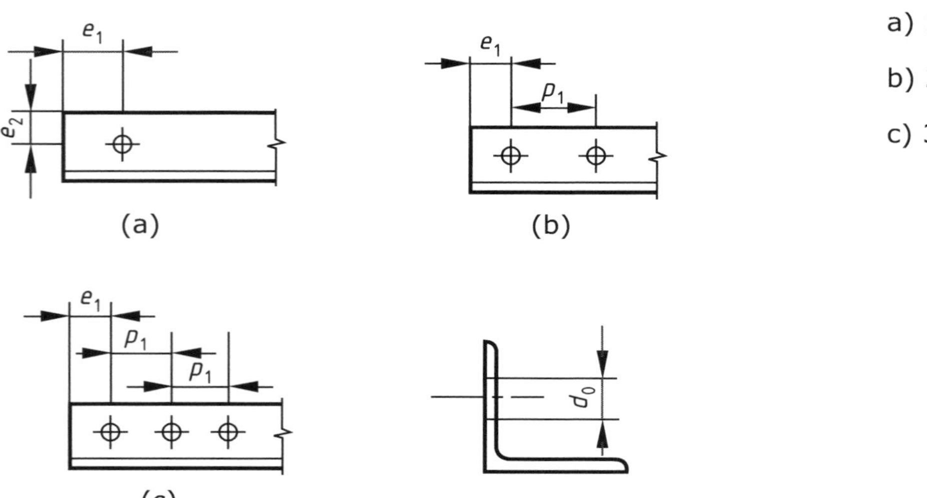

Figure 3.9 — Angles connected by one leg

Clause 3.10.2 introduces a new concept of block tearing (involving a combination of shear and tension failure) and is relatively self explanatory.

Clause 3.10.3 covers the point referred to in the commentary to Part 1.1 where a tensile load is applied eccentrically to a cross-section for fabrication or practical reasons. To cover this effect a reduction in area of the cross-section is defined.

4 Welded connections

4.1 General

(1) The provisions in this section apply to weldable structural steels conforming to EN 1993-1-1 and to material thicknesses of 4 mm and over. The provisions also apply to joints in which the mechanical properties of the weld metal are compatible with those of the parent metal, see 4.2.

For welds in thinner material reference should be made to EN 1993 Part 1.3 and for welds in structural hollow sections in material thicknesses of 2,5 mm and over guidance is given section 7 of this Standard.

For stud welding reference should be made to EN 1994-1-1.

NOTE Further guidance on stud welding can be found in EN ISO 14555 and EN ISO 13918.

(2)P Welds subject to fatigue shall also satisfy the principles given in EN 1993-1-9.

(3) Quality level C according to EN ISO 25817 is usually required, if not otherwise specified. The frequency of inspection of welds should be specified in accordance with the rules in 2.8 Reference Standards: Group 7. The quality level of welds should be chosen according to EN ISO 25817. For the quality level of welds used in fatigue loaded structures, see EN 1993-1-9.

(4) Lamellar tearing shall be avoided.

(5) Guidance on lamellar tearing is given in EN 1993-1-10.

4.2 Welding consumables

(1) All welding consumables should conform to the relevant standards specified in 2.8 Reference Standards; Group 5.

(2) The specified yield strength, ultimate tensile strength, elongation at failure and minimum Charpy V-notch energy value of the filler metal, should be equivalent to, or better than that specified for the parent material.

NOTE Generally it is safe to use electrodes that are overmatched with regard to the steel grades being used.

4.3 Geometry and dimensions

4.3.1 Type of weld

(1) This Standard covers the design of fillet welds, fillet welds all round, butt welds, plug welds and flare groove welds. Butt welds may be either full penetration butt welds or partial penetration butt welds. Both fillet welds all round and plug welds may be either in circular holes or in elongated holes.

(2) The most common types of joints and welds are illustrated in EN 12345.

4.3.2 Fillet welds

4.3.2.1 General

(1) Fillet welds may be used for connecting parts where the fusion faces form an angle of between 60° and 120°.

(2) Angles smaller than 60° are also permitted. However, in such cases the weld should be considered to be a partial penetration butt weld.

(3) For angles greater than 120° the resistance of fillet welds should be determined by testing in accordance with EN 1990 Annex D: Design by testing.

(4) Fillet welds finishing at the ends or sides of parts should be returned continuously, full size, around the corner for a distance of at least twice the leg length of the weld, unless access or the configuration of the joint renders this impracticable.

NOTE In the case of intermittent welds this rule applies only to the last intermittent fillet weld at corners.

(5) End returns should be indicated on the drawings.

(6) For eccentricity of single-sided fillet welds, see 4.12.

4.3.2.2 Intermittent fillet welds

(1) Intermittent fillet welds shall not be used in corrosive conditions.

(2) In an intermittent fillet weld, the gaps (L_1 or L_2) between the ends of each length of weld L_w should fulfil the requirement given in Figure 4.1.

(3) In an intermittent fillet weld, the gap (L_1 or L_2) should be taken as the smaller of the distances between the ends of the welds on opposite sides and the distance between the ends of the welds on the same side.

(4) In any run of intermittent fillet weld there should always be a length of weld at each end of the part connected.

(5) In a built-up member in which plates are connected by means of intermittent fillet welds, a continuous fillet weld should be provided on each side of the plate for a length at each end equal to at least three-quarters of the width of the narrower plate concerned (see Figure 4.1).

4.3.3 Fillet welds all round

(1) Fillet welds all round, comprising fillet welds in circular or elongated holes, may be used only to transmit shear or to prevent the buckling or separation of lapped parts.

(2) The diameter of a circular hole, or width of an elongated hole, for a fillet weld all round should not be less than four times the thickness of the part containing it.

(3) The ends of elongated holes should be semi-circular, except for those ends which extend to the edge of the part concerned.

(4) The centre to centre spacing of fillet welds all round should not exceed the value necessary to prevent local buckling, see Table 3.3.

4.5 Design resistance of a fillet weld

4.5.1 Length of welds

(1) The effective length of a fillet weld l_{eff} should be taken as the length over which the fillet is full-size. This may be taken as the overall length of the weld reduced by twice the effective throat thickness a. Provided that the weld is full size throughout its length including starts and terminations, no reduction in effective length need be made for either the start or the termination of the weld.

(2) A fillet weld with an effective length less than 30 mm or less than 6 times its throat thickness, whichever is larger, should not be designed to carry load.

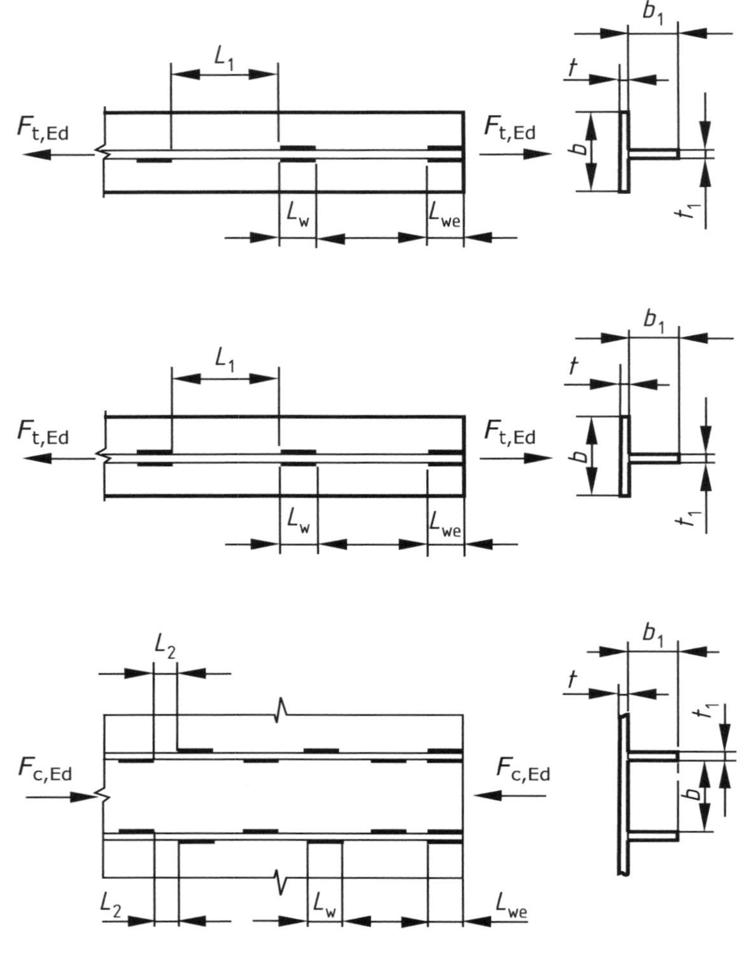

The larger of $L_{we} \geq 0,75\ b$ and $0,75\ b_1$

For build-up members in tension:

The smallest of $L_1 \leq 16\ t$ and $16\ t_1$ and 200 mm

For build-up members in compression or shear:

The smallest of $L_2 \leq 12\ t$ and $12\ t_1$ and $0,25\ b$ and 200 mm

Figure 4.1 — Intermittent fillet welds

4.5.2 Effective throat thickness

(1) The effective throat thickness, *a*, of a fillet weld should be taken as the height of the largest triangle (with equal or unequal legs) that can be inscribed within the fusion faces and the weld surface, measured perpendicular to the outer side of this triangle, see Figure 4.3.

(2) The effective throat thickness of a fillet weld should not be less than 3 mm.

(3) In determining the design resistance of a deep penetration fillet weld, account may be taken of its additional throat thickness, see Figure 4.4, provided that preliminary tests show that the required penetration can consistently be achieved.

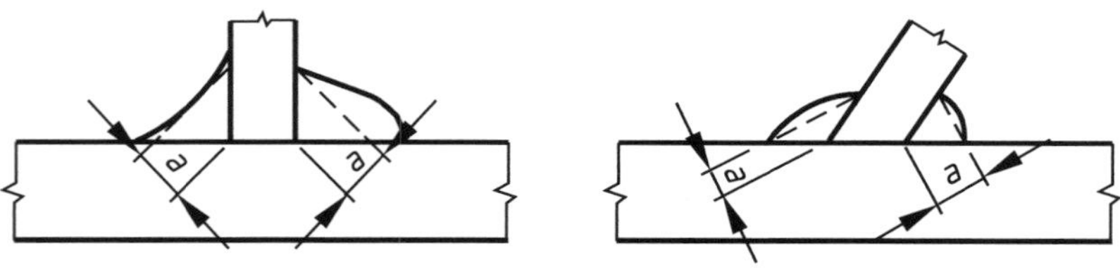

Figure 4.3 — Throat thickness of a fillet weld

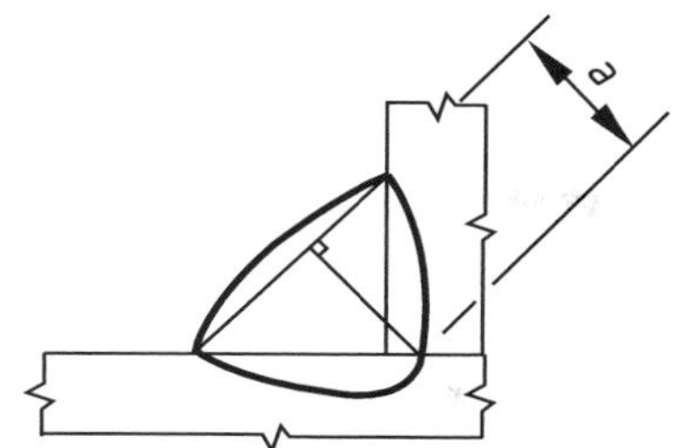

Figure 4.4 — Throat thickness of a deep penetration fillet weld

4.5.3 Design resistance of fillet welds

4.5.3.1 General

(1) The design resistance of a fillet weld should be determined using either the Directional method given in 4.5.3.2 or the Simplified method given in 4.5.3.3

4.5.3.2 Directional method

(1) In this method, the forces transmitted by a unit length of weld are resolved into components parallel and transverse to the longitudinal axis of the weld and normal and transverse to the plane of its throat.

(2) The design throat area A_w should be taken as $A_w = \Sigma a \, l_{eff}$.

(3) The location of the design throat area should be assumed to be concentrated in the root.

(4) A uniform distribution of stress is assumed on the throat section of the weld, leading to the normal stresses and shear stresses shown in Figure 4.5, as follows:

$\sigma_\perp$ is the normal stress perpendicular to the throat
$\sigma_\parallel$ is the normal stress parallel to the axis of the weld
$\tau_\perp$ is the shear stress (in the plane of the throat) perpendicular to the axis of the weld
$\tau_\parallel$ is the shear stress (in the plane of the throat) parallel to the axis of the weld.

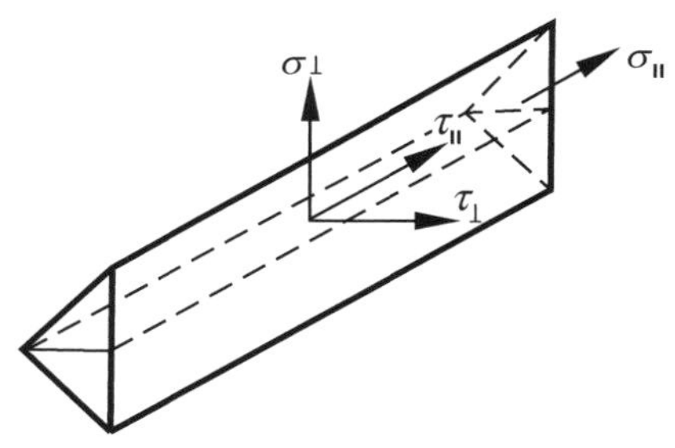

Figure 4.5 — Stresses on the throat section of a fillet weld

(5) The normal stress $\sigma_\parallel$ parallel to the axis is not considered when verifying the design resistance of the weld.

(6) The design resistance of the fillet weld will be sufficient if the following are both satisfied:

$$\left[\sigma_\perp^2 + 3\left(\tau_\perp^2 + \tau_{\parallel}^2\right)\right]^{0,5} \leq f_u / \left(\beta_w \gamma_{M2}\right) \quad \text{and} \quad \sigma_\perp \leq 0,9\, f_u / \gamma_{M2} \qquad (4.1)$$

where:

f_u is the nominal ultimate tensile strength of the weaker part joined;
β_w is the appropriate correlation factor taken from Table 4.1.

(7) Welds between parts with different material strength grades should be designed using the properties of the material with the lower strength grade.

Table 4.1 — Correlation factor β_w for fillet welds

Standard and steel grade			Correlation factor β_w
EN 10025	**EN 10210**	**EN 10219**	
S 235 S 235 W	S 235 H	S 235 H	0,8
S 275 S 275 N/NL S 275 M/ML	S 275 H S 275 NH/NLH	S 275 H S 275 NH/NLH S 275 MH/MLH	0,85
S 355 S 355 N/NL S 355 M/ML S 355 W	S 355 H S 355 NH/NLH	S 355 H S 355 NH/NLH S 355 MH/MLH	0,9
S 420 N/NL S 420 M/ML		S 420 MH/MLH	1,0
S 460 N/NL S 460 M/ML S 460 Q/QL/QL1	S 460 NH/NLH	S 460 NH/NLH S 460 MH/MLH	1,0

4.5.3.3 Simplified method for design resistance of fillet weld

(1) Alternatively to 4.5.3.2 the design resistance of a fillet weld may be assumed to be adequate if, at every point along its length, the resultant of all the forces per unit length transmitted by the weld satisfy the following criterion:

$$F_{w,Ed} \leq F_{w,Rd} \qquad (4.2)$$

where:

$F_{w,Ed}$ is the design value of the weld force per unit length;
$F_{w,Rd}$ is the design weld resistance per unit length.

(2) Independent of the orientation of the weld throat plane to the applied force, the design resistance per unit length $F_{w,Rd}$ should be determined from:

$$F_{w,Rd} = f_{vw,d}\, a \qquad (4.3)$$

where:

$f_{vw.d}$ is the design shear strength of the weld.

(3) The design shear strength $f_{vw.d}$ of the weld should be determined from:

$$f_{vw,d} = \frac{f_u / \sqrt{3}}{\beta_w \gamma_{M2}} \qquad (4.4)$$

where:

f_u and β_w are defined in 4.5.3.2(6).

4.6 Design resistance of fillet welds all round

(1) The design resistance of a fillet weld all round should be determined using one of the methods given in 4.5.

Clause 4.5 concerns detailing practice and rules for fillet welds (intermittent, all round, short lengths, effective lengths) and also the design resistance of fillet welds. As regards the design resistance the strength of the weld is effectively calculated across its throat thickness and clause 4.5.3 then deals with resolving this resistance directionally to correspond to the applied design forces. Two methods are given (see 4.5.3.2 and 4.5.3.3), the simplified method removing the need for considering the orientation of the applied force at the expense of using a reduced weld resistance.

4.9 Distribution of forces

(1) The distribution of forces in a welded connection may be calculated on the assumption of either elastic or plastic behaviour in conformity with 2.4 and 2.5.

(2) It is acceptable to assume a simplified load distribution within the welds.

(3) Residual stresses and stresses not subjected to transfer of load need not be included when checking the resistance of a weld. This applies specifically to the normal stress parallel to the axis of a weld.

(4) Welded joints should be designed to have adequate deformation capacity. However, ductility of the welds should not be relied upon.

(5) In joints where plastic hinges may form, the welds should be designed to provide at least the same design resistance as the weakest of the connected parts.

(6) In other joints where deformation capacity for joint rotation is required due to the possibility of excessive straining, the welds require sufficient strength not to rupture before general yielding in the adjacent parent material.

(7) If the design resistance of an intermittent weld is determined by using the total length l_{tot}, the weld shear force per unit length $F_{w,Ed}$ should be multiplied by the factor $(e+l)/l$, see Figure 4.7.

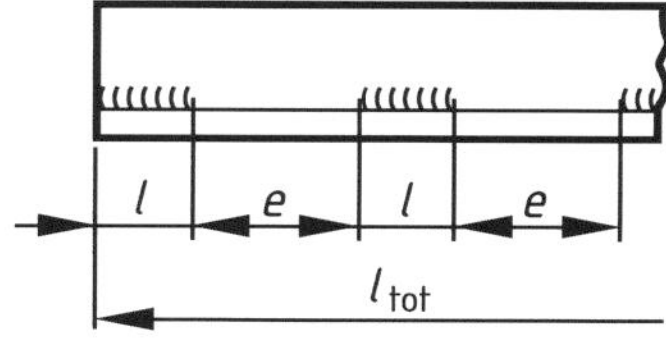

Figure 4.7 — Calculation of weld forces for intermittent welds

4.11 Long joints

(1) In lap joints the design resistance of a fillet weld should be reduced by multiplying it by a reduction factor β_{Lw} to allow for the effects of non-uniform distribution of stress along its length.

(2) The provisions given in 4.11 do not apply when the stress distribution along the weld corresponds to the stress distribution in the adjacent base metal, as, for example, in the case of a weld connecting the flange and the web of a plate girder.

(3) In lap joints longer than 150a the reduction factor β_{Lw} should be taken as $\beta_{Lw.1}$ given by:

$$\beta_{Lw.1} = 1,2 - 0,2L_j / (150a) \text{ but } \beta_{Lw.1} \leq 1,0 \quad (4.9)$$

where:

L_j is the overall length of the lap in the direction of the force transfer.

(4) For fillet welds longer than 1,7 metres connecting transverse stiffeners in plated members, the reduction factor β_{Lw} may be taken as $\beta_{Lw.2}$ given by:

$$\beta_{Lw.2} = 1,1 - L_w / 17 \text{ but } \beta_{Lw.2} \leq 1,0 \text{ and } \beta_{Lw.2} \geq 0,6 \quad (4.10)$$

where:

L_w is the length of the weld (in metres).

5 Analysis, classification and modelling

5.1 Global analysis

5.1.1 General

(1) The effects of the behaviour of the joints on the distribution of internal forces and moments within a structure, and on the overall deformations of the structure, should generally be taken into account, but where these effects are sufficiently small they may be neglected.

(2) To identify whether the effects of joint behaviour on the analysis need be taken into account, a distinction may be made between three simplified joint models as follows:

- simple, in which the joint may be assumed not to transmit bending moments;
- continuous, in which the behaviour of the joint may be assumed to have no effect on the analysis;
- semi-continuous, in which the behaviour of the joint needs to be taken into account in the analysis.

(3) The appropriate type of joint model should be determined from Table 5.1, depending on the classification of the joint and on the chosen method of analysis.

(4) The design moment-rotation characteristic of a joint used in the analysis may be simplified by adopting any appropriate curve, including a linearised approximation (e.g. bi-linear or tri-linear), provided that the approximate curve lies wholly below the design moment-rotation characteristic.

Table 5.1 — Type of joint model

Method of global analysis	Classification of joint		
Elastic	Nominally pinned	Rigid	Semi-rigid
Rigid-Plastic	Nominally pinned	Full-strength	Partial-strength
Elastic-Plastic	Nominally pinned	Rigid and full-strength	Semi-rigid and partial-strength Semi-rigid and full-strength Rigid and partial-strength
Type of joint model	Simple	Continuous	Semi-continuous

5.1.2 Elastic global analysis

(1) The joints should be classified according to their rotational stiffness, see 5.2.2.

(2) The joints shall have sufficient strength to transmit the forces and moments acting at the joints resulting from the analysis.

(3) In the case of a semi-rigid joint, the rotational stiffness S_j corresponding to the bending moment $M_{j,Ed}$ should generally be used in the analysis. If $M_{j,Ed}$ does not exceed 2/3 $M_{j,Rd}$ the initial rotational stiffness $S_{j,ini}$ may be taken in the global analysis, see Figure 5.1(a).

(4) As a simplification to 5.1.2(3), the rotational stiffness may be taken as $S_{j,ini} / \eta$ in the analysis, for all values of the moment $M_{j,Ed}$, as shown in Figure 5.1(b), where η is the stiffness modification coefficient from Table 5.2.

(5) For joints connecting H or I sections S_j is given in 6.3.1.

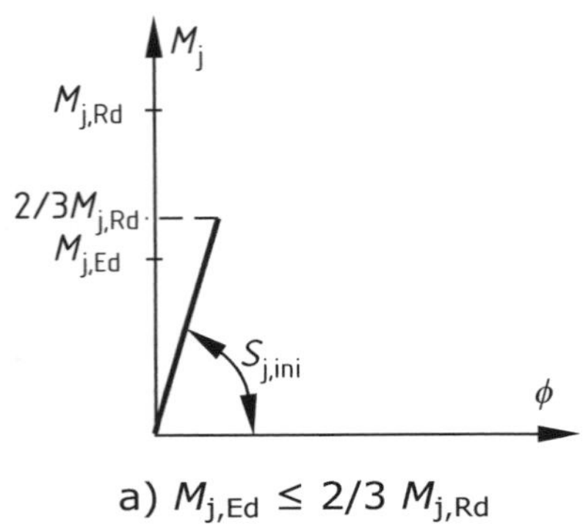

a) $M_{j,Ed} \leq 2/3\ M_{j,Rd}$

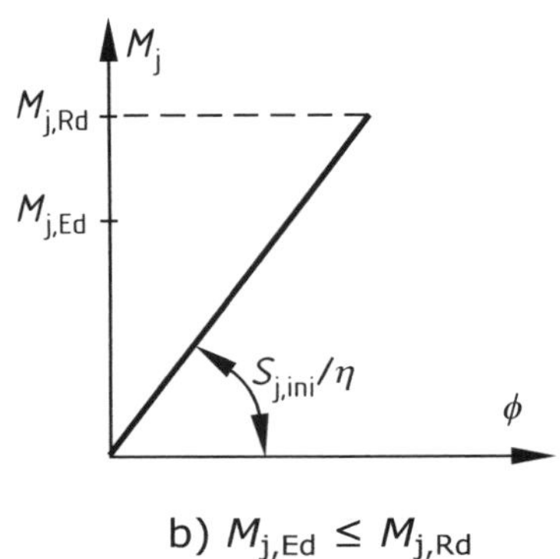

b) $M_{j,Ed} \leq M_{j,Rd}$

Figure 5.1 — Rotational stiffness to be used in elastic global analysis

Table 5.2 — Stiffness modification coefficient η

Type of connection	Beam-to-column joints	Other types of joints (beam-to-beam joints, beam splices, column base joints)
Welded	2	3
Bolted end-plate	2	3
Bolted flange cleats	2	3,5
Base plates	–	3

5.1.3 Rigid-plastic global analysis

(1) The joints should be classified according to their strength, see 5.2.3.

(2) For joints connecting H or I sections $M_{j,Rd}$ is given in 6.2.

(3) For joints connecting hollow sections the method given in section 7 may be used.

(4) The rotation capacity of a joint shall be sufficient to accommodate the rotations resulting from the analysis.

(5) For joints connecting H or I sections the rotation capacity should be checked according to 6.4.

5.1.4 Elastic-plastic global analysis

(1) The joints should be classified according to both stiffness (see 5.2.2) and strength (see 5.2.3).

(2) For joints connecting H or I sections $M_{j,Rd}$ is given in 6.2, S_j is given in 6.3.1 and ϕ_{Cd} is given in 6.4.

(3) For joints connecting hollow sections the method given in section 7 may be used.

(4) The moment rotation characteristic of the joints should be used to determine the distribution of internal forces and moments.

(5) As a simplification, the bi-linear design moment-rotation characteristic shown in Figure 5.2 may be adopted. The stiffness modification coefficient η should be obtained from Table 5.2.

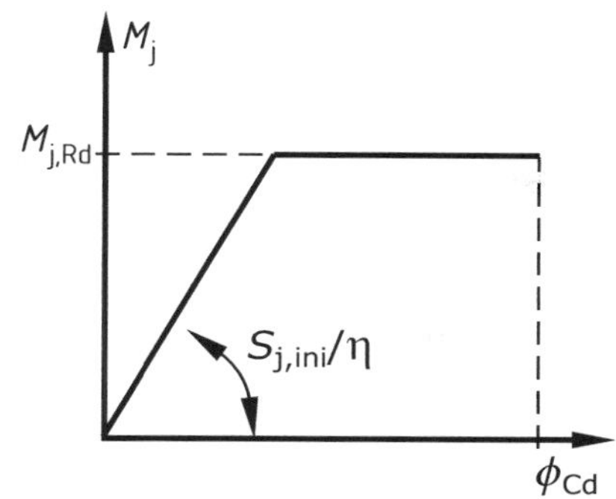

Figure 5.2 — Simplified bi-linear design moment-rotation characteristic

5.2 Classification of joints

5.2.1 General

(1) The details of all joints shall fulfil the assumptions made in the relevant design method, without adversely affecting any other part of the structure.

(2) Joints may be classified by their stiffness (see 5.2.2) and by their strength (see 5.2.3).

NOTE The National Annex may give additional information on the classification of joints by their stiffness and strength to that given in 5.2.2.1(2).

NA 2.6 Clause 5.2.1(2) Classification of joints

For buildings the following guidance may be used to classify joints.

Nominally pinned joints are described as "Simple Connections" in UK practice. Connections designed in accordance with the principles given in the publication "Joints in Steel Construction - Simple Connections" [1] may be classified as nominally pinned joints.

Ductile, partial strength joints are described as "Ductile Connections" in UK practice. They are used in plastically designed semi-continuous frames. Braced semi-continuous frames may be designed using the principles given in the publication "Semi-continuous design of braced frames" [2] with connections designed to the principles given in Section 2 of "Joints in Steel Construction - Moment Connections" [3]. Unbraced semi-continuous frames (known as wind moment frames) may be designed using the principles given in the publication "Wind-moment design of Low rise Frames" [4].

Until experience is gained with the numerical method of calculating rotational stiffness given in BS EN 1993-1-8:2005, 6.3 and the classification by stiffness method given in BS EN 1993-1-8:2005, 5.2.2, semi-continuous elastic design should only be used where it is supported by test evidence according to BS EN 1993-1-8:2005, 5.2.2.1(2) or where it is based on satisfactory performance in a similar situation.

Connections designed in accordance with the principles given in the publication "Joints in Steel Construction - Moment Connections" [3] may be classified on the basis of the guidance given in Section 2.5 of the same publication.

5.2.2 Classification by stiffness

5.2.2.1 General

(1) A joint may be classified as rigid, nominally pinned or semi-rigid according to its rotational stiffness, by comparing its initial rotational stiffness $S_{j,ini}$ with the classification boundaries given in 5.2.2.5.

NOTE Rules for the determination of $S_{j,ini}$ for joints connecting H or I sections are given in 6.3.1. Rules for the determination of $S_{j,ini}$ for joints connecting hollow sections are not given in this Standard.

(2) A joint may be classified on the basis of experimental evidence, experience of previous satisfactory performance in similar cases or by calculations based on test evidence.

5.2.2.2 Nominally pinned joints

(1) A nominally pinned joint shall be capable of transmitting the internal forces, without developing significant moments which might adversely affect the members or the structure as a whole.

(2) A nominally pinned joint shall be capable of accepting the resulting rotations under the design loads.

5.2.2.3 Rigid joints

(1) Joints classified as rigid may be assumed to have sufficient rotational stiffness to justify analysis based on full continuity.

5.2.2.4 Semi-rigid joints

(1) A joint which does not meet the criteria for a rigid joint or a nominally pinned joint should be classified as a semi-rigid joint.

NOTE Semi-rigid joints provide a predictable degree of interaction between members, based on the design moment-rotation characteristics of the joints.

(2) Semi-rigid joints should be capable of transmitting the internal forces and moments.

5.2.2.5 Classification boundaries

(1) Classification boundaries for joints other than column bases are given in 5.2.2.1(1) and Figure 5.4.

(2) Column bases may be classified as rigid provided the following conditions are satisfied:

- in frames where the bracing system reduces the horizontal displacement by at least 80 % and where the effects of deformation may be neglected
  - if $\bar{\lambda}_0 \leq 0,5$; (5.2a)
  - if $0,5 < \bar{\lambda}_0 < 3,93$ and $S_{j,ini} \geq 7\left(2\bar{\lambda}_0 - 1\right) EI_c / L_c$; (5.2b)
  - if $\bar{\lambda}_0 \geq 3,93$ and $S_{j,ini} \geq 48\, EI_c / L_c$ (5.2c)
- otherwise if $S_{j,ini} \geq 30\, EI_c / L_c$ (5.2d)

where:

$\bar{\lambda}_0$ is the slenderness of a column in which both ends are assumed to be pinned;
I_c, L_c are as given in Figure 5.4.

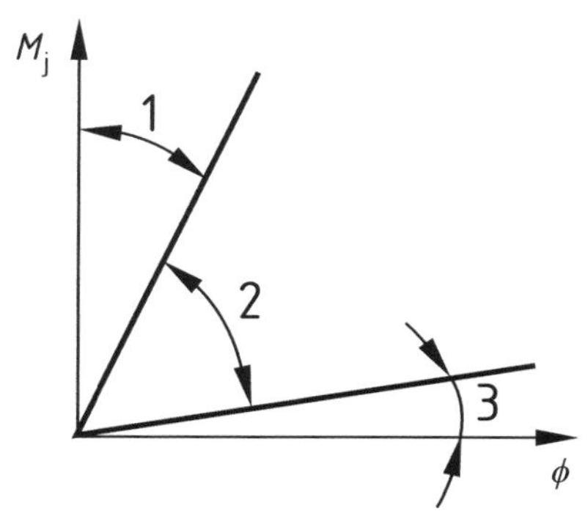

Zone 1: rigid, if $S_{j,ini} \geq K_b \, EI_b \, / \, L_b$

where

$K_b = 8$ for frames where the bracing system reduces the horizontal displacement by at least 80 %

$K_b = 25$ for other frames, provided that in every storey $K_b/K_c \geq 0,1$ *)

Zone 2: semi-rigid

All joints in zone 2 should be classified as semi-rigid. Joints in zones 1 or 3 may optionally also be treated as semi-rigid.

Zone 3: nominally pinned, if $S_{j,ini} \leq 0,5 \, EI_b \, / \, L_b$

*) For frames where $K_b/K_c < 0,1$ the joints should be classified as semi-rigid.

Key:

K_b is the mean value of I_b/L_b for all the beams at the top of that storey;
K_c is the mean value of I_c/L_c for all the columns in that storey;
I_b is the second moment of area of a beam;
I_c is the second moment of area of a column;
L_b is the span of a beam (centre-to-centre of columns);
L_c is the storey height of a column.

Figure 5.4 — Classification of joints by stiffness

5.2.3 Classification by strength

5.2.3.1 General

(1) A joint may be classified as full-strength, nominally pinned or partial strength by comparing its design moment resistance $M_{j,Rd}$ with the design moment resistances of the members that it connects. When classifying joints, the design resistance of a member should be taken as that member adjacent to the joint.

5.2.3.2 Nominally pinned joints

(1) A nominally pinned joint shall be capable of transmitting the internal forces, without developing significant moments which might adversely affect the members or the structure as a whole.

(2) A nominally pinned joint shall be capable of accepting the resulting rotations under the design loads.

(3) A joint may be classified as nominally pinned if its design moment resistance $M_{j,Rd}$ is not greater than 0,25 times the design moment resistance required for a full-strength joint, provided that it also has sufficient rotation capacity.

5.2.3.3 Full-strength joints

(1) The design resistance of a full strength joint shall be not less than that of the connected members.

(2) A joint may be classified as full-strength if it meets the criteria given in Figure 5.5.

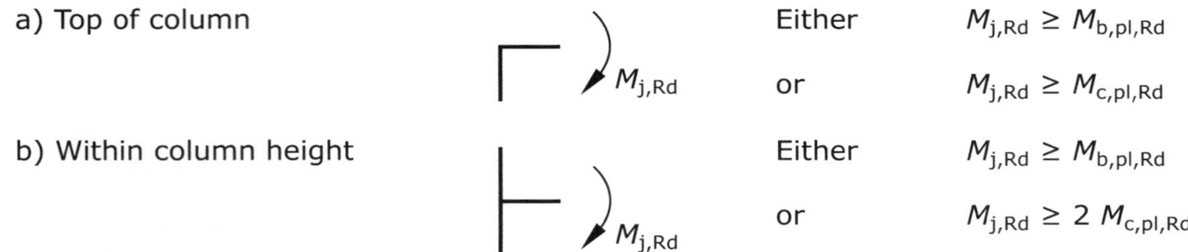

Key:

$M_{b,pl,Rd}$ is the design plastic moment resistance of a beam;
$M_{c,pl,Rd}$ is the design plastic moment resistance of a column.

Figure 5.5 — Full-strength joints

5.2.3.4 Partial-strength joints

(1) A joint which does not meet the criteria for a full-strength joint or a nominally pinned joint should be classified as a partial-strength joint.

6 Structural joints connecting H or I sections

6.1 General

6.1.1 Basis

(1) This section contains design methods to determine the structural properties of joints in frames of any type. To apply these methods, a joint should be modelled as an assembly of basic components, see 1.4(1).

(2) The basic components used in this Standard are identified in Table 6.1 and their properties should be determined in accordance with the provisions given in this Standard. Other basic components may be used provided their properties are based on tests or analytical and numerical methods supported by tests, see EN 1990.

NOTE The design methods for basic joint components given in this Standard are of general application and can also be applied to similar components in other joint configurations. However the specific design methods given for determining the design moment resistance, rotational stiffness and rotation capacity of a joint are based on an assumed distribution of internal forces for joint configurations indicated in Figure 1.2. For other joint configurations, design methods for determining the design moment resistance, rotational stiffness and rotation capacity should be based on appropriate assumptions for the distribution of internal forces.

6.1.2 Structural properties

6.1.2.1 Design moment-rotation characteristic

(1) A joint may be represented by a rotational spring connecting the centre lines of the connected members at the point of intersection, as indicated in Figure 6.1 (a) and (b) for a single-sided beam-to-column joint configuration. The properties of the spring can be expressed in the form of a design moment-rotation characteristic that describes the relationship between the bending moment $M_{j,Ed}$ applied to a joint and the corresponding rotation ϕ_{Ed} between the connected members. Generally the design moment-rotation characteristic is non-linear as indicated in Figure 6.1(c).

(2) A design moment-rotation characteristic, see Figure 6.1(c), should define the following three main structural properties:

- moment resistance;
- rotational stiffness;
- rotation capacity.

NOTE In certain cases the actual moment-rotation behaviour of a joint includes some rotation due to such effects as bolt slip, lack of fit and, in the case of column bases, foundation-soil interactions. This can result in a significant amount of initial hinge rotation that may need to be included in the design moment-rotation characteristic.

(3) The design moment-rotation characteristics of a beam-to-column joint shall be consistent with the assumptions made in the global analysis of the structure and with the assumptions made in the design of the members, see EN 1993-1-1.

(4) The design moment-rotation characteristic for joints and column bases of I and H sections as obtained from 6.3.1(4) may be assumed to satisfy the requirements of 5.1.1(4) for simplifying this characteristic for global analysis purposes.

6.1.2.2 Design moment resistance

(1) The design moment resistance $M_{j,Rd}$, which is equal to the maximum moment of the design moment-rotation characteristic, see Figure 6.1(c), should be taken as that given by 6.1.3(4).

6.1.2.3 Rotational stiffness

(1) The rotational stiffness S_j, which is the secant stiffness as indicated in Figure 6.1(c), should be taken as that given by 6.3.1(4). For a design moment-rotation characteristic this definition of S_j applies up to the rotation ϕ_{Xd} at which $M_{j,Ed}$ first reaches $M_{j,Rd}$, but not for larger rotations, see Figure 6.1(c). The initial rotational stiffness $S_{j,ini}$, which is the slope of the elastic range of the design moment-rotation characteristic, should be taken as that given by 6.1.3(4).

6.1.2.4 Rotation capacity

(1) The design rotation capacity ϕ_{Cd} of a joint, which is equal to the maximum rotation of the design moment-rotation characteristic, see Figure 6.1(c), should be taken as that given by 6.1.3(4).

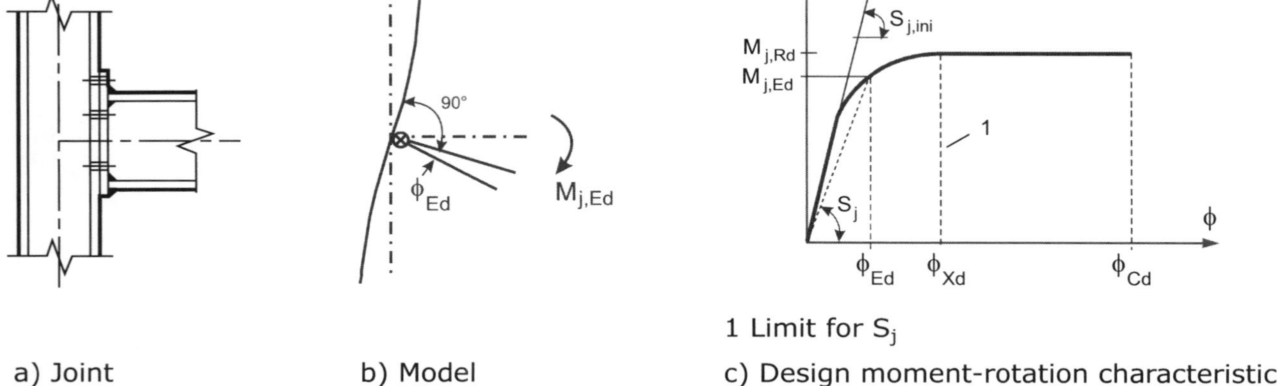

1 Limit for S_j

a) Joint b) Model c) Design moment-rotation characteristic

Figure 6.1 — Design moment-rotation characteristic for a joint

6.1.3 Basic components of a joint

(1) The design moment-rotation characteristic of a joint should depend on the properties of its basic components, which should be among those identified in 6.1.3(2).

(2) The basic joint components should be those identified in Table 6.1, together with the reference to the application rules which should be used for the evaluation of their structural properties.

(3) Certain joint components may be reinforced. Details of the different methods of reinforcement are given in 6.2.4.3 and 6.2.6.

(4) The relationships between the properties of the basic components of a joint and the structural properties of the joint should be those given in the following clauses:

- for moment resistance in 6.2.7 and 6.2.8;
- for rotational stiffness in 6.3.1;
- for rotation capacity in 6.4.

Table 6.1 — Basic joint components

	Component		Reference to application rules		
			Design resistance	Stiffness coefficient	Rotation capacity
1	Column web panel in shear	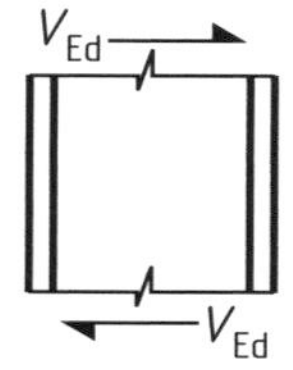 V_{Ed} / V_{Ed}	6.2.6.1	6.3.2	6.4.2 and 6.4.3
2	Column web in transverse compression	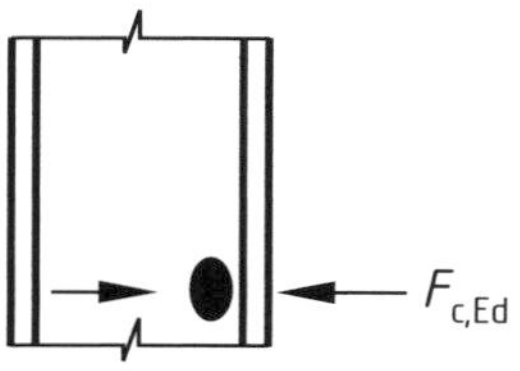 $F_{c,Ed}$	6.2.6.2	6.3.2	6.4.2 and 6.4.3
3	Column web in transverse tension	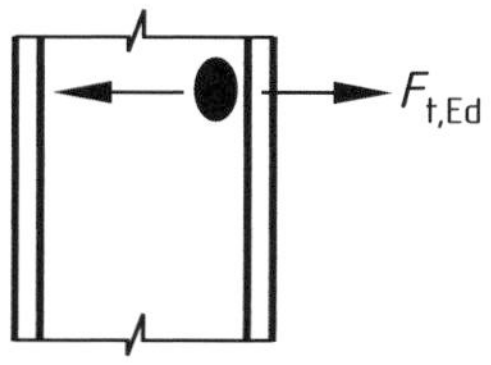 $F_{t,Ed}$	6.2.6.3	6.3.2	6.4.2 and 6.4.3
4	Column flange in bending	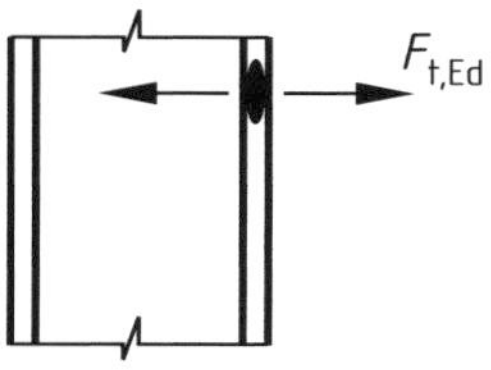 $F_{t,Ed}$	6.2.6.4	6.3.2	6.4.2 and 6.4.3
5	End-plate in bending	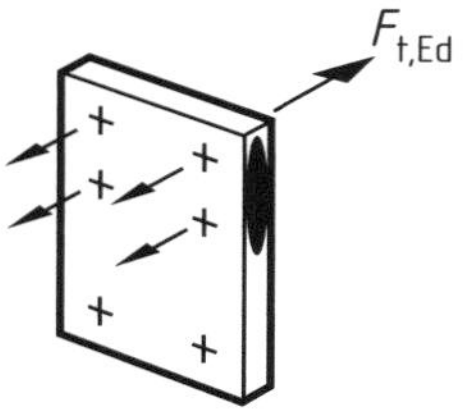 $F_{t,Ed}$	6.2.6.5	6.3.2	6.4.2
6	Flange cleat in bending	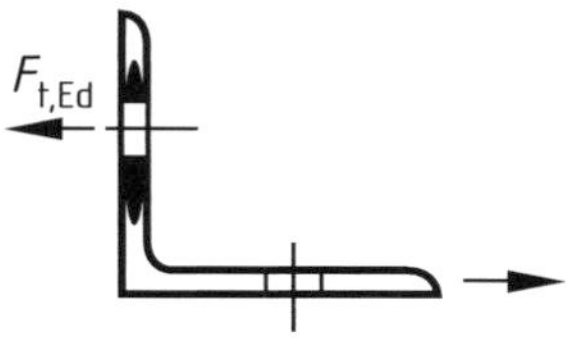 $F_{t,Ed}$	6.2.6.6	6.3.2	6.4.2

Component			Reference to application rules		
			Design resistance	Stiffness coefficient	Rotation capacity
7	Beam or column flange and web in compression	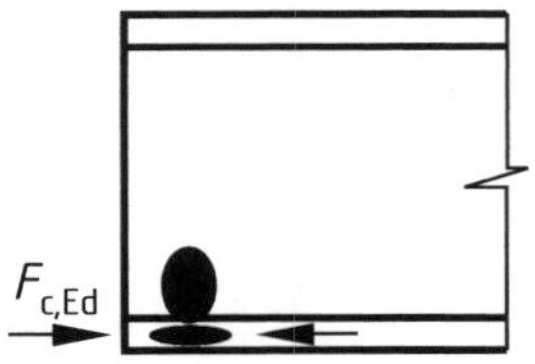 $F_{c,Ed}$	6.2.6.7	6.3.2	*)
8	Beam web in tension	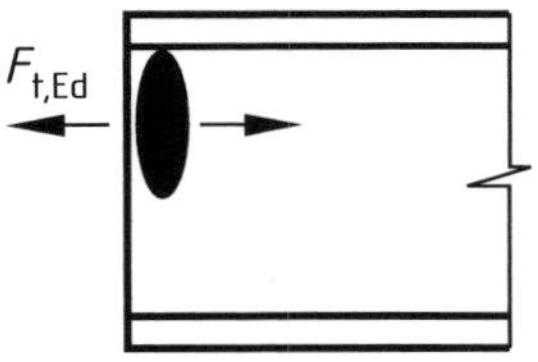 $F_{t,Ed}$	6.2.6.8	6.3.2	*)
9	Plate in tension or compression	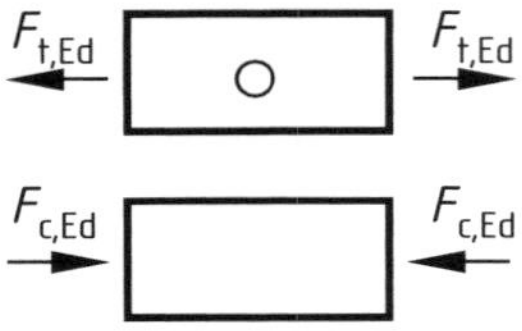 $F_{t,Ed}$ $F_{t,Ed}$ $F_{c,Ed}$ $F_{c,Ed}$	in tension: – EN 1993-1-1 in compression: – EN 1993-1-1	6.3.2	*)
10	Bolts in tension	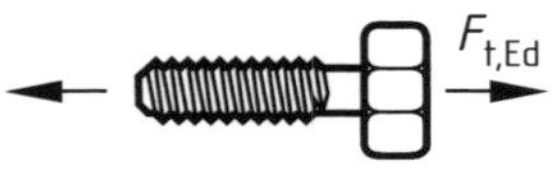 $F_{t,Ed}$	With column flange: – 6.2.6.4 with end-plate: – 6.2.6.5 with flange cleat: – 6.2.6.6	6.3.2	6.4.2
11	Bolts in shear	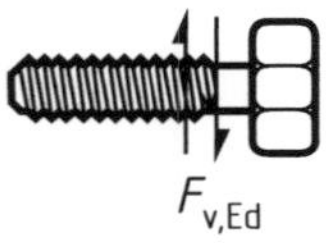 $F_{v,Ed}$	3.6	6.3.2	6.4.2
12	Bolts in bearing (on beam flange, column flange, end-plate or cleat)	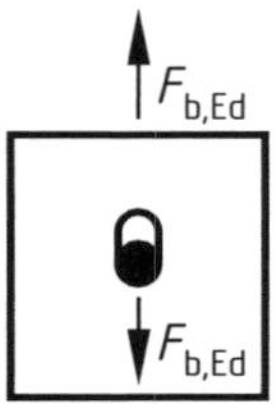 $F_{b,Ed}$ $F_{b,Ed}$	3.6	6.3.2	*)
*) No information available in this part.					

Component			Reference to application rules		
			Design resistance	Stiffness coefficient	Rotation capacity
13	Concrete in compression including grout		6.2.6.9	6.3.2	*)
14	Base plate in bending under compression		6.2.6.10	6.3.2	*)
15	Base plate in bending under tension		6.2.6.11	6.3.2	*)
16	Anchor bolts in tension		6.2.6.12	6.3.2	*)
17	Anchor bolts in shear		6.2.2	*)	*)
18	Anchor bolts in bearing		6.2.2	*)	*)
19	Welds		4	6.3.2	*)
20	Haunched beam		6.2.6.7	6.3.2	*)
*) No information available in this part.					

Sections 5 and 6 (introductory part only) are included without detailed commentary as coherent and understandable statements concerning the classification of joints and the effect of this classification on the analysis and modelling methods to be used (see section 5) and the corresponding resistance calculations to be applied (see section 6) for H and I sections. Table 6.1 is a useful checklist for designers of the 'links in the chain' of the load path through a joint, some or all requiring checking at the detailed design stage. Reference to the full code is recommended for further details.

Bibliography

Standards publications

For dated references, only the edition cited applies. For undated references, the latest edition of the referenced document (including any amendments) applies.

BS 4620:1970, *Specification for rivets for general engineering purposes*

BS EN ISO 898-1, *Mechanical properties of fasteners made of carbon steel and alloy steel – Part 1: Bolts, screws and studs*

BS EN 14399-4, *High-strength structural bolting assemblies for preloading – System HV – Part 4: Hexagon bolt and nut assemblies*

BS EN 14399-8, *High-strength structural bolting assemblies for preloading – System HV – Part 8: Hexagon fit bolts and nut assemblies*

Other publications

[1] Joints in Steel Construction. Simple Connections, BCSA, SCI publication No. P212, Jointly published by the British Constructional Steelwork Association and the Steel Construction Institute, 2002.

[2] Design of semi-continuous braced frames, SCI publication No. P183, The Steel Construction Institute, 1997.

[3] Joints in Steel Construction. Moment Connections, BCSA, SCI publication No. P207, jointly published by the British Constructional Steelwork Association and the Steel Construction Institute, 1995.

[4] Wind-moment design of low rise frames, SCI publication No. P263, The Steel Construction Institute, 1999.

Chapter 4 — Extracts from Eurocode 4: Design of composite steel and concrete structures

The Eurocode extracts in this chapter are taken from EN 1994-1-1:2004 (incorporating corrigendum April 2009), *Eurocode 4: Design of composite steel and concrete structures — Part 1-1 General rules and rules for buildings.*

Text altered by CEN corrigendum April 2009 is indicated in the text by [AC1) (AC1].

A useful additional reference is: Designers' guide to EN 1994-1-1: Eurocode 4: Design of composite steel and concrete structures, Part 1.1 : General rules and rules for buildings [1].

The National Annex extracts are taken from NA to BS EN 1994-1-1:2004 *UK National Annex to Eurocode 4: Design of composite steel and concrete structures – Part 1-1: General rules and rules for buildings.*

The full list of the contents of EN 1994-1-1 follows, and is given for reference purposes. (Bold items are covered in this chapter.)

Section 5 Structural analysis
5.1 Structural modelling for analysis
5.1.1 Structural modelling and basic assumptions
5.1.2 Joint modelling
5.1.3 Ground-structure interaction
5.2 Structural stability
5.2.1 Effects of deformed geometry of the structure
5.2.2 Methods of analysis for buildings
5.3 Imperfections
5.3.1 Basis
5.3.2 Imperfections in buildings
5.3.2.1 General
5.3.2.2 Global imperfections
5.3.2.3 Member imperfections
5.4 Calculation of action effects
5.4.1 Methods of global analysis
5.4.1.1 General
5.4.1.2 Effective width of flanges for shear lag
5.4.2 Linear elastic analysis
5.4.2.1 General
5.4.2.2 Creep and shrinkage
5.4.2.3 Effects of cracking of concrete
5.4.2.4 Stages and sequence of construction
5.4.2.5 Temperature effects
5.4.2.6 Pre-stressing by controlled imposed deformations
5.4.3 Non-linear global analysis
5.4.4 Linear elastic analysis with limited redistribution for buildings
5.4.5 Rigid plastic global analysis for buildings
5.5 Classification of cross-sections
5.5.1 General
5.5.2 Classification of composite sections without concrete encasement
5.5.3 Classification of composite sections for buildings with concrete encasement
Section 6 Ultimate limit states
6.1 Beams
6.1.1 Beams for buildings
6.1.2 Effective width for verification of cross-sections
6.2 Resistances of cross-sections of beams
6.2.1 Bending resistance
6.2.1.1 General
6.2.1.2 Plastic resistance moment $M_{pl,Rd}$ of a composite cross-section
6.2.1.3 Plastic resistance moment of sections with partial shear connection in buildings
6.2.1.4 Non-linear resistance to bending
6.2.1.5 Elastic resistance to bending
6.2.2 Resistance to vertical shear
6.2.2.1 Scope
6.2.2.2 Plastic resistance to vertical shear
6.2.2.3 Shear buckling resistance
6.2.2.4 Bending and vertical shear
6.3 Resistance of cross-sections of beams for buildings with partial encasement
6.3.1 Scope
6.3.2 Bending resistance
6.3.3 Resistance to vertical shear
6.3.4 Bending and vertical shear
6.4 Lateral-torsional buckling of composite beams
6.4.1 General
6.4.2 Verification of lateral-torsional buckling of continuous composite beams with cross-sections in Class 1, 2 and 3 for buildings
6.4.3 Simplified verification for buildings without direct calculation

6.8.3 Fatigue strength
6.8.4 Internal forces and fatigue loadings
6.8.5 Stresses
6.8.5.1 General
6.8.5.2 Concrete
6.8.5.3 Structural steel
6.8.5.4 Reinforcement
6.8.5.5 Shear connection
6.8.6 Stress ranges
6.8.6.1 Structural steel and reinforcement
6.8.6.2 Shear connection
6.8.7 Fatigue assessment based on nominal stress ranges
6.8.7.1 Structural steel, reinforcement and concrete
6.8.7.2 Shear connection

Section 7 Serviceability limit states

7.1 General

7.2 Stresses

7.2.1 General

7.2.2 Stress limitation for buildings

7.3 Deformations in buildings

7.3.1 Deflections

7.3.2 Vibration

7.4 Cracking of concrete

7.4.1 General

7.4.2 Minimum reinforcement

7.4.3 Control of cracking due to direct loading

Section 8 Composite joints in frames for buildings

8.1 Scope
8.2 Analysis, modelling and classification
8.2.1 General
8.2.2 Elastic global analysis
8.2.3 Classification of joints
8.3 Design methods
8.3.1 Basis and scope
8.3.2 Resistance
8.3.3 Rotational stiffness
8.3.4 Rotation capacity
8.4 Resistance of components
8.4.1 Scope
8.4.2 Basic joint components
8.4.2.1 Longitudinal steel reinforcement in tension
8.4.2.2 Steel contact plate in compression
8.4.3 Column web in transverse compression
8.4.4 Reinforced components
8.4.4.1 Column web panel in shear
8.4.4.2 Column web in compression

Section 9 Composite slabs with profiled steel sheeting for buildings

9.1 General

9.1.1 Scope

9.1.2 Definitions

9.1.2.1 Types of shear connection

9.2 Detailing provisions

9.2.1 Slab thickness and reinforcement

9.2.2 Aggregate
9.2.3 Bearing requirements

9.3 Actions and action effects

9.3.1 Design situations

9.3.2 Actions for profiled steel sheeting as shuttering

9.3.3 Actions for composite slab

Foreword

National Annex for EN 1994-1-1

This standard gives values with notes indicating where national choices may have to be made. Therefore the National Standard implementing EN 1994-1-1 has a National Annex containing all Nationally Determined Parameters to be used for the design of buildings and civil engineering works to be constructed in the relevant country.

Section 1 General

1.1 Scope

1.1.1 Scope of Eurocode 4

(1) Eurocode 4 applies to the design of composite structures and members for buildings and civil engineering works. It complies with the principles and requirements for the safety and serviceability of structures, the basis of their design and verification that are given in EN 1990 – Basis of structural design.

(2) Eurocode 4 is concerned only with requirements for resistance, serviceability, durability and fire resistance of composite structures. Other requirements, e.g. concerning thermal or sound insulation, are not considered.

(3) Eurocode 4 is intended to be used in conjunction with:

EN 1990 Basis of structural design
EN 1991 Actions on structures
ENs, hENs, ETAGs and ETAs for construction products relevant for composite structures
EN 1090 Execution of steel structures – Technical requirements
EN 13670 Execution of concrete structures
EN 1992 Design of concrete structures
EN 1993 Design of steel structures
EN 1997 Geotechnical design
EN 1998 Design of structures for earthquake resistance, when composite structures are built in seismic regions.

(4) Eurocode 4 is subdivided in various parts:

Part 1-1: General rules and rules for buildings
Part 1-2: Structural fire design
Part 2: Bridges.

In 1.1.1(4), the bold text indicates the parts of Eurocode 4 that are covered in this chapter.

1.1.2 Scope of Part 1-1 of Eurocode 4

(1) Part 1-1 of Eurocode 4 gives a general basis for the design of composite structures together with specific rules for buildings.

(2) The following subjects are dealt with in Part 1-1:

Section 1: General
Section 2: Basis of design
Section 3: Materials
Section 4: Durability
Section 5: Structural analysis
Section 6: Ultimate limit states

Section 7: Serviceability limit states
Section 8: Composite joints in frames for buildings
Section 9: Composite slabs with profiled steel sheeting for buildings

Scope of Part 1-2 of Eurocode 4

This part deals with the design of composite structures for the accidental situation of fire exposure and identifies differences from, or supplements to, normal temperature design.

Scope of Part 2 of Eurocode 4

This part gives the basic rules for the design of composite construction for bridges.

1.5 Definitions

1.5.2 Additional terms and definitions used in this standard

1.5.2.1
composite member
a structural member with components of concrete and of structural or cold-formed steel, interconnected by shear connection so as to limit the longitudinal slip between concrete and steel and the separation of one component from the other

1.5.2.2
shear connection
an interconnection between the concrete and steel components of a composite member that has sufficient strength and stiffness to enable the two components to be designed as parts of a single structural member

1.5.2.6
composite slab
a slab in which profiled steel sheets are used initially as permanent shuttering and subsequently combine structurally with the hardened concrete and act as tensile reinforcement in the finished floor

1.5.2.9
propped structure or member
a structure or member where the weight of concrete elements is applied to the steel elements which are supported in the span, or is carried independently until the concrete elements are able to resist stresses

1.5.2.10
un-propped structure or member
a structure or member in which the weight of concrete elements is applied to steel elements which are unsupported in the span

1.5.2.11
un-cracked flexural stiffness
the stiffness $E_a I_1$ of a cross-section of a composite member where I_1 is the second moment of area of the effective equivalent steel section calculated assuming that concrete in tension is un-cracked

1.5.2.12
cracked flexural stiffness
the stiffness $E_a I_2$ of a cross-section of a composite member where I_2 is the second moment of area of the effective equivalent steel section calculated neglecting concrete in tension but including reinforcement

1.6 Symbols

For the purpose of this Standard the following symbols apply.

Latin upper case letters

A	Cross-sectional area of the effective composite section neglecting concrete in tension
A_a	Cross-sectional area of the structural steel section
A_b	Cross-sectional area of bottom transverse reinforcement
A_{bh}	Cross-sectional area of bottom transverse reinforcement in a haunch
A_c	Cross-sectional area of concrete
A_{ct}	Cross-sectional area of the tensile zone of the concrete
A_p	Cross-sectional area of profiled steel sheeting
A_{pe}	Effective cross-sectional area of profiled steel sheeting
A_s	Cross-sectional area of reinforcement
A_{sf}	Cross-sectional area of transverse reinforcement
A_t	Cross-sectional area of top transverse reinforcement
E_a	Modulus of elasticity of structural steel
$E_{c,eff}$	Effective modulus of elasticity for concrete
E_{cm}	Secant modulus of elasticity of concrete
E_s	Design value of modulus of elasticity of reinforcing steel
F_ℓ	Design longitudinal force per stud
F_t	Design transverse force per stud
I	Second moment of area of the effective composite section neglecting concrete in tension
I_a	Second moment of area of the structural steel section
I_c	Second moment of area of the un-cracked concrete section
I_1	Second moment of area of the effective equivalent steel section assuming that the concrete in tension is un-cracked
I_2	Second moment of area of the effective equivalent steel section neglecting concrete in tension but including reinforcement
L	Length; span; effective span
L_e	Equivalent span
L_i	Span
L_s	Shear span
M	Bending moment
M_a	Contribution of the structural steel section to the design plastic resistance moment of the composite section
$M_{el,Rd}$	Design value of the elastic resistance moment of the composite section
M_{pa}	Design value of the plastic resistance moment of the effective cross-section of the profiled steel sheeting
$M_{pl,a,Rd}$	Design value of the plastic resistance moment of the structural steel section
$M_{pl,Rd}$	Design value of the plastic resistance moment of the composite section with full shear connection
M_{pr}	Reduced plastic resistance moment of the profiled steel sheeting
M_{Rd}	Design value of the resistance moment of a composite section or joint
M_{Rk}	Characteristic value of the resistance moment of a composite section or joint
N	Compressive normal force; number of stress range cycles; number of shear connectors
N_a	Design value of the normal force in the structural steel section
N_c	Design value of the compressive normal force in the concrete flange
$N_{c,f}$	Design value of the compressive normal force in the concrete flange with full shear connection
$N_{c,el}$	Compressive normal force in the concrete flange corresponding to $M_{el,Rd}$
$N_{pl,a}$	Design value of the plastic resistance of the structural steel section to normal force
N_s	Design value of the plastic resistance of the steel reinforcement to normal force
N_{sd}	Design value of the plastic resistance of the reinforcing steel to tensile normal force
$P_{\ell,Rd}$	Design value of the shear resistance of a single stud connector corresponding to F_ℓ
$P_{pb,Rd}$	Design value of the bearing resistance of a stud
P_{Rd}	Design value of the shear resistance of a single connector
P_{Rk}	Characteristic value of the shear resistance of a single connector
$P_{t,Rd}$	Design value of the shear resistance of a single stud connector corresponding to F_t
$V_{a,Ed}$	Design value of the shear force acting on the structural steel section

$V_{b,Rd}$ Design value of the shear buckling resistance of a steel web
V_{Ed} Design value of the shear force acting on the composite section
V_{ld} Design value of the resistance of the end anchorage
$V_{l,Rd}$ Design value of the resistance to shear
$V_{pl,Rd}$ Design value of the plastic resistance of the composite section to vertical shear
$V_{pl,a,Rd}$ Design value of the plastic resistance of the structural steel section to vertical shear
V_{Rd} Design value of the resistance of the composite section to vertical shear
$V_{v,Rd}$ Design value of the resistance of a composite slab to vertical shear

Latin lower case letters

a Spacing between parallel beams; diameter or width; distance
b Width of the flange of a steel section; width of slab
b_b Width of the bottom of the concrete rib
b_{eff} Total effective width
$b_{eff,1}$ Effective width at mid-span for a span supported at both ends
$b_{eff,2}$ Effective width at an internal support
b_{ei} Effective width of the concrete flange on each side of the web
b_{em} Effective width of a composite slab
b_f Width of the flange of a steel section
b_i Geometric width of the concrete flange on each side of the web
b_r Width of rib of profiled steel sheeting
b_s Distance between centres of adjacent ribs of profiled steel sheeting
b_0 Distance between the centres of the outstand shear connectors; mean width of a concrete rib (minimum width for re-entrant sheeting profiles); width of haunch
c Width of the outstand of a steel flange; effective perimeter of reinforcing bar
d Clear depth of the web of the structural steel section; diameter of the shank of a stud connector; overall diameter of circular hollow steel section; minimum transverse dimension of a column
d_{do} Diameter of the weld collar to a stud connector
d_p Distance between the centroidal axis of the profiled steel sheeting and the extreme fibre of the composite slab in compression
d_s Distance between the steel reinforcement in tension to the extreme fibre of the composite slab in compression; distance between the longitudinal reinforcement in tension and the centroid of the beam's steel section
e Eccentricity of loading; distance from the centroidal axis of profiled steel sheeting to the extreme fibre of the composite slab in tension
e_p Distance from the plastic neutral axis of profiled steel sheeting to the extreme fibre of the composite slab in tension
e_s Distance from the steel reinforcement in tension to the extreme fibre of the composite slab in tension
f_{cd} Design value of the cylinder compressive strength of concrete
f_{ck} Characteristic value of the cylinder compressive strength of concrete at 28 days
$f_{ct,eff}$ Mean value of the effective tensile strength of the concrete
f_{ctm} Mean value of the axial tensile strength of concrete
$f_{ct,0}$ Reference strength for concrete in tension
f_{lctm} Mean value of the axial tensile strength of lightweight concrete
f_{sd} Design value of the yield strength of reinforcing steel
f_{sk} Characteristic value of the yield strength of reinforcing steel
f_u Specified ultimate tensile strength
f_y Nominal value of the yield strength of structural steel
f_{yd} Design value of the yield strength of structural steel
$f_{yp,d}$ Design value of the yield strength of profiled steel sheeting
h Overall depth; thickness
h_a Depth of the structural steel section
h_c Depth of the concrete encasement to a steel section; thickness of the concrete flange; thickness of concrete above the main flat surface of the top of the ribs of the sheeting
h_f Thickness of concrete flange; thickness of finishes
h_n Position of neutral axis
h_p Overall depth of the profiled steel sheeting excluding embossments
h_s Depth between the centroids of the flanges of the structural steel section; distance between the longitudinal reinforcement in tension and the centre of compression

h_{sc}	Overall nominal height of a stud connector
k	Amplification factor for second-order effects; coefficient; empirical factor for design shear resistance
k_c	Coefficient
k_ℓ	Reduction factor for resistance of a headed stud used with profiled steel sheeting parallel to the beam
k_s	Rotational stiffness; coefficient
k_t	Reduction factor for resistance of a headed stud used with profiled steel sheeting transverse to the beam
k_ϕ	Parameter
ℓ	Length of the beam in hogging bending adjacent to the joint
m	Slope of fatigue strength curve; empirical factor for design shear resistance
n	Modular ratio; number of shear connectors
n_f	Number of connectors for full shear connection
n_L	Modular ratio depending on the type of loading
n_r	Number of stud connectors in one rib
n_0	Modular ratio for short-term loading
s	Longitudinal spacing centre-to-centre of the stud shear connectors; slip
s_t	Transverse spacing centre-to-centre of the stud shear connectors
t	Age; thickness
t_f	Thickness of a flange of the structural steel section
t_w	Thickness of the web of the structural steel section
t_0	Age at loading
v_{Ed}	Design longitudinal shear stress
x_{pl}	Distance between the plastic neutral axis and the extreme fibre of the concrete slab in compression
y	Cross-section axis parallel to the flanges
z	Cross-section axis perpendicular to the flanges; lever arm
z_0	Vertical distance

Greek upper case letters

$\Delta\sigma$	Stress range
$\Delta\sigma_c$	Reference value of the fatigue strength at 2 million cycles
$\Delta\sigma_E$	Equivalent constant amplitude stress range
$\Delta\sigma_{E,glob}$	Equivalent constant amplitude stress range due to global effects
$\Delta\sigma_{E,loc}$	Equivalent constant amplitude stress range due to local effects
$\Delta\sigma_{E,2}$	Equivalent constant amplitude stress range related to 2 million cycles
$\Delta\sigma_s$	Increase of stress in steel reinforcement due to tension stiffening of concrete
$\Delta\sigma_{s,equ}$	Damage equivalent stress range
$\Delta\tau$	Range of shear stress for fatigue loading
$\Delta\tau_c$	Reference value of the fatigue strength at 2 million cycles
$\Delta\tau_E$	Equivalent constant amplitude stress range
$\Delta\tau_{E,2}$	Equivalent constant amplitude range of shear stress related to 2 million cycles
$\Delta\tau_R$	Fatigue shear strength
Ψ	Coefficient

Greek lower case letters

α	Factor; parameter
α_{cr}	Factor by which the design loads would have to be increased to cause elastic instability
α_M	Coefficient related to bending of a composite column
$\alpha_{M,y}$, α_{Mz}	Coefficient related to bending of a composite column about the *y-y* axis and the *z-z* axis respectively
α_{st}	Ratio
β	Factor; transformation parameter
β_c, β_i	Parameters
γ_C	Partial factor for concrete
γ_F	Partial factor for actions, also accounting for model uncertainties and dimensional variations
γ_{Ff}	Partial factor for equivalent constant amplitude stress range

γ_{M}	Partial factor for a material property, also accounting for model uncertainties and dimensional variations
γ_{M0}	Partial factor for structural steel applied to resistance of cross-sections, see EN 1993-1-1, 6.1(1)
γ_{M1}	Partial factor for structural steel applied to resistance of members to instability assessed by member checks, see EN 1993-1-1, 6.1(1)
γ_{Mf}	Partial factor for fatigue strength
$\gamma_{Mf,s}$	Partial factor for fatigue strength of studs in shear
γ_{P}	Partial factor for pre-stressing action
γ_{S}	Partial factor for reinforcing steel
γ_{V}	Partial factor for design shear resistance of a headed stud
γ_{VS}	Partial factor for design shear resistance of a composite slab
δ	Factor; steel contribution ratio; central deflection
δ_{max}	Sagging vertical deflection
δ_{s}	Deflection of steel sheeting under its own weight plus the weight of wet concrete
$\delta_{s,max}$	Limiting value of δ_{s}
δ_{u}	Maximum slip measured in a test at the characteristic load level
δ_{uk}	Characteristic value of slip capacity
ε	$\sqrt{235 / f_{y}}$, where f_{y} is in N/mm^2
η	Degree of shear connection; coefficient
η_{a}, η_{ao}	Factors related to the confinement of concrete
η_{c}, η_{co}, η_{cL}	Factors related to the confinement of concrete
θ	Angle
λ, λ_{v}	Damage equivalent factors
λ_{glob}, λ_{ldz}	Damage equivalent factors for global effects and local effects, respectively
$\bar{\lambda}$	Relative slenderness
$\bar{\lambda}_{LT}$	Relative slenderness for lateral-torsional buckling
μ	Coefficient of friction; nominal factor
μ_{d}	Factor related to design for compression and uniaxial bending
μ_{dy}, μ_{dz}	Factor μ_{d} related to plane of bending
ν	Reduction factor to allow for the effect of longitudinal compression on resistance in shear; parameter related to deformation of the shear connection
ν_{a}	Poisson's ratio for structural steel
ξ	Parameter related to deformation of the shear connection
ρ	Parameter related to reduced design bending resistance accounting for vertical shear
ρ_{s}	Parameter; reinforcement ratio
$\sigma_{com,c,Ed}$	Longitudinal compressive stress in the encasement due to the design normal force
$\sigma_{c,Rd}$	Local design strength of concrete
σ_{ct}	Extreme fibre tensile stress in the concrete
$\sigma_{max,f}$	Maximum stress due to fatigue loading
$\sigma_{min,f}$	Minimum stress due to fatigue loading
$\sigma_{s,max,f}$	Stress in the reinforcement due to the bending moment $M_{Ed,max,f}$
$\sigma_{s,min,f}$	Stress in the reinforcement due to the bending moment $M_{Ed,min,f}$
σ_{s}	Stress in the tension reinforcement
$\sigma_{s,max}$	Stress in the reinforcement due to the bending moment M_{max}
$\sigma_{s,max,0}$	Stress in the reinforcement due to the bending moment M_{max}, neglecting concrete in tension
$\sigma_{s,0}$	Stress in the tension reinforcement neglecting tension stiffening of concrete
τ_{Rd}	Design shear strength
τ_{u}	Value of longitudinal shear strength of a composite slab determined from testing
$\tau_{u,Rd}$	Design value of longitudinal shear strength of composite slab
$\tau_{u,Rk}$	Characteristic value of longitudinal shear strength of a composite slab
ϕ	Diameter (size) of a steel reinforcing bar; damage equivalent impact factor
$\phi*$	Diameter (size) of a steel reinforcing bar
φ_{t}	Creep coefficient
φ (t,t_{0})	Creep coefficient, defining creep between times t and t_{0}, related to elastic deformation at 28 days
χ	Reduction factor for flexural buckling
χ_{LT}	Reduction factor for lateral-torsional buckling
ψ_{L}	Creep multiplier

Section 2 Basis of design

2.1 Requirements

(1)P The design of composite structures shall be in accordance with the general rules given in EN 1990.

(2)P The supplementary provisions for composite structures given in this Section shall also be applied.

2.2 Principles of limit states design

(1)P For composite structures, relevant stages in the sequence of construction shall be considered.

The influence of the method of construction – propped or un-propped – should be carefully considered. In un-propped construction, the bare steel beam (or metal deck in the case of an un-propped composite slab) is required to safely carry the wet concrete and temporary actions arising during construction. See also 5.4.2.4.

2.3 Basic variables

2.3.1 Actions and environmental influences

(1) Actions to be used in design may be obtained from the relevant parts of EN 1991.

(2)P In verification for steel sheeting as shuttering, account shall be taken of the ponding effect (increased depth of concrete due to the deflection of the sheeting).

For further guidance on when ponding should be considered and how this may be done, see 9.3.2.

2.3.2 Material and product properties

(1) Unless otherwise given by Eurocode 4, actions caused by time-dependent behaviour of concrete should be obtained from EN 1992-1-1.

2.3.3 Classification of actions

(1)P The effects of shrinkage and creep of concrete and non-uniform changes of temperature result in internal forces in cross-sections, and curvatures and longitudinal strains in members; the effects that occur in statically determinate structures, and in statically indeterminate structures when compatibility of the deformations is not considered, shall be classified as primary effects.

(2)P In statically indeterminate structures the primary effects of shrinkage, creep and temperature are associated with additional action effects, such that the total effects are compatible; these shall be classified as secondary effects and shall be considered as indirect actions.

For buildings the effects of shrinkage may sometimes be ignored – see 3.1(4) and 7.3.1(8).

2.4 Verification by the partial factor method

2.4.1.2 Design values of material or product properties

(2)P For concrete, a partial factor γ_C shall be applied. The design compressive strength shall be given by:

$$f_{cd} = f_{ck} / \gamma_C \quad (2.1)$$

where the characteristic value f_{ck} shall be obtained by reference to EN 1992-1-1, 3.1 for normal concrete and to EN 1992-1-1, 11.3 for lightweight concrete.

NOTE The value for γ_C is that used in EN 1992-1-1.

(3)P For steel reinforcement, a partial factor γ_S shall be applied.

NOTE The value for γ_S is that used in EN 1992-1-1.

(4)P For structural steel, steel sheeting and steel connecting devices, partial factors γ_M shall be applied. Unless otherwise stated, the partial factor for structural steel shall be taken as γ_{M0}.

NOTE Values for γ_M are those given in EN 1993.

(5)P For shear connection, a partial factor γ_V shall be applied.

NOTE The value for γ_V may be given in the National Annex. The recommended value for γ_v is 1,25.

The National Annex refers to γ_V in NA.2.3.

NA 2.3 Clause 2.4.1.2(5) Partial factor, γ_V

The value of γ_v may vary depending on the form of slab, geometry of decking, and the size and layout of shear studs. Use the recommended value unless shear stud resistances given in non-contradictory complementary information (see NA.4) would justify the use of an alternative value.

NA.4 refers the reader to the website www.steel-ncci.co.uk for non-contradictory complementary information. The number of studs in a trough, type of decking and other details (e.g. the position of reinforcing mesh) may have a considerable effect on shear stud resistances and the designer should check that the resistance used in calculations is appropriate for the as-built condition. For scheme design, a value of γ_v of 1,25 is reasonable but the guidance provided in non-contradictory complementary information should be consulted for the final design.

(6)P For longitudinal shear in composite slabs, a partial factor γ_{VS} shall be applied.

NOTE The value for γ_{VS} may be given in the National Annex. The recommended value for γ_{VS} is 1,25.

The National Annex refers to γ_{VS} in NA.2.4.

NA 2.4 Clause 2.4.1.2(6) Partial factor, γ_{VS}

Use the recommended value.

2.4.1.4 Design resistances

(1)P For composite structures, design resistances shall be determined in accordance with EN 1990, expression (6.6a) or expression (6.6c).

2.4.2 Combination of actions

(1) The general formats for combinations of actions are given in EN 1990, Section 6.

NOTE For buildings, the combination rules may be given in the National Annex to Annex A of EN 1990.

Section 3 Materials

3.1 Concrete

(1) Unless otherwise given by Eurocode 4, properties should be obtained by reference to EN 1992-1-1, 3.1 for normal concrete and to EN 1992-1-1, 11.3 for lightweight concrete.

(2) This Part of EN 1994 does not cover the design of composite structures with concrete strength classes lower than C20/25 and LC20/22 and higher than C60/75 and LC60/66.

(3) Shrinkage of concrete should be determined taking account of the ambient humidity, the dimensions of the element and the composition of the concrete.

(4) Where composite action is taken into account in buildings, the effects of autogenous shrinkage may be neglected in the determination of stresses and deflections.

NOTE Experience shows that the values of shrinkage strain given in EN 1992-1-1 can give overestimates of the effects of shrinkage in composite structures. Values for shrinkage of concrete may be given in the National Annex. Recommended values for composite structures for buildings are given in Annex C.

3.2 Reinforcing steel

(1) Properties should be obtained by reference to EN 1992-1-1, 3.2.

(2) For composite structures, the design value of the modulus of elasticity E_s may be taken as equal to the value for structural steel given in EN 1993-1-1, 3.2.6.

3.3 Structural steel

(1) Properties should be obtained by reference to EN 1993-1-1, 3.1 and 3.2.

(2) The rules in this Part of EN 1994 apply to structural steel of nominal yield strength not more than 460 N/mm^2.

3.5 Profiled steel sheeting for composite slabs in buildings

(2) The rules in this Part of EN 1994 apply to the design of composite slabs with profiled steel sheets manufactured from steel in accordance with EN 10025, cold formed steel sheet in accordance with EN 10149-2 or EN 10149-3 or galvanised steel sheet in accordance with [AC1) EN 10326. (AC1]

NOTE The minimum value for the nominal thickness t of steel sheets may be given in the National Annex. The National Annex refers to *t* in NA.2.7. The recommended value is 0,70 mm.

NA 2.7 Clause 3.5(2) Nominal thickness, *t*, of steel sheets

The nominal bare metal thickness of the sheeting can be a minimum of 0.70 mm.

Section 4 Durability

4.2 Profiled steel sheeting for composite slabs in buildings

(1)P The exposed surfaces of the steel sheeting shall be adequately protected to resist the particular atmospheric conditions.

(3) A zinc coating of total mass 275 g/m^2 (including both sides) is sufficient for internal floors in a non-aggressive environment, but the specification may be varied depending on service conditions.

Section 5 Structural analysis

5.1 Structural modelling for analysis

5.1.1 Structural modelling and basic assumptions

(1)P The structural model and basic assumptions shall be chosen in accordance with EN 1990, 5.1.1 and shall reflect the anticipated behaviour of the cross-sections, members, joints and bearings.

(3) Analysis of composite slabs with profiled steel sheeting in buildings should be in accordance with Section 9.

5.1.2 Joint modelling

(1) The effects of the behaviour of the joints on the distribution of internal forces and moments within a structure, and on the overall deformations of the structure, may generally be neglected, but where such effects are significant (such as in the case of semi-continuous joints) they should be taken into account, see Section 8 and EN 1993-1-8.

(2) To identify whether the effects of joint behaviour on the analysis need be taken into account, a distinction may be made between three joint models as follows, see 8.2 and EN 1993-1-8, 5.1.1:

- simple, in which the joint may be assumed not to transmit bending moments;
- continuous, in which the stiffness and/or resistance of the joint allow full continuity of the members to be assumed in the analysis;
- semi-continuous, in which the behaviour of the joint needs to be taken into account in the analysis.

Section 8 is not included in these extracts. Many composite buildings are designed assuming simple joints, with the beams assumed to be simply supported and the resistance to lateral loads provided by a bracing system. A summary of the alternative design methods can be found in Composite Construction [2].

5.2 Structural stability

5.2.1 Effects of deformed geometry of the structure

(1) The action effects may generally be determined using either:

- first-order analysis, using the initial geometry of the structure
- second-order analysis, taking into account the influence of the deformation of the structure.

(2)P The effects of the deformed geometry (second-order effects) shall be considered if they increase the action effects significantly or modify significantly the structural behaviour.

(3) First-order analysis may be used if the increase of the relevant internal forces or moments caused by the deformations given by first-order analysis is less than 10 %. This condition may be assumed to be fulfilled if the following criterion is satisfied:

$$\alpha_{cr} \geq 10 \qquad (5.1)$$

where:

α_{cr} is the factor by which the design loading would have to be increased to cause elastic instability.

(4)P In determining the stiffness of the structure, appropriate allowances shall be made for cracking and creep of concrete and for the behaviour of the joints.

5.2.2 Methods of analysis for buildings

(1) Beam-and-column type plane frames may be checked for sway mode failure with first-order analysis if the criterion (5.1) is satisfied for each storey. In these structures α_{cr} may be calculated using the expression given in EN 1993-1-1, 5.2.1(4), provided that the axial compression in the beams is not significant and appropriate allowances are made for cracking of concrete, see 5.4.2.3, creep of concrete, see 5.4.2.2 and for the behaviour of the joints, see 8.2 and EN 1993-1-8, 5.1.

(2) Second-order effects may be included indirectly by using a first-order analysis with appropriate amplification.

(3) If second-order effects in individual members and relevant member imperfections are fully accounted for in the global analysis of the structure, individual stability checks for the members are unnecessary.

(7) For structures in which the columns are structural steel, stability may also be verified by member checks based on buckling lengths, in accordance with EN 1993-1-1, 5.2.2(8) and 6.3.

5.2.2(8) is not included in these extracts.

5.3 Imperfections

5.3.2 Imperfections in buildings

5.3.2.1 General

(1) Equivalent geometric imperfections, see 5.3.2.2 and 5.3.2.3, should be used, with values that reflect the possible effects of global imperfections and of local imperfections, unless the effects of local imperfections are included in the resistance formulae for member design, see 5.3.2.3.

(4) Imperfections within steel compression members should be considered in accordance with EN 1993-1-1, 5.3.2 and 5.3.4.

5.3.2.2 Global imperfections

(1) The effects of imperfections should be allowed for in accordance with EN 1993-1-1, 5.3.2.

5.3.2.3 Member imperfections

(3) For steel members the effects of imperfections are incorporated within the formulae given for buckling resistance, see EN 1993-1-1, 6.3.

5.4 Calculation of action effects

5.4.1 Methods of global analysis

5.4.1.1 General

(1) Action effects may be calculated by elastic global analysis, even where the resistance of a cross-section is based on its plastic or non-linear resistance.

(2) Elastic global analysis should be used for serviceability limit states, with appropriate corrections for non-linear effects such as cracking of concrete.

(4)P The effects of shear lag and of local buckling shall be taken into account if these significantly influence the global analysis.

(5) The effects of local buckling of steel elements on the choice of method of analysis may be taken into account by classifying cross-sections, see 5.5.

5.4.1.2 Effective width of flanges for shear lag

(1)P Allowance shall be made for the flexibility of steel or concrete flanges affected by shear in their plane (shear lag) either by means of rigorous analysis, or by using an effective width of flange.

(3) The effective width of concrete flanges should be determined in accordance with the following provisions.

(4) When elastic global analysis is used, a constant effective width may be assumed over the whole of each span. This value may be taken as the value $b_{\mathrm{eff},1}$ at mid-span for a span supported at both ends, or the value $b_{\mathrm{eff},2}$ at the support for a cantilever.

(5) At mid-span or an internal support, the total effective width b_{eff}, see Figure 5.1, may be determined as:

$$b_{\mathrm{eff}} = b_0 + \Sigma b_{\mathrm{ei}} \qquad (5.3)$$

where:

b_0 is the distance between the centres of the outstand shear connectors;

b_{ei} is the value of the effective width of the concrete flange on each side of the web and taken as L_e / 8 but not greater than the geometric width b_i . The value b_i should be taken as the distance from the outstand shear connector to a point mid-way between adjacent webs, measured at mid-depth of the concrete flange, except that at a free edge b_i is the distance to the free edge. The length L_e should be taken as the approximate distance between points of zero bending moment. For typical continuous composite beams, where a moment envelope from various load arrangements governs the design, and for cantilevers, L_e may be assumed to be as shown in Figure 5.1.

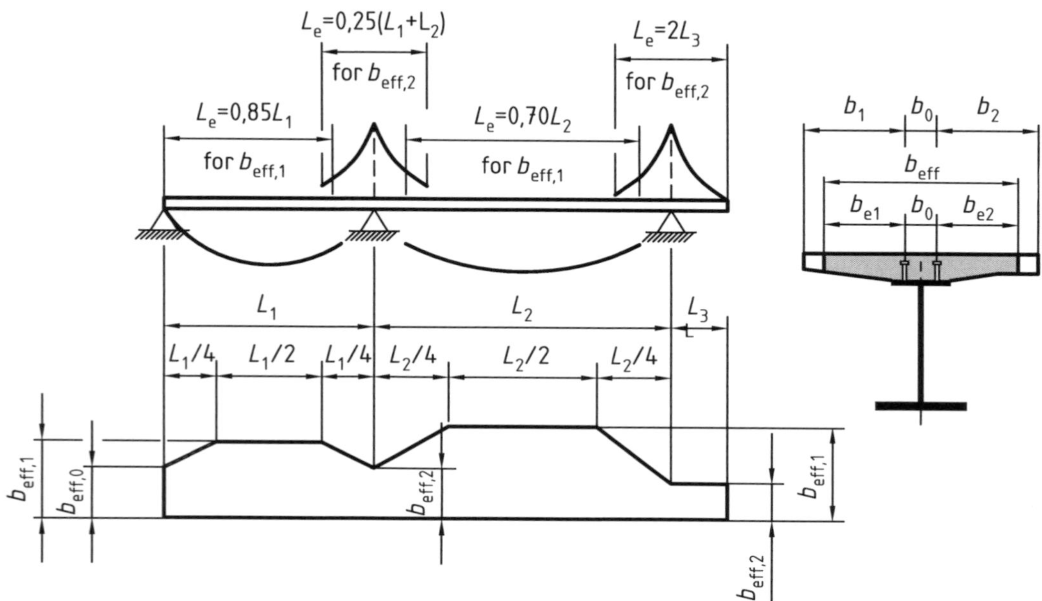

Figure 5.1 — Equivalent spans, for effective width of concrete flange

(6) The effective width at an end support may be determined as:

$$b_{\mathrm{eff}} = b_0 + \Sigma \beta_i \, b_{\mathrm{ei}} \qquad (5.4)$$

with:

$$\beta_i = (0,55 + 0,025\, L_e / b_{\mathrm{ei}}) \leq 1,0 \qquad (5.5)$$

where:

b_{ei} is the effective width, see (5), of the end span at mid-span and L_e is the equivalent span of the end span according to Figure 5.1.

(7) The distribution of the effective width between supports and midspan regions may be assumed to be as shown in Figure 5.1.

(9) For analysis of building structures, b_0 may be taken as zero and b_i measured from the centre of the web.

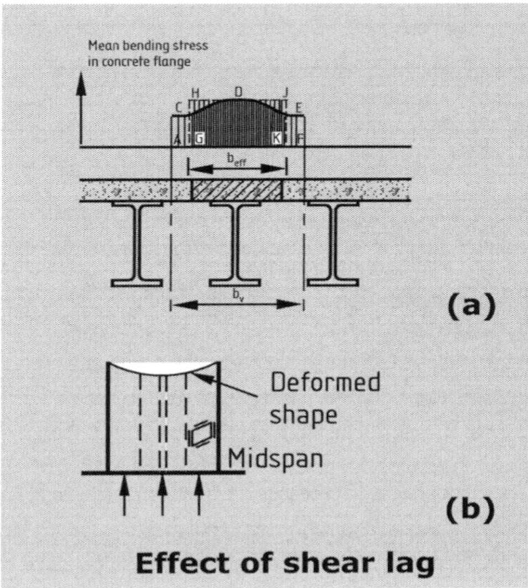

Effect of shear lag

Shear lag is illustrated in the adjacent figure. Initially, plane sections do not remain plane after bending and this deformation results in a non-linear distribution of bending stress across the width of the concrete flange. The concept of an effective width is to replace the actual centre-to-centre distance between beams with a reduced width over which the bending stress is assumed to be constant. The effective width, b_{eff}, is obtained by equating area GHJK with ACDEF, as shown in (a), left.

Note that for a simply supported composite beam a constant effective width, taken as the midspan value, may be assumed over the whole span. See 6.1.2(2) and 6.2.1.5

5.4.2 Linear elastic analysis

5.4.2.1 General

(1) Allowance should be made for the effects of cracking of concrete, creep and shrinkage of concrete, sequence of construction and pre-stressing.

5.4.2.2 Creep and shrinkage

(1)P Appropriate allowance shall be made for the effects of creep and shrinkage of concrete.

(2) Except for members with both flanges composite, the effects of creep may be taken into account by using modular ratios n_L for the concrete. The modular ratios depending on the type of loading (subscript L) are given by:

$$n_L = n_0 \left(1 + \psi_L \varphi_t\right) \tag{5.6}$$

where:

n_0 is the modular ratio E_a / E_{cm} for short-term loading;
E_{cm} is the secant modulus of elasticity of the concrete for short-term loading according to EN 1992-1-1, Table 3.1 or Table 11.3.1;
φ_t is the creep coefficient $\varphi(t,t_0)$ according to EN 1992-1-1, 3.1.4 or 11.3.3, depending on the age (t) of concrete at the moment considered and the age (t_0) at loading,
ψ_L is the creep multiplier depending on the type of loading, which should be taken as 1,1 for permanent loads, 0,55 for primary and secondary effects of shrinkage and 1,5 for pre-stressing by imposed deformations.

(4) For shrinkage, the age of loading should generally be assumed to be one day.

(11) For simplification in structures for buildings that satisfy expression (5.1) or 5.2.2(1), are not mainly intended for storage and are not pre-stressed by controlled imposed deformations,

the effects of creep in composite beams may be taken into account by replacing concrete areas A_c by effective equivalent steel areas A_c / n for both short-term and long-term loading, where n is the nominal modular ratio corresponding to an effective modulus of elasticity for concrete $E_{c,eff}$ taken as $E_{cm} / 2$.

The approach is to use a transformed section i.e. the concrete is converted into an equivalent area of steel using an appropriate value for the ratio of moduli for steel and concrete. In choosing a value of E for concrete, the effects of creep should be taken into account; thus the duration of load becomes important, and so a distinction should be made between propped and un-propped construction. In general, an average value can be used for the modular ratio (n) but for warehouses and other buildings intended mainly for storage it is necessary to distinguish between short-term and long-term effects by calculating two transformed sections with n_0 and n_L for use with long and short term loads separately.

5.4.2.3 Effects of cracking of concrete

(1)P Appropriate allowance shall be made for the effects of cracking of concrete.

(2) The following method may be used for the determination of the effects of cracking in composite beams with concrete flanges. First the envelope of the internal forces and moments for the characteristic combinations, see EN 1990, 6.5.3, including long-term effects should be calculated using the flexural stiffness $E_a I_1$ of the un-cracked sections. This is defined as "un-cracked analysis". In regions where the extreme fibre tensile stress in the concrete due to the envelope of global effects exceeds twice the strength f_{ctm} or f_{lctm} , see EN1992-1-1, Table 3.1 or Table 11.3.1, the stiffness should be reduced to $E_a I_2$, see 1.5.2.12. This distribution of stiffness may be used for ultimate limit states and for serviceability limit states. A new distribution of internal forces and moments, and deformation if appropriate, is then determined by re-analysis. This is defined as "cracked analysis".

(3) For continuous composite beams with the concrete flanges above the steel section and not pre-stressed, including beams in frames that resist horizontal forces by bracing, the following simplified method may be used. Where all the ratios of the length of adjacent continuous spans (shorter/longer) between supports are at least 0,6, the effect of cracking may be taken into account by using the flexural stiffness $E_a I_2$ over 15 % of the span on each side of each internal support, and as the un-cracked values $E_a I_1$ elsewhere.

For simply-supported beams the effects of cracking on the analysis are not relevant but cracking still needs to be controlled for serviceability – see 7.4.

5.4.2.4 Stages and sequence of construction

(1)P Appropriate analysis shall be made to cover the effects of staged construction including where necessary separate effects of actions applied to structural steel and to wholly or partially composite members.

(2) The effects of sequence of construction may be neglected in analysis for ultimate limit states other than fatigue, for composite members where all cross-sections are in Class 1 or 2 and in which no allowance for lateral-torsional buckling is necessary.

5.4.2.5 Temperature effects

(2) Temperature effects may normally be neglected in analysis for the ultimate limit states other than fatigue, for composite members where all cross-sections are in Class 1 or Class 2 and in which no allowance for lateral-torsional buckling is necessary.

5.4.4 Linear elastic analysis with limited redistribution for buildings

(1) Provided that second-order effects need not be considered, linear elastic analysis with limited redistribution may be applied to continuous beams and frames for verification of limit states other than fatigue.

(2) The bending moment distribution given by a linear elastic global analysis according to 5.4.2 may be redistributed in a way that satisfies equilibrium and takes account of the effects of inelastic behaviour of materials, and all types of buckling.

(4) For ultimate limit state verifications other than for fatigue, the elastic bending moments in composite beams may be modified according to (5) – (7) where:

- the beam is a continuous composite member, or part of a frame that resists horizontal forces by bracing,
- the beam is connected by rigid and full-strength joints, or by one such joint and one nominally-pinned joint,
- for a partially-encased composite beam, either it is established that rotation capacity is sufficient for the degree of redistribution adopted, or the contribution of the reinforced concrete encasement in compression is neglected when calculating the resistance moment at sections where the bending moment is reduced,
- each span is of uniform depth and
- no allowance for lateral-torsional buckling is necessary.

(5) Where (4) applies, the bending moments in composite beams determined by linear elastic global analysis may be modified:

- by reducing maximum hogging moments by amounts not exceeding the percentages given in Table 5.1, or
- in beams with all cross-sections in Classes 1 or 2 only, by increasing maximum hogging moments by amounts not exceeding 10 %, for un-cracked elastic analysis or 20 % for cracked elastic analysis, see 5.4.2.3,

unless it is verified that the rotation capacity permits a higher value.

Table 5.1 — Limits to redistribution of hogging moments, per cent of the initial value of the bending moment to be reduced

Class of cross-section in hogging moment region	1	2	3	4
For un-cracked analysis	40	30	20	10
For cracked analysis	25	15	10	0

(6) For grades of structural steel higher than S355, redistribution should only be applied to beams with all cross-sections in Class 1 and Class 2. The redistribution should not exceed 30 % for an un-cracked analysis and 15 % for a cracked analysis, unless it is demonstrated that the rotation capacity permits a higher value.

5.5 Classification of cross-sections

5.5.1 General

(1)P The classification system defined in EN 1993-1-1, 5.5.2 applies to cross-sections of composite beams.

(5) For cross-sections in Class 1 and 2 with bars in tension, reinforcement used within the effective width should have a ductility Class B or C, see EN 1992-1-1, Table C.1. Additionally for a section whose resistance moment is determined by 6.2.1.2, 6.2.1.3 or 6.2.1.4, a minimum area of reinforcement A_s within the effective width of the concrete flange should be provided to satisfy the following condition:

$$A_s \geq \rho_s A_c \tag{5.7}$$

with

$$\rho_s = \delta \frac{f_y}{235} \frac{f_{ctm}}{f_{sk}} \sqrt{k_c} \qquad (5.8)$$

where:

A_c is the effective area of the concrete flange;
f_y is the nominal value of the yield strength of the structural steel in N/mm^2;
f_{sk} is the characteristic yield strength of the reinforcement;
f_{ctm} is the mean tensile strength of the concrete, see EN1992-1-1, Table 3.1 or Table 11.3.1;
k_c is a coefficient given in 7.4.2;
δ is equal to 1,0 for Class 2 and equal to 1,1 for Class 1 cross-sections at which plastic hinge rotation is required.

(6) Welded mesh should not be included in the effective section unless it has been shown to have sufficient ductility, when built into a concrete slab, to ensure that it will not fracture.

(7) In global analysis for stages in construction, account should be taken of the class of the steel section at the stage considered.

6.2.1.4 is not included in these extracts.

5.5.2 Classification of composite sections without concrete encasement

(1) A steel compression flange that is restrained from buckling by effective attachment to a concrete flange by shear connectors may be assumed to be in Class 1 if the spacing of connectors is in accordance with 6.6.5.5.

(2) The classification of other steel flanges and webs in compression in composite beams without concrete encasement should be in accordance with EN 1993-1-1, Table 5.2. An element that fails to satisfy the limits for Class 3 should be taken as Class 4.

(3) Cross-sections with webs in Class 3 and flanges in Classes 1 or 2 may be treated as an effective cross-section in Class 2 with an effective web in accordance with EN1993-1-1, 6.2.2.4.

Section 6 Ultimate limit states

6.1 Beams

6.1.1 Beams for buildings

(1)P Composite beams are defined in 1.5.2. Typical types of cross-section are shown in Figure 6.1 with either a solid slab or a composite slab. Partially–encased beams are those in which the web of the steel section is encased by reinforced concrete and shear connection is provided between the concrete and the steel components.

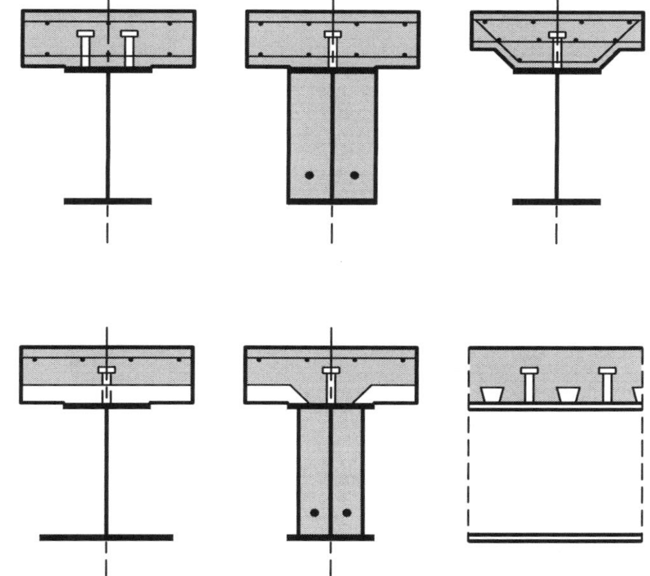

Figure 6.1 — Typical cross-sections of composite beams

(2) Design resistances of composite cross-sections in bending or/and vertical shear should be determined in accordance with 6.2 for composite beams with steel sections and 6.3 for partially-encased composite beams.

(3)P Composite beams shall be checked for:

- resistance of critical cross-sections (6.2 and 6.3);
- resistance to lateral-torsional buckling (6.4);
- resistance to shear buckling (6.2.2.3) and transverse forces on webs (6.5);
- resistance to longitudinal shear (6.6).

(4)P Critical cross-sections include:

- sections of maximum bending moment;
- supports;
- sections subjected to concentrated loads or reactions;
- places where a sudden change of cross-section occurs, other than a change due to cracking of concrete.

(6) For checking resistance to longitudinal shear, a critical length consists of a length of the interface between two critical cross-sections. For this purpose critical cross-sections also include:

- free ends of cantilevers;
- in tapering members, sections so chosen that the ratio of the greater to the lesser plastic resistance moments (under flexural bending of the same direction) for any pair of adjacent cross-sections does not exceed 1,5.

(7)P The concepts "full shear connection" and "partial shear connection" are applicable only to beams in which plastic theory is used for calculating bending resistances of critical cross-sections. A span of a beam, or a cantilever, has full shear connection when increase in the number of shear connectors would not increase the design bending resistance of the member. Otherwise, the shear connection is partial.

NOTE Limits to the use of partial shear connection are given in 6.6.1.2.

6.1.2 Effective width for verification of cross-sections

(1) The effective width of the concrete flange for verification of cross-sections should be determined in accordance with 5.4.1.2 taking into account the distribution of effective width between supports and mid-span regions.

(2) As a simplification for buildings, a constant effective width may be assumed over the whole region in sagging bending of each span. This value may be taken as the value $b_{eff,1}$ at mid-span. The same assumption applies over the whole region in hogging bending on both sides of an intermediate support. This value may be taken as the value $b_{eff,2}$ at the relevant support.

6.2 Resistances of cross-sections of beams

6.2.1 Bending resistance

6.2.1.1 General

(1)P The design bending resistance shall be determined by rigid-plastic theory only where the effective composite cross-section is in Class 1 or Class 2 and where pre-stressing by tendons is not used.

(2) Elastic analysis and non-linear theory for bending resistance may be applied to cross-sections of any class.

(4)P The tensile strength of concrete shall be neglected.

6.2.1.2 Plastic resistance moment $M_{pl,Rd}$ of a composite cross-section

(1) The following assumptions should be made in the calculation of $M_{pl,Rd}$:

a) there is full interaction between structural steel, reinforcement, and concrete;
b) the effective area of the structural steel member is stressed to its design yield strength f_{yd} in tension or compression;
c) the effective areas of longitudinal reinforcement in tension and in compression are stressed to their design yield strength f_{sd} in tension or compression. Alternatively, reinforcement in compression in a concrete slab may be neglected;
d) the effective area of concrete in compression resists a stress of 0,85 f_{cd}, constant over the whole depth between the plastic neutral axis and the most compressed fibre of the concrete, where f_{cd} is the design cylinder compressive strength of concrete.

Typical plastic stress distributions are shown in Figure 6.2.

(3) Where plastic theory is used and reinforcement is in tension, that reinforcement should be in accordance with 5.5.1(5).

(4)P For buildings, profiled steel sheeting in compression shall be neglected.

(5) For buildings, any profiled steel sheeting in tension included within the effective section should be assumed to be stressed to its design yield strength $f_{yp,d}$.

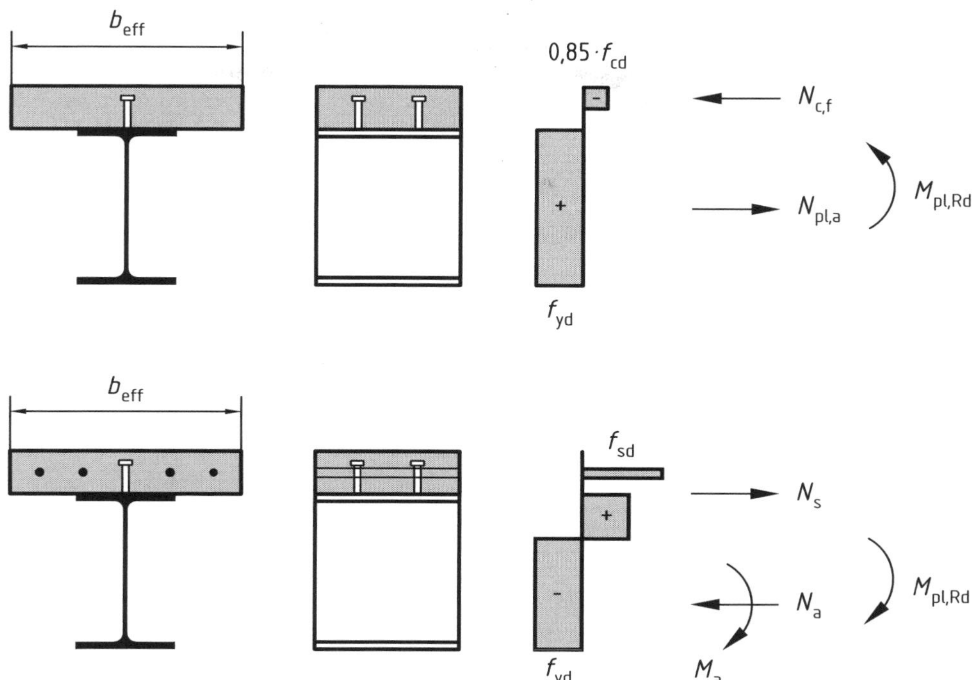

Figure 6.2 — Examples of plastic stress distributions for a composite beam with a solid slab and full shear connection in sagging and hogging bending

6.2.1.3 Plastic resistance moment of sections with partial shear connection in buildings

(1) In regions of sagging bending, partial shear connection in accordance with 6.6.1 and 6.6.2.2 may be used in composite beams for buildings.

(2) Unless otherwise verified, the plastic resistance moment in hogging bending should be determined in accordance with 6.2.1.2 and appropriate shear connection should be provided to ensure yielding of reinforcement in tension.

(3) Where ductile shear connectors are used, the resistance moment of the critical cross-section of the beam M_{Rd} may be calculated by means of rigid plastic theory in accordance with 6.2.1.2, except that a reduced value of the compressive force in the concrete flange N_c should be used in place of the force N_{cf} given by 6.2.1.2(1)(d). The ratio $\eta = N_c / N_{c,f}$ is the degree of shear connection. The location of the plastic neutral axis in the slab should be determined by the new force N_c , see Figure 6.4. There is a second plastic neutral axis within the steel section, which should be used for the classification of the web.

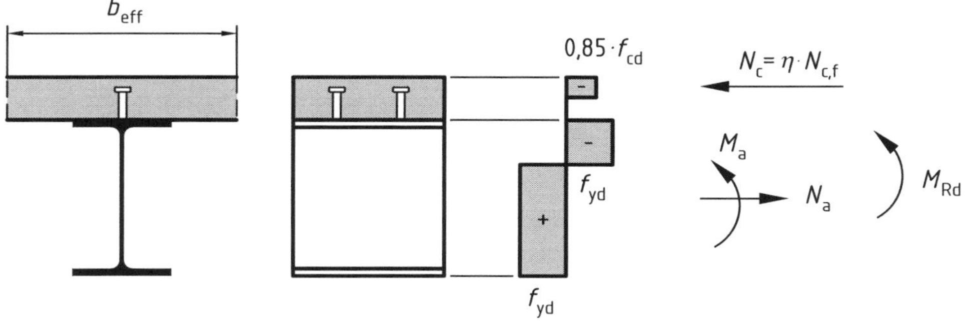

Figure 6.4 — Plastic stress distribution under sagging bending for partial shear connection

(4) The relation between M_{Rd} and N_c in (3) is qualitatively given by the convex curve ABC in Figure 6.5 where $M_{pl,a,Rd}$ and $M_{pl,Rd}$ are the design plastic resistances to sagging bending of the structural steel section alone, and of the composite section with full shear connection, respectively.

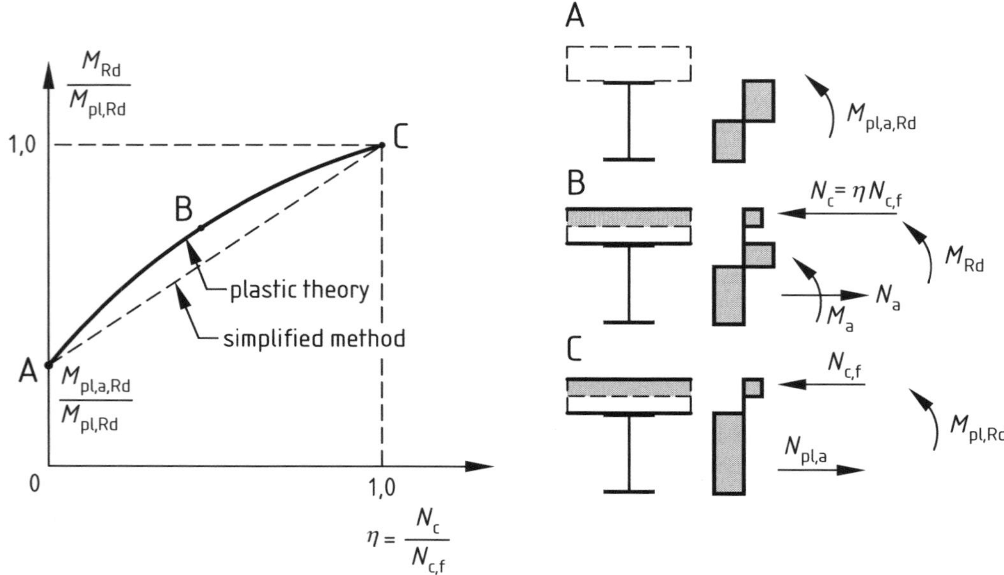

Figure 6.5 — Relation between M_{Rd} and N_c (for ductile shear connectors)

(5) For the method given in (3), a conservative value of M_{Rd} may be determined by the straight line AC in Figure 6.5:

AC1) $$M_{Rd} = M_{pl,a,Rd} + (M_{pl,Rd} - M_{pl,a,Rd}) \frac{N_c}{N_{c,f}} \quad (6.1)$$ (AC1

6.2.1.5 Elastic resistance to bending

(1) Stresses should be calculated by elastic theory, using an effective width of the concrete flange in accordance with 6.1.2. For cross-sections in Class 4, the effective structural steel section should be determined in accordance with EN 1993-1-5, 4.3.

(2) In the calculation of the elastic resistance to bending based on the effective cross-section, the limiting stresses should be taken as:

- f_{cd} in concrete in compression;
- f_{yd} in structural steel in tension or compression;
- f_{sd} in reinforcement in tension or compression. Alternatively, reinforcement in compression in a concrete slab may be neglected.

(3)P Stresses due to actions on the structural steelwork alone shall be added to stresses due to actions on the composite member.

(4) Unless a more precise method is used, the effect of creep should be taken into account by use of a modular ratio according to 5.4.2.2.

6.2.2 Resistance to vertical shear

6.2.2.1 Scope

(1) Clause 6.2.2 applies to composite beams with a rolled or welded structural steel section with a solid web, which may be stiffened.

6.2.2.2 Plastic resistance to vertical shear

(1) The resistance to vertical shear $V_{pl,Rd}$ should be taken as the resistance of the structural steel section $V_{pl,a,Rd}$ unless the value for a contribution from the reinforced concrete part of the beam has been established.

(2) The design plastic shear resistance $V_{pl,a,Rd}$ of the structural steel section should be determined in accordance with EN 1993-1-1, 6.2.6.

6.2.2.3 Shear buckling resistance

(1) The shear buckling resistance $V_{b,Rd}$ of an uncased steel web should be determined in accordance with EN 1993-1-5, 5.

6.2.2.4 Bending and vertical shear

(1) Where the vertical shear force V_{Ed} exceeds half the shear resistance V_{Rd} given by $V_{pl,Rd}$ in 6.2.2.2 or $V_{b,Rd}$ in 6.2.2.3, whichever is the smaller, allowance should be made for its effect on the resistance moment.

(2) For cross-sections in Class 1 or 2, the influence of the vertical shear on the resistance to bending may be taken into account by a reduced design steel strength $(1 - \rho) f_{yd}$ in the shear area as shown in Figure 6.7 where:

$$\rho = (2V_{Ed} / V_{Rd} - 1)^2 \qquad (6.5)$$

and V_{Rd} is the appropriate resistance to vertical shear, determined in accordance with 6.2.2.2 or 6.2.2.3.

[AC1⟩ (3) For cross-sections in Class 3 and 4, EN 1993-1-5, 7.1 is applicable using as M_{Ed} the total bending moment in the considered cross-section and both $M_{pl,Rd}$ and $M_{f,Rd}$ for the composite cross-section. ⟨AC1]

M_{Ed}, $M_{pl,Rd}$ and $M_{f,Rd}$ are terms used in an interaction equation for shear force, bending moment and axial force (equation 7.1 of EN 1993 Part 1-5) usually applied to non-composite cross-sections fabricated from plates. For non-composite sections, $M_{pl,Rd}$ and $M_{f,Rd}$ refer to resistances of the steel cross-section alone but when applied to Class 3 and 4 composite sections (rolled or plated) they are calculated for the composite section.

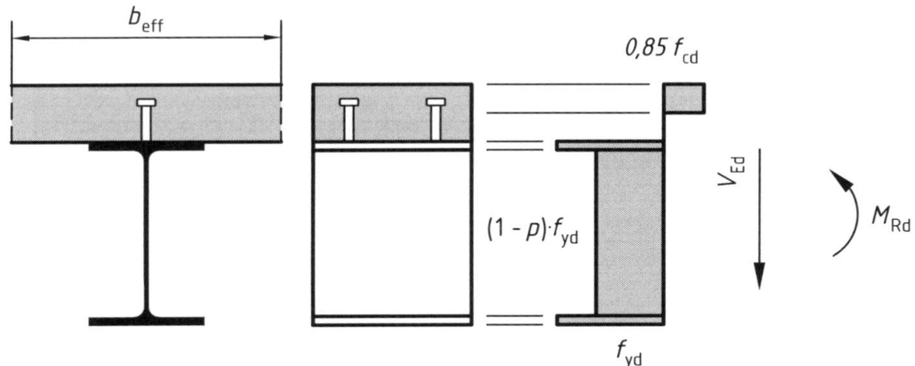

Figure 6.7 — Plastic stress distribution modified by the effect of vertical shear

6.4 Lateral-torsional buckling of composite beams

6.4.1 General

(1) A steel flange that is attached to a concrete or composite slab by shear connection in accordance with 6.6 may be assumed to be laterally stable, provided that lateral instability of the concrete slab is prevented.

6.4.3 Simplified verification for buildings without direct calculation

(1) A continuous beam (or a beam within a frame that is composite throughout its length) with Class 1, 2 or 3 cross-sections may be designed without additional lateral bracing when the following conditions are satisfied:

a) Adjacent spans do not differ in length by more than 20 % of the shorter span. Where there is a cantilever, its length does not exceed 15 % of that of the adjacent span.
b) The loading on each span is uniformly distributed, and the design permanent load exceeds 40 % of the total design load.
c) The top flange of the steel member is attached to a reinforced concrete or composite slab by shear connectors in accordance with 6.6.
d) The same slab is also attached to another supporting member approximately parallel to the composite beam considered, to form an inverted-U frame as illustrated in Figure 6.11.
e) If the slab is composite, it spans between the two supporting members of the inverted-U frame considered.
f) At each support of the steel member, its bottom flange is laterally restrained and its web is stiffened. Elsewhere, the web may be un-stiffened.
g) If the steel member is an IPE section or an HE section that is not partially encased, its depth h does not exceed the limit given in Table 6.1.
h) If the steel member is partially encased in concrete according to 5.5.3(2), its depth h does not exceed the limit given in Table 6.1 by more than 200 mm for steel grades up to S355 and by 150 mm for grades S420 and S460.

NOTE Provisions for other types of steel section may be given in the National Annex.

Table 6.1 — Maximum depth *h* (mm) of uncased steel member for which clause 6.4.3 is applicable

Steel member	Nominal steel grade			
	S 235	S 275	S 355	S 420 and S 460
IPE	600	550	400	270
HE	800	700	650	500

NA 2.8 Clause 6.4.3(1)(h) Other types of steel section

For BS 4-1 or similar I and H steel sections the guidance given in 6.4.3(1) may be applied where the section parameter is less than or equal to the limiting values given in Table NA 1.

The section parameter is determined as follows.

$$\left(1+\frac{t_w h_s}{4 b_f t_f}\right)\left(\frac{h_s}{t_w}\right)^{0.75}\left(\frac{t_f}{b_f}\right)^{0.25}$$

Where:

t_w is the web thickness
t_f is the flange thickness
b_f is the breadth of the bottom flange
$h_s = h - t_f$
h is the depth of the section

Table NA 1 — Section parameter limits

	Section parameter limit for steel grade			
	S235	S275	S355	S420 and S460
Uncased web	15.1	13.9	12.3	10.8
Encased web	15.1	18.0	15.8	13.9

6.6 Shear connection

6.6.1 General

6.6.1.1 Basis of design

(1) Clause 6.6 is applicable to composite beams and, as appropriate, to other types of composite member.

(2)P Shear connection and transverse reinforcement shall be provided to transmit the longitudinal shear force between the concrete and the structural steel element, ignoring the effect of natural bond between the two.

(3)P Shear connectors shall have sufficient deformation capacity to justify any inelastic redistribution of shear assumed in design.

(4)P Ductile connectors are those with sufficient deformation capacity to justify the assumption of ideal plastic behaviour of the shear connection in the structure considered.

(5) A connector may be taken as ductile if the characteristic slip capacity δ_{uk} is at least 6 mm.

NOTE An evaluation at δ_{uk} is given in Annex B.

(9) Headed stud shear connectors in accordance with 6.6.5.7 may be assumed to provide sufficient resistance to uplift, unless the shear connection is subjected to direct tension.

(13) For buildings, the number of connectors should be at least equal to the total design shear force for the ultimate limit state, determined according to 6.6.2, divided by the design resistance of a single connector P_{Rd}. For stud connectors the design resistance should be determined according to 6.6.3 or 6.6.4, as appropriate.

(14)P If all cross-sections are in Class 1 or Class 2, in buildings partial shear connection may be used for beams. The number of connectors shall then be determined by a partial connection theory taking into account the deformation capacity of the shear connectors.

In buildings it is common for the steel beam to be designed to carry the loads during construction (the wet concrete and temporary construction loads) i.e. un-propped construction. Once the concrete has hardened, $M_{pl,Rd}$ of the resulting composite section may be considerably in excess of the applied moments at the ultimate limit state. By reducing the number of shear connectors, the resistance of the composite section M_{Rd} may be matched more closely to the applied moment. This is termed partial shear connection and provides some economy in the provision of connectors but is most helpful because in some cases (particularly where composite slabs are used) it proves physically impossible to accommodate the required number for full interaction.

6.6.1.2 Limitation on the use of partial shear connection in beams for buildings

(1) Headed studs with an overall length after welding not less than 4 times the diameter, and with a shank of nominal diameter not less than 16 mm and not greater than 25 mm, may be considered as ductile within the following limits for the degree of shear connection, which is defined by the ratio $\eta = n / n_f$:

For steel sections with equal flanges:

$L_e \leq 25$: $\quad \eta \geq 1 - \left(\frac{355}{f_y}\right)(0,75 - 0,03\,L_e), \quad \eta \geq 0,4$ (6.12)

$L_e > 25$: $\quad \eta \geq 1$ (6.13)

where:

L_e is the distance in sagging bending between points of zero bending moment in metres; for typical continuous beams, L_e may be assumed to be as shown in Figure 5.1;

AC1) n_f (AC1 is the number of connectors for full shear connection determined for that length of beam in accordance with 6.6.1.1(13) and 6.6.2.2(2);

n is the number of shear connectors provided within that same length.

6.6.1.3 Spacing of shear connectors in beams for buildings

(1)P The shear connectors shall be spaced along the beam so as to transmit longitudinal shear and to prevent separation between the concrete and the steel beam, considering an appropriate distribution of design longitudinal shear force.

(3) Ductile connectors may be spaced uniformly over a length between adjacent critical cross-sections as defined in 6.1.1 provided that:

- all critical sections in the span considered are in Class 1 or Class 2,
- η satisfies the limit given by 6.6.1.2 and
- the plastic resistance moment of the composite section does not exceed 2,5 times the plastic resistance moment of the steel member alone.

6.6.2 Longitudinal shear force in beams for buildings

6.6.2.2 Beams in which plastic theory is used for resistance of cross-sections

(1)P The total design longitudinal shear shall be determined in a manner consistent with the design bending resistance, taking account of the difference in the normal force in concrete or structural steel over a critical length.

(2) For full shear connection, reference should be made to 6.2.1.2, or 6.3.2, as appropriate.

(3) For partial shear connection, reference should be made to 6.2.1.3 or 6.3.2, as appropriate.

6.3.2 relates to partially encased sections and is not included in these extracts.

6.6.3 Headed stud connectors in solid slabs and concrete encasement

6.6.3.1 Design resistance

(1) The design shear resistance of a headed stud automatically welded in accordance with EN 14555 should be determined from:

$$P_{Rd} = \frac{0,8\, f_u\, \pi\, d^2 / 4}{\gamma_V} \tag{6.18}$$

or:

$$P_{Rd} = \frac{0,29\, \alpha d^2 \sqrt{f_{ck} E_{cm}}}{\gamma_V} \qquad (6.19)$$

whichever is smaller, with:

$$\alpha = 0,2\left(\frac{h_{sc}}{d}+1\right) \quad \text{for } 3 \le h_{sc}/d \le 4 \qquad (6.20)$$

$$\alpha = 1 \quad \text{for } h_{sc}/d > 4 \qquad (6.21)$$

where:

γ_V is the partial factor;
d is the diameter of the shank of the stud, 16 mm ≤ d ≤ 25 mm;
f_u is the specified ultimate tensile strength of the material of the stud but not greater than 500 N/mm^2;
[AC1⟩ f_{ck} ⟨AC1] is the characteristic cylinder compressive strength of the concrete at the age considered, of density not less than 1750 kg/m^3;
h_{sc} is the overall nominal height of the stud.

NOTE The value for γ_V may be given in the National Annex. The recommended value for γ_V is 1,25.

The National Annex refers to γ_V in NA.2.9.

NA 2.9 Clause 6.6.3.1(1) Partial factor, γ_V

The recommended values are given in NA 2.3.

NA 2.3 is included in these extracts after 2.4.1.2(5).

The characteristic value of the shear resistance of a single connector P_{Rk} may also be determined by tests. Details are given in Annex B (not included in these extracts).

6.6.4 Design resistance of headed studs used with profiled steel sheeting in buildings

6.6.4.1 Sheeting with ribs parallel to the supporting beams

(1) The studs are located within a region of concrete that has the shape of a haunch, see Figure 6.12. Where the sheeting is continuous across the beam, the width of the haunch b_0 is equal to the width of the trough as given in Figure 9.2. Where the sheeting is not continuous, b_0 is defined in a similar way as given in Figure 6.12. The depth of the haunch should be taken as h_p, the overall depth of the sheeting excluding embossments.

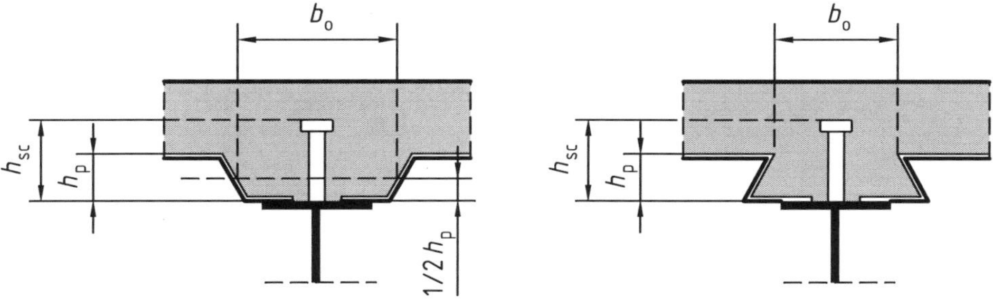

Figure 6.12 — Beam with profiled steel sheeting parallel to the beam

(2) The design shear resistance should be taken as the resistance in a solid slab, see 6.6.3.1, multiplied by the reduction factor k_ℓ given by the following expression:

$$k_\ell = 0,6 \frac{b_0}{h_p} \left(\frac{h_{sc}}{h_p} - 1 \right) \leq 1,0 \qquad (6.22)$$

where:

h_{sc} is the overall height of the stud, but not greater than h_p + 75 mm.

The behaviour of a stud connector in a rib of profiled steel sheeting is more complex than that in a solid slab and the resistance is reduced by the factor k_l to account for the shape of the surrounding concrete.

6.6.4.2 Sheeting with ribs transverse to the supporting beams

(1) Provided that the conditions given in (2) and (3) are satisfied, the design shear resistance should be taken as the resistance in a solid slab, calculated as given by 6.6.3.1 (except that f_u should not be taken as greater than 450 N/mm^2) multiplied by the reduction factor k_t given by:

$$k_t = \frac{0,7}{\sqrt{n_r}} \frac{b_0}{h_p} \left(\frac{h_{sc}}{h_p} - 1 \right) \qquad (6.23)$$

where:

AC1 n_r is the number of stud connectors in one rib at the beam intersection, not to exceed two in calculation of the reduction factor k_t and of the longitudinal shear resistance of the connection. Other symbols are as defined in Figure 6.13. AC1

(2) The factor k_t should not be taken greater than the appropriate value $k_{t,max}$ given in Table 6.2.

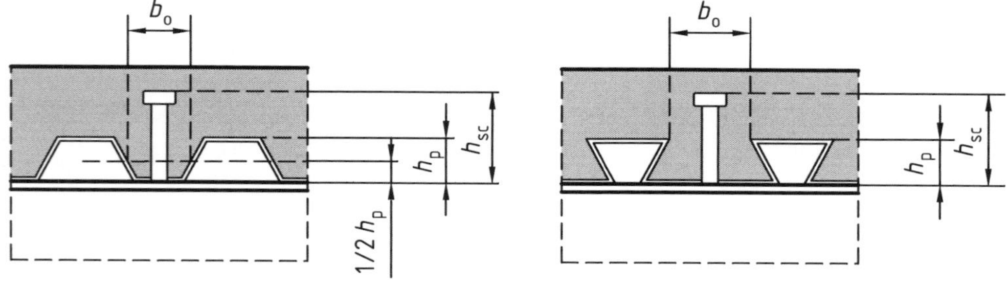

Figure 6.13 — Beam with profiled steel sheeting transverse to the beam

Table 6.2 — Upper limits $k_{t,max}$ for the reduction factor k_t

Number of stud connectors per rib	Thickness t of sheet (mm)	Studs not exceeding 20 mm in diameter and welded through profiled steel sheeting	Profiled sheeting with holes and studs 19 mm or 22mm in diameter
$n_r = 1$	≤ 1,0	0,85	0,75
	> 1,0	1,0	0,75
$n_r = 2$	≤ 1,0	0,70	0,60
	> 1,0	0,8	0,60

(3) The values for k_t given by (1) and (2) are applicable provided that:

- the studs are placed in ribs with a height h_p not greater than 85 mm and a width b_0 not less than h_p and
- for through deck welding, the diameter of the studs is not greater than 20 mm, or for holes provided in the sheeting, the diameter of the studs is not greater than 22 mm.
- for holes provided in the sheeting, the diameter of the studs is not greater than 22 mm.

The behaviour of a stud connector in a rib of profiled steel sheeting is more complex than that in a solid slab and the resistance is reduced by the factor k_t to account for the shape of the surrounding concrete.

6.6.4.3 Biaxial loading of shear connectors

(1) Where the shear connectors are provided to produce composite action both for the beam and for the composite slab, the combination of forces acting on the stud should satisfy the following:

$$\frac{F_\ell^2}{P_{\ell,\mathrm{Rd}}^2} + \frac{F_t^2}{P_{t,\mathrm{Rd}}^2} \leq 1 \qquad (6.24)$$

where:

F_ℓ is the design longitudinal force caused by composite action in the beam;
F_t is the design transverse force caused by composite action in the slab, see Section 9;

$P_{\ell,\mathrm{Rd}}$ and $P_{t,\mathrm{Rd}}$ are the corresponding design shear resistances of the stud.

6.6.5 Detailing of the shear connection and influence of execution

6.6.5.2 Cover and concreting for buildings

(1)P The detailing of shear connectors shall be such that concrete can be adequately compacted around the base of the connector.

(2) If cover over the connector is required, the minimum cover should be:

a) not less than 20 mm, or
b) as recommended by EN 1992-1-1, Table 4.4 for reinforcing steel, less 5 mm, whichever is the greater.

6.6.5.3 Local reinforcement in the slab

(1) Where the shear connection is adjacent to a longitudinal edge of a concrete slab, transverse reinforcement provided in accordance with 6.6.6 should be fully anchored in the concrete between the edge of the slab and the adjacent row of connectors.

(2) To prevent longitudinal splitting of the concrete flange caused by the shear connectors, the following additional recommendations should be applied where the distance from the edge of the concrete flange to the centreline of the nearest row of shear connectors is less than 300 mm:

a) transverse reinforcement should be supplied by U-bars passing around the shear connectors,
b) where headed studs are used as shear connectors, the distance from the edge of the concrete flange to the centre of the nearest stud should not be less than $6d$, where d is the nominal diameter of the stud, and the U-bars should be not less than $0{,}5d$ in diameter and
c) the U-bars should be placed as low as possible while still providing sufficient bottom cover.

6.6.5.5 Spacing of connectors

(1)P Where it is assumed in design that the stability of either the steel or the concrete member is ensured by the connection between the two, the spacing of the shear connectors shall be sufficiently close for this assumption to be valid.

(2) Where a steel compression flange that would otherwise be in AC1 Class 3 or Class 4 AC1 is assumed to be in Class 1 or Class 2 because of restraint from shear connectors, the centre-to-centre spacing of the shear connectors in the direction of compression should not be greater than the following limits:

- where the slab is in contact over the full length (e.g. solid slab): $22\, t_f \sqrt{235 / f_y}$
- where the slab is not in contact over the full length (e.g. slab with ribs transverse to the beam): $15\, t_f \sqrt{235 / f_y}$

where:

t_f is the thickness of the flange;
f_y is the nominal yield strength of the flange in N/mm^2.

In addition, the clear distance from the edge of a compression flange to the nearest line of shear connectors should not be greater than $9\, t_f \sqrt{235 / f_y}$.

(3) In buildings, the maximum longitudinal centre-to-centre spacing of shear connectors should not be greater than 6 times the total slab thickness nor 800 mm.

6.6.5.7 Headed stud connectors

(1) The overall height of a stud should be not less than 3*d*, where *d* is the diameter of the shank.

(4) The spacing of studs in the direction of the shear force should be not less than 5*d*; the spacing in the direction transverse to the shear force should be not less than 2,5*d* in solid slabs and 4*d* in other cases.

(5) Except when the studs are located directly over the web, the diameter of a welded stud should not be greater than 2,5 times the thickness of that part to which it is welded, unless test information is provided to establish the resistance of the stud as a shear connector.

6.6.5.8 Headed studs used with profiled steel sheeting in buildings

(1) The nominal height of a connector should extend not less than 2*d* above the top of the steel deck, where *d* is the diameter of the shank.

(3) Where the sheeting is such that studs cannot be placed centrally within a trough, they should be placed alternately on the two sides of the trough, throughout the length of the span.

6.6.6 Longitudinal shear in concrete slabs

6.6.6.1 General

(1)P Transverse reinforcement in the slab shall be designed for the ultimate limit state so that premature longitudinal shear failure or longitudinal splitting shall be prevented.

(2)P The design longitudinal shear stress for any potential surface of longitudinal shear failure within the slab v_{Ed} shall not exceed the design longitudinal shear strength of the shear surface considered.

(3) The length of the shear surface b-b shown in Figure 6.15 should be taken as equal to $2h_{sc}$ plus the head diameter for a single row of stud shear connectors or staggered stud connectors, or as equal to $(2h_{sc} + s_t)$ plus the head diameter for stud shear connectors arranged in pairs, where h_{sc} is the height of the studs and s_t is the transverse spacing centre-to-centre of the studs.

6.6.6.2 Design resistance to longitudinal shear

(1) The design shear strength of the concrete flange (shear planes a-a illustrated in Figure 6.15) should be determined in accordance with EN 1992-1-1, 6.2.4.

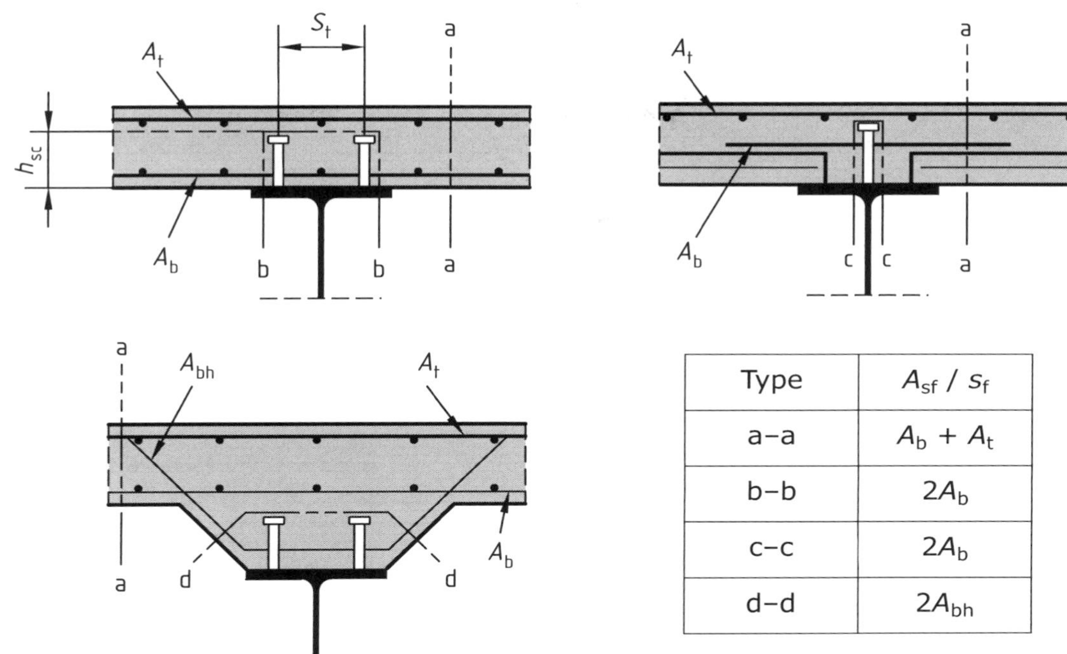

Type	A_{sf} / s_f
a–a	$A_b + A_t$
b–b	$2A_b$
c–c	$2A_b$
d–d	$2A_{bh}$

Figure 6.15 — Typical potential surfaces of shear failure

(2) In the absence of a more accurate calculation the design shear strength of any surface of potential shear failure in the flange or a haunch may be determined from EN 1992-1-1, 6.2.4(4). For a shear surface passing around the shear connectors (e.g. shear surface b-b in Figure 6.15), the dimension h_f should be taken as the length of the shear surface.

6.6.6.3 Minimum transverse reinforcement

(1) The minimum area of reinforcement should be determined in accordance with EN 1992-1-1, 9.2.2(5) using definitions appropriate to transverse reinforcement.

6.6.6.4 Longitudinal shear and transverse reinforcement in beams for buildings

(1) Where profiled steel sheeting is used and the shear surface passes through the depth of the slab (e.g. shear surface a-a in Figure 6.16), the dimension h_f should be taken as the thickness of the concrete above the sheeting.

(2) Where profiled steel sheeting is used transverse to the beam and the design resistances of the studs are determined using the appropriate reduction factor k_t as given in 6.6.4.2, it is not necessary to consider shear surfaces of type b-b in Figure 6.16.

(3) Unless verified by tests, for surfaces of type c-c in Figure 6.16 the depth of the sheeting should not be included in h_f.

(4) Where profiled steel sheeting with mechanical or frictional interlock and with ribs transverse to the beam is continuous across the top flange of the steel beam, its contribution to the transverse reinforcement for a shear surface of type a-a may be allowed for by replacing expression (6.21) in EN 1992-1-1, 6.2.4(4) by:

$$\left(A_{sf}\, f_{yd} / s_f\right) + A_{pe}\, f_{yp,d} > v_{Ed}\, h_f / \cot\theta \qquad (6.25)$$

where:

A_{pe} is the cross-sectional area of the profiled steel sheeting per unit length of the beam; for sheeting with holes, the net area should be used;

$f_{yp,d}$ is its design yield strength.

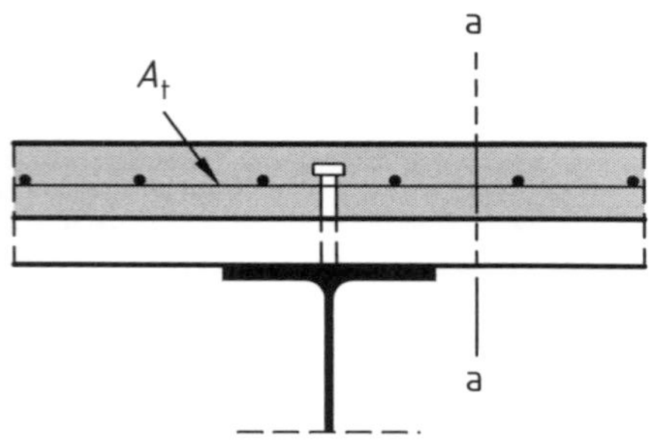

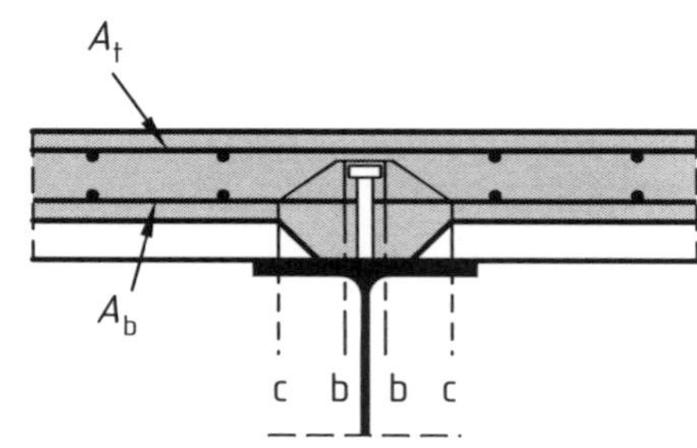

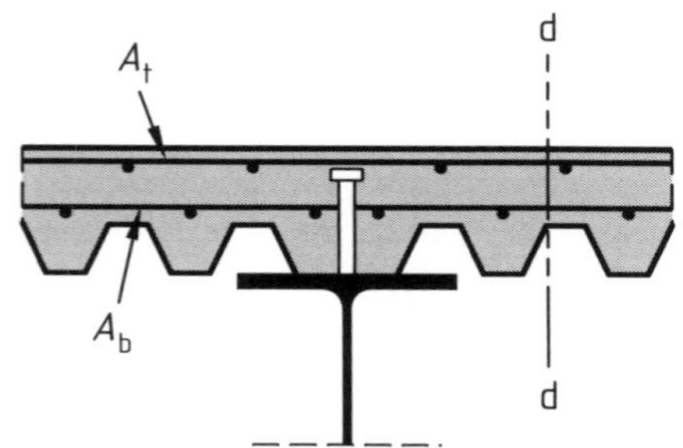

Type	A_{sf} / s_f
a–a	A_t
b–b	$2A_b$
c–c	$2A_b$
d–d	$A_t + A_b$

Figure 6.16 — Typical potential surfaces of shear failure where profiled steel sheeting is used

(5) Where the profiled steel sheeting with ribs transverse to the beam is discontinuous across the top flange of the steel beam, and stud shear connectors are welded to the steel beam directly through the profiled steel sheets, the term [AC1) $A_{pe} f_{yp,d}$ (AC1] in expression (6.25) should be replaced by:

[AC1) $P_{pb,Rd} / s$ but $\leq A_{pe} f_{yp,d}$ (AC1] (6.26)

where:

$P_{pb,Rd}$ is the design bearing resistance of a headed stud welded through the sheet according to 9.7.4;

s is the longitudinal spacing centre-to-centre of the studs effective in anchoring the sheeting.

(6) With profiled steel sheeting, the requirement for minimum reinforcement relates to the area of concrete above the sheeting.

Section 7 Serviceability limit states

7.1 General

(1)P A structure with composite members shall be designed and constructed such that all relevant serviceability limit states are satisfied according to the principles of 3.4 of EN 1990.

7.2 Stresses

7.2.1 General

(1)P Calculation of stresses for beams at the serviceability limit state shall take into account the following effects, where relevant:

- shear lag;
- creep and shrinkage of concrete;
- cracking of concrete and tension stiffening of concrete;
- sequence of construction;
- increased flexibility resulting from significant incomplete interaction due to slip of shear connection;
- inelastic behaviour of steel and reinforcement, if any;
- torsional and distorsional warping, if any.

(2) Shear lag may be taken into account according to 5.4.1.2.

(3) Unless a more accurate method is used, effects of creep and shrinkage may be taken into account by use of modular ratios according to 5.4.2.2.

(4) In cracked sections the primary effects of shrinkage may be neglected when verifying stresses.

(5)P In section analysis the tensile strength of concrete shall be neglected.

(8) The effects of incomplete interaction may be ignored, where full shear connection is provided and where, in case of partial shear connection in buildings, 7.3.1(4) applies.

7.2.2 Stress limitation for buildings

(1) Stress limitation is not required for beams if, in the ultimate limit state, no verification of fatigue is required and no pre-stressing by tendons and/or by controlled imposed deformations (e.g. jacking of supports) is provided.

(3) If required, the stress limitations for concrete and reinforcement given in EN 1992-1-1, 7.2 apply.

Eurocode 4 does not specify a "permissible stress" limit. Some plasticity at the serviceability limit state may occur, whether in the mid-span (which does not greatly influence the deflection), or on the intermediate supports in the case of a continuous beam (the effect on the deflection is taken account of - see 7.3.1(7)).

In (3) "If required" refers to situations where crack widths need to be controlled.

7.3 Deformations in buildings

7.3.1 Deflections

(1) Deflections due to loading applied to the steel member alone should be calculated in accordance with EN 1993-1-1.

(2) Deflections due to loading applied to the composite member should be calculated using elastic analysis in accordance with Section 5.

(3) The reference level for the sagging vertical deflection δ_{max} of un-propped beams is the upper-side of the composite beam. Only where the deflection can impair the appearance of the building should the underside of the beam be taken as reference level.

(4) The effects of incomplete interaction may be ignored provided that:

a) the design of the shear connection is in accordance with 6.6,
b) either not less shear connectors are used than half the number for full shear connection, or the forces resulting from an elastic behaviour and which act on the shear connectors in the serviceability limit state do not exceed P_{Rd} and
c) in case of a ribbed slab with ribs transverse to the beam, the height of the ribs does not exceed 80 mm.

(5) The effect of cracking of concrete in hogging moment regions on the deflection should be taken into account by adopting the methods of analysis given in 5.4.2.3.

(7) For the calculation of deflection of un-propped beams, account may be taken of the influence of local yielding of structural steel over a support by multiplying the bending moment at the support, determined according to the methods given in this clause, with an additional reduction factor as follows:

- $f_2 = 0,5$ if f_y is reached before the concrete slab has hardened;
- $f_2 = 0,7$ if f_y is reached after concrete has hardened.

This applies for the determination of the maximum deflection but not for pre-camber.

(8) Unless specifically required by the client, the effect of curvature due to shrinkage of normal weight concrete need not be included when the ratio of span to overall depth of the beam is not greater than 20.

7.3.2 Vibration

(1) The dynamic properties of floor beams should satisfy the criteria in EN1990, A1.4.4.

7.4 Cracking of concrete

7.4.1 General

(3) As a simplified and conservative alternative, crack width limitation to acceptable width can be achieved by ensuring a minimum reinforcement defined in 7.4.2, and bar spacing or diameters not exceeding the limits defined in 7.4.3.

(4) In cases where beams in buildings are designed as simply supported although the slab is continuous and the control of crack width is of no interest, the longitudinal reinforcement provided within the effective width of the concrete slab according to 6.1.2 should be not less than:

- 0,4 % of the area of the concrete, for propped construction;
- 0,2 % of the area of concrete, for un-propped construction.

The reinforcement should extend over a length of $0.25L$ each side of an internal support, or $L/2$ for a cantilever, where L is the length of the relevant span or the length of the cantilever respectively. No account should be taken of any profiled steel sheeting. The maximum spacing of the bars should be in accordance with 9.2.1(5) for a composite slab, or with EN 1992-1-1, 9.3.1.1(3) for a solid concrete flange.

7.4.2 Minimum reinforcement

(1) Unless a more accurate method is used in accordance with EN 1992-1-1, 7.3.2(1), in all sections without pre-stressing by tendons and subjected to significant tension due to restraint of imposed deformations (e.g. primary and secondary effects of shrinkage), in combination or

not with effects of direct loading the required minimum reinforcement area A_s for the slabs of composite beams is given by:

$$A_s = k_s \, k_c \, k \, f_{ct,eff} \, A_{ct} / \sigma_s \qquad (7.1)$$

where:

$f_{ct,eff}$ is the mean value of the tensile strength of the concrete effective at the time when cracks may first be expected to occur. Values of $f_{ct,eff}$ may be taken as those for f_{ctm}, see EN 1992-1-1, Table 3.1, or as f_{lctm}, see Table 11.3.1, as appropriate, taking as the class the strength at the time cracking is expected to occur. When the age of the concrete at cracking cannot be established with confidence as being less than 28 days, a minimum tensile strength of 3 N/mm^2 may be adopted;

k is a coefficient which allows for the effect of non-uniform self-equilibrating stresses which may be taken as 0,8;

k_s is a coefficient which allows for the effect of the reduction of the normal force of the concrete slab due to initial cracking and local slip of the shear connection, which may be taken as 0,9;

k_c is a coefficient which takes account of the stress distribution within the section immediately prior to cracking and is given by:

$$k_c = \frac{1}{1 + h_c / (2\, z_o)} + 0,3 \le 1,0 \qquad (7.2)$$

h_c is the thickness of the concrete flange, excluding any haunch or ribs;

z_o is the vertical distance between the centroids of the un-cracked concrete flange and the un-cracked composite section, calculated using the modular ratio n_0 for short-term loading;

σ_s is the maximum stress permitted in the reinforcement immediately after cracking. This may be taken as its characteristic yield strength f_{sk}. A lower value, depending on the bar size, may however be needed to satisfy the required crack width limits. This value is given in Table 7.1;

A_{ct} is the area of the tensile zone (caused by direct loading and primary effects of shrinkage) immediately prior to cracking of the cross-section. For simplicity the area of the concrete section within the effective width may be used.

Table 7.1 — Maximum bar diameters for high bond bars

Steel stress σ_s (N/mm^2)	Maximum bar diameter ϕ* (mm) for design crack width w_k		
	w_k=0,4mm	w_k=0,3mm	w_k=0,2mm
160	40	32	25
200	32	25	16
240	20	16	12
280	16	12	8
320	12	10	6
360	10	8	5
400	8	6	4
450	6	5	–

Section 9 Composite slabs with profiled steel sheeting for buildings

9.1 General

9.1.1 Scope

(1)P This Section deals with composite floor slabs spanning only in the direction of the ribs. Cantilever slabs are included. It applies to designs for building structures where the imposed loads are predominantly static, including industrial buildings where floors may be subject to moving loads.

9.1.2 Definitions

9.1.2.1 Types of shear connection

(1)P The profiled steel sheet shall be capable of transmitting horizontal shear at the interface between the sheet and the concrete; pure bond between steel sheeting and concrete is not considered effective for composite action. Composite behaviour between profiled sheeting and concrete shall be ensured by one or more of the following means, see Figure 9.1:

a) mechanical interlock provided by deformations in the profile (indentations or embossments);
b) frictional interlock for profiles shaped in a re-entrant form;
c) end anchorage provided by welded studs or another type of local connection between the concrete and the steel sheet, only in combination with (a) or (b);
d) end anchorage by deformation of the ribs at the end of the sheeting, only in combination with (b).

Other means are not excluded but are not within the scope of this Standard.

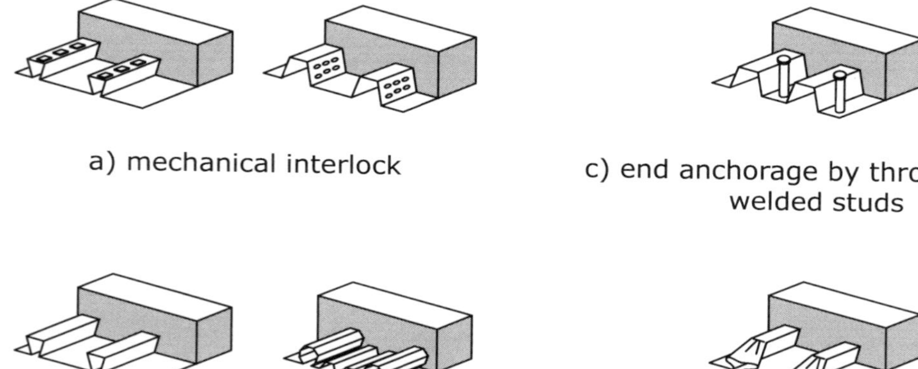

a) mechanical interlock

c) end anchorage by through-deck welded studs

b) frictional interlock

d) end anchorage by deformation of the ribs

Figure 9.1 — Typical forms of interlock in composite slabs

9.2 Detailing provisions

9.2.1 Slab thickness and reinforcement

(1)P The overall depth of the composite slab h shall be not less than 80 mm. The thickness of concrete h_c above the main flat surface of the top of the ribs of the sheeting shall be not less than 40 mm.

(2)P If the slab is acting compositely with the beam or is used as a diaphragm, the total depth shall be not less than 90 mm and h_c shall be not less than 50 mm.

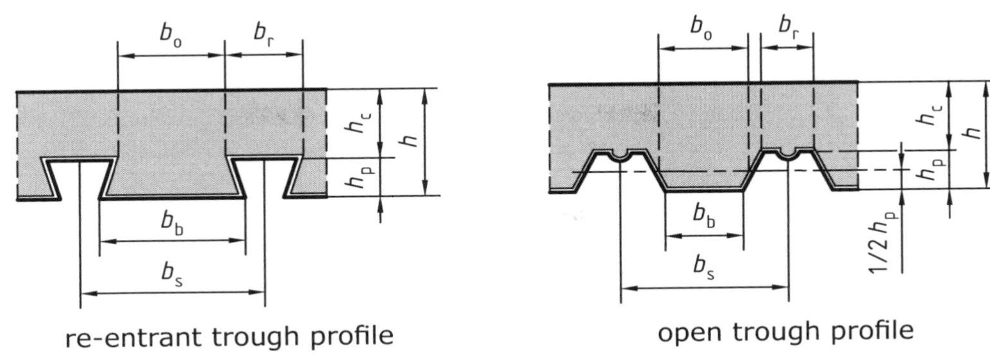

Figure 9.2 — Sheet and slab dimensions

9.3 Actions and action effects

9.3.1 Design situations

(2)P The following situations shall be considered:

a) Profiled steel sheeting as shuttering: Verification is required for the behaviour of the profiled steel sheeting while it is acting as formwork for the wet concrete. Account shall be taken of the effect of props, if any.

b) Composite slab: Verification is required for the floor slab after composite behaviour has commenced and any props have been removed.

9.3.2 Actions for profiled steel sheeting as shuttering

(1)The following loads should be taken into account in calculations for the steel deck as shuttering:

- weight of concrete and steel deck;
- construction loads including local heaping of concrete during construction, in accordance with EN 1991-1-6, 4.11.2;
- storage load, if any;
- "ponding" effect (increased depth of concrete due to deflection of the sheeting).

(2) If the central deflection δ of the sheeting under its own weight plus that of the wet concrete, calculated for serviceability, is less than 1/10 of the slab depth, the ponding effect may be ignored in the design of the steel sheeting. If this limit is exceeded, this effect should be allowed for. It may be assumed in design that the nominal thickness of the concrete is increased over the whole span by $0{,}7\delta$.

9.3.3 Actions for composite slab

(1) Loads and load arrangements should be in accordance with EN 1991-1-1.

(2) In design checks for the ultimate limit state, it may be assumed that the whole of the loading acts on the composite slab, provided this assumption is also made in design for longitudinal shear.

9.4 Analysis for internal forces and moments

9.4.1 Profiled steel sheeting as shuttering

(1) The design of the profiled steel sheeting as shuttering should be in accordance with EN1993-1-3.

9.4.2 Analysis of composite slab

(1) The following methods of analysis may be used for ultimate limit states:

a) Linear elastic analysis with or without redistribution;

b) Rigid plastic global analysis provided that it is shown that sections where plastic rotations are required have sufficient rotation capacity;
c) Elastic-plastic analysis, taking into account the non-linear material properties.

(2) Linear methods of analysis should be used for serviceability limit states.

(5) A continuous slab may be designed as a series of simply supported spans. Nominal reinforcement in accordance with 9.8.1 should be provided over intermediate supports.

9.5 Verification of profiled steel sheeting as shuttering for ultimate limit states

(1) Verification of the profiled steel sheeting for ultimate limit states should be in accordance with EN 1993-1-3. Due consideration shall be given to the effect of embossments or indentations on the design resistances.

9.6 Verification of profiled steel sheeting as shuttering for serviceability limit states

(1) Section properties shall be determined in accordance with EN 1993-1-3.

(2) The deflection δ_s of the sheeting under its own weight plus the weight of wet concrete, excluding the construction load, should not exceed $\delta_{s,max}$.

NOTE Values for $\delta_{s,max}$ may be given in the National Annex. The recommended value is *L*/180 where *L* is the effective span between supports (props being supports in this context).

The National Annex refers to $\delta_{s,max}$ in NA.2.15.

NA 2.15 Clause 9.6(2) Limit for the deflection of sheeting, $\delta_{s,max}$

The following limits are recommended.

$\delta_{s,max}$ = L/180 but less than 20mm where the loads from ponding are ignored (see **9.3.2**(2) of BS EN 1994-1-1: 2004)

$\delta_{s,max}$ = L/130 but less than 30mm where the loads from ponding are included (see **9.3.2**(2) of BS EN 1994-1-1: 2004)

9.7 Verification of composite slabs for the ultimate limit states

9.7.1 Design criterion

(1)P The design values of internal forces shall not exceed the design values of resistance for the relevant ultimate limit states.

9.7.2 Flexure

(1) In case of full shear connection the bending resistance M_{Rd} of any cross-section should be determined by plastic theory in accordance with 6.2.1.2(1) but with the design yield strength of the steel member (sheeting) taken as that for the sheeting, $f_{yp,d}$.

(5) The sagging bending resistance of a cross-section with the neutral axis above the sheeting should be calculated from the stress distribution in Figure 9.5.

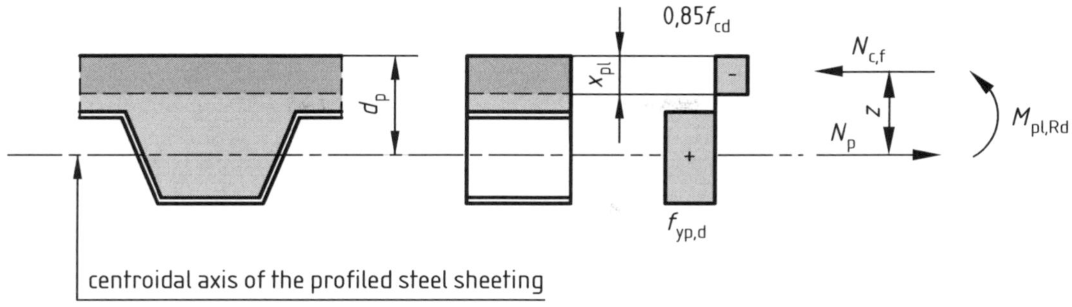

Figure 9.5 — Stress distribution for sagging bending if the neutral axis is above the steel sheeting

(6) The sagging bending resistance of a cross-section with the neutral axis in the sheeting should be calculated from the stress distribution in Figure 9.6.

For simplification z and M_{pr} may be determined with the following expressions respectively:

$$z = h - 0,5\,h_c - e_p + (e_p - e)\frac{N_{cf}}{A_{pe}\,f_{yp,d}} \tag{9.5}$$

$$M_{pr} = 1,25\,M_{pa}\left(1 - \frac{N_{cf}}{A_{pe}\,f_{yp,d}}\right) \le M_{pa} \tag{9.6}$$

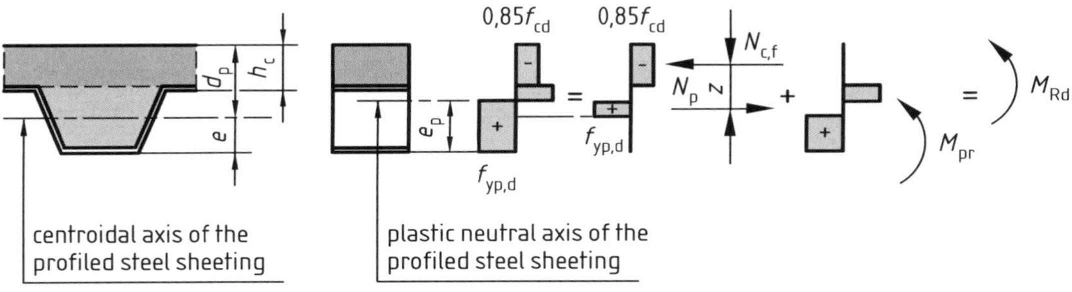

Figure 9.6 — Stress distribution for sagging bending if neutral axis is in the steel sheeting

(7) If the contribution of the steel sheeting is neglected the hogging bending resistance of a cross-section should be calculated from the stress distribution in Figure 9.7.

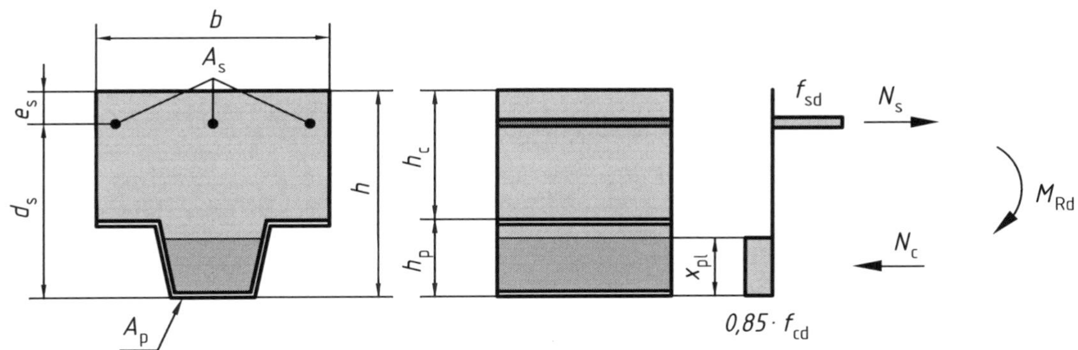

Figure 9.7 — Stress distribution for hogging bending

9.7.3 Longitudinal shear for slabs without end anchorage

(1)P The provisions in this clause 9.7.3 apply to composite slabs with mechanical or frictional interlock (types (a) and (b) as defined in 9.1.2.1).

(2) The design resistance against longitudinal shear should be determined by the *m-k* method, see (4) and (5) below, or by the partial connection method as given in (7) – (10). The partial connection method should be used only for composite slabs with a ductile longitudinal shear behaviour.

(4) If the *m-k* method is used it should be shown that the maximum design vertical shear V_{Ed} for a width of slab b does not exceed the design shear resistance $V_{l,Rd}$ determined from the following expression:

$$V_{l,Rd} = \frac{b\,d_p}{\gamma_{Vs}}\left(\frac{m\,A_p}{b\,L_s} + k\right) \tag{9.7}$$

where:

b, d_p are in mm;
A_p is the nominal cross-section of the sheeting in mm^2;
m, k are design values for the empirical factors in N/mm^2 obtained from slab tests meeting the basic requirements of the *m-k* method;
L_s is the shear span in mm and defined in (5) below;
γ_{Vs} is the partial safety factor for the ultimate limit state.

NOTE 1 The value for γ_{Vs} may be given in the National Annex. The recommended value for γ_{Vs} is 1,25.

The National Annex refers to γ_{Vs} in NA.2.16.

NOTE 2 The test method as given in Annex B may be assumed to meet the basic requirements of the m-k method.

NOTE 3 In expression (9.7) the nominal cross-section A_p is used because this value is normally used in the test evaluation to determine m and k.

NA 2.16 Clause 9.7.3(4) Partial factor, γ_{Vs}

The recommended values are given in **NA 2.4**.

NA 2.4 is included in these extracts after clause 2.4.1.2(6). NA 2.4 states 'use the recommended value'.

(5) For design, L_s should be taken as:

- $L/4$ for a uniform load applied to the entire span length;
- the distance between the applied load and the nearest support for two equal and symmetrically placed loads;
- for other loading arrangements, including a combination of distributed and asymmetrical point loads, an assessment should be made based upon test results or by the following approximate calculation. The shear span should be taken as the maximum moment divided by the greater support reaction.

(6) Where the composite slab is designed as continuous, it is permitted to use an equivalent isostatic span for the determination of the resistance. The span length should be taken as:

- $0{,}8L$ for internal spans;
- $0{,}9L$ for external spans.

9.7.3(7)–(10) are not included in these extracts.

Isostatic means statically determinate i.e. for the purpose of calculating $V_{l,Rd}$ the continuous span may be considered as an equivalent simply supported span of the length noted in (6).

This clause will be relevant in cases where the composite slab is not connected to the supporting beams or walls below e.g. where the beams are not designed to act compositely or the slab is supported by concrete or masonry walls. In other cases 9.7.4 applies.

9.7.4 Longitudinal shear for slabs with end anchorage

(1) Unless a contribution to longitudinal shear resistance by other shear devices is shown by testing, the end anchorage of type (c), as defined in 9.1.2.1, should be designed for the tensile force in the steel sheet at the ultimate limit state.

(3) The design resistance $P_{pb.Rd}$ of a headed stud welded through the steel sheet used for end anchorage should be taken as the smaller of the design shear resistance of the stud in accordance with 6.6.3.1 or the bearing resistance of the sheet determined with the following expression:

$$P_{pb,Rd} = k_{\varphi}\, d_{do}\, t\, f_{yp,d} \qquad (9.10)$$

with:

$$k_{\varphi} = 1 + a / d_{do} \leq 6{,}0 \qquad (9.11)$$

where:

d_{do} is the diameter of the weld collar which may be taken as 1,1 times the diameter of the shank of the stud;

a is the distance from the centre of the stud to the end of the sheeting, to be not less than 1,5 d_{do};

t is the thickness of the sheeting.

This clause applies where composite slabs are used in conjunction with composite beams and headed shear connectors are therefore provided.

9.7.5 Vertical shear

(1) The vertical shear resistance $V_{v,Rd}$ of a composite slab over a width equal to the distance between centres of ribs should be determined in accordance with EN 1992-1-1, 6.2.2.

9.8 Verification of composite slabs for serviceability limit states

9.8.1 Cracking of concrete

(2) Where continuous slabs are designed as simply-supported in accordance with 9.4.2(5), the cross-sectional area of the anti-crack reinforcement above the ribs should be not less than 0,2 % of the cross-sectional area of the concrete on top of the steel sheet for un-propped construction and 0,4 % of this cross-sectional area for propped construction.

9.8.2 Deflection

(4) Calculations of deflections may be omitted if both:

- the span to depth ratio does not exceed the limits given in EN 1992-1-1, 7.4, for lightly stressed concrete, and
- the condition of (6) below, for neglect of the effects of end slip, is satisfied.

(5) For an internal span of a continuous slab where the shear connection is as defined in 9.1.2.1(a), (b) or (c), the deflection may be determined using the following approximations:

- the second moment of area may be taken as the average of the values for the cracked and un-cracked section;
- for concrete, an average value of the modular ratio for both long- and short-term effects may be used.

(6) For external spans, no account need be taken of end slip if the initial slip load in tests (defined as the load causing an end slip of 0,5 mm) exceeds 1,2 times the design service load.

For a slab in sagging, the depth of the slab considered in calculating the span to depth ratio should be taken as the distance from the top of the slab to the centroidal axis of the profiled sheeting.

Bibliography

EN 1991-1-5: Actions on structures: Thermal actions – to be published.

EN 1991-1-6: Actions on structures: Actions during execution – to be published.

EN 13670: Requirements for the execution of concrete structures – to be published.

EN ISO 13918: 1998 Welding – Studs and ceramic ferrules for arc stud welding (ISO 13918:1998).

EN ISO 14555: 1998 Welding – Arc stud welding of metallic materials (ISO 14555:1998).

Bibliography

Standards publications

For dated references, only the edition cited applies. For undated references, the latest edition of the referenced document (including any amendments) applies.

BS 4-1, *Structural steel sections – Part 1: specification for hot-rolled sections*

BS EN 1994-2:2005, *Eurocode 4 – Design of composite steel and concrete structures – Part 2: General rules and rules for bridges*

Useful references

[1] Johnson RP, Anderson D. Designers' guide to EN 1994-1-1: Eurocode 4: Design of composite steel and concrete structures, Part 1.1: General rules and rules for buildings. England: Thomas Telford Ltd; 2004.

[2] Nethercot DA, editor. Composite Construction. England: London; 2003.

Chapter 5 — Extracts from Eurocode 5: Design of timber structures

The Eurocode extracts in this chapter are taken from EN 1995-1-1:2004+A1:2008 (incorporating corrigendum no.1 June 2006), *Eurocode 5: Design of timber structures — Part 1-1: General — Common rules and rules for buildings*.

Tags indicating changes to CEN text carry the number of the CEN amendment. Text altered by CEN amendment A1 is indicated by [A1⟩ ⟨A1].

The National Annex extracts are taken from NA to BS EN 1995-1-1:2004+A1:2008 (Incorporating National Amendment No. 1), *UK National Annex to Eurocode 5: Design of timber structures - Part 1-1: General - Common rules and rules for buildings*

The full list of contents of EN 1995-1-1 follows, and is given for reference purposes. (Bold items are covered in this chapter.)

3.2 Solid timber
3.3 Glued laminated timber
3.4 Laminated veneer lumber (LVL)
3.5 Wood-based panels
3.6 Adhesives
3.7 Metal fasteners
Section 4 Durability
4.1 Resistance to biological organisms
4.2 Resistance to corrosion
Section 5 Basis of structural analysis
5.1 General
5.2 Members
5.3 Connections
5.4 Assemblies
5.4.1 General
5.4.2 Frame structures
5.4.3 Simplified analysis of trusses with punched metal plate fasteners
5.4.4 Plane frames and arches
Section 6 Ultimate limit states
6.1 Design of cross-sections subjected to stress in one principal direction
6.1.1 General
6.1.2 Tension parallel to the grain
6.1.3 Tension perpendicular to the grain
6.1.4 Compression parallel to the grain
6.1.5 Compression perpendicular to the grain
6.1.6 Bending
6.1.7 Shear
6.1.8 Torsion
6.2 Design of cross-sections subjected to combined stresses
6.2.1 General
6.2.2 Compression stresses at an angle to the grain
6.2.3 Combined bending and axial tension
6.2.4 Combined bending and axial compression
6.3 Stability of members
6.3.1 General
6.3.2 Columns subjected to either compression or combined compression and bending
6.3.3 Beams subjected to either bending or combined bending and compression
6.4 Design of cross-sections in members with varying cross-section or curved shape
6.4.1 General
6.4.2 Single tapered beams
6.4.3 Double tapered, curved and pitched cambered beams
6.5 Notched members
6.5.1 General
6.5.2 Beams with a notch at the support
6.6 System strength
Section 7 Serviceability limit states
7.1 Joint slip
7.2 Limiting values for deflections of beams
7.3 Vibrations
7.3.1 General
7.3.2 Vibrations from machinery
7.3.3 Residential floors
Section 8 Connections with metal fasteners
8.1 General
8.1.1 Fastener requirements
8.1.2 Multiple fastener connections
8.1.3 Multiple shear plane connections

Section 10 Structural detailing and control
10.1 General
10.2 Materials
10.3 Glued joints
10.4 Connections with mechanical fasteners
10.4.1 General
10.4.2 Nails
10.4.3 Bolts and washers
10.4.4 Dowels
10.4.5 Screws
10.5 Assembly
10.6 Transportation and erection
10.7 Control
10.8 Special rules for diaphragm structures
10.8.1 Floor and roof diaphragms
10.8.2 Wall diaphragms
10.9 Special rules for trusses with punched metal plate fasteners
10.9.1 Fabrication
10.9.2 Erection
Annex A (Informative): Block shear and plug shear failure at multiple dowel-type steel-to-timber connections
Annex B (Informative): Mechanically jointed beams
B.1 Simplified analysis
B.1.1 Cross-sections
B.1.2 Assumptions
B.1.3 Spacings
B.1.4 Deflections resulting from bending moments
B.2 Effective bending stiffness
B.3 Normal stresses
B.4 Maximum shear stress
B.5 Fastener load
Annex C (Informative): Built-up columns
C.1 General
C.1.1 Assumptions
C.1.2 Load carrying capacity
C.2 Mechanically jointed columns
C.2.1 Effective slenderness ratio
C.2.2 Load on fasteners
C.2.3 Combined loads
C.3 Spaced columns with packs or gussets
C.3.1 Assumptions
C.3.2 Axial load-carrying capacity
C.3.3 Load on fasteners, gussets or packs
C.4 Lattice columns with glued or nailed joints
C.4.1 Assumptions
C.4.2 Load-carrying capacity
C.4.3 Shear forces
Annex D (Informative): Bibliography

Section 1 General

1.1 Scope

The basic principles apply to all types of timber structure. However, there are special structures such as masts, cooling towers, platforms and equipment installations that are likely to require additional consideration. EN 1995-2 is the Eurocode for timber bridges. The structural aspects of fire are covered by EN 1995-1-2.

The Eurocodes are unable to address all the aspects of traditional construction that have been employed for centuries. In particular, many aspects of traditional carpentry remain beyond the capability of engineering analysis, yet they have proven satisfactory.

Serviceability of timber building structures is to some extent addressed, but innovative, larger, or more complex structures may require special investigation with advanced dynamic analyses.

Basic consideration of durability of elements, structures and connections is touched upon in Section 4.

Execution is covered to the extent that is necessary to indicate the quality of the construction materials and products that should be used, and the standard of workmanship on site needed to conform to the assumptions made in the design rules. Additional requirements for structural detailing and control in relation to timber structures are given in Section 10 of EN 1995-1-1.

The Parts of EN 1995

The European Standard EN 1995 comprises the following Parts:

- EN 1995-1-1:2004, *Eurocode 5: Design of timber structures — General — Common rules and rules for buildings*
- EN 1995-1-2:2004, *Eurocode 5: Design of timber structures — General — Structural fire design*
- EN 1995-2:2004, *Eurocode 5: Design of timber structures — Bridges*

Scope of Part 1-1 of Eurocode 5

EN 1995 describes the principles and requirements for safety, serviceability and durability of timber structures. It is based on the limit state concept used in conjunction with a partial factor method. For the design of new structures, EN 1995 is intended to be used, for direct application, together with EN 1990 and relevant Parts of EN 1991. Numerical values for partial factors and other reliability parameters are recommended as basic values that provide an acceptable level of reliability. They have been selected assuming that an appropriate level of workmanship and of quality management applies.

Scope of Part 1-2 of Eurocode 5

This part deals with the design of timber structures for the accidental situation of fire exposure and identifies differences from, or supplements to, normal temperature design. Only passive methods of fire protection are considered - active methods of fire protection are not covered. It addresses the need to avoid premature collapse of the structure and to limit the spread of fire.

Scope of Part 2 of Eurocode 5

This part gives the basic rules for bridges.

1.5 Terms and definitions

1.5.1 General

(1)P The terms and definitions of EN 1990:2002 clause 1.5 apply.

1.5.2 Additional terms and definitions used in this present standard

1.5.2.1
Characteristic value
refer to EN 1990:2002 subclause 1.5.4.1

1.5.2.2
Dowelled connection
connection made with a circular cylindrical rod usually of steel, with or without a head, fitting tightly in prebored holes and used for transferring loads perpendicular to the dowel axis

1.5.2.3
Equilibrium moisture content
the moisture content at which wood neither gains nor loses moisture to the surrounding air

1.5.2.4
Fibre saturation point
moisture content at which the wood cells are completely saturated

1.5.2.5
LVL
laminated veneer lumber, defined according to EN 14279 and EN 14374

1.5.2.6
Laminated timber deck
plate made of abutting parallel and solid laminations connected together by nails or screws or prestressing or gluing

1.5.2.7
Moisture content
mass of water in wood expressed as a proportion of its oven-dry mass

1.5.2.8
Racking
effect caused by horizontal actions in the plane of a wall

1.5.2.9
Stiffness property
property used in the calculation of the deformation of the structure, such as modulus of elasticity, shear modulus, slip modulus

1.5.2.10
Slip modulus
property used in the calculation of the deformation between two members of a structure

1.6 Symbols used in EN 1995-1-1

For the purpose of EN 1995-1-1, the following symbols apply.

Latin upper case letters

A	Cross-sectional area
[A1) A_{ef}	Effective area of the total contact surface between a punched metal plate fastener and the timber; Effective contact area in compression perpendicular to the grain (A1]
A_f	Cross-sectional area of flange
$A_{net,t}$	Net cross-sectional area perpendicular to the grain
$A_{net,v}$	Net shear area parallel to the grain
C	Spring stiffness
$E_{0,05}$	Fifth percentile value of modulus of elasticity
E_d	Design value of modulus of elasticity
E_{mean}	Mean value of modulus of elasticity
$E_{mean,fin}$	Final mean value of modulus of elasticity

F	Force
$F_{A,Ed}$	Design force acting on a punched metal plate fastener at the centroid of the effective area
$F_{A,min,d}$	Minimum design force acting on a punched metal plate fastener at the centroid of the effective area
$F_{ax,Ed}$	Design axial force on fastener
$F_{ax,Rd}$	Design value of axial withdrawal capacity of the fastener
$F_{ax,Rk}$	Characteristic axial withdrawal capacity of the fastener
F_c	Compressive force
F_d	Design force
$F_{d,ser}$	Design force at the serviceability limit state
$F_{f,Rd}$	Design load-carrying capacity per fastener in wall diaphragm
$F_{i,c,Ed}$	Design compressive reaction force at end of shear wall
$F_{i,t,Ed}$	Design tensile reaction force at end of shear wall
$F_{i,vert,Ed}$	Vertical load on wall
$F_{i,v,Rd}$	Design racking resistance of panel *i* (in 9.2.4.2) or wall *i* (in 9.2.4.3)
F_{la}	Lateral load
$F_{M,Ed}$	Design force from a design moment
F_t	Tensile force
[A1) $F_{t,Rk}$	Characteristic tensile resistance of connection (A1]
$F_{v,0,Rk}$	Characteristic load-carrying capacity of a connector along the grain
$F_{v,Ed}$	Design shear force per shear plane of fastener; Horizontal design effect on wall diaphragm
$F_{v,Rd}$	Design load-carrying capacity fastener per shear plane fastener; Design racking load capacity
$F_{v,Rk}$	Characteristic load-carrying capacity per shear plane per fastener
$F_{v,w,Ed}$	Design shear force acting on web
$F_{x,Ed}$	Design value of a force in x-direction
$F_{y,Ed}$	Design value of a force in y-direction
$F_{x,Rd}$	Design value of plate capacity in x-direction
$F_{y,Rd}$	Design value of plate capacity in y-direction
$F_{x,Rk}$	Characteristic plate capacity in x-direction
$F_{y,Rk}$	Characteristic plate capacity in y-direction
$G_{0,05}$	Fifth percentile value of shear modulus
G_d	Design value of shear modulus
G_{mean}	Mean value of shear modulus
H	Overall rise of a truss
I_f	Second moment of area of flange
I_{tor}	Torsional moment of inertia
I_z	Second moment of area about the weak axis
K_{ser}	Slip modulus
K_u	Final slip modulus
$L_{net,t}$	Net width of the cross-section perpendicular to the grain
$L_{net,v}$	Net length of the fracture area in shear
$M_{A,Ed}$	Design moment acting on a punched metal plate fastener
$M_{ap,d}$	Design moment at apex zone
M_d	Design moment
$M_{y,Rk}$	Characteristic yield moment of fastener
N	Axial force
$R_{90,d}$	Design splitting capacity
$R_{90,k}$	Characteristic splitting capacity
$R_{ax,d}$	Design load-carrying capacity of an axially loaded connection
$R_{ax,k}$	Characteristic load-carrying capacity of an axially loaded connection
$R_{ax,\alpha,k}$	Characteristic load-carrying capacity at an angle to grain
R_d	Design value of a load-carrying capacity
$R_{ef,k}$	Effective characteristic load-carrying capacity of a connection
$R_{iv,d}$	Design racking capacity of a wall
R_k	Characteristic load-carrying capacity
$R_{sp,k}$	Characteristic splitting capacity
$R_{to,k}$	Characteristic load-carrying capacity of a toothed plate connector
$R_{v,d}$	Design racking capacity of a wall diaphragm
V	Shear force; Volume

V_u, V_l	Shear forces in upper and lower part of beam with a hole
W_y	Section modulus about axis y
X_d	Design value of a strength property
X_k	Characteristic value of a strength property

Latin lower case letters

a	Distance
a_1	Spacing, parallel to grain, of fasteners within one row
A1⟩ $a_{1,CG}$	End distance of centre of gravity of the threaded part of screw in the member ⟨A1
a_2	Spacing, perpendicular to grain, between rows of fasteners
A1⟩ $a_{2,CG}$	Edge distance of centre of gravity of the threaded part of screw in the member ⟨A1
$a_{3,c}$	Distance between fastener and unloaded end
$a_{3,t}$	Distance between fastener and loaded end
$a_{4,c}$	Distance between fastener and unloaded edge
$a_{4,t}$	Distance between fastener and loaded edge
a_{bow}	Maximum bow of truss member
$a_{bow,perm}$	Maximum permitted bow of truss member
a_{dev}	Maximum deviation of truss
$a_{dev,perm}$	Maximum permitted deviation of truss
b	Width
b_i	Width of panel i (in 9.2.4.2) or wall i (in 9.2.4.3)
b_{net}	Clear distance between studs
b_w	Web width
A1⟩ d	Diameter; Outer thread diameter
d_1	Inner thread diameter ⟨A1
d_c	Connector diameter
d_{ef}	Effective diameter
A1⟩ d_h	Head diameter of screws ⟨A1
$f_{h,i,k}$	Characteristic embedment strength of timber member i
$f_{a,0,0}$	Characteristic anchorage capacity per unit area for $\alpha = 0°$ and $\beta = 0°$
$f_{a,90,90}$	Characteristic anchorage capacity per unit area for $\alpha = 90°$ and $\beta = 90°$
$f_{a,\alpha,\beta,k}$	Characteristic anchorage strength
A1⟩ $f_{ax,k}$	Characteristic pointside withdrawal strength for nails; Characteristic withdrawal strength ⟨A1
$f_{ax,k}$	Characteristic withdrawal parameter for nails
$f_{c,0,d}$	Design compressive strength along the grain
$f_{c,w,d}$	Design compressive strength of web
$f_{f,c,d}$	Design compressive strength of flange
$f_{c,90,k}$	Characteristic compressive strength perpendicular to the grain
$f_{f,t,d}$	Design tensile strength of flange
$f_{h,k}$	Characteristic embedment strength
$f_{head,k}$	Characteristic pull through parameter for nails
f_I	Fundamental frequency
$f_{m,k}$	Characteristic bending strength
$f_{m,y,d}$	Design bending strength about the principal y-axis
$f_{m,z,d}$	Design bending strength about the principal z-axis
$f_{m,\alpha,d}$	Design bending strength at an angle α to the grain
$f_{t,0,d}$	Design tensile strength along the grain
$f_{t,0,k}$	Characteristic tensile strength along the grain
$f_{t,90,d}$	Design tensile strength perpendicular to the grain
$f_{t,w,d}$	Design tensile strength of the web
$f_{u,k}$	Characteristic tensile strength of bolts
$f_{v,0,d}$	Design panel shear strength
$f_{v,ax,\alpha,k}$	Characteristic withdrawal strength at an angle α to grain
$f_{v,ax,90,k}$	Characteristic withdrawal strength perpendicular to grain
$f_{v,d}$	Design shear strength
h	Depth; Height of wall
h_{ap}	Depth of the apex zone
h_d	Hole depth
h_e	Embedment depth

h Loaded edge distance

h_{ef} Effective depth

$h_{f,c}$ Depth of compression flange

$h_{f,t}$ Depth of tensile flange

h_{rl} Distance from lower edge of hole to bottom of member

h_{ru} Distance from upper edge of hole to top of member

h_{w} Web depth

i Notch inclination

$k_{c,y}$ or $k_{c,z}$ Instability factor

[A1⟩ k_{cr} Crack factor for shear resistance ⟨A1]

k_{crit} Factor used for lateral buckling

k_{d} Dimension factor for panel

k_{def} Deformation factor

k_{dis} Factor taking into account the distribution of stresses in an apex zone

$k_{f,1}$, $k_{f,2}$, $k_{f,3}$ Modification factors for bracing resistance

k_{h} Depth factor

$k_{i,q}$ Uniformly distributed load factor

k_{m} Factor considering redistribution of bending stresses in a cross-section

k_{mod} Modification factor for duration of load and moisture content

k_{n} Sheathing material factor

k_{r} Reduction factor

$k_{R,red}$ Reduction factor for load-carrying capacity

k_{s} Fastener spacing factor; Modification factor for spring stiffness

$k_{s,red}$ Reduction factor for spacing

k_{shape} Factor depending on the shape of the cross-section

k_{sys} System strength factor

k_{v} Reduction factor for notched beams

k_{vol} Volume factor

k_{y} or k_{z} Instability factor

$l_{a,min}$ Minimum anchorage length for a glued-in rod

l Span; contact length

l_{A} Support distance of a hole

l_{ef} Effective length; Effective length of distribution

l_{V} Distance from a hole to the end of the member

l_{Z} Spacing between holes

m Mass per unit area

n_{40} Number of frequencies below 40 Hz

n_{ef} Effective number of fasteners

p_{d} Distributed load

q_{i} Equivalent uniformly distributed load

r Radius of curvature

s Spacing

s_{0} Basic fastener spacing

r_{in} Inner radius

t Thickness

t_{pen} Penetration depth

u_{creep} Creep deformation

u_{fin} Final deformation

$u_{fin,G}$ Final deformation for a permanent action G

$u_{fin,Q,1}$ Final deformation for leading variable action Q_1

$u_{fin,Q,i}$ Final deformation for accompanying variable actions Q_i

u_{inst} Instantaneous deformation

$u_{inst,G}$ Instantaneous deformation for a permanent action G

$u_{inst,Q,1}$ Instantaneous deformation leading variable action Q_1

$u_{inst,Q,i}$ Instantaneous deformation accompanying variable actions Q_i

w_{c} Precamber

w_{creep} Creep deflection

w_{fin} Final deflection

w_{inst} Instantaneous deflection

$w_{net,fin}$ Net final deflection

v Unit impulse velocity response

Greek lower case letters

Symbol	Description
α	Angle between the x-direction and the force for a punched metal plate; Angle between a force and the direction of grain; Angle between the direction of the Load and the loaded edge (or end)
β	Angle between the grain direction and the force for a punched metal plate
β_c	Straightness factor
γ	Angle between the x-direction and the timber connection line for a punched metal plate
γ_M	Partial factor for material properties, also accounting for model uncertainties and dimensional variations
λ_y	Slenderness ratio corresponding to bending about the y-axis
λ_z	Slenderness ratio corresponding to bending about the z-axis
$\lambda_{rel,y}$	Relative slenderness ratio corresponding to bending about the y-axis
$\lambda_{rel,z}$	Relative slenderness ratio corresponding to bending about the z-axis
[A1) ρ_a	Associated density (A1]
ρ_k	Characteristic density
ρ_m	Mean density
$\sigma_{c,0,d}$	Design compressive stress along the grain
$\sigma_{c,\alpha,d}$	Design compressive stress at an angle α to the grain
$\sigma_{f,c,d}$	Mean design compressive stress of flange
$\sigma_{f,c,max,d}$	Design compressive stress of extreme fibres of flange
$\sigma_{f,t,d}$	Mean design tensile stress of flange
$\sigma_{f,t,max,d}$	Design tensile stress of extreme fibres of flange
$\sigma_{m,crit}$	Critical bending stress
$\sigma_{m,y,d}$	Design bending stress about the principal y-axis
$\sigma_{m,z,d}$	Design bending stress about the principal z-axis
$\sigma_{m,\alpha,d}$	Design bending stress at an angle α to the grain
σ_N	Axial stress
$\sigma_{t,0,d}$	Design tensile stress along the grain
$\sigma_{t,90,d}$	Design tensile stress perpendicular to the grain
$\sigma_{w,c,d}$	Design compressive stress of web
$\sigma_{w,t,d}$	Design tensile stress of web
τ_d	Design shear stress
$\tau_{F,d}$	Design anchorage stress from axial force
$\tau_{M,d}$	Design anchorage stress from moment
$\tau_{tor,d}$	Design shear stress from torsion
ψ_0	Factor for combination value of a variable action
ψ_2	Factor for quasi-permanent value of a variable action
ζ	Modal damping ratio

Section 2 Basis of design

This section is based on EN 1990, and hence it follows the CEN-ratified common safety format that applies to all of the Eurocodes. In a timber context, background to this is given in: STEP 1, Lecture A2 [1].

For timber structures, mechanical resistance involving both ultimate limit states conditions and serviceability limit states depends markedly upon effects not always noted in other materials. These affect elements, structures and connections. They entail duration of load effects, moisture content, which is in turn related to ambient conditions that may be cyclical, and size or volume effects. Consequently in this section, special principles and application rules start to be introduced that are timber-specific. Moisture content with mechanical properties, and duration of load influences, are introduced in: STEP 1, Lecture A4 [1].

2.1 Requirements

2.1.1 Basic requirements

(1)P The design of timber structures shall be in accordance with EN 1990:2002.

(2)P The supplementary provisions for timber structures given in this section shall also be applied.

2.2 Principles of limit state design

2.2.1 General

(1)P The design models for the different limit states shall, as appropriate, take into account the following:

- different material properties (e.g. strength and stiffness);
- different time-dependent behaviour of the materials (duration of load, creep);
- different climatic conditions (temperature, moisture variations);
- different design situations (stages of construction, change of support conditions).

2.2.2 Ultimate limit states

(1)P The analysis of structures shall be carried out using the following values for stiffness properties:

- for a first order linear elastic analysis of a structure, whose distribution of internal forces is not affected by the stiffness distribution within the structure (e.g. all members have the same time-dependent properties), mean values shall be used;
- for a first order linear elastic analysis of a structure, whose distribution of internal forces is affected by the stiffness distribution within the structure (e.g. composite members containing materials having different time-dependent properties), final mean values adjusted to the load component causing the largest stress in relation to strength shall be used;
- for a second order linear elastic analysis of a structure, design values, not adjusted for duration of load, shall be used.

NOTE 1 For final mean values adjusted to the duration of load, see 2.3.2.2(2).

NOTE 2 For design values of stiffness properties, see 2.4.1(2)P.

2.2.3 Serviceability limit states

(1)P The deformation of a structure which results from the effects of actions (such as axial and shear forces, bending moments and joint slip) and from moisture shall remain within appropriate limits, having regard to the possibility of damage to surfacing materials, ceilings, floors, partitions and finishes, and to the functional needs as well as any appearance requirements.

(2) The instantaneous deformation, u_{inst}, see Figure 7.1, under an action should be calculated for the characteristic combination of actions, see EN 1990, clause 6.5.3(2) a), using mean values of the appropriate moduli of elasticity, shear moduli and slip moduli.

(3) The final deformation, u_{fin}, see Figure 7.1, should be calculated for the quasi-permanent combination of actions, see EN 1990, clause 6.5.3(2) c).

2.3 Basic variables

2.3.1 Actions and environmental influences

2.3.1.1 General

(1) Actions to be used in design may be obtained from the relevant parts of EN 1991.

NOTE 1 The relevant parts of EN 1991 for use in design include:

EN 1991-1-1 Densities, self-weight and imposed loads
EN 1991-1-3 Snow loads
EN 1991-1-4 Wind loads
EN 1991-1-5 Thermal actions
EN 1991-1-6 Actions during execution
EN 1991-1-7 Accidental actions due to impact and explosions

(2)P Duration of load and moisture content affect the strength and stiffness properties of timber and wood based elements and shall be taken into account in the design for mechanical resistance and serviceability.

(3)P Actions caused by the effects of moisture content changes in the timber shall be taken into account.

2.3.1.2 Load-duration classes

Orders of accumulated duration of load have to be estimated in timber design. Here, they are related to the characteristic loads, and tabulated in connection with load-duration classes. Experience, which includes calibration against earlier structural codes that have been found to be satisfactory, and which entails engineering judgement, has been backed by large programmes of research. These steps have led to relatively simplified tabulations. Damage accumulation effects in timber have also been studied and modelled, as well as duration of load effects and their moisture dependency.

Using these tables, together with strength and stiffness factors relating to further classifications that are given later, permits many commonly-occurring design situations to be handled. However, temporary structures, designing for unusual phases of erection, and other special conditions such as those occurring after accidents, may entail investigation and judgement on the part of the engineer.

For further information, refer to the following publication: CIB. Structural Timber Design Code (Publication 66). International Council for Research and Innovation in Building and Construction; 1983 [11].

(1)P The load-duration classes are characterised by the effect of a constant load acting for a certain period of time in the life of the structure. For a variable action the appropriate class shall be determined on the basis of an estimate of the typical variation of the load with time.

(2)P Actions shall be assigned to one of the load-duration classes given in Table 2.1 for strength and stiffness calculations.

Table 2.1 — Load-duration classes

Load-duration class	Order of accumulated duration of characteristic load
Permanent	more than 10 years
Long-term	6 months – 10 years
Medium-term	1 week – 6 months
Short-term	less than one week
Instantaneous	

NOTE Examples of load-duration assignment are given in Table 2.2. Since climatic loads (snow, wind) vary between countries, the assignment of load-duration classes may be specified in the National Annex.

EN 1995-1-1, Table 2.2 is implemented nationally in the UK by using Table NA.1.

Table NA.1 — Load-duration classes

Load-duration class	Duration	Examples of loading
Permanent	More than 10 years	Self-weight
Long-term	6 months to 10 years	Storage loading (including in lofts), water tanks
Medium-term	1 week to 6 months	Imposed floor loading
Short-term	Less than 1 week	Snow, maintenance or man loading on roofs, residual structure after accidental event
Instantaneous		Wind, impact loading, explosion

2.3.1.3 Service classes

Notionally, the mean temperature and relative humidity of the air surrounding an element or structure provide parameters to define three service classes.

The concept of service class is somewhat simplistic, but it is a practical notion. It recognizes the fundamental hygroscopicity of wood. Timber and all related materials are sensitive to this effect, and in a structure, the components take time to come to equilibrium with the surrounding climate, even when this is relatively constant. An introduction, together with a good set of further references, can be found in: STEP 1, Lecture A4 [1].

Whilst service classes cannot be claimed to relate directly to real meteorological climates, research has demonstrated that there are valid links. Consequently, this helps to justify the judgements made here by the code-writers.

(1)P Structures shall be assigned to one of the service classes given below:

NOTE 1 The service class system is mainly aimed at assigning strength values and for calculating deformations under defined environmental conditions.

NOTE 2 Information on the assignment of structures to service classes given in (2)P, (3)P and (4)P may be given in the National Annex.

(2)P Service class 1 is characterised by a moisture content in the materials corresponding to a temperature of 20°C and the relative humidity of the surrounding air only exceeding 65 % for a few weeks per year.

NOTE In service class 1 the average moisture content in most softwoods will not exceed 12 %.

(3)P Service class 2 is characterized by a moisture content in the materials corresponding to a temperature of 20°C and the relative humidity of the surrounding air only exceeding 85 % for a few weeks per year.

NOTE In service class 2 the average moisture content in most softwoods will not exceed 20 %.

(4)P Service class 3 is characterised by climatic conditions leading to higher moisture contents than in service class 2.

EN 1995-1-1, **2.3.1.3**(1)P is implemented nationally in the UK for common timber constructions by using Table NA.2.

Table NA.2 — Service classes

Type of construction	Service class
Cold roofs	2
Warm roofs	1
Intermediate floors	1
Ground floors	2
Timber-frame walls, internal and party walls	1
Timber-frame walls, external walls	2
External uses where member is protected from direct wetting	2
External uses, fully exposed	3

2.4 Verification by the partial factor method

Section 3, to which this contains a forward reference, is based on the safety format of EN 1990. The partial factor γ_m for material properties and resistances have a similar basis and format to γ_m values in Eurocodes for other materials. However, materials used in timber structures also require special adjustments. First introduced here is an important modification factor, k_{mod} – the modification taking into account the effect of the duration of load and moisture content. The modification factor k_{mod} is further discussed in the commentary on Section 3.

The partial factor for material properties and resistances, γ_M, is given in EN 1995-1-1, Table 2.3 for fundamental combinations (see EN 1990, Section 6) and for accidental combinations (EN 1990, Section 6). In the latter case, it invariably takes the value of unity, inferring a lower reliability index for emergency situations.

However, for the majority of design purposes, the choice of γ_M depends upon the generic material type or element (solid timber, glulam, LVL, panel material or connection unit). Generally speaking, the principle is followed that the greater the control during production of the semi-finished element or product, the less strict the value assigned to this partial factor.

2.4.1 Design value of material property

(1)P The design value X_d of a strength property shall be calculated as:

$$X_d = k_{mod} \frac{X_k}{\gamma_M} \tag{2.14}$$

where:

X_k is the characteristic value of a strength property;
γ_M is the partial factor for a material property;
k_{mod} is a modification factor taking into account the effect of the duration of load and moisture content.

NOTE 1 Values of k_{mod} are given in 3.1.3.

NOTE 2 The recommended partial factors for material properties (γ_M) are given in Table 2.3. Information on the National choice may be found in the National Annex.

EN 1995-1-1, Table 2.3 is implemented nationally in the UK by using Table NA.3.

Table NA.3 — Partial factors γ_M for material properties and resistances

Fundamental combinations	
Solid timber, untreated	1,3
Solid timber, preservative-treated	1,3
Glued laminated timber	1,25
LVL, plywood, OSB	1,2
Particleboard	1,3
Fibreboards, hard	1,3
Fibreboards, medium	1,3
Fibreboards, MDF	1,3
Fibreboards, soft	1,3
Connections (except for punched metal plate fasteners)	1,3
Punched metal plate fasteners, anchorage strength	1,3
Punched metal plate fasteners, plate (steel) strength	1,15
Accidental combinations	1,0

(2)P The design member stiffness property E_d shall be calculated as:

$$E_d = \frac{E_{mean}}{\gamma_M} \tag{2.15}$$

$$G_d = \frac{G_{mean}}{\gamma_M} \tag{2.16}$$

where:

E_{mean} is the mean value of modulus of elasticity;
G_{mean} is the mean value of shear modulus.

2.4.2 Design value of geometrical data

(1) Geometrical data for cross-sections and systems may be taken as nominal values from product standards hEN or drawings for the execution.

(2) Design values of geometrical imperfections specified in this standard comprise the effects of

- geometrical imperfections of members;
- the effects of structural imperfections from fabrication and erection;
- inhomogeneity of materials (e.g. due to knots).

2.4.3 Design resistances

(1)P The design value R_d of a resistance (load carrying capacity) shall be calculated as:

$$R_d = k_{mod} \frac{R_k}{\gamma_M} \tag{2.17}$$

where:

R_k is the characteristic value of load-carrying capacity;
γ_M is the partial factor for a material property,
k_{mod} is a modification factor taking into account the effect of the duration of load and moisture content.

NOTE 1 Values of k_{mod} are given in 3.1.3.

NOTE 2 For partial factors, see 2.4.1.

Section 3 Material properties

The general principles in assigning the partial factor values γ_M (see Table 2.3) and the modification factors (see Table 3.1), have been described elsewhere. Since these relate to important engineering fundamentals that students should understand, they are briefly discussed herein. The same principles may in future be applied to innovative materials or elements used in expert designs following Eurocode-type formats, or in assessing suitability for future code inclusion, or for reference by related standards.

The following considerations applied to the partial factor assignments of this code, and to the choice of tabulated modification factors linked to these via the following expression:

$$G_d = \frac{G_{mean}}{\gamma_M} \quad (2.16)$$

1. Significant quantities of the standardized generic material group (solid timber, glulam, LVL etc.) or element type (connections, innovative fasteners etc.) are expected to be available on an ongoing basis in order for them to be considered. EN 1995-1-1 and its supporting standards should not be regarded as trial documents for very innovative or unusual materials or element types.
2. Adequate test data and fundamentals are necessary, linked to the basis of design. For timber, these include measured descriptions of load duration and moisture response. These make it possible to allocate the characteristic mechanical properties and associated performance descriptions via the modification procedures used in EN 1995-1-1.
3. The materials or elements are required to be converted, manufactured, graded and controlled in a manner conforming to standards developed in accordance with the CEN rules.
4. Product marking and accompanying documentation is also required by the harmonized products standards, so that compliance with 1 to 3 above can be verified.

3.1.3 Strength modification factors for service classes and load-duration classes

(1) The values of the modification factor k_{mod} given in Table 3.1 should be used.

(2) If a load combination consists of actions belonging to different load-duration classes a value of k_{mod} should be chosen which corresponds to the action with the shortest duration, e.g. for a combination of dead load and a short-term load, a value of k_{mod} corresponding to the short-term load should be used.

The tabulated strength modification factors denoted k_{mod} for service class and load duration classes, apply to ultimate limit states conditions. Note the important guidance that a value of k_{mod} should be chosen which corresponds to the action with the shortest duration. It is commonly the case that the actions within a combination change to varying durations, and this effect should be carefully studied.

3.1.4 Deformation modification factors for service classes

(1) The values of the deformation factors k_{def} given in Table 3.2 should be used.

Another modification factor denoted k_{def} also relating to service class, is provided here, but this is used under serviceability limit states conditions, so further commentary on this is provided under Section 7.

3.2 Solid timber

[A1⟩ (1)P Timber members shall comply with EN 14081-1.

NOTE Strength classes for timber are given in EN 338. ⟨A1]

There is a large series of potential combinations of strength grades and species with the considerable variety of options for timber supplies. Hence many sets of characteristic values for strength graded structural timber are possible. To simplify this, a strength class system was devised, described in EN 338. The standard strength classes comprise nine classes for coniferous species and poplar (which, because of its low density, is treated like a conifer) and six classes for all of the other broad-leaved species. Sizes and permissible deviations are also important to the structural designer – these are given in EN 336.

Characteristic strength and stiffness properties and density values are available for each class, and rules exist for the allocation of timbers to the classes. Visual grades and species are assigned to strength classes by EN 1912. With machine strength grading, the process itself determines whether a combination will match a particular class.

The test procedures for physical and mechanical properties to which these standards refer are stated in EN 408. Characteristic values of mechanical properties and density for individual species or grade combinations are also admissible for design purposes; these are required to be defined according to specific rules, stated in EN 384.

(2) The effect of member size on strength may be taken into account.

(3) For rectangular solid timber with a characteristic timber density $\rho_k \leq 700$ kg/m^3, the reference depth in bending or width (maximum cross-sectional dimension) in tension is 150 mm. For depths in bending or widths in tension of solid timber less than 150 mm the characteristic values for $f_{m,k}$ and $f_{t,0,k}$ may be increased by the factor k_h, given by:

$$k_h = \min\begin{cases}\left(\dfrac{150}{h}\right)^{0,2} \\ 1,3\end{cases} \tag{3.1}$$

where h is the depth for bending members, in mm.

[A1] Table 3.1 — Values of k_{mod}

Material	Standard	Service Class	Load-duration class				
			Permanent action	Long term action	Medium term action	Short term action	Instant-aneous action
Solid timber	EN 14081-1	1 2 3	0,60 0,60 0,50	0,70 0,70 0,55	0,80 0,80 0,65	0,90 0,90 0,70	1,10 1,10 0,90
Glued laminated timber	EN 14080	1 2 3	0,60 0,60 0,50	0,70 0,70 0,55	0,80 0,80 0,65	0,90 0,90 0,70	1,10 1,10 0,90
LVL	EN 14374 EN 14279	1 2 3	0,60 0,60 0,50	0,70 0,70 0,55	0,80 0,80 0,65	0,90 0,90 0,70	1,10 1,10 0,90
Plywood	EN 636 Type EN 636-1 Type EN 636-2 Type EN 636-3	 1 2 3	 0,60 0,60 0,50	 0,70 0,70 0,55	 0,80 0,80 0,65	 0,90 0,90 0,70	 1,10 1,10 0,90

Material	Standard	Service Class	Load-duration class				
			Permanent action	Long term action	Medium term action	Short term action	Instant-aneous action
OSB	EN 300						
	OSB/2	1	0,30	0,45	0,65	0,85	1,10
	OSB/3, OSB/4	1	0,40	0,50	0,70	0,90	1,10
	OSB/3, OSB/4	2	0,30	0,40	0,55	0,70	0,90
Particle-board	EN 312						
	Type P4, Type P5	1	0,30	0,45	0,65	0,85	1,10
	Type P5	2	0,20	0,30	0,45	0,60	0,80
	Type P6, Type P7	1	0,40	0,50	0,70	0,90	1,10
	Type P7	2	0,30	0,40	0,55	0,70	0,90
Fibre-board, hard	EN 622-2						
	HB.LA, HB.HLA1 or 2	1	0,30	0,45	0,65	0,85	1,10
	HB.HLA1 or 2	2	0,20	0,30	0,45	0,60	0,80
Fibre-board, medium	EN 622-3						
	MBH.LA1 or 2	1	0,20	0,40	0,60	0,80	1,10
	MBH.HLS1 or 2	1	0,20	0,40	0,60	0,80	1,10
	MBH.HLS1 or 2	2	–	–	–	0,45	0,80
Fibre-board, MDF	EN 622-5						
	MDF.LA, MDF. HLS	1	0,20	0,40	0,60	0,80	1,10
	MDF.HLS	2	–	–	–	0,45	0,80

A1

3.3 Glued laminated timber

Glued laminated timber (glulam) is defined by EN 386 as a means of forming structural members by bonding together timber laminations, with their grain running essentially parallel.

The relevant harmonized European Standard is EN 14080. This specifies the requirements for glued laminated timber, having deviations from the target sizes within the tolerances of EN 390.

The harmonized standard incorporates a number of provisions. Amongst the most significant, the physical and mechanical properties of glulam, upon which its code-referenced strength classes (EN 1194) are based, are derived from test principles in EN 408. The same fundamentals are applied to this material as are applied to solid timber, to which the latter also relates.

EN 301 addresses the phenolic and amino plastic adhesives that "traditionally" i.e. since about 1950, have been used in bonding the laminations of most structural glulam. Recently, certain types of one-component moisture curing polyurethane (PU) adhesives have been introduced extensively by the industry (See EN 14080 Annex D). These are used both for finger joints in the laminations (see EN 385), and for the production of glulam members by bonding the laminations.

EN 350 (two parts) deals with the natural durability and treatability of selected wood species of importance in Europe, including those used to manufacture glulam.

The requirements for large finger joints in glulam are also given in the harmonized standard, EN 14080. "Large finger joints" are those made in glulam after the semi-finished product has been manufactured. They thus connect elements across a whole series of laminations, or even introduce sharp corner connections e.g. for portal frames. These are now of economic importance, are covered by EN 387, and are further discussed in STEP 2, Lecture D8 [2].

(3) For rectangular glued laminated timber, the reference depth in bending or width in tension is 600 mm. For depths in bending or widths in tension of glued laminated timber less than 600 mm the characteristic values for $f_{m,k}$ and $f_{t,0,k}$ may be increased by the factor k_h, given by

$$k_h = \min \begin{cases} \left(\dfrac{600}{h}\right)^{0,1} \\ 1,1 \end{cases} \tag{3.2}$$

where h is the depth for bending members or width for tensile members, in mm.

With glulam, both the characteristic bending strength and the characteristic tensile strength are benchmarked to a dimension of 600 mm. This differs from solid timber, whose reference depth or width is 150 mm. Expression 3.2 facilitates adjustment of properties for depths/widths other than 600 mm.

A1⟩ Table 3.2 — Values of k_{def} for timber and wood-based materials

Material	Standard	Service class		
		1	2	3
Solid timber	EN 14081-1	0,60	0,80	2,00
Glued Laminated timber	EN 14080	0,60	0,80	2,00
LVL	EN 14374, EN 14279	0,60	0,80	2,00
Plywood	EN 636 Type EN 636-1 Type EN 636-2 Type EN 636-3	 0,80 0,80 0,80	 – 1,00 1,00	 – – 2,50
OSB	EN 300 OSB/2 OSB/3, OSB/4	 2,25 1,50	 – 2,25	 – –
Particleboard	EN 312 Type P4 Type P5 Type P6 Type P7	 2,25 2,25 1,50 1,50	 – 3,00 – 2,25	 – – – –
Fibreboard, hard	EN 622-2 HB.LA HB.HLA1, HB.HLA2	 2,25 2,25	 – 3,00	 – –
Fibreboard, medium	EN 622-3 MBH.LA1, MBH.LA2 MBH.HLS1, MBH.HLS2	 3,00 3,00	 – 4,00	 – –

Table 3.2 — Values of k_{def} for timber and wood-based materials (continued)

Material	Standard	Service class		
		1	2	3
Fibreboard, MDF	EN 622-5 MDF.LA MDF.HLS	 2,25 2,25	 – 3,00	 – –

A1

3.4 Laminated veneer lumber (LVL)

Laminated veneer lumber (LVL) is defined by the harmonized European Standard, EN 14374, as a composite of wood veneers with wood fibres primarily orientated along the length of the grain direction of the face veneers. A similar product, cross-laminated LVL (LVL-Cross), has a certain number of orthogonal veneers, but fewer in proportion to the total section than balanced plywood. Both standard LVL and LVL-Cross are used essentially as a prismatic-shaped structural element. Useful plate or diaphragm action is achievable with the second type, but even here, primary emphasis is on single-direction spanning.

Key code and harmonized standard cross-references are as follows.
Physical and mechanical properties of LVL are based on EN 408, as for solid timber and glulam. Quality tests for the veneer bonding and pressing stages are based on those for plywood, notably EN 314 (two parts), since for manufacturing purposes, LVL is essentially made as plywood, then cut longitudinally into structural elements. EN 350 addresses the natural durability of the species from which the LVL is manufactured.

Most of the applications and requirements of large finger joints for glulam also apply to LVL. Use of these in service class 3 is not recommended.

Fabrication outlines and examples in use of LVL can be found in STEP 1, Lecture A9 [1].

Because of its close control through all stages of production, attention to aspects such as automated veneer drying, grading and blending, and precision moisture contents and section sizes, LVL has characteristic physical and mechanical properties superior to almost all wood-based alternatives. Its coefficient of variation is extremely low, leading to high characteristic properties. This combined with its absolute lightness (European LVL is made primarily from spruce), means that its use worldwide is growing rapidly.

(3) The reference depth in bending is 300 mm. For depths in bending not equal to 300 mm the characteristic value for $f_{m,k}$ should be multiplied by the factor k_h, given by

$$k_h = \min \begin{cases} \left(\dfrac{300}{h}\right)^s \\ 1,2 \end{cases} \tag{3.3}$$

where:

h is the depth of the member, in mm;
s is the size effect exponent, refer to 3.4(5)P.

(4) The reference length in tension is 3000 mm. For lengths in tension not equal to 3000 mm the characteristic value for $f_{t,0,k}$ should be multiplied by the factor k_l given by

$$k_l = \min \begin{cases} \left(\frac{3000}{l}\right)^{s/2} \\ 1,1 \end{cases} \tag{3.4}$$

where l is the length, in mm.

(5)P The size effect exponent s for LVL shall be taken as declared in accordance with EN 14374.

3.5 Wood-based panels

Not all wood-based panels are suitable for structures as many are manufactured for other purposes. The relevant harmonized standard, EN 13986, states the general characteristics, means of evaluation of conformity, and marking requirements, for structural wood based-panels.

Plywood is classed as suitable for structures, provided it is a type that conforms to EN 13986. A classic wood-based panel material produced on the basis of a well-established technology, it is used for many structural components, including thin webbed beams (I-beams and boxed beams) that are addressed in Section 9 of this chapter. The European Standard EN 1995 also addresses "thin-flanged beams", better known as stressed skin panels, and these also entail design using materials such as plywood.

An understanding of how the critical design properties of plywood are handled by EN 1995 and its referenced standards will enable the student to appreciate how the more recently introduced wood-based panels such as OSB, particleboards and fibreboards, are also dealt with. Further guidance can be found in STEP 1, Lecture A11 [1].

The standard EN 12369 provides information on the characteristic values for use in designing structures incorporating wood-based panels. Part 2 deals with structural plywood. Although principles are similar for other permissible web materials, Section 9 of this guide includes a commentary on thin webbed beams that concentrates mainly on I beams or boxed beams manufactured with plywood webs.

When applying characteristic values of mechanical properties in the design of elements made of plywood, it is essential to differentiate between the material's various types and modes of behaviour. Plywood is manufactured to produce material of a balanced, layered nature, and typically the grain orientations in adjacent veneers are at right angles to each other. This, together with the fact that it is used for plate or planar elements, rather than simply as prismatic members, means the engineer has a far greater range of mechanical properties to consider. Not only is plywood orthotropic, like timber, but also differentiation should be made between:

1. properties in the direction of the grain of the outer layers of veneer, conventionally denoted by symbol 0;

2. properties perpendicular to the grain direction of the outer veneers, conventionally denoted by symbol 90.

Furthermore, dependent upon the application, it may be necessary to examine performance, e.g. bending strength, perpendicular to the plane of the panel or in the plane of the panel.

Shear strength also has both a principal mode that is perpendicular to the flat planes (panel shear, or "shear through the thickness") and another that is parallel to the flat-wise planes (planar, or "rolling shear"). In general terms, panel shear strengths are much higher than planar shear strengths, but in components, the latter are often alleviated by much higher contact areas, e.g. those between webs and flanges, which should, however, be checked in design.

Compared with solid timber, essential stiffness properties similarly proliferate. Associated with the bending, tension and compression properties, are moduli of elasticity that vary considerably according to mode, because of the pronounced orthotropicity both of the wood and of the panel system. There are also shear moduli, denoted by symbol G, that are needed for certain design purposes, such as estimating deformations due to shear within thin-webbed beams.

The types and modes of mechanical property for plywood are summarized in Table A of this commentary. This shows diagrammatically, and in notes, the characteristic strengths and moduli of elasticity whose properties are required. See EN 12369-2 for further information, including strength classes, and see STEP 1, Lecture A10 [1] for comprehensive explanations of the structural behaviour of plywood.

Direction a)	Direction b)	Mechanical Property
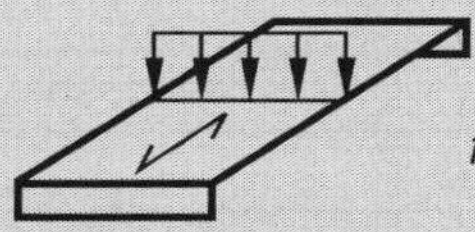 $f_{m,0,k}$	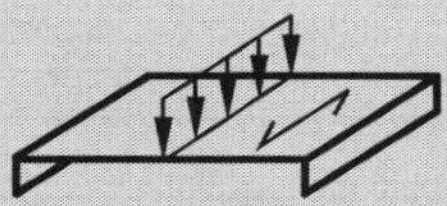 $f_{m,90,k}$	Bending perpendicular to plane. a) Parallel to face grain. b) Perpendicular to face grain.
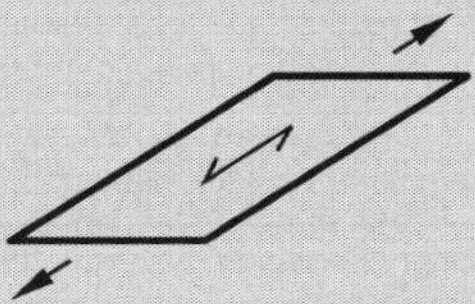 $f_{t,0,k}$	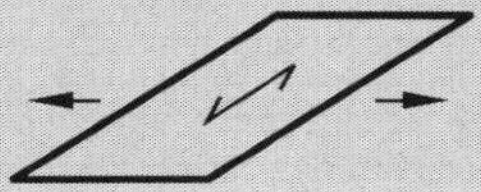 $f_{t,90,k}$	In-plane tension. a) Parallel to face grain. b) Perpendicular to face grain.
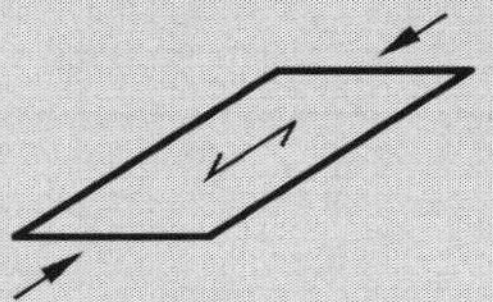 $f_{c,0,k}$	 $f_{c,90,k}$	In-plane compression. a) Parallel to face grain. b) Perpendicular to face grain.
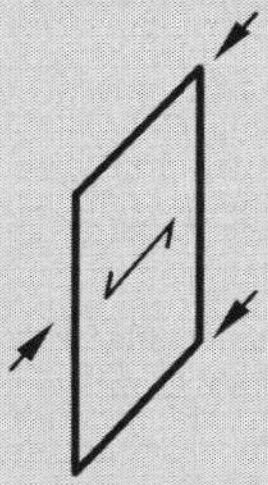 $f_{v,k}$	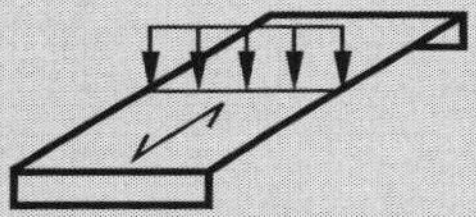 $f_{r,k}$	Shear. a) Panel shear stress. b) Planar shear stress.
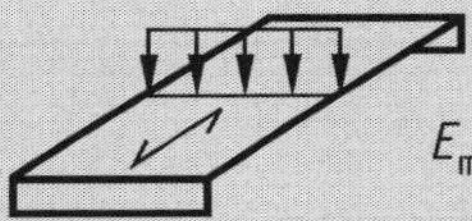 $E_{m,0,mean}$	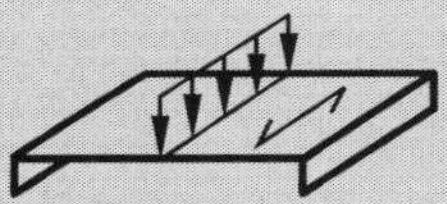 $E_{m,90,mean}$	Modulus of elasticity in bending perpendicular to plane. a) Parallel to face grain. b) Perpendicular to face grain.
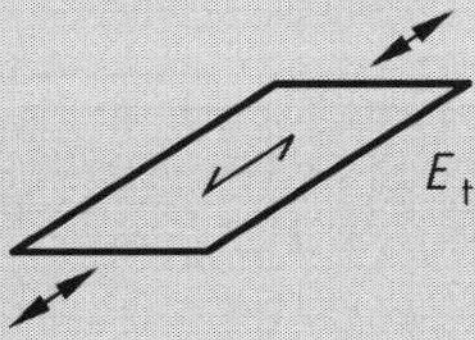 $E_{t(c),0,mean}$	 $E_{t(c),90,mean}$	Modulus of elasticity for in-plane tension and compression. a) Parallel to face grain. b) Perpendicular to face grain.

Table A — The main types of mechanical property for plywood – characteristic strengths and moduli of elasticity.

Note that in addition to the properties outlined in Table A, designers need to take account of properties similar to those of concern with solid timber, glulam or LVL, such as density, moisture content, swelling or shrinkage, and load duration response. Durability is also addressed, according to service class and hazard conditions.

(1)P Wood-based panels shall comply with EN 13986 and LVL used as panels shall comply with EN 14279.

(2) The use of softboards according to EN 622-4 should be restricted to wind bracing and should be designed by testing.

An overview of the various structural timber adhesives is provided in STEP 1, Lecture A12 [1]. This briefly discusses adhesive bonding, approval routes, compositions of the families, classifications, and applications. Types of bonded connection in timber structures are also outlined.

Resorcinol-formaldehyde (RF), phenol-resorcinol-formaldehyde (PRF) and urea-formaldehyde (UF) adhesives have been the workhorses of timber engineering for many years. EN 301 addresses all three. Certain formulations of polyurethane adhesive (PU) are beginning to be covered by the support standards, and are already extensively adopted by glulam manufacturers in continental Europe and the Nordic region, on the basis of private type testing and approvals – see commentary on glulam.

None of these families are suitable for very wide gap-filling applications. Appropriate epoxy adhesive formulations, already extensively used elsewhere in construction (see Guide to Structural Use of Adhesives [3]), are entering use for applications in timber engineering such as bonded-in rod connections (see GIROD – Glued in rods for timber structures [4]). Work has started on standardization and code-formatted design fundamentals.

3.6 Adhesives

(1)P Adhesives for structural purposes shall produce joints of such strength and durability that the integrity of the bond is maintained in the assigned service class throughout the expected life of the structure.

(2) Adhesives which comply with Type I specification as defined in EN 301 may be used in all service classes.

(3) Adhesives which comply with Type II specification as defined in EN 301 should only be used in service classes 1 or 2 and not under prolonged exposure to temperatures in excess of 50°C.

Section 4 Durability

If kept permanently and perfectly dry, all timber is capable of lasting for a very long period of time, e.g. millennia. Many effects that are perceived as ageing are due either to changes that have taken place in the moisture content of sections of the member or structure throughout its lifetime, or to past or continuing biodeterioration, or to combinations of these two effects.

The sapwood of all species of timber, both conifers and broadleaves, is perishable. Therefore in all situations above hazard class 2 (EN 335-1) and in some hazard class 2 and service class 2 or 3 (EN 1995-1-1) situations, sapwood should be excluded, through specification and by inspection during manufacture.

Fungal attack occurs in timber which has a higher moisture content (generally between 20 % and 30 %). In the absence of termites, e.g. normally in the UK, insect attack will not occur unless:

a) sapwood is present;
b) the timber experiences reasonably prolonged or permanent conditions leading to a similar moisture content threshold to that for risk of fungal attack.

Nowadays, for many designers, limiting or eliminating these conditions without resorting to preservative treatment is the preferred aim. The fundamental approaches to this are outlined later.

Important further advice is also to be found in "Moisture in timber" [5] and in "Timber decay in buildings. The conservation approach to treatment" [6].

4.1 Resistance to biological organisms

(1)P Timber and wood-based materials should either have adequate natural durability in accordance with EN 350-2 for the particular hazard class (defined in EN 335-1, EN 335-2 and EN 335-3), or be given a preservative treatment selected in accordance with EN 351-1 and EN 460.

NOTE 1 Preservative treatment may affect the strength and stiffness properties.

NOTE 2 Rules for specification of preservation treatments are given in EN 350-2 and EN 335.

Particularly in external or high hazard class environments, structural timber members may experience deleterious effects due to weathering and exposure. Precipitation and solar radiation (also cyclical surface drying by the wind), combined with periods of wetting, exacerbate this tendency. Effects can be reduced by:

1. timber protection as a design-planning concept – leading to detailing for durability;
2. using timber species with adequate natural durability;
3. chemical protection of timber – essentially entailing treatment by a pressure preservative process.

To achieve approach 1), a suitable form of partial or complete covering of the key structural elements is usually necessary. This may be combined with 2) or 3). If option 3) is the partial or complete solution, then it should be realized that machining members when manufacturing a structure removes the surface layers – by definition, the zones of section that are most at risk. Therefore, treatments should be carried out on elements that are as near completion as possible, including ensuring (where they exist) that holes, grooves and mortises are already machined. Specialist advice from the manufacturer and treater is invaluable.

If the designer considers how to avoid or strictly limit the following conditions, it will substantially improve durability:

a) standing water avoidance, through appropriate inclination of exposed near-horizontal surfaces;

b) excluding traps, pockets etc., where water infiltrates and damp dust, soil, or algal growth accumulates;
c) eliminating direct absorption of water (e.g. capillary absorption into end-grain from concrete floors or foundations).

Item c) is best achieved through elevation of the elements e.g. setting posts or columns on raised bases (also through use of appropriate slopes or barriers).

Positive "detailing for durability" measures also include:

- selecting an appropriate geometry for the initial structure, which maximizes possibilities for natural ventilation and protection of all timber parts;
- appropriate sealing and/or cover plates to limit fissures and de-laminations, especially at locations where the end-grain would otherwise be exposed;
- ensuring appropriate initial moisture content and reducing moisture changes; achieved through adequate surface protection – local "roofs" and covers that may themselves be sloped for water shedding, are examples.

Where elements are located near the ground, there is often an especially high risk of increased moisture content. Potential hazards include insufficient ventilation due to growth of vegetation between the timber and the ground, bouncing and splashing of precipitation, or poor surface drainage in the vicinity. Covering the ground by a membrane and/or coarse gravel to deter vegetation, increasing the distance or isolating the timber parts from the ground level can reduce these risks.

References to protective design can be found in STEP 1, Lectures A14 and A15 [1], and STEP 2, Lecture E17 [2].

4.2 Resistance to corrosion

(1)P Metal fasteners and other structural connections shall, where necessary, either be inherently corrosion-resistant or be protected against corrosion.

(2) Examples of minimum corrosion protection or material specifications for different service classes (see 2.3.1.3) are given in Table 4.1.

Table 4.1 — Examples of minimum specification for material protection against corrosion for fasteners (related to ISO 2081)

Fastener	Service Class[b]		
	1	2	3
Nails and screws with $d \leq 4$ mm	None	Fe/Zn 12c[a]	Fe/Zn 25c[a]
Bolts, dowels, nails and screws with $d > 4$ mm	None	None	Fe/Zn 25c[a]
Staples	Fe/Zn 12c[a]	Fe/Zn 12c[a]	Stainless steel
Punched metal plate fasteners and steel plates up to 3 mm thickness	Fe/Zn 12c[a]	Fe/Zn 12c[a]	Stainless steel
Steel plates from 3 mm up to 5 mm in thickness	None	Fe/Zn 12c[a]	Fe/Zn 25c[a]
Steel plates over 5 mm thickness	None	None	Fe/Zn 25c[a]

[a] If hot dip zinc coating is used, Fe/Zn 12c should be replaced by Z275 and Fe/Zn 25c by Z350 in accordance with EN 10147

[b] For especially corrosive conditions consideration should be given to heavier hot dip coatings or stainless steel.

Section 5 Basis of structural analysis

5.1 General

(1)P Calculations shall be performed using appropriate design models (supplemented, if necessary, by tests) involving all relevant variables. The models shall be sufficiently precise to predict the structural behaviour, commensurate with the standard of workmanship likely to be achieved, and with the reliability of the information on which the design is based.

5.2 Members

(1)P The following shall be taken into account by the structural analysis:

- deviations from straightness;
- inhomogeneities of the material.

NOTE Deviations from straightness and inhomogeneities are taken into account implicitly by the design methods given in this standard.

(2)P Reductions in the cross-sectional area shall be taken into account in the member strength verification.

(3) Reductions in the cross-sectional area may be ignored for the following cases:

- nails and screws with a diameter of 6 mm or less, driven without pre-drilling;
- holes in the compression area of members, if the holes are filled with a material of higher stiffness than the wood.

(4) When assessing the effective cross-section at a joint with multiple fasteners, all holes within a distance of half the minimum fastener spacing measured parallel to the grain from a given cross-section should be considered as occurring at that cross-section.

Section 6 Ultimate limit states

In addressing section 6, both the student and the tutor will find that it is in the nature of the layout of the Eurocodes materials design suite (EN 1992 to EN 1996 inclusive) that, unlike some of the more traditional codes such as BS 5268, not all of the rules for the design of a particular structural class of member are to be found at a single position in the text. Instead, a more didactically rigorous approach was taken by the leading drafting technical committee, which all were obliged to follow. This has advantages for precision, non-ambiguity and commonality of presentation among all materials. However, it does give rise to less immediacy of interpretation.

For example, in order to master the design of even quite a simple column, the student needs to read carefully and to understand:

1. "Design of cross sections subjected to stress in one principal direction" (for dealing with compression parallel to the grain);
2. "Design of cross sections subjected to combined stresses" (for combined bending and axial compression); and
3. "Stability of Members" (for members subjected to compression and bending (columns).

There are important forward references that should not be missed. For example, at the foot of 6.1.4, "NOTE Rules for the instability of members are given in 6.3." Also the last phrase of 6.2.4 states, "(3) A check should also be made of the instability condition (see 6.3)."

Hence, the only safe procedure is that at the very least, the user should carefully read from start to finish, each major section of the code (section 6 in this instance). They should then be in a better position to revisit specific clauses for a particular design purpose. Copious use should also be made of additional guidance e.g. the STEP Lectures guidance documents and other worked examples referenced herein (see the "Useful references" in Annex D at the end of this chapter).

6.1 Design of cross-sections subjected to stress in one principal direction

6.1.1 General

(1) Clause 6.1 applies to straight solid timber, glued laminated timber or wood-based structural products of constant cross-section, whose grain runs essentially parallel to the length of the member. The member is assumed to be subjected to stresses in the direction of only one of its principal axes (see Figure 6.1).

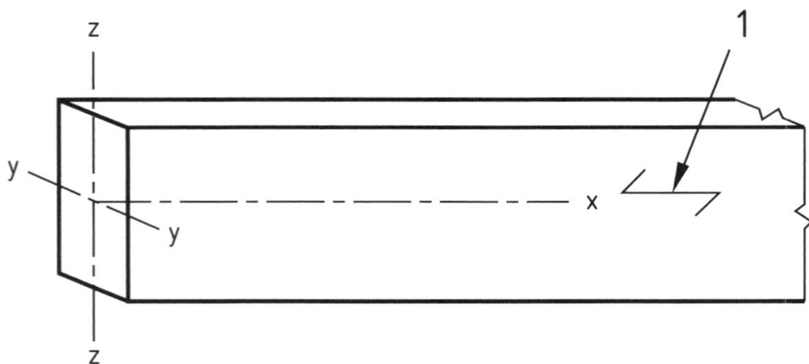

Key
1 Direction of grain

Figure 6.1 — Member Axes

6.1.2 Tension parallel to the grain

(1)P The following expression shall be satisfied:

$$\sigma_{t,0,d} \leq f_{t,0,d} \tag{6.1}$$

where:

$\sigma_{t,0,d}$ is the design tensile stress along the grain;
$f_{t,0,d}$ is the design tensile strength along the grain.

6.1.4 Compression parallel to the grain

(1)P The following expression shall be satisfied:

$$\sigma_{c,0,d} \leq f_{c,0,d} \tag{6.2}$$

where:

$\sigma_{c,0,d}$ is the design compressive stress along the grain;
$f_{c,0,d}$ is the design compressive strength along the grain.

NOTE Rules for the instability of members are given in 6.3.

6.1.5 Compression perpendicular to the grain

[A1⟩ (1)P The following expression shall be satisfied:

$$\sigma_{c,90,d} \leq k_{c,90}\, f_{c,90,d} \tag{6.3}$$

with:

$$\sigma_{c,90,d} = \frac{F_{c,90,d}}{A_{ef}} \tag{6.4}$$

where:

$\sigma_{c,90,d}$ is the design compressive stress in the contact area perpendicular to the grain;
$F_{c,90,d}$ is the design compressive load perpendicular to the grain;
A_{ef} is the effective contact area in compression perpendicular to the grain;
$f_{c,90,d}$ is the design compressive strength perpendicular to the grain;
$k_{c,90}$ is a factor taking into account the load configuration, the possibility of splitting and the degree of compressive deformation. ⟨A1]

6.1.6 Bending

(1)P The following expressions shall be satisfied:

$$\frac{\sigma_{m,y,d}}{f_{m,y,d}} + k_m \frac{\sigma_{m,z,d}}{f_{m,z,d}} \leq 1 \tag{6.11}$$

$$k_m \frac{\sigma_{m,y,d}}{f_{m,y,d}} + \frac{\sigma_{m,z,d}}{f_{m,z,d}} \leq 1 \tag{6.12}$$

where:

$\sigma_{m,y,d}$ and $\sigma_{m,z,d}$ are the design bending stresses about the principal axes as shown in Figure 6.1;
$f_{m,y,d}$ and $f_{m,z,d}$ are the corresponding design bending strengths.

NOTE The factor k_m makes allowance for redistribution of stresses and the effect of inhomogeneities of the material in a cross-section.

(2) The value of the factor k_m should be taken as follows:

For solid timber, glued laminated timber and LVL:
for rectangular sections: $k_m = 0,7$
for other cross-sections: $k_m = 1,0$
For other wood-based structural products, for all cross-sections: $k_m = 1,0$

(3)P A check shall also be made of the instability condition (see 6.3).

6.1.7 Shear

(1)P For shear with a stress component parallel to the grain, see Figure 6.5(a), as well as for shear with both stress components perpendicular to the grain, see Figure 6.5(b), the following expression shall be satisfied:

$$\tau_d \leq f_{v,d} \qquad (6.13)$$

where:

τ_d is the design shear stress;
$f_{v,d}$ is the design shear strength for the actual condition.

NOTE The shear strength for rolling shear is approximately equal to twice the tension strength perpendicular to grain.

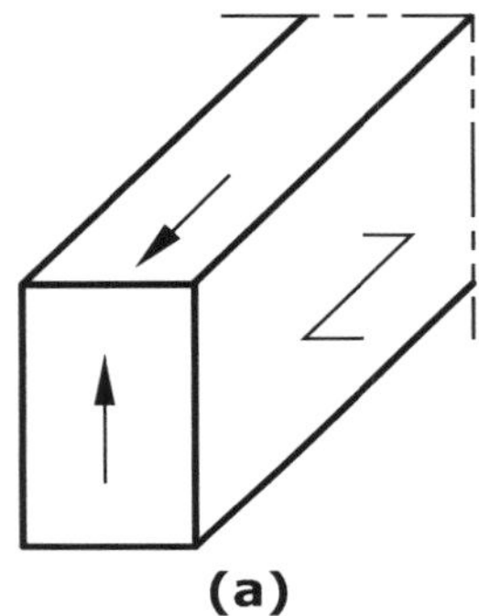
(a)

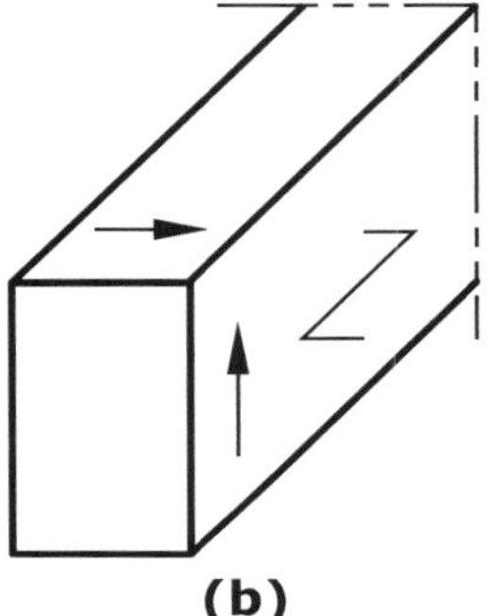
(b)

Figure 6.5 — (a) Member with a shear stress component parallel to the grain (b) Member with both stress components perpendicular to the grain (rolling shear)

6.2 Design of cross sections subjected to combined stresses

Unless they are adequately restrained along their length, columns, or more generally "beam-columns" (elements subjected to combined flexure and compression), are prone to flexural buckling. The primary influences on buckling resistance are the effective buckling length (which depends on the type of restraint at each end and on any partial bracing along the length), slenderness ratio (commonly represented by the symbol I and calculated as the effective buckling length divided by the radius of gyration), compressive and bending strength in the axial direction, and modulus of elasticity in bending. For solid rectangular sections the radius of gyration is the cross-sectional depth measured in the direction of buckling divided by the square root of 12. Geometric parameters and structural imperfections also have an effect. These influences vary according to the type of material (e.g. grade of solid timber) or quality of semi-finished product (e.g. glulam, LVL).

The buckling expressions of EN 1995-1-1 may be presented as interaction curves, as explained by Blass in STEP 1, Lecture B6 [1]. In such diagrams, ratios of axial force to axial resistance are plotted against ratios of applied moment to ultimate moment. Visualizing the interaction in this way illustrates the fact that the code expressions are based on a second order analysis. In this, the capability of timber to behave plastically under compression is taken into account (see Strength model for glulam columns [7]).

The design of columns with $\lambda > 30$, and subjected to bending due to lateral loading and eccentricity, is based on a linear interaction of buckling resistance and bending strength.

The principal factors influencing actual buckling lengths, and the approximate solutions for choice of effective lengths, are discussed by Blass in STEP 1, Lecture B7 [1]. Practical cases are presented for common element end-constraint conditions, and for flexural-compression zones of portal frames and arches.

6.2.3 Combined bending and axial tension

(1)P The following expressions shall be satisfied:

$$\frac{\sigma_{t,0,d}}{f_{t,0,d}} + \frac{\sigma_{m,y,d}}{f_{m,y,d}} + k_m \frac{\sigma_{m,z,d}}{f_{m,z,d}} \leq 1 \qquad (6.17)$$

$$\frac{\sigma_{t,0,d}}{f_{t,0,d}} + k_m \frac{\sigma_{m,y,d}}{f_{m,y,d}} + \frac{\sigma_{m,z,d}}{f_{m,z,d}} \leq 1 \qquad (6.18)$$

(2) The values of k_m given in 6.1.6 apply.

6.2.4 Combined bending and axial compression

(1)P The following expressions shall be satisfied:

$$\left(\frac{\sigma_{c,0,d}}{f_{c,0,d}}\right)^2 + \frac{\sigma_{m,y,d}}{f_{m,y,d}} + k_m \frac{\sigma_{m,z,d}}{f_{m,z,d}} \leq 1 \qquad (6.19)$$

$$\left(\frac{\sigma_{c,0,d}}{f_{c,0,d}}\right)^2 + k_m \frac{\sigma_{m,y,d}}{f_{m,y,d}} + \frac{\sigma_{m,z,d}}{f_{m,z,d}} \leq 1 \qquad (6.20)$$

(2)P The values of k_m given in 6.1.6 apply.

NOTE To check the instability condition, a method is given in 6.3.

6.3 Stability of members

6.3.2 Columns subjected to either compression or combined compression and bending

Beam instability in a timber context is discussed in STEP 1, Lecture B3 [1]. The classic expressions set out in Theory of Elastic Stability [8] are related to timber research such as that described in Lateral Stability of Glue Laminated Beams [9].

The expression (6.32)(below) is closely similar to that shown to be generally appropriate for rectangular sections in the above classic references. Whilst the code strictly states it to be applicable to "softwood with solid rectangular section", the basis for the small difference in the constant, and the reason for the restriction to "softwood" is unclear. In the absence of alternative advice, it is likely that the expression will be applied to all materials covered by the code.

The student should also be aware that in practical design, many cases are covered by sub-clause 6.3.3 (5), permitting great simplification.

(1) The relative slenderness ratios should be taken as:

$$\lambda_{rel,y} = \frac{\lambda_y}{\pi}\sqrt{\frac{f_{c,0,k}}{E_{0,05}}} \qquad (6.21)$$

and

$$\lambda_{rel,z} = \frac{\lambda_z}{\pi}\sqrt{\frac{f_{c,0,k}}{E_{0,05}}} \qquad (6.22)$$

where:

λ_y and $\lambda_{rel,y}$ are slenderness ratios corresponding to bending about the *y*-axis (deflection in the *z*-direction);

λ_z and $\lambda_{rel,z}$ are slenderness ratios corresponding to bending about the *z*-axis (deflection in the *y*-direction);

$E_{0,05}$ is the fifth percentile value of the modulus of elasticity parallel to the grain.

(2) Where both $\lambda_{rel,z} \leq 0{,}3$ and $\lambda_{rel,y} \leq 0{,}3$ the stresses should satisfy the expressions (6.19) and (6.20) in 6.2.4.

(3) In all other cases the stresses, which will be increased due to deflection, should satisfy the following expressions:

$$\frac{\sigma_{c,0,d}}{k_{c,y} f_{c,0,d}} + \frac{\sigma_{m,y,d}}{f_{m,y,d}} + k_m \frac{\sigma_{m,z,d}}{f_{m,z,d}} \leq 1 \qquad (6.23)$$

$$\frac{\sigma_{c,0,d}}{k_{c,z} f_{c,0,d}} + k_m \frac{\sigma_{m,y,d}}{f_{m,y,d}} + \frac{\sigma_{m,z,d}}{f_{m,z,d}} \leq 1 \qquad (6.24)$$

where the symbols are defined as follows:

$$k_{c,y} = \frac{1}{k_y + \sqrt{k_y^2 - \lambda_{rel,y}^2}} \qquad (6.25)$$

$$k_{c,z} = \frac{1}{k_z + \sqrt{k_z^2 - \lambda_{rel,z}^2}} \qquad (6.26)$$

$$k_y = 0{,}5\left(1 + \beta_c\left(\lambda_{rel,y} - 0{,}3\right) + \lambda_{rel,y}^2\right) \qquad (6.27)$$

$$k_z = 0{,}5\left(1 + \beta_c\left(\lambda_{rel,z} - 0{,}3\right) + \lambda_{rel,z}^2\right) \qquad (6.28)$$

where:

β_c is a factor for members within the straightness limits defined in Section 10:

$$\beta_c = \begin{cases} 0{,}2 & \text{for solid timber} \\ 0{,}1 & \text{for glued laminated timber and LVL} \end{cases} \qquad (6.29)$$

k_m as given in 6.1.6.

6.3.3 Beams subjected to either bending or combined bending and compression

(1)P Lateral torsional stability shall be verified both in the case where only a moment M_y exists about the strong axis *y* and where a combination of moment M_y and compressive force N_c exists.

(2) The relative slenderness for bending should be taken as:

$$\lambda_{rel,m} = \sqrt{\frac{f_{m,k}}{\sigma_{m,crit}}} \qquad (6.30)$$

where $\sigma_{m,crit}$ is the critical bending stress calculated according to the classical theory of stability, using 5-percentile stiffness values.

The critical bending stress should be taken as:

$$\sigma_{m,crit} = \frac{M_{y,crit}}{W_y} = \frac{\pi\sqrt{E_{0,05} I_z G_{0,05} I_{tor}}}{l_{ef} W_y} \quad (6.31)$$

where:

$E_{0,05}$ is the fifth percentile value of modulus of elasticity parallel to grain;
$G_{0,05}$ is the fifth percentile value of shear modulus parallel to grain;
I_z is the second moment of area about the weak axis z.
I_{tor} is the torsional moment of inertia;
l_{ef} is the effective length of the beam, depending on the support conditions and the load configuration, according to Table 6.1;
W_y is the section modulus about the strong axis y.

For softwood with solid rectangular cross-section, $\sigma_{m,crit}$ should be taken as:

$$\sigma_{m,crit} = \frac{0,78b^2}{hl_{ef}} E_{0,05} \quad (6.32)$$

where:

b is the width of the beam;
h is the depth of the beam.

(3) In the case where only a moment M_y exists about the strong axis y, the stresses should satisfy the following expression:

$$\sigma_{m,d} \leq k_{crit} f_{m,d} \quad (6.33)$$

where:

$\sigma_{m,d}$ is the design bending stress;
$f_{m,d}$ is the design bending strength;
k_{crit} is a factor which takes into account the reduced bending strength due to lateral buckling.

Table 6.1 — Effective length as a ratio of the span

Beam type	Loading typel	l_{ef}/l[a]
Simply supported	Constant moment Uniformly distributed load Concentrated force at the middle of the span	1,0 0,9 0,8
Cantilever	Uniformly distributed load Concentrated force at the free end	0,5 0,8
[a] The ratio between the effective length l_{ef} and the span l is valid for a beam with torsionally restrained supports and loaded at the centre of gravity. If the load is applied at the compression edge of the beam, l_{ef} should be increased by $2h$ and may be decreased by $0,5h$ for a load at the tension edge of the beam.		

(4) For beams with an initial lateral deviation from straightness within the limits defined in Section 10, k_{crit} may be determined from expression (6.34).

$$k_{crit} = \begin{cases} 1 & \text{for } \lambda_{rel,m} \leq 0,75 \\ 1,56 - 0,57\,\lambda_{rel,m} & \text{for } 0,75 < \lambda_{rel,m} \leq 1,4 \\ \dfrac{1}{\lambda_{rel,m}^2} & \text{for } 1,4 < \lambda_{rel,m} \end{cases} \quad (6.34)$$

(5) The factor k_{crit} may be taken as 1,0 for a beam where lateral displacement of its compressive edge is prevented throughout its length and where torsional rotation is prevented at its supports.

A1) (6) In the case where a combination of moment M_y about the strong axis y and compressive force N_c exists, the stresses should satisfy the following expression:

$$\left(\frac{\sigma_{m,d}}{k_{crit}\, f_{m,d}}\right)^2 + \frac{\sigma_{c,0,d}}{k_{c,z}\, f_{c,0,d}} \leq 1 \qquad (6.35)$$

where:

$\sigma_{m,d}$ is the design bending stress;
$\sigma_{c,0,d}$ is the design compressive stress parallel to grain;
$f_{c,0,d}$ is the design compressive strength parallel to grain;
$k_{c,z}$ is given by expression (6.26). (A1

6.5 Notched members

6.5.1 General

(1)P The effects of stress concentrations at the notch shall be taken into account in the strength verification of members.

(2) The effect of stress concentrations may be disregarded in the following cases:

- tension or compression parallel to the grain;
- bending with tensile stresses at the notch if the taper is not steeper than 1:i = 1:10, that is $i \geq 10$, see Figure 6.10a;
- bending with compressive stresses at the notch, see Figure 6.10b.

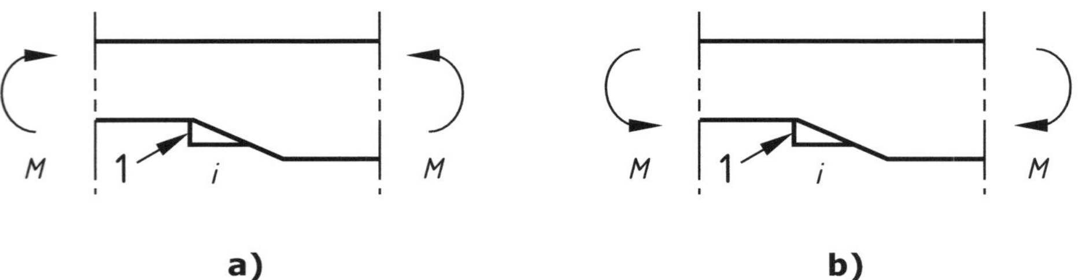

Figure 6.10 — Bending at a notch: a) with tensile stresses at the notch, b) with compressive stresses at the notch

6.5.2 Beams with a notch at the support

(1) For beams with rectangular cross-sections and where grain runs essentially parallel to the length of the member, the shear stresses at the notched support should be calculated using the effective (reduced) depth h_{ef} (see Figure 6.11).

(2) It should be verified that

$$\tau_d = \frac{1,5V}{bh_{ef}} \leq k_v\, f_{v,d} \qquad (6.60)$$

where k_v is a reduction factor defined as follows:

- For beams notched at the opposite side to the support (see Figure 6.11b)

$$k_v = 1,0 \qquad (6.61)$$

– For beams notched on the same side as the support (see Figure 6.11a)

$$k_v = \min \begin{cases} 1 \\ \dfrac{k_n \left(1 + \dfrac{1,1\, i^{1,5}}{\sqrt{h}}\right)}{\sqrt{h}\left(\sqrt{\alpha(1-\alpha)} + 0,8\dfrac{x}{h}\sqrt{\dfrac{1}{\alpha} - \alpha^2}\right)} \end{cases} \qquad (6.62)$$

where:

i is the notch inclination (see Figure 6.11a);
h is the beam depth in mm;
x is the distance from line of action of the support reaction to the corner of the notch, in mm;

$$\alpha = \frac{h_{ef}}{h}$$

$$k_n = \begin{cases} 4,5 & \text{for LVL} \\ 5 & \text{for solid timber} \\ 6,5 & \text{for glued laminated timber} \end{cases} \qquad (6.63)$$

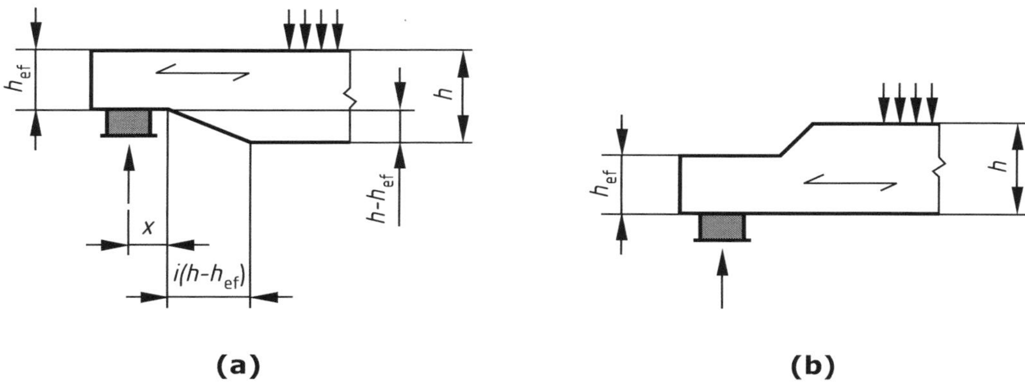

Figure 6.11 — End-notched beams

6.6 System strength

(1) When several equally spaced similar members, components or assemblies are laterally connected by a continuous load distribution system, the member strength properties may be multiplied by a system strength factor k_{sys}.

(2) Provided the continuous load-distribution system is capable of transferring the loads from one member to the neighbouring members, the factor k_{sys} should be 1,1.

(3) The strength verification of the load distribution system should be carried out assuming the loads are of short-term duration.

NOTE For roof trusses with a maximum centre to centre distance of 1,2m it may be assumed that tiling battens, purlins or panels can transfer the load to the neighbouring trusses provided that these load-distribution members are continuous over at least two spans, and any joints are staggered.

(4) For laminated timber decks or floors the values of k_{sys} given in Figure 6.12 should be used.

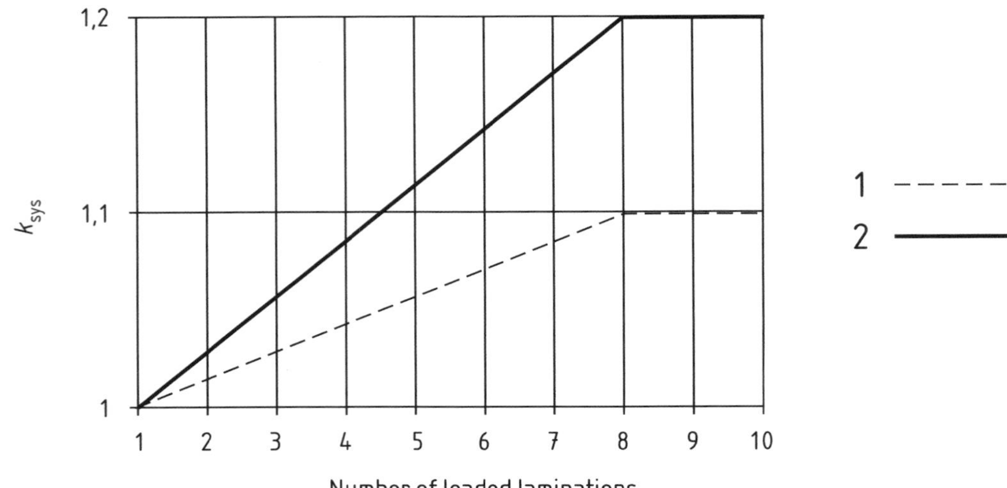

Key
1 Nailed or screwed laminations
2 Laminations pre-stressed or glued together

Figure 6.12 — System strength factor k_{sys} for laminated deck plates of solid timber or glued laminated members

Section 7 Serviceability limit states

7.1 Joint slip

(1) For joints made with dowel-type fasteners the slip modulus K_{ser} per shear plane per fastener under service load should be taken from Table 7.1 with ρ_m in kg/m^3 and d or d_c in mm. For the definition of d_c, see EN 13271.

NOTE In EN 26891 the symbol used is k_s instead of K_{ser}.

Table 7.1 — Values of K_{ser} for fasteners and connectors in N/mm in timber-to-timber and wood-based panel-to-timber connections

Fastener type	K_{ser}
Dowels Bolts with or without clearance[a] Screws Nails (with pre-drilling)	$\rho_m^{1,5}\, d\, /\, 23$
Nails (without pre-drilling)	$\rho_m^{1,5}\, d^{0,8}\, /\, 30$
Staples	$\rho_m^{1,5}\, d^{0,8}\, /\, 80$
Split-ring connectors type A according to EN 912 Shear-plate connectors type B according to EN 912	$\rho_m\, d_c\, /\, 2$
Toothed-plate connectors: – Connectors types C1 to C9 according to EN 912 – Connectors type C10 and C11 according to EN 912	 $1,5\, \rho_m\, d_c\, /\, 4$ $\rho_m\, d_c\, /\, 2$
[a] The clearance should be added separately to the deformation.	

(3) For steel-to-timber or concrete-to-timber connections, K_{ser} should be based on ρ_m for the timber member and may be multiplied by 2,0.

7.2 Limiting values for deflections of beams

(1) The components of deflection resulting from a combination of actions (see 2.2.3(5)) are shown in Figure 7.1, where the symbols are defined as follows, see 2.2.3:

- w_c is the precamber (if applied);
- w_{inst} is the instantaneous deflection;
- w_{creep} is the creep deflection;
- w_{fin} is the final deflection;
- $w_{net,fin}$ is the net final deflection.

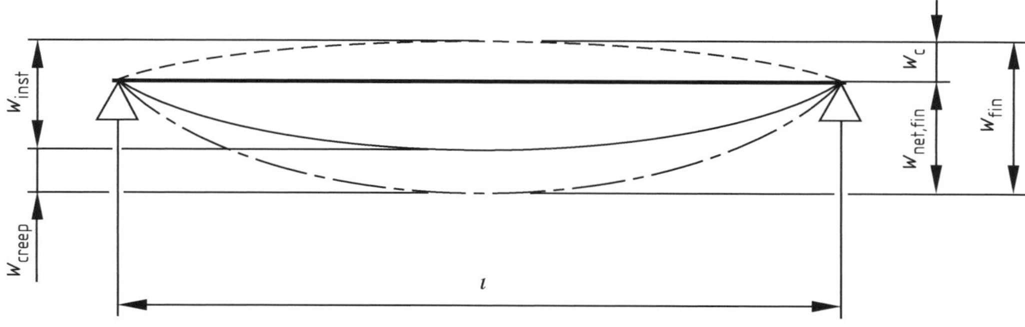

Figure 7.1 — Components of deflection

(2) The net deflection below a straight line between the supports, $w_{net,fin}$, should be taken as:

$$w_{net, fin} = w_{inst} + w_{creep} - w_c = w_{fin} - w_c \qquad (7.2)$$

NOTE The recommended range of limiting values of deflections for beams with span l is given in Table 7.2 depending upon the level of deformation deemed to be acceptable. Information on National choice may be found in the National Annex.

Table 7.2 — Examples of limiting values for deflections of beams

	w_{inst}	$w_{net,fin}$	w_{fin}
Beam on two supports	$l/300$ to $l/500$	$l/250$ to $l/350$	$l/150$ to $l/300$
Cantilevering beams	$l/150$ to $l/250$	$l/125$ to $l/175$	$l/75$ to $l/150$

EN 1995-1-1, 7.2(2) and Table 7.2 is implemented nationally in the UK as guidance by using Table NA.4.

The limiting values given in Table NA.5 take into account creep deformations.

Table NA.5 — Limiting values for deflections of individual beams

Type of member	**Limiting value for net final deflections of individual beams, $w_{net,fin}$**	
	A member of span, l between two supports	**A member with a cantilever, l**
Roof or floor members with a plastered or plasterboard ceiling	$l/250$	$l/125$
Roof or floor members without a plastered or plasterboard ceiling	$l/150$	$l/75$
NOTE When calculating $w_{net,fin}$, w_{fin} should be calculated as u_{fin} in accordance with BS EN 1995-1-1:2004+A1:2008, 2.2.3(5).		

Section 8 Connections with metal fasteners

8.1 General

Whilst the title of section 8 refers to "metal fasteners", the types covered by the referenced standards are all expected to be of ferrous materials. The great majority of the research that led to the design rules that follow was based on the premise that if the fastener fails it develops one or more distinct plastic hinges. Hence for the rules to be applicable, a plain carbon steel dowel-type fastener is taken to be the genotype, and other similar "dowel-type fasteners" are matched to this. Fasteners of very hardened, brittle materials, should not be used for designs following these principles without special investigations.

Ultimate limit states design of connections with metal fasteners

A dowelled connection is defined in (1.5.2.2). Dowel-type fasteners whose design is addressed by EN 1995-1-1 are: nails, staples, bolts, plain steel dowels and screws. Split ring, shear plate and toothed plate connectors (EN 1995-1-1, 8.9 and 8.10) require use of bolt, nut and washer sets in order to complete the connection (see Figure 8.12). Hence design for these also entails understanding of dowel-type fasteners.

The principal influences on the load-carrying capability of laterally loaded dowelled connections are:

1. the geometry and yield moment of the fastener(s);
2. embedding strength of the solid timber, glulam, LVL, or structural wood-based panel concerned;
3. the geometry of the connection.

With regard to point 1), whilst a plain steel dowel has no head or special shank or thread shape, and is perfectly cylindrical other than perhaps containing small chamfered portions at the ends, other dowel type fasteners including nails, bolts and screws, approximate sufficiently closely to the plain type to be treated with the same set of design expressions, provided that the actual geometry is controlled by the appropriate reference standards with this in mind.

The embedding strength 2), is not really a pure material property, but a system property that is a convenient concept for design and for assessment by means of a standard test, namely EN 383. For the purposes of the design expressions presented in this section, embedding strength is assumed to increase linearly with increasing timber density, a reasonable assumption, since density and compressive strength properties are quite well correlated in most species and types.

Because it is not a pure property, embedding strength itself actually depends upon:

a. density of the elements being connected;
b. diameter of the fastener;
c. angle between force resultant and grain direction;
d. friction between fastener and timber.

Splitting in timber connections is an undesirable, brittle failure mode. In the main, it is avoided by following the well-established spacing rules given in this section (e.g. 8.3.1.2).

During the preliminary design and detailing, the spacing rules should interrelate with the geometry of the connection, (see list item 3 above).

To prevent splitting, it is also necessary to follow the rules for connection forces at an angle to the grain when these occur (8.1.4). Informative Annex A, contains guidance on a recently-studied mode of failure involving shear failure of volumes of timber around a group of fasteners.

8.1.2 Multiple fastener connections

(2)P It shall be taken into account that the load-carry capacity of a multiple fastener connection consisting of fasteners of the same type and dimension, may be lower than the summation of the individual load-carrying capacities for each fastener.

Effects that have to be taken into account include:

1. reduction of load carrying capacity of multiple fastener connections compared with that of one made with a single fastener (an arrangement that rarely occurs);
2. spacing rules, giving minimum distances from edges, ends and between fasteners, to achieve the requested strength capacities and stiffness;
3. influence of angle between principal force resultant and grain of the timber;
4. effect of alternating loads, where relevant;
5. rules for arrangements in which load is carried by more than one type of fastener within a single connection.

(4) For one row of fasteners parallel to the grain direction, the effective characteristic load-carrying capacity parallel to the row, $F_{v,ef,Rk}$, should be taken as:

$$F_{v,\,ef,\,Rk} = n_{ef}\, F_{v,\,Rk} \tag{8.1}$$

where:

$F_{v,ef,Rk}$ is the effective characteristic load-carrying capacity of one row of fasteners parallel to the grain;
n_{ef} is the effective number of fasteners in line parallel to the grain;
$F_{v,Rk}$ is the characteristic load-carrying capacity of each fastener parallel to the grain.

NOTE Values of n_{ef} for rows parallel to grain are given in 8.3.1.1(8) and 8.5.1.1(4).

8.1.3 Multiple shear plane connections

(1) In multiple shear plane connections the resistance of each shear plane should be determined by assuming that each shear plane is part of a series of three-member connections.

8.1.4 Connection forces at an angle to the grain

(1)P When a force in a connection acts at an angle to the grain, (see Figure 8.1), the possibility of splitting caused by the tension force component, $F_{Ed} \sin \alpha$, perpendicular to the grain, shall be taken into account.

(2)P To take account of the possibility of splitting caused by the tension force component, $F_{Ed} \sin \alpha$, perpendicular to the grain, the following shall be satisfied:

$$F_{v,\,Ed} \leq F_{90,\,Rd} \tag{8.2}$$

with

$$F_{v,\,Ed} = \max \begin{cases} F_{v,\,Ed,\,1} \\ F_{v,\,Ed,\,2} \end{cases} \tag{8.3}$$

where:

$F_{90,Rd}$ is the design splitting capacity, calculated from the characteristic splitting capacity $F_{90,Rk}$ according to 2.4.3;

$F_{v,Ed,1}$, $F_{v,Ed,2}$ are the design shear forces on either side of the connection. (See Figure 8.1).

(3) For softwoods, the characteristic splitting capacity for the arrangement shown in Figure 8.1 should be taken as:

$$F_{90,\mathrm{Rk}} = 14bw\sqrt{\frac{h_\mathrm{e}}{\left(1-\frac{h_\mathrm{e}}{h}\right)}} \tag{8.4}$$

where:

$$w = \begin{cases} \max\begin{cases}\left(\frac{w_\mathrm{pl}}{100}\right)^{0,35} \\ 1\end{cases} & \text{for punched metal plate fasteners} \\ 1 & \text{for all other fasteners}\end{cases} \tag{8.5}$$

and:

$F_{90,\mathrm{Rk}}$ is the characteristic splitting capacity, in N;
w is a modification factor;
h_e is the loaded edge distance to the centre of the most distant fastener or to the edge of the punched metal plate fastener, in mm;
h is the timber member height, in mm;
b is the member thickness, in mm;
w_pl is the width of the punched metal plate fastener parallel to the grain, in mm.

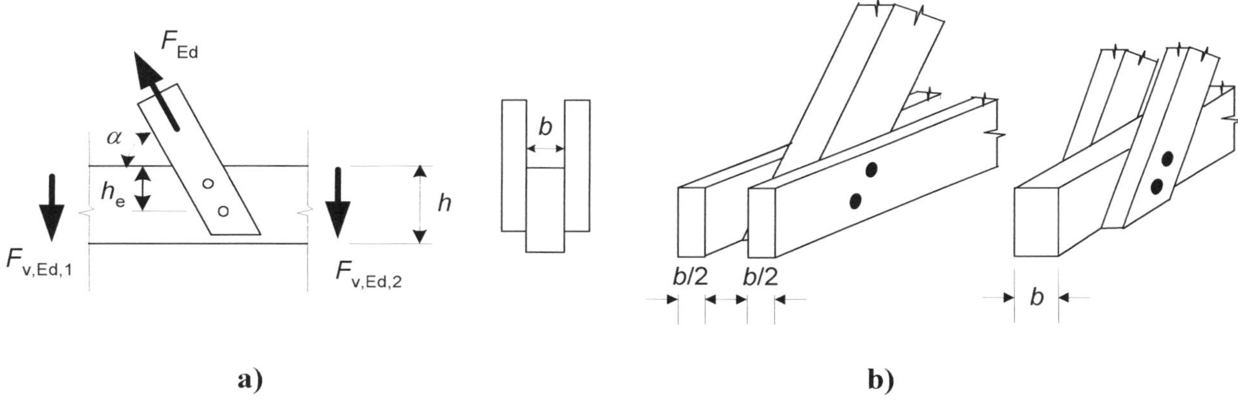

Figure 8.1 — Inclined force transmitted by a connection

8.2 Lateral load-carrying capacity of metal dowel-type fasteners

8.2.1 General

(1)P For the determination of the characteristic load-carrying capacity of connections with metal dowel-type fasteners the contributions of the yield strength, the embedment strength, and the withdrawal strength of the fastener shall be considered.

8.2.2 Timber-to-timber and panel-to-timber connections

Former design codes had an empirical basis for mechanically-fastened timber connection design. Data were entirely tabular, and a variety of procedures were followed for short-term tests on the various types of fastener concerned, as well as for the analysis and reductions to code format. To follow a similar route for EN 1995-1-1 would not have eliminated anomalies between apparent performance of the various types; nor would it have been feasible with a programme of testing of acceptable scope and duration.

Characteristic values for laterally-loaded dowel connections were able to be predicted from the geometry and yield moment of the fasteners, the embedding strength of the timber and the geometry of the connection, using a harmonized theory that applied to all of the types and materials combinations. This was first propounded by the Danish researcher K. W. Johansen in his 1949 paper "Theory of timber connections" [10]. His theoretical expressions were subsequently amplified and validated by tests on replications of structural-sized connection assemblies.

(1) The characteristic load-carrying capacity for nails, staples, bolts, dowels and screws per shear plane per fastener, should be taken as the minimum value found from the following expressions:

- For fasteners in single shear

$$F_{v,Rk} = \min \begin{cases} f_{h,1,k}\, t_1\, d & \text{(a)} \\ f_{h,2,k}\, t_2\, d & \text{(b)} \\ \dfrac{f_{h,1,k}\, t_1\, d}{1+\beta}\left[\sqrt{\beta + 2\beta^2\left[1+\dfrac{t_2}{t_1}+\left(\dfrac{t_2}{t_1}\right)^2\right]+\beta^3\left(\dfrac{t_2}{t_1}\right)^2} - \beta\left(1+\dfrac{t_2}{t_1}\right)\right] + \dfrac{F_{ax,Rk}}{4} & \text{(c)} \\ 1,05\,\dfrac{f_{h,1,k}\, t_1\, d}{2+\beta}\left[\sqrt{2\beta(1+\beta)+\dfrac{4\beta(2+\beta)M_{y,Rk}}{f_{h,1,k}\, d\, t_1^2}} - \beta\right] + \dfrac{F_{ax,Rk}}{4} & \text{(d)} \\ 1,05\,\dfrac{f_{h,1,k}\, t_2\, d}{1+2\beta}\left[\sqrt{2\beta^2(1+\beta)+\dfrac{4\beta(1+2\beta)M_{y,Rk}}{f_{h,1,k}\, d\, t_2^2}} - \beta\right] + \dfrac{F_{ax,Rk}}{4} & \text{(e)} \\ 1,15\sqrt{\dfrac{2\beta}{1+\beta}}\sqrt{2M_{y,Rk}\, f_{h,1,k}\, d} + \dfrac{F_{ax,Rk}}{4} & \text{(f)} \end{cases} \qquad (8.6)$$

- For fasteners in double shear:

$$F_{v,Rk} = \min \begin{cases} f_{h,1,k}\, t_1\, d & \text{(g)} \\ 0,5\, f_{h,2,k}\, t_2\, d & \text{(h)} \\ 1,05\,\dfrac{f_{h,1,k}\, t_1\, d}{2+\beta}\left[\sqrt{2\beta(1+\beta)+\dfrac{4\beta(2+\beta)M_{y,Rk}}{f_{h,1,k}\, d\, t_1^2}} - \beta\right] + \dfrac{F_{ax,Rk}}{4} & \text{(j)} \\ 1,15\sqrt{\dfrac{2\beta}{1+\beta}}\sqrt{2M_{y,Rk}\, f_{h,1,k}\, d} + \dfrac{F_{ax,Rk}}{4} & \text{(k)} \end{cases} \qquad (8.7)$$

with:

$$\beta = \frac{f_{h,2,k}}{f_{h,1,k}} \qquad (8.8)$$

where:

$F_{v,Rk}$ is the characteristic load-carrying capacity per shear plane per fastener;
t_i is the timber or board thickness or penetration depth, with i either 1 or 2, see also 8.3 to 8.7;
$f_{h,i,k}$ is the characteristic embedment strength in timber member i;
d is the fastener diameter;
$M_{y,Rk}$ is the characteristic fastener yield moment;
β is the ratio between the embedment strength of the members;
$F_{ax,Rk}$ is the characteristic axial withdrawal capacity of the fastener, see (2).

NOTE Plasticity of joints can be assured when relatively slender fasteners are used. In that case, failure modes (f) and (k) are governing.

8.2.3 Steel-to-timber connections

(1) The characteristic load-carrying capacity of a steel-to-timber connection depends on the thickness of the steel plates. Steel plates of thickness less than or equal to 0,5*d* are classified

as thin plates and steel plates of thickness greater than or equal to d with the tolerance on hole diameters being less than 0,1d are classified as thick plates. The characteristic load-carrying capacity of connections with steel plate thickness between a thin and a thick plate should be calculated by linear interpolation between the limiting thin and thick plate values.

(2)P The strength of the steel plate shall be checked.

(3) The characteristic load-carrying capacity for nails, bolts, dowels and screws per shear plane per fastener should be taken as the minimum value found from the following expressions:

– For a thin steel plate in single shear:

$$F_{v,Rk} = \min \begin{cases} 0,4\, f_{h,k}\, t_1\, d & \text{(a)} \\ 1,15\sqrt{2M_{y,Rk}\, f_{h,k}\, d} + \dfrac{F_{ax,Rk}}{4} & \text{(b)} \end{cases} \tag{8.9}$$

– For a thick steel plate in single shear:

A1)

$$F_{v,Rk} = \min \begin{cases} f_{h,k}\, t_1\, d & \text{(c)} \\ f_{h,k}\, t_1\, d\left[\sqrt{2 + \dfrac{4M_{y,Rk}}{f_{h,k}\, d\, t_1^2}} - 1\right] + \dfrac{F_{ax,Rk}}{4} & \text{(d)} \\ 2,3\sqrt{M_{y,Rk}\, f_{h,k}\, d} + \dfrac{F_{ax,Rk}}{4} & \text{(e)} \end{cases} \tag{8.10}$$

(A1

– For a steel plate of any thickness as the central member of a double shear connection:

$$F_{v,Rk} = \min \begin{cases} f_{h,1,k}\, t_1\, d & \text{(f)} \\ f_{h,1,k}\, t_1\, d\left[\sqrt{2 + \dfrac{4M_{y,Rk}}{f_{h,1,k}\, d\, t_1^2}} - 1\right] + \dfrac{F_{ax,Rk}}{4} & \text{(g)} \\ 2,3\sqrt{M_{y,Rk}\, f_{h,1,k}\, d} + \dfrac{F_{ax,Rk}}{4} & \text{(h)} \end{cases} \tag{8.11}$$

– For thin steel plates as the outer members of a double shear connection:

$$F_{v,Rk} = \min \begin{cases} 0,5\, f_{h,2,k}\, t_2\, d & \text{(j)} \\ 1,15\sqrt{2M_{y,Rk}\, f_{h,2,k}\, d} + \dfrac{F_{ax,Rk}}{4} & \text{(k)} \end{cases} \tag{8.12}$$

– For thick steel plates as the outer members of a double shear connection:

$$F_{v,Rk} = \min \begin{cases} 0,5\, f_{h,2,k}\, t_2\, d & \text{(l)} \\ 2,3\sqrt{M_{y,Rk}\, f_{h,2,k}\, d} + \dfrac{F_{ax,Rk}}{4} & \text{(m)} \end{cases} \tag{8.13}$$

where:

$F_{v,Rk}$ is the characteristic load-carrying capacity per shear plane per fastener;
$f_{h,k}$ is the characteristic embedment strength in the timber member;
t_1 is the smaller of the thickness of the timber side member or the penetration depth;
t_2 is the thickness of the timber middle member;
d is the fastener diameter;
$M_{y,Rk}$ is the characteristic fastener yield moment;
$F_{ax,Rk}$ is the characteristic withdrawal capacity of the fastener.

NOTE 1 The different failure modes are illustrated in Figure 8.3

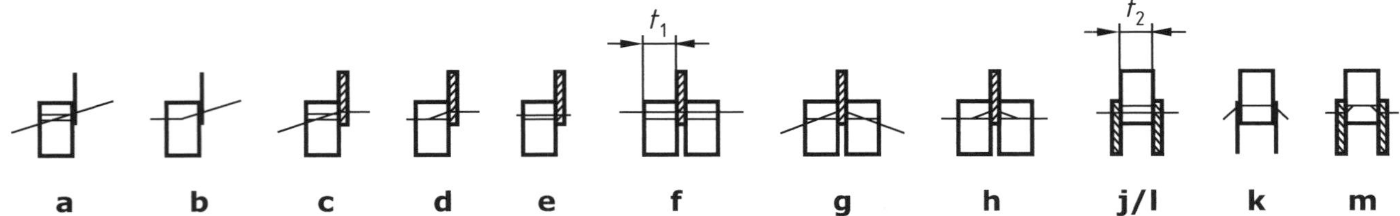

Figure 8.3 — Failure modes for steel-to-timber connections

Using the parameters described above, the expressions shown above predict ultimate strength from either a specific type of bearing failure in the timber, e.g. EN 1995-1-1, Figure 8.2, (1) a, b, c, (2) g, h, or from formation of one or more plastic hinges in the fastener, EN 1995-1-1, Figure 8.2, (1) d, e, f, (2) j, k. In practice, combinations of these types do occur, and it should be recognized that the theory is somewhat idealized. Nevertheless these types of failure have been shown by test, and the benefit of the approach is that by linking diagrammatic modes such as those shown here with expressions such as (EN 1995-1-1, 8.6 to 8.8) the designer is able to predict the likely failure mode of a proposed detail and make adjustments accordingly to attain the required performance and geometry.

(4) For the limitation of the rope effect $F_{ax,Rk}$ (8.2.2(2)) applies.

(5)P It shall be taken into account that the load-carrying capacity of steel-to-timber connections with a loaded end may be reduced by failure along the circumference of the fastener group.

8.3 Nailed connections

8.3.1 Laterally loaded nails

8.3.1.1 General

(1) The symbols for the thicknesses in single and double shear connections (see Figure 8.4) are defined as follows:

t_1 is:

- the headside thickness in a single shear connection;
- the minimum of the headside timber thickness and the pointside penetration in a double shear connection;

t_2 is:

- the pointside penetration in a single shear connection;
- the central member thickness in a double shear connection.

A1 (2) Timber should be pre-drilled when:

- the characteristic density of the timber is greater than 500 kg/m^3;
- the diameter d of the nail exceeds 6 mm. A1

(3) For square and grooved nails, the nail diameter d should be taken as the side dimension.

(4) For smooth nails produced from wire with a minimum tensile strength of 600 N/mm^2, the following characteristic values for yield moment should be used:

$$M_{y,Rk} = \begin{cases} 0,3\, f_u\, d^{2,6} & \text{for round nails} \\ 0,45\, f_u\, d^{2,6} & \text{for square and grooved nails} \end{cases} \qquad (8.14)$$

where:

$M_{y,Rk}$ is the characteristic value for the yield moment, in Nmm;
d is the nail diameter as defined in EN 14592, in mm;
f_u is the tensile strength of the wire, in N/mm^2.

(5) For nails with diameters up to 8 mm, the following characteristic embedment strengths in timber and LVL apply:

– without predrilled holes

$$f_{h,k} = 0,082\,\rho_k\,d^{-0,3} \quad \text{N/mm}^2 \tag{8.15}$$

– with predrilled holes

$$f_{h,k} = 0,082\,(1 - 0,01\,d)\,\rho_k \quad \text{N/mm}^2 \tag{8.16}$$

where:

ρ_k is the characteristic timber density, in kg/m^3;
d is the nail diameter, in mm.

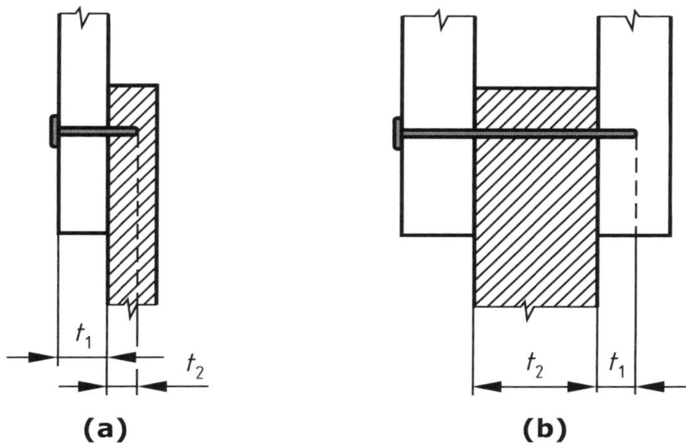

Figure 8.4 — Definitions of t_1 and t_2 (a) single shear connection, (b) double shear connection

(6) For nails with diameters greater than 8 mm the characteristic embedment strength values for bolts according to 8.5.1 apply.

(7) In a three-member connection, nails may overlap in the central member provided (t – t_2) is greater than $4d$ (see Figure 8.5).

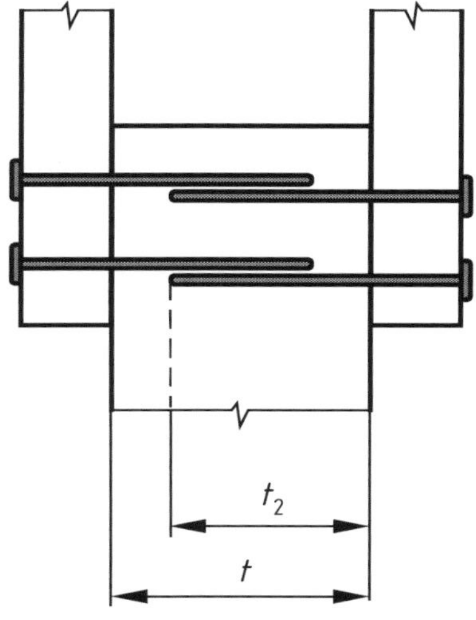

Figure 8.5 — Overlapping nails

(8) For one row of n nails parallel to the grain, unless the nails of that row are staggered perpendicular to grain by at least $1d$ (see figure 8.6), the load-carrying capacity parallel to the grain (see 8.1.4.2) should be calculated using the effective number of fasteners n_{ef}, where:

$$n_{ef} = n^{k_{ef}} \tag{8.17}$$

where:

n_{ef} is the effective number of nails in the row;
n is the number of nails in a row;
k_{ef} is given in Table 8.1.

Table 8.1 — Values of k_{ef}

Spacing[a]	k_{ef}	
	Not predrilled	Predrilled
$a_1 \geq 14d$	1,0	1,0
$a_1 = 10d$	0,85	0,85
$a_1 = 7d$	0,7	0,7
$a_1 = 4d$	–	0,5

[a] For intermediate spacings, linear interpolation of k_{ef} is permitted

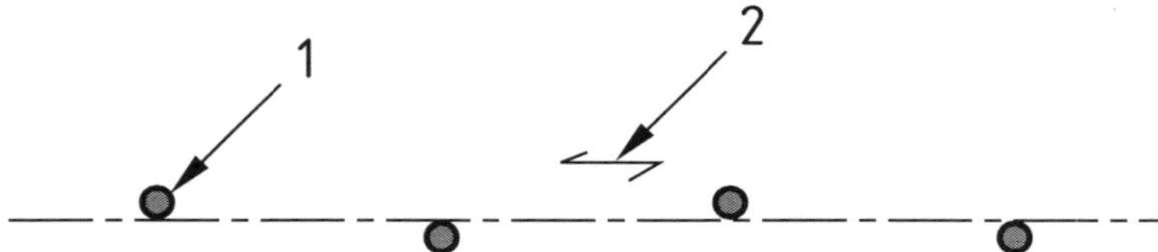

Key
1 Nail
2 Grain direction

Figure 8.6 — Nails in a row parallel to grain staggered perpendicular to grain by *d*

(9) There should be at least two nails in a connection.

(10) Requirements for structural detailing and control of nailed connections are given in 10.4.2.

8.3.1.2 Nailed timber-to-timber connections

(1) For smooth nails the pointside penetration length should be at least $8d$.

(2) For nails other than smooth nails, as defined in EN 14592, the pointside penetration length should be at least $6d$.

(3) Nails in end grain should not be considered capable of transmitting lateral forces.

(4) As an alternative to 8.3.1.2(3), for nails in end grain the following rules apply:

- In secondary structures smooth nails may be used. The design values of the load-carrying capacity should be taken as 1/3 of the values for nails installed at right angles to the grain;

- Nails other than smooth nails, as defined in EN 14592, may be used in structures other than secondary structures. The design values of the load-carrying capacity should be taken as 1/3 of the values for smooth nails of equivalent diameter installed at right angles to the grain, provided that:
  - the nails are only laterally loaded;
  - there are at least three nails per connection;
  - the pointside penetration is at least 10*d*;
  - the connection is not exposed to service class 3 conditions;
  - the prescribed spacings and edge distances given in Table 8.2 are satisfied.

NOTE 1 An example of a secondary structure is a fascia board nailed to rafters.

NOTE 2 The recommendation application rule is given in 8.3.1.2(3). The National choice may be specified in the National annex.

EN 1995-1-1, 8.3.1.2(4) is implemented nationally in the UK by using the application rules provided in 8.3.1.2(4).

(5) Minimum spacings and edge and end distances are given in Table 8.2, where (see Figure 8.7):

a_1 is the spacing of nails within one row parallel to grain;
a_2 is the spacing of rows of nails perpendicular to grain;
$a_{3,c}$ is the distance between nail and unloaded end;
$a_{3,t}$ is the distance between nail and loaded end;
$a_{4,c}$ is the distance between nail and unloaded edge;
$a_{4,t}$ is the distance between nail and loaded edge;
α is the angle between the force and the grain direction.

Table 8.2 — Minimum spacings and edge and end distances for nails

Spacing or distance (see Figure 8.7)	Angle α	Minimum spacing or end/edge distance		
		without predrilled holes		with predrilled holes
		$\rho k \leq 420$ kg/m^3	420 kg/m^3 < $\rho k \leq 500$ kg/m^3	
Spacing a_1 (parallel to grain)	$0° \leq \alpha \leq 360°$	d < 5 mm: $(5+5\|\cos \alpha\|)d$ $d \geq 5$ mm: $(5+7\|\cos \alpha\|)d$	$(7+8\|\cos \alpha\|)d$	$(4+\|\cos \alpha\|)d$
Spacing a_2 (perpendicular to grain)	$0° \leq \alpha \leq 360°$	$5d$	$7d$	$(3+\|\sin \alpha\|)d$
Distance $a_{3,t}$ (loaded end)	$-90° \leq \alpha \leq 90°$	$(10+5\|\cos \alpha\|)d$	$(15+5\|\cos \alpha\|)d$	$(7+5\|\cos \alpha\|)d$
Distance $a_{3,c}$ (unloaded end)	$90° \leq \alpha \leq 270°$	$10d$	$15d$	$7d$
Distance $a_{4,t}$ (loaded edge)	$0° \leq \alpha \leq 180°$	d < 5 mm: $(5+2\|\sin \alpha\|)d$ $d \geq 5$ mm: $(5+5\|\sin \alpha\|)d$	d < 5 mm: $(7+2\|\sin \alpha\|)d$ $d \geq 5$ mm: $(7+5\|\sin \alpha\|)d$	d < 5 mm: $(3+2\|\sin \alpha\|)d$ $d \geq 5$ mm: $(3+4\|\sin \alpha\|)d$
Distance $a_{4,c}$ (unloaded edge)	$180° \leq \alpha \leq 360°$	$5d$	$7d$	$3d$

(6) Timber should be pre-drilled when the thickness of the timber members is smaller than

$$t = \max \begin{cases} 7d \\ (13d - 30)\dfrac{\rho_k}{400} \end{cases} \qquad (8.18)$$

where:

t is the minimum thickness member to avoid pre-drilling, in mm;
ρ_k is the characteristic timber density in kg/m^3;
d is the nail diameter, in mm.

8.3.1.4 Nailed steel-to-timber connections

(1) The minimum edge and end distances for nails given in Table 8.2 apply. Minimum nail spacings are those given in Table 8.2, multiplied by a factor of 0,7.

8.3.2 Axially loaded nails

[A1) (1)P Nails used to resist permanent or long-term axial loading shall be threaded.

NOTE The following definition of threaded nails is given in EN 14592: Nail that has its shank profiled or deformed over a part of its length of minimum 4,5 d (4,5 times the nominal diameter) and that has a characteristic withdrawal parameter $f_{ax,k}$ greater than or equal to 6 N/mm^2 when measured on timber with a characteristic density of 350 kg/m^3 when conditioned to constant mass at 20 °C and 65% relative humidity. (A1]

(2) For threaded nails, only the threaded part should be considered capable of transmitting axial load.

(3) Nails in end grain should be considered incapable of transmitting axial load.

(4) The characteristic withdrawal capacity of nails, $F_{ax,Rk}$, for nailing perpendicular to the grain (Figure 8.8 (a) and for slant nailing (Figure 8.8 (b)), should be taken as the smaller of the values found from the following expressions:

– For nails other than smooth nails, as defined in EN 14592:

$$F_{ax,Rk} = \begin{cases} f_{ax,k}\, d\, t_{pen} & \text{(a)} \\ f_{head,k}\, d_h^2 & \text{(b)} \end{cases} \qquad (8.23)$$

– For smooth nails:

$$F_{ax,Rk} = \begin{cases} f_{ax,k}\, d\, t_{pen} & \text{(a)} \\ f_{ax,k}\, d\, t + f_{head,k}\, d_h^2 & \text{(b)} \end{cases} \qquad (8.24)$$

where:

$f_{ax,k}$ is the characteristic pointside withdrawal strength;
$f_{head,k}$ is the characteristic headside pull-through strength;
d is the nail diameter according to 8.3.1.1;
t_{pen} is the pointside penetration length or the length of the threaded part in the pointside member;
t is the thickness of the headside member;
d_h is the nail head diameter.

(5) The characteristic strengths $f_{ax,k}$ and $f_{head,k}$ should be determined by tests in accordance with EN 1382, EN 1383 and EN 14358 unless specified in the following.

(6) For smooth nails with a pointside penetration of at least 12*d*, the characteristic values of the withdrawal and pull-through strengths should be found from the following expressions:

$$f_{\mathrm{ax,k}} = 20 \times 10^{-6}\,\rho_{\mathrm{k}}^{2} \tag{8.25}$$

$$f_{\mathrm{head,k}} = 70 \times 10^{-6}\,\rho_{\mathrm{k}}^{2} \tag{8.26}$$

where:

ρ_{k} is the characteristic timber density in kg/m^3;

(7) For smooth nails, the pointside penetration t_{pen} should be at least 8*d*. For nails with a pointside penetration smaller than 12*d* the withdrawal capacity should be multiplied by ($t_{\mathrm{pen}}/4d$ −2). For threaded nails, the pointside penetration should be at least 6*d*. For nails with a pointside penetration smaller than 8*d* the withdrawal capacity should be multiplied by ($t_{\mathrm{pen}}/2d$ −3).

(8) For structural timber which is installed at or near fibre saturation point, and which is likely to dry out under load, the values of $f_{\mathrm{ax,k}}$ and $f_{\mathrm{head,k}}$ should be multiplied by 2/3.

(9) The spacings, end and edge distances for laterally loaded nails apply to axially loaded nails.

[A1⟩ (10) For slant nailing the distance to the loaded end should be at least 10*d* (see Figure 8.8(b)). There should be at least two slant nails in a connection. ⟨A1]

8.5 Bolted connections

Bolted and dowelled joints

Design rules are provided for various types of bolted and dowelled connections. The rules for spacings, end and edge distances are given and the influence of load-to-grain angle is dealt with. Empirical equations for the embedding strengths of the members and the fastener yield moments are given. The effect of system properties (e.g. fastener surface friction) on the characteristic load-carrying capacity of the joints is addressed.

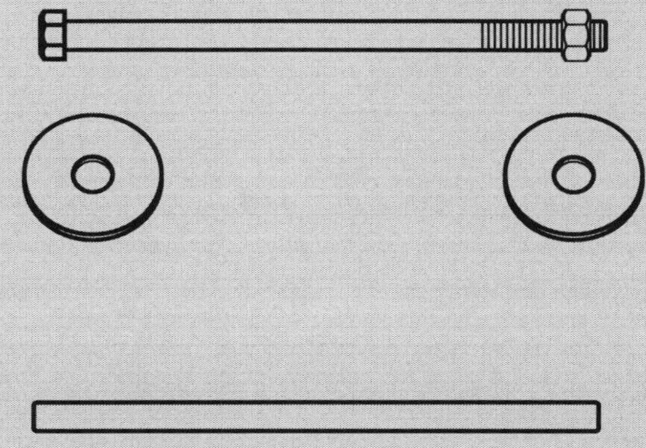

Figure B — Bolt with washer and dowel

Bolts (see Figure B) are dowel-type fasteners with heads and nuts. They should be tightened so that the members fit closely, and they should be re-tightened if necessary when the timber has reached equilibrium moisture content. Bolt holes may have a diameter not more than 1 mm larger then the bolt. If a bolt is fitted in a hole which is not greater than its shank, the design method for dowelled joints is applied. Washers with a side length or diameter of at least 3*d* and a thickness of at least 0,3*d* (*d* is the bolt diameter) should be used under the head and nut. Washers should have a full bearing area.

Joints with dowels are used in timber construction to transmit high forces. This economic type of joint is easy to produce. In large dowelled connections, it may be necessary to replace some dowels with fitted bolts to maintain the form of the joint. Dowelled joints are stiff, compared with bolted joints. Therefore, bolted joints should not be used in construction where large deformations impair the serviceability.

8.5.1 Laterally loaded bolts

8.5.1.1 General and bolted timber-to-timber connections

(1) For bolts the following characteristic value for the yield moment should be used:

$$M_{y,Rk} = 0,3\, f_{u,k}\, d^{2,6} \tag{8.30}$$

where:

$M_{y,Rk}$ is the characteristic value for the yield moment, in Nmm;
$f_{u,k}$ is the characteristic tensile strength, in N/mm^2;
d is the bold diameter, in mm.

(2) For bolts up to 30 mm diameter, the following characteristic embedment strength values in timber should be used, at an angle α to the grain:

$$f_{h,\alpha,k} = \frac{f_{h,0,k}}{k_{90}\sin^2\alpha + \cos^2\alpha} \tag{8.31}$$

$$f_{h,0,k} = 0,082\,(1 - 0,01d)\,\rho_k \tag{8.32}$$

where:

$$k_{90} = \begin{cases} 1,35 + 0,015d & \text{for softwoods} \\ 1,30 + 0,015d & \text{for LVL} \\ 0,90 + 0,015d & \text{for hardwoods} \end{cases} \tag{8.33}$$

and:

$f_{h,0,k}$ is the characteristc embedment strength parallel to grain, in N/mm^2;
ρ_k is the characteristic timber density, in kg/m^3;
α is the angle of the load to the grain;
d is the bolt diameter, in mm.

(3) Minimum spacing and edge and end distances should be taken from Table 8.4, with symbols illustrated in Figure 8.7.

Table 8.4 — Minimum values of spacing and edge and end distances for bolts

Spacing and end/edge distances (see Figure 8.7)	Angle	Minimum spacing or distance
a_1 (parallel to grain)	$0° \le \alpha \le 360°$	$(4 + \|\cos \alpha\|)\, d$
a_2 (perpendicular to grain)	$0° \le \alpha \le 360°$	$4d$
$a_{3,t}$ (loaded end)	$-90° \le \alpha \le 90°$	max (7 d; 80 mm)
$a_{3,c}$ (unloaded end)	$90° \le \alpha < 150°$ $150° \le \alpha < 210°$ $210° \le \alpha \le 270°$	A1 $(1 + 6\|\sin \alpha\|)\, d$ $4d$ $(1 + 6\|\sin \alpha\|)\, d$ A1
$a_{4,t}$ (loaded edge)	$0° \le \alpha \le 180°$	max $[(2 + 2\|\sin \alpha\|)\, d;\ 3d]$
$a_{4,c}$ (unloaded edge)	$180° \le \alpha \le 360°$	$3d$

(4) For one row of n bolts parallel to the grain direction, the load-carrying capacity parallel to grain, see 8.1.2(4), should be calculated using the effective number of bolts n_{ef} where:

$$n_{ef} = \min \begin{cases} n \\ n^{0,9} \sqrt[4]{\dfrac{a_1}{13d}} \end{cases} \tag{8.34}$$

where:

a_1 is the spacing between bolts in the grain direction;
d is the bolt diameter;
n is the number of bolts in the row.

For loads perpendicular to grain, the effective number of fasteners should be taken as

$$n_{ef} = n \tag{8.35}$$

For angles $0° < \alpha < 90°$ between load and grain direction, n_{ef} may be determined by linear interpolation between expressions (8.34) and (8.35).

(5) Requirements for minimum washer dimensions and thickness in relation to bolt diameter are given in 10.4.3.

8.5.1.3 Bolted steel-to-timber connections

(1) The rules given in 8.2.3 apply.

8.5.2 Axially loaded bolts

(1) The axial load-bearing capacity and withdrawal capacity of a bolt should be taken as the lower value of:

- the bolt tensile capacity;
- the load-bearing capacity of either the washer or (for steel-to-timber connections) the steel plate.

(2) The bearing capacity of a washer should be calculated assuming a characteristic compressive strength on the contact area of $3{,}0f_{c,90,k}$.

(3) The bearing capacity per bolt of a steel plate should not exceed that of a circular washer with a diameter which is the minimum of:

- $12t$, where t is the plate thickness;
- $4d$, where d is the bolt diameter.

8.6 Dowelled connections

Dowels (see Figure B) are slender cylindrical rods made of steel, usually with a smooth surface. The minimum diameter covered by the code is 6 mm. The tolerances on the dowel are −0,0/+0,1 mm and the pre-drilled holes in the timber member should have a diameter not greater then the dowel itself. The holes in steel in steel members may be pre-drilled 1 mm larger than the dowel diameter and due allowance may be made for any extra slip that may occur.

(1) The rules given in 8.5.1, except 8.5.1.1(3), apply.

(2) The minimum dowel diameter should be greater than 6 mm and the maximum 30 mm.

(3) Minimum spacing and edge and end distances are given in Table 8.5, with symbols illustrated in Figure 8.7.

(4) Requirements for dowel hole tolerances are given in 10.4.4.

Table 8.5 — Minimum spacings and edge and end distances for dowels

Spacing and end/edge distances (see Figure 8.7)	Angle	Minimum spacing or edge/end distance
a_1 (parallel to grain)	$0° \leq \alpha \leq 360°$	$(3 + 2\lvert\cos\alpha\rvert)\,d$
a_2 (perpendicular to grain)	$0° \leq \alpha \leq 360°$	$3d$
$a_{3,t}$ (loaded end)	$-90° \leq \alpha \leq 90°$	max (7 d; 80 mm)
$a_{3,c}$ (unloaded end)	$90° \leq \alpha < 150°$ $150° \leq \alpha < 210°$ $210° \leq \alpha \leq 270°$	max ($a_{3,t}\lvert\sin\alpha\rvert$) d; $3d$) $3d$ max ($a_{3,t}\lvert\sin\alpha\rvert$) d; $3d$)
$a_{4,t}$ (loaded edge)	$0° \leq \alpha \leq 180°$	max [(2 + 2$\lvert\sin\alpha\rvert$) d; $3d$]
$a_{4,c}$ (unloaded edge)	$180° \leq \alpha \leq 360°$	$3d$

8.7 Screwed connections

Wood screws (see Figure C) are especially suitable for steel-to-timber and panel-to-timber joints, but they can also be used for timber-to-timber joints. Such screwed joints are mainly designed as single shear joints.

Screws with a diameter greater then 5 mm should be turned into pre-drilled holes to prevent splitting of the wood. The holes should be pre-drilled over the length of the unthreaded shank with the diameter of the smooth shank and over the threaded portion with a diameter of about 70 per cent of the shank diameter. Screws should be inserted by turning and not by driving with a hammer, otherwise the load carrying capacity will decrease significantly.

Requirements referring to design and material of the screws will be detailed in a European product standard that is currently being drafted. In the design expressions, d should be taken as the diameter of the screw measured on the smooth shank. The diameter d of coach screws varies from 8 mm to 20 mm, the diameter of countersunk head or round head screws varies from 4 mm to 8 mm. The root diameter in the threaded portion d_1 is about 70 per cent of the diameter measured on the smooth shank. The depth of the thread h_1 varies from 0,125d to 0,14d, the threadpitch h_2 from 0,4d to 0,5d. The length of the threaded portion is about 60 per cent of the total length of the shank.

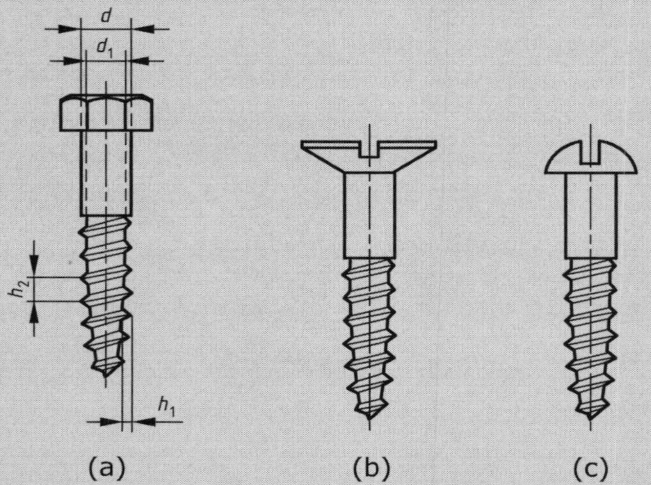

Figure C — Typical wood screws: (a) coach screw (b) countersunk head (c) round head

8.7.1 Laterally loaded screws

(1)P The effect of the threaded part of the screw shall be taken into account in determining the load-carrying capacity, by using an effective diameter d_{ef}.

(2) For smooth shank screws, where the outer thread diameter is equal to the shank diameter, the rules given in 8.2 apply, provided that:

- The effective diameter d_{ef} is taken as the smooth shank diameter;
- The smooth shank penetrates into the member containing the point of the screw by not less than $4d$.

(3) Where the conditions in (2) are not satisfied, the screw load-carrying capacity should be calculated using an effective diameter d_{ef} taken as 1,1 times the thread root diameter.

(4) For smooth shank screws with a diameter $d > 6$ mm, the rules in 8.5.1 apply.

(5) For smooth shank screws with a diameter of 6 mm or less, the rules of 8.3.1 apply.

(6) Requirements for structural detailing and control of screwed joints are given in 10.4.5.

8.7.2 Axially loaded screws

[A1⟩ (1)P For the verification of resistance of axially loaded screws, the following failure modes shall be taken into account:

- the withdrawal failure of the threaded part of the screw;
- the tear-off failure of the screw head of screws used in combination with steel plates, tear-off resistance of the screw head should be greater than the tensile strength of the screw;
- the pull-through failure of the screw head;
- the tensile failure of the screw;
- the buckling failure of the screw when loaded in compression;
- failure along the circumference of a group of screws used in conjunction with steel plates (block shear or plug shear).

(2) Minimum spacings and end and edge distances for axially loaded screws, see Figure 8.11a, should be taken from Table 8.6, provided the timber thickness $t \geq 12d$.

Table 8.6 — Minimum spacings and end and edge distances for axially loaded screws

Minimum screw spacing in a plane parallel to the grain a_1	Minimum screw spacing perpendicular to a plane parallel to the grain a_2	Minimum end distance of the centre of gravity of the threaded part of the screw in the member $a_{1,cg}$	Minimum edge distance of the centre of gravity of the threaded part of the screw in the member $a_{2,cg}$
$7d$	$5d$	$10d$	$4d$

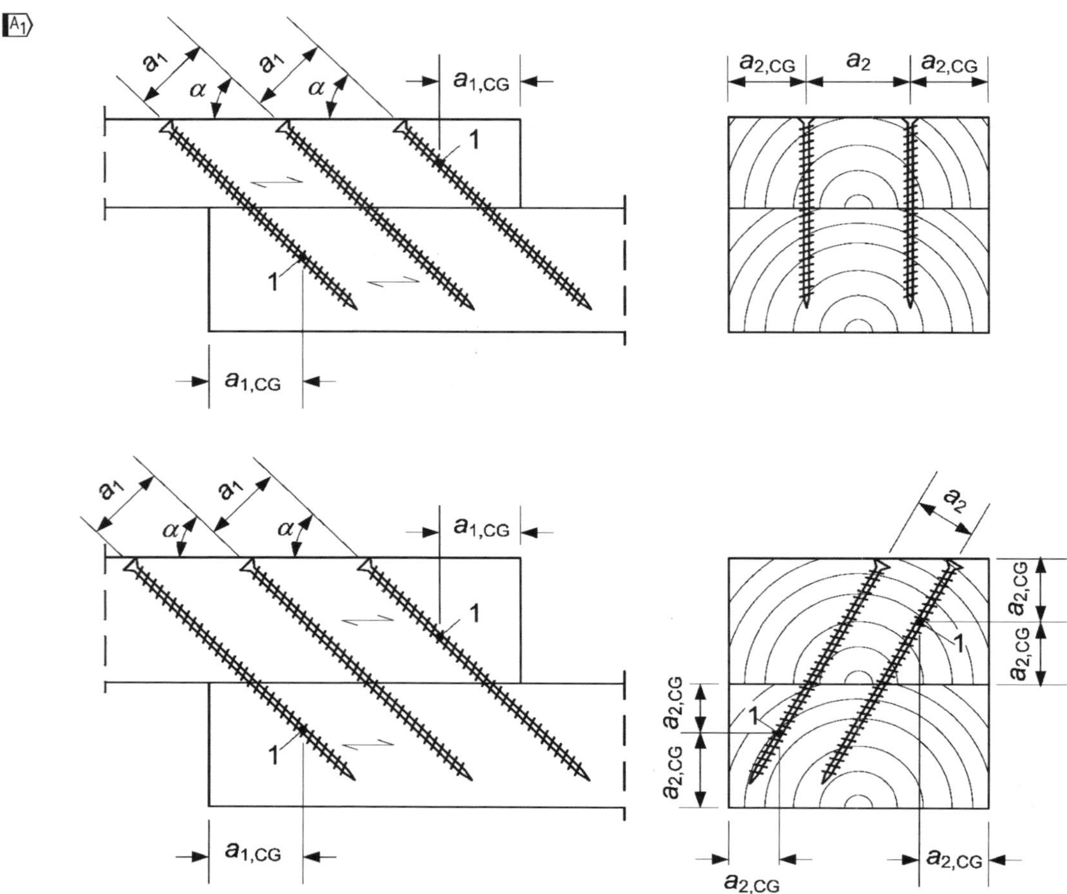

Key: 1 Centre of gravity of the threaded part of the screw in the member

Figure 8.11.a — Spacings and end and edge distances

(3) The minimum point side penetration length of the threaded part should be $6d$.

(4) For connections with screws in accordance with EN 14592 with

- $6 \text{ mm} \leq d \leq 12 \text{ mm}$
- $0{,}6 \leq d_1/d \leq 0{,}75$

where

d is the outer thread diameter;

d_1 is the inner thread diameter

the characteristic withdrawal capacity should be taken as:

$$F_{ax,k,Rk} = \frac{n_{ef} f_{ax,k} d \ell_{ef} k_d}{1{,}2\cos^2\alpha + \sin^2\alpha} \quad (8.38)$$

where:

$$f_{ax,k} = 0{,}52\, d^{-0,5} \ell_{ef}^{-0,1} \rho_k^{0,8} \quad (8.39)$$

$$k_d = \min\begin{cases} \dfrac{d}{8} \\ 1 \end{cases} \quad (8.40)$$

A1) $F_{ax,\alpha,Rk}$ is the characteristic withdrawal capacity of the connection at an angle α to the grain, in N;
$f_{ax,k}$ is the characteristic withdrawal strength perpendicular to the grain, in N/mm^2;
n_{ef} is the effective number of screws, see 8.7.2(8);
ℓ_{ef} is the penetration length of the threaded part, in mm;
ρ_k is the characteristic density, in kg/m^3;
α is the angle between the screw axis and the grain direction, with $\alpha \geq 30°$.

NOTE Failure modes in the steel or in the timber around the screw are brittle, i.e. with small ultimate deformation and therefore have a limited possibility for stress redistribution.

(5) Where the requirements with respect to the outer and inner thread diameter given in (4) are not satisfied, the characteristic withdrawal capacity, $F_{ax,\alpha,Rk}$, should be taken as:

$$F_{ax,\alpha,Rk} = \frac{n_{ef} f_{ax,k} d \ell_{ef}}{1,2\cos^2\alpha + \sin^2\alpha}\left(\frac{\rho_k}{\rho_a}\right)^{0,8} \quad (8.40a)$$

where

$f_{ax,k}$ is the characteristic withdrawal parameter perpendicular to the grain determined in accordance with EN 14592 for the associated density ρ_a;

ρ_a is the associated density for $f_{ax,k}$, in kg/m^3

and the other symbols are explained in (4).

(6) The characteristic pull-through resistance of connections with axially loaded screws should be taken as:

$$F_{ax,\alpha,Rk} = n_{ef} f_{head,k} d_h^2 \left(\frac{\rho_k}{\rho_a}\right)^{0,8} \quad (8.40b)$$

where:

$F_{ax,\alpha,Rk}$ is the characteristic pull-through capacity of the connection at an angle α to the grain in N, with $\alpha \geq 30°$;

$f_{head,k}$ is the characteristic pull-through parameter of the screw determined in accordance with EN 14592 for the associated density ρ_a;

d_h is the diameter of the screw head in mm

and the other symbols are explained in (4).

(7) The characteristic tensile resistance of the connection (head tear-off or tensile capacity of shank), $F_{t,Rk}$, should be taken as:

$$F_{t,Rk} = n_{ef} f_{tens,k} \quad (8.40c)$$

where

$f_{tens,k}$ is the characteristic tensile capacity of the screw determined in accordance with EN 14592;

n_{ef} is the effective number of screws, see 8.7.2(8).

(8) For a connection with a group of screws loaded by a force component parallel to the shank, the effective number of screws is given by:

$$n_{ef} = n^{0,9} \quad (8.41)$$

where

n_{ef} is the effective number of screws;

n is the number of screws acting together in a connection. (A1

8.9 Split ring and shear plate connectors

Various forms of ring and shear-plate connectors exist. The load-carrying behaviour of connections with ring, or shear-plate connectors, is based in part on the theory of dowel type fasteners. The possible failure modes for different load-grain angles and their effect on the design values of the connection strength are taken into account. Special attention is required to the spacing, end and edge distances of the connectors in a connection.

Ring and shear-plate connectors are used in laterally loaded timber-to-timber and steel-to-timber joints as well as for timber-to-timber joints. Shear-plate connectors are normally installed before the assembly of the structure and the joints are demountable (see Figure D).

Ring and shear plate connectors are available in a variety of shapes and sizes, with diameters ranging from 60 mm to 260 mm. They are always circular because they are placed into pre-cut grooves produced by rotary cutters and are made from aluminium cast alloy, steel or cast iron. Those connectors commonly used in Europe are specified in EN 912 "Timber fasteners-Specifications for connectors for timber". In EN 912 ring connectors are denoted as Type A whereas shear-plate connectors are listed as Type B.

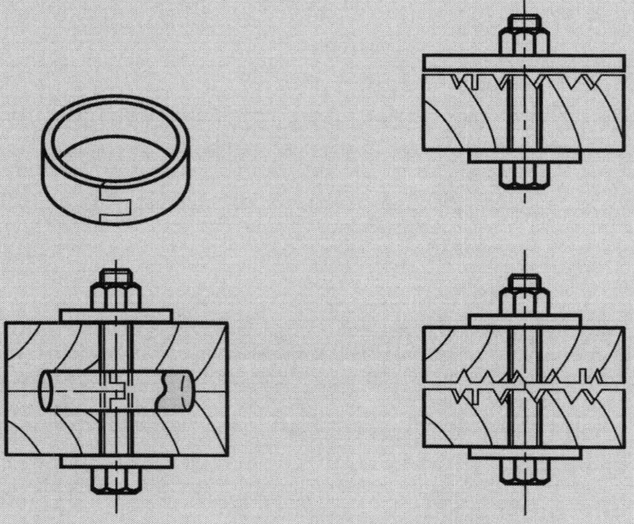

Figure D — Ring connection (left) and shear-plate connection (right)

(1) For connections made with ring connectors of type A or shear plate connectors of type B according to EN 912 and EN 14545, and with a diameter not bigger than 200 mm, the characteristic load-carrying capacity parallel to grain, $F_{v,0,Rk}$ per connector and per shear plane should be taken as:

$$F_{v,0,Rk} = \min \begin{cases} k_1\, k_2\, k_3\, k_4 \left(35\, d_c^{1,5}\right) & \text{(a)} \\ k_1\, k_3\, h_e \left(31,5\, d_c\right) & \text{(b)} \end{cases} \qquad (8.61)$$

where:

$F_{v,0,Rk}$ is the characteristic load-carrying capacity parallel to the grain, in N;
d_c is the connector diameter, in mm;
h_e is the embedment depth, in mm;
k_i are modification factors, with i = 1 to 4, defined below.

(2) The minimum thickness of the outer timber members should be $2,25h_e$, and of the inner timber member should be $3,75h_e$, where h_e is the embedment depth, see Figure 8.12.

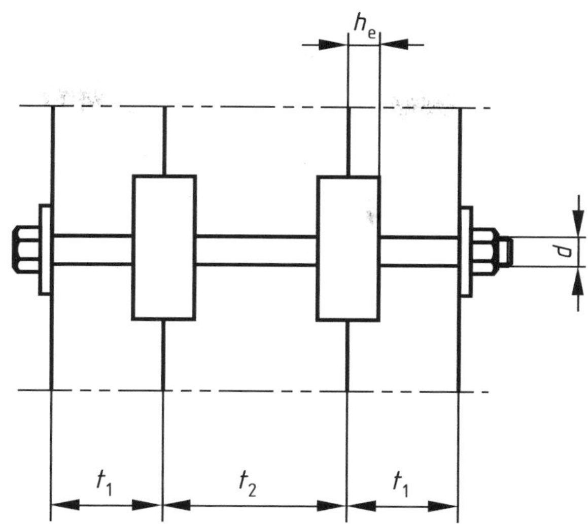

Figure 8.12 — Dimensions for connections with split ring and shear plate connectors

(3) The factor k_1 should be taken as:

$$k_1 = \min \begin{cases} 1 \\ \dfrac{t_1}{3h_e} \\ \dfrac{t_2}{5h_e} \end{cases} \tag{8.62}$$

(4) The factor k_2 applies to a loaded end ($-30° \leq \alpha \leq 30°$) and should be taken as:

$$k_2 = \min \begin{cases} k_a \\ \dfrac{a_{3,t}}{2d_c} \end{cases} \tag{8.63}$$

where:

$$k_a = \begin{cases} 1,25 & \text{for connections with one connector per shear plane} \\ 1,0 & \text{for connections with more than one connector per shear plane} \end{cases} \tag{8.64}$$

$a_{3,t}$ is given in Table 8.7.

For other values of α, $k_2 = 1,0$.

(5) The factor k_3 should be taken as:

$$k_3 = \min \begin{cases} 1,75 \\ \dfrac{\rho_k}{350} \end{cases} \tag{8.65}$$

where ρ_k is the characteristic density of the timber, in kg/m^3.

(6) The factor k_4, which depends on the materials connected, should be taken as:

$$k_4 = \begin{cases} 1,0 & \text{for timber-to-timber connections} \\ 1,1 & \text{for steel-to-timber connections} \end{cases} \tag{8.66}$$

(7) For connections with one connector per shear plane loaded in an unloaded end situation ($150° \leq \alpha \leq 210°$), the condition (a) in expression (8.61) should be disregarded.

(8) For a force at an angle α to the grain, the characteristic load-carrying capacity, $F_{\alpha,Rk}$ per connector per shear plane should be calculated using the following expression:

$$F_{v,\alpha,Rk} = \frac{F_{v,0,Rk}}{k_{90}\sin^2\alpha + \cos^2\alpha} \qquad (8.67)$$

with:

$$k_{90} = 1,3 + 0,001d_c \qquad (8.68)$$

where:

$F_{v,0,Rk}$ is the characteristic load-carrying capacity of the connector for a force parallel to grain according to expression (8.61);

d_c is the connector diameter, in mm.

(9) Minimum spacing and edge and end distances are given in Table 8.7, with the symbols illustrated in Figure 8.7.

Table 8.7 — Minimum spacings and edge and end distances for ring and shear plate connectors

Spacing and end/edge distances (see Figure 8.7)	Angle to grain	Minimum spacings or edge/end distances
a_1 (parallel to grain)	$0° \le \alpha \le 360°$	$(1,2 + 0,8\lvert\cos\alpha\rvert)\ d_c$
a_2 (perpendicular to grain)	$0° \le \alpha \le 360°$	$1,2d_c$
$a_{3,t}$ (loaded end)	$-90° \le \alpha \le 90°$	$1,5d_c$
$a_{3,c}$ (unloaded end)	$90° \le \alpha < 150°$ $150° \le \alpha < 210°$ $210° \le \alpha \le 270°$	$(0,4 + 1,6\lvert\sin\alpha\rvert)\ d_c$ $1,2d_c$ $(0,4 + 1,6\lvert\sin\alpha\rvert)\ d_c$
$a_{4,t}$ (loaded edge)	$0° \le \alpha \le 180°$	$(0,6 + 0,2\lvert\sin\alpha\rvert)\ d_c$
$a_{4,c}$ (unloaded edge)	$180° \le \alpha \le 360°$	$0,6d_c$

(10) When the connectors are staggered (see Figure 8.13), the minimum spacings parallel and perpendicular to the grain should comply with the following expression:

$$(k_{a1})^2 + (k_{a2})^2 \ge 1 \quad \text{with} \quad \begin{cases} 0 \le k_{a1} \le 1 \\ 0 \le k_{a2} \le 1 \end{cases} \qquad (8.69)$$

where:

k_{a1} is a reduction factor for the minimum distance parallel to the grain;

k_{a2} is a reduction factor for the minimum distance perpendicular to the grain.

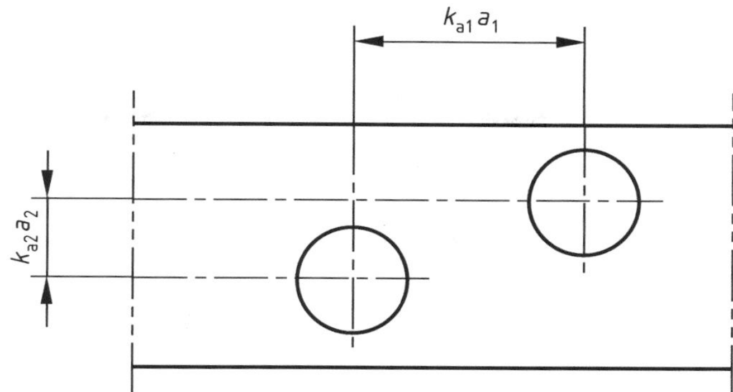

Figure 8.13 — Reduced distances for connectors

(11) The spacing parallel to grain, $k_{a1}\, a_1$ may further be reduced by multiplication by a factor $k_{s,red}$, with $0{,}5 \leq k_{s,red} \leq 1{,}0$, provided that the load-carrying capacity is multiplied by a factor

$$k_{R,\,red} = 0{,}2 + 0{,}8\, k_{s,\,red} \tag{8.70}$$

(12) For a row of connectors parallel to the grain, the load-carrying capacity in that direction should be calculated using the effective number of connectors n_{ef} where:

$$n_{ef} = 2 + \left(1 - \frac{n}{20}\right)(n - 2) \tag{8.71}$$

where:

n_{ef} is the effective number of connectors;
n is the number of connectors in a line parallel to grain.

(13) Connectors should be considered as positioned parallel to the grain where $k_{a2}\, a_2 < 0{,}5\, k_{a1}\, a_1$.

Punched metal plate fasteners

An introduction to connections made with punched metal plate fasteners is found in STEP 1, Lecture C11 [1]. These devices form the basis of sophisticated proprietary pre-fabricated component manufacturing systems, entailing specialist computer-aided design and manufact-uring. Sufficient understanding of these structures is not possible through study of the code alone, hence it was decided to omit these from this guide. Those wishing to follow the subject, as a special topic, will find copious information in the Reference indicated, in the standards referenced by the full code, and through searching appropriate web sites.

Toothed-plate connector joints

There are various forms of toothed timber connectors. The load bearing behaviour of connections with these is broadly based on the methods employed for the dowel type fasteners. The failure modes and their impact on the design values of the connection strength are dependent on careful attention to the required spacing, end and edge distance of the connectors.

Toothed plate connectors are used in laterally loaded timber-to-timber and steel-to-timber joints, generally in combination with bolts. While ring and shear-plate connectors are placed into pre-cut grooves, toothed plate connectors are pressed into the timber members to be connected. Double-sided toothed plate connectors are used in timber-to-timber joints; single-sided connectors may also be used if the connectors are installed before the assembly of the structure or if the joints should be demountable (see Figure E). Single-sided connectors are also used for steel-to-timber joints. Because of the need to press the teeth into the timber, toothed-plate connectors can only be used in timber with a characteristic density of not more than 500 kg/m^3.

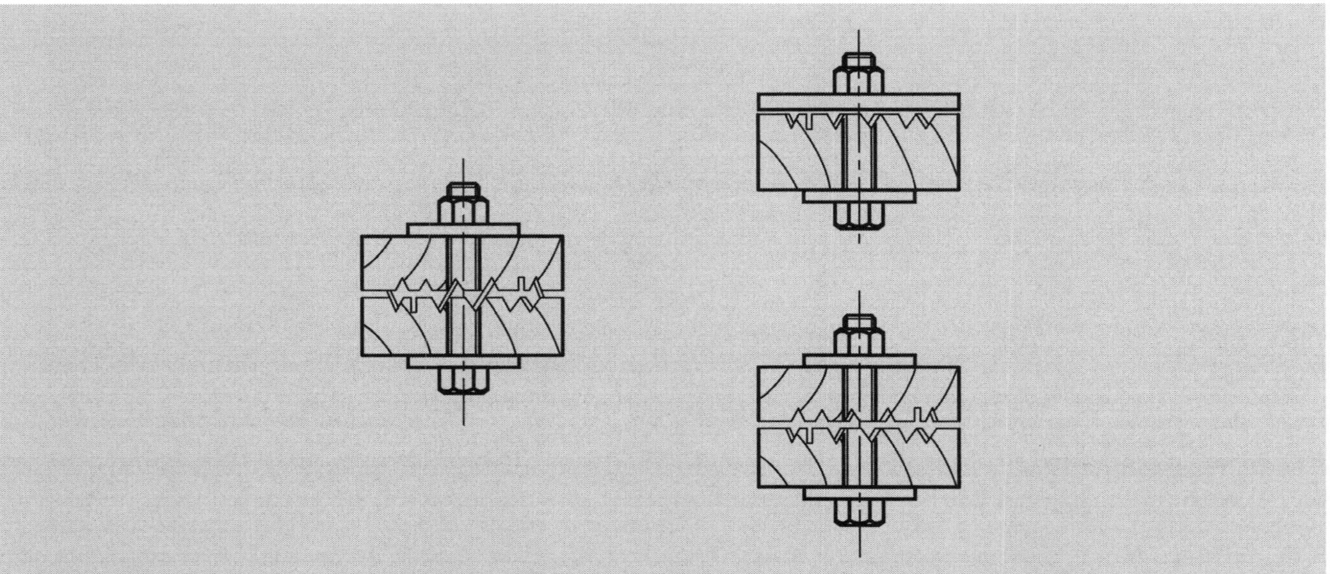

Figure E — Double-sided (left) and single-sided (right) toothed-plate connector

Toothed plate connectors are available in a variety of shapes and sizes, with diameters ranging from 38 mm 165 mm. They are mostly circular but square and oval shapes are also available. The connectors are either made of cold rolled band steel, hot-dipped galvanized mild steel or malleable cast iron.

Section 9 Components and assemblies

9.1 Components

9.1.1 Glued thin-webbed beams

(1) If a linear variation of strain over the depth of the beam is assumed, the axial stresses in the wood-based flanges should satisfy the following expressions:

$$\sigma_{f,c,max,d} \leq f_{m,d} \tag{9.1}$$

$$\sigma_{f,t,max,d} \leq f_{m,d} \tag{9.2}$$

$$\sigma_{f,c,d} \leq k_c\, f_{c,0,d} \tag{9.3}$$

$$\sigma_{f,t,d} \leq f_{t,0,d} \tag{9.4}$$

where:

$\sigma_{f,c,max,d}$ is the extreme fibre flange design compressive stress;
$\sigma_{f,t,max,d}$ is the extreme fibre flange design tensile stress;
$\sigma_{f,c,d}$ is the mean flange design compressive stress;
$\sigma_{f,t,d}$ is the mean flange design tensile stress;
k_c is a factor which takes into account lateral instability.

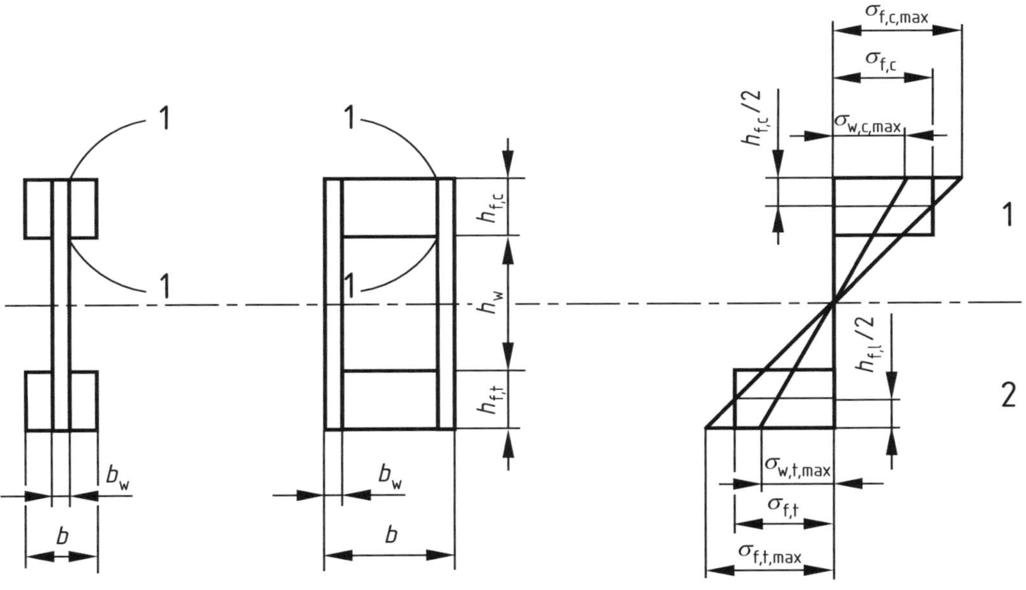

Key
1 Compression
2 Tension

Figure 9.1 — Thin-webbed beams

(3) The factor k_c may be determined (conservatively, especially for box beams) according to 6.3.2 with

$$\lambda_z = \sqrt{12}\left(\frac{l_c}{b}\right) \tag{9.5}$$

where:

l_c is the distance between the sections where lateral deflection of the compressive flange is prevented;
b is given in Figure 9.1.

If a special investigation is made with respect to the lateral instability of the beam as a whole, it may be assumed that $k_c = 1,0$.

(4) The axial stresses in the webs should satisfy the following expressions:

$$\sigma_{w,c,d} \leq f_{c,w,d} \tag{9.6}$$

$$\sigma_{w,t,d} \leq f_{t,w,d} \tag{9.7}$$

where:

$\sigma_{w,c,d}$ and $\sigma_{w,t,d}$ are the design compressive and tensile stresses in the webs;
$f_{c,w,d}$ and $f_{t,w,d}$ are the design compressive and tensile bending strengths of the webs.

(5) Unless other values are given, the design in-plane bending strength of the webs should be taken as the design tensile or compressive strength.

(6)P It shall be verified that any glued splices have sufficient strength.

(7) Unless a detailed buckling analysis is made it should be verified that:

$$h_w \leq 70 b_w \tag{9.8}$$

and:

$$F_{v,w,Ed} \leq \begin{cases} b_w h_w \left(1 + \dfrac{0,5(h_{f,t} + h_{f,c})}{h_w}\right) f_{v,0,d} & \text{for} \quad h_w \leq 35 b_w \\ 35 b_w^2 \left(1 + \dfrac{0,5(h_{f,t} + h_{f,c})}{h_w}\right) f_{v,0,d} & \text{for} \quad 35 b_w \leq h_w \leq 70 b_w \end{cases} \tag{9.9}$$

where:

$F_{v,w,Ed}$ is the design shear force acting on each web;
h_w is the clear distance between flanges;
$h_{f,c}$ is the compressive flange depth;
$h_{f,t}$ is the tensile flange depth;
b_w is the width of each web;
$f_{v,0,d}$ is the design panel shear strength.

(8) For webs of wood-based panels, it should, for sections 1-1 in Figure 9.1, be verified that:

$$\tau_{mean,d} \leq \begin{cases} f_{v,90,d} & \text{for } h_f \leq 4\, b_{ef} \\ f_{v,90,d} \left(\dfrac{4 b_{ef}}{h_f}\right)^{0,8} & \text{for } h_f > 4\, b_{ef} \end{cases} \tag{9.10}$$

where:

$\tau_{mean,d}$ is the design shear stress at the sections 1-1, assuming a uniform stress distribution;
$f_{v,90,d}$ is the design planar (rolling) shear strength of the web;
h_f is either $h_{f,c}$ or $h_{f,t}$.

$$b_{ef} = \begin{cases} b_w & \text{for boxed beams} \\ b_w / 2 & \text{for I-beams} \end{cases} \tag{9.11}$$

9.2 Assemblies

9.2.1 Trusses

(1) For trusses which are loaded predominantly at the nodes, the sum of the combined bending and axial compressive stress ratios given in expressions (6.19) and (6.20) should be limited to 0,9.

(2) For members in compression, the effective column length for in-plane strength verification should generally be taken as the distance between two adjacent points of contraflexure.

(6)P A check shall be made that the lateral (out-of-plane) stability of the truss members is adequate.

(7)P The joints shall be capable of transferring the forces which may occur during handling and erection.

(8) All joints should be capable of transferring a force $F_{r,d}$ acting in any direction within the plane of the truss. $F_{r,d}$ should be assumed to be of short-term duration, acting on timber in service class 2, with the value:

$$F_{r,d} = 1,0 + 0,1L \tag{9.18}$$

where:

$F_{r,d}$ is in kN;
L is the overall length of the truss, in m.

9.2.5 Bracing

9.2.5.1 General

(1)P Structures which are not otherwise adequately stiff shall be braced to prevent instability or excessive deflection.

(2)P The stress caused by geometrical and structural imperfections, and by induced deflections (including the contribution of any joint slip) shall be taken into account.

(3)P The bracing forces shall be determined on the basis of the most unfavourable combination of structural imperfections and induced deflections.

9.2.5.2 Single members in compression

(1) For single elements in compression, requiring lateral support at intervals a (see Figure 9.9), the initial deviations from straightness between supports should be within $a/500$ for glued laminated or LVL members, and $a/300$ for other members.

(2) Each intermediate support should have a minimum spring stiffness C

$$C = k_s \frac{N_d}{a} \tag{9.34}$$

where:

k_s is a modification factor;
N_d is the mean design compressive force in the element;
a is the bay length (see Figure 9.9).

NOTE For k_s, see note in 9.2.5.3(1)

(3) The design stabilizing force F_d at each support should be taken as:

$$F_d = \begin{cases} \dfrac{N_d}{k_{f,1}} & \text{for solid timber} \\ \dfrac{N_d}{k_{f,2}} & \text{for glued laminated timber and LVL} \end{cases} \qquad (9.35)$$

where $k_{f,1}$ and $k_{f,2}$ are modification factors.

NOTE For $k_{f,1}$ and $k_{f,2}$, see note in 9.2.5.3(1)

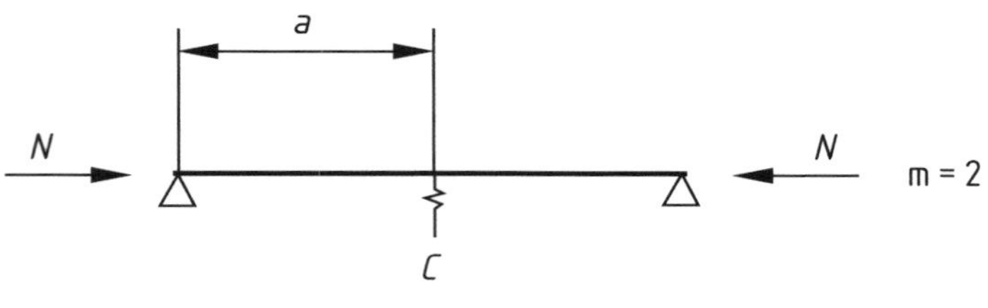

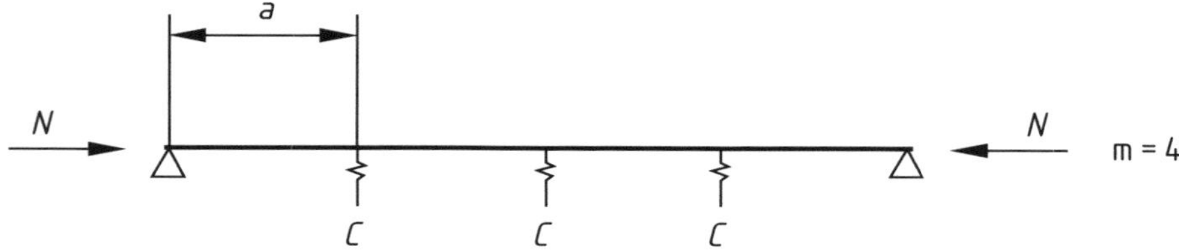

Figure 9.9 — Examples of single members in compression braced by lateral supports

(4) The design stabilizing force F_d for the compressive edge of a rectangular beam should be determined in accordance with 9.2.5.2(3)

where:

$$N_d = (1 - k_{crit}) \frac{M_d}{h} \qquad (9.36)$$

The value of k_{crit} should be determined from 6.3.3(4) for the unbraced beam, and M_d is the maximum design moment acting on the beam of depth h.

9.2.5.3 Bracing of beam or truss systems

(1) For a series of n parallel members which require lateral supports at intermediate nodes A,B, etc. (see Figure 9.10) a bracing system should be provided, which, in addition to the effects of external horizontal load (e.g. wind), should be capable of resisting an internal stability load per unit length q, as follows:

$$q_d = k_l \frac{nN_d}{k_{f,3}\, l} \qquad (9.37)$$

where:

$$k_l = \min \begin{cases} 1 \\ \sqrt{\dfrac{15}{l}} \end{cases} \qquad (9.38)$$

N_d is the mean design compressive force in the member;
l is the overall span of the stabilizing system, in m;
$k_{f,3}$ is a modification factor.

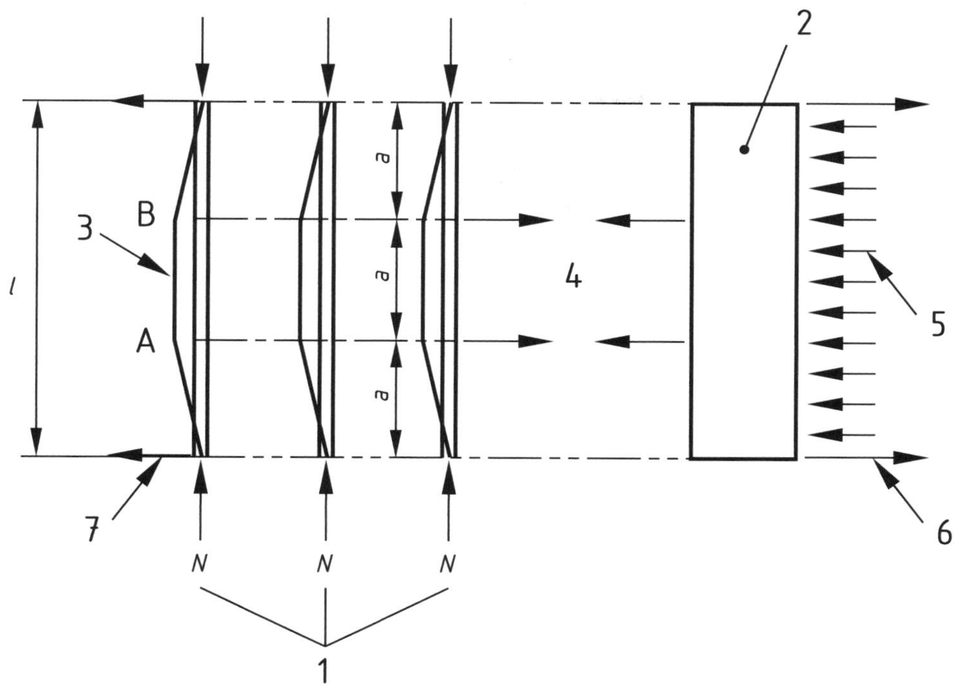

Key
1 *n* members of truss system
2 Bracing
3 Deflection of truss system due to imperfections and second order effects
4 Stabilizing forces
5 External load on bracing
6 Reaction forces of bracing due to external loads
7 Reaction forces of truss system due to stabilizing forces

Figure 9.10 — Beam or truss system requiring lateral supports

NOTE The values of the modification factors k_s, $k_{f,1}$, $k_{f,2}$ and $k_{f,3}$ depend on influences such as workmanship, span etc. Ranges of values are given in Table 9.2 where the recommended values are underlined. The National choice may be given in the National Annex.

EN 1995-1-1, Table 9.2 is implemented nationally in the UK by using Table NA.7.

Table NA.7 — Values of modification factors for bracing systems

Modification factor	Value
k_s	4
$k_{f,1}$	60
$k_{f,2}$	100
$k_{f,3}$	50 (members spaced at ≤ 600 mm) 40 (members spaced at > 600 mm)

(2) The horizontal deflection of the bracing system due to force q_d and any other external load (e.g. wind), should not exceed l/500.

Section 10 Structural detailing and control

10.1 General

(1)P The provisions given in this section are prerequisite requirements for the design rules given in this standard to apply.

10.2 Materials

(1) The deviation from straightness measured midway between the supports should, for columns and beams where lateral instability can occur, or members in frames, be limited to 1/500 times the length of glued laminated timber or LVL members and to 1/300 times the length of solid timber. The limitations on bow in most strength grading rules are inadequate for the selection of material for these members and particular attention should therefore be paid to their straightness.

(2) Timber and wood-based components and structural elements should not be unnecessarily exposed to climatic conditions more severe than those expected in the finished structure.

(3) Before being used in construction, timber should be dried as near as practicable to the moisture content appropriate to its climatic condition in the completed structure. If the effects of any shrinkage are not considered important, or if parts that are unacceptably damaged are replaced, higher moisture contents may be accepted during erection provided that it is ensured that the timber can dry to the desired moisture content.

10.3 Glued joints

(1) Where bond strength is a requirement for ultimate limit state design, the manufacture of glued joints should be subject to quality control, to ensure that the reliability and quality of the joint is in accordance with the technical specification.

(2) The adhesive manufacturer's recommendations with respect to mixing, environmental conditions for application and curing, moisture content of members and all factors relevant to the proper use of the adhesive should be followed.

(3) For adhesives which require a conditioning period after initial set, before attaining full strength, the application of load to the joint should be restricted for the necessary time.

10.4 Connections with mechanical fasteners

10.4.1 General

(1)P Wane, splits, knots or other defects shall be limited in the region of the connection such that the load-carrying capacity of the connection is not reduced.

10.4.2 Nails

(1) Unless otherwise specified, nails should be driven in at right angles to the grain and to such depth that the surfaces of the nail heads are flush with the timber surface.

(2) Unless otherwise specified, slant nailing should be carried out in accordance with Figure 8.8(b).

(3) The diameter of pre-drilled holes should not exceed 0,8d, where d is the nail diameter.

10.4.3 Bolts and washers

(1) Bolt holes in timber should have a diameter not more than 1 mm larger than the bolt. Bolt holes in steel plates should have a diameter not more than 2 mm or 0,1d (whichever is the greater) larger than the bolt diameter d.

(2) Washers with a side length or a diameter of at least $3d$ and a thickness of at least $0,3d$ should be used under the head and nut. Washers should have a full bearing area.

(3) Bolts and lag screws should be tightened so that the members fit closely, and they should be re-tightened if necessary when the timber has reached equilibrium moisture content to ensure that the load-carrying capacity and stiffness of the structure is maintained.

(4) The minimum diameter requirements given in Table 10.1 apply to bolts used with timber connectors, where:

d_c is the connector diameter, in mm;
d is the bolt diameter, in mm;
d_1 is the diameter of the centre hole of the connector.

Table 10.1 — Requirements for diameters of bolts used with timber connectors

Type of connector EN 912	d_c	d **minimum**	d **maximum**
	mm	mm	mm
A1 - A6	≤ 130	12	24
A1, A4, A6	> 130	$0,1d_c$	24
B		$d_1 - 1$	d_1

10.5 Assembly

(1) The structure should be assembled in such a way that over-stressing of its members or connections is avoided. Members which are warped, split or badly fitting at the joints should be replaced.

10.6 Transportation and erection

(1) The over-stressing of members during storage, transportation or erection should be avoided. If the structure is loaded or supported in a different manner than in the finished building the temporary condition should be considered as a relevant load case, including any possible dynamic actions. In the case of structural framework, e.g. framed arches, portal frames, special care should be taken to avoid distortion during hoisting from the horizontal to the vertical position.

Annex D (Informative): Bibliography

EN 338 Structural timber – Strength classes
EN 1194 Glued laminated timber – Strength classes and determination of characteristic values

Bibliography

Standards publications

For dated references, only the edition cited applies. For undated references, the latest edition of the referenced document (including any amendments) applies.

A1 PD 6693-1-1, *Guidance to Eurocode 5: Design of timber structures – Part 1: General – Common rules and rules for buildings*. (In preparation.) A1

BS EN 1990:2002, *Eurocode – Basis of structural design*.

BS EN 1991 (all parts), *Eurocode 1 – Actions on structures*.

Useful references

[1] Blass HJ et al, editors. Timber engineering STEP 1. Netherlands: Centrum Hout; 1995.
[2] Blass HJ et al, editors. Timber engineering STEP 2. Netherlands: Centrum Hout; 1995.
[3] IStructE. Guide to structural use of adhesives. The Institute of Structural Engineers. England: London; 1999.
[4] Glued in rods for timber structures. Sweden: SP Swedish National Testing and Research Institute; 2002.
[5] Moisture in timber. Wood information sheet 4-14. England: TRADA Technology Ltd; 1999.
[6] Ridout, B. Timber decay in buildings - The conservation approach to treatment. England: Spon Press; 1999.
[7] Blass, HJ. Strength model for glulam columns. CIB W18/IUFRO S 5.02 (Paper 19-2-2). 1986; Florence, Italy.
[8] Timoshenko S, Gere JM. Theory of elastic stability. 2nd ed. New York, US: McGraw-Hill Book Co. Inc; 1961.
[9] Hooley RF, Madsen B. Lateral stability of glue laminated beams. Journal of the Structural Division, ASCE. 1964;ST3:201-218.
[10] Johansen KW. Theory of timber connections. International Association for Bridge and Structural Engineering. 1949;9:249-262.
[11] CIB. Structural Timber Design Code (Publication 66). International Council for Research and Innovation in Building and Construction; 1983.

Chapter 6 — Extracts from Eurocode 6: Design of masonry structures

The extracts in this chapter are taken from EN 1996-1-1:2005 (incorporating corrigenda February 2006 and July 2009), *Eurocode 6: Design of masonry structures — Part 1-1: Rules for reinforced and unreinforced masonry structures.*

Text altered by CEN corrigendum July 2009 is indicated in the text by AC1 AC1.

The National Annex extracts are taken from NA to BS EN 1996-1-1:2005, *UK National Annex to Eurocode 6: Design of masonry structures - Part 1-1: General rules for reinforced and unreinforced masonry structures*

Eurocode 6 has been developed to enable the designer to use the following types of masonry unit: clay, calcium silicate, aggregate concrete, autoclaved aerated concrete (aac), manufactured stone and natural stone. European standards for these materials are in an advanced state of preparation and are supported by numerous standards for other materials and test methods.

The European Standard EN 1996 comprises the following Parts:
EN 1996-1-1, *General rules for reinforced and unreinforced masonry structures*;
EN 1996-1-2, *Structural fire design*;
EN 1996-2, *Design, selection of materials and execution of masonry*;
EN 1996-3, *Simplified calculation methods.*

Selected extracts from EN 1996-1-1 are included in this guide, but reinforced masonry, prestressed masonry and confined masonry have been omitted.

The full list of contents of EN 1996-1-1 follows, and is given for reference purposes. (Bold items are covered in this chapter.)

8 Detailing
8.1 Masonry details
8.1.1 Masonry materials
8.1.2 Minimum thickness of wall
8.1.3 Minimum area of wall
8.1.4 Bonding of masonry
8.1.5 Mortar joints
8.1.6 Bearings under concentrated loads
8.2 Reinforcement details
8.2.1 General
8.2.2 Cover to reinforcing steel
8.2.3 Minimum area of reinforcement
8.2.4 Size of reinforcing steel
8.2.5 Anchorage and laps
8.2.6 Restraint of compression reinforcing steel
8.2.7 Spacing of reinforcing steel
8.3 Prestressing details
8.4 Confined masonry details
8.5 Connection of walls
8.5.1 Connection of walls to floors and roofs
8.5.2 Connection between walls
8.6 Chases and recesses on walls
8.6.1 General
8.6.2 Vertical chases and recesses
8.6.3 Horizontal and inclined chases
8.7 Damp proof courses
8.8 Thermal and long term movement
9 Execution
9.1 General
9.2 Design of structural members
9.3 Loading of masonry
Annex A (informative)
Consideration of partial factors relating to execution
Annex B (informative)
Method for calculating the eccentricity of a stability core
Annex C (informative)
A simplified method for calculating the out-of-plane eccentricity of loading on walls
Annex D (informative)
Determination of ρ_3 and ρ_4
Annex E (informative) Bending moment coefficients, α_2, in single leaf laterally loaded wall panels of thickness less than or equal to 250 mm
Annex F (informative) Limiting height and length to thickness ratios for walls under the serviceability limit state
Annex G (informative) Reduction factor for slenderness and eccentricity
Annex H (informative) Enhancement factor as given in 6.1.3
Annex I (informative) Adjustment of lateral load for walls supported on three or four edges subjected to out-of-plane horizontal loading and vertical loading
Annex J (informative) Reinforced masonry members subjected to shear loading: enhancement of f_{vd}

1. General

The scope of EN 1996-1-1 is not given in full.

1.1 Scope

1.1.1 Scope of Eurocode 6

(1)P Eurocode 6 applies to the design of buildings and civil engineering works, or parts thereof, in unreinforced, reinforced, prestressed and confined masonry.

(2)P Eurocode 6 deals only with the requirements for resistance, serviceability and durability of structures. Other requirements, for example, concerning thermal or sound insulation, are not considered.

(3)P Execution is covered to the extent that is necessary to indicate the quality of the construction materials and products that should be used and the standard of workmanship on site needed to comply with the assumptions made in the design rules.

(4)P Eurocode 6 does not cover the special requirements of seismic design. Provisions related to such requirements are given in Eurocode 8 "Design of structures in seismic regions" which complements, and is consistent with, Eurocode 6.

(5)P Numerical values of the actions on buildings and civil engineering works to be taken into account in the design are not given in Eurocode 6. They are provided in Eurocode 1.

EN 1996-1-1 describes the principles and requirements for safety, serviceability and durability of masonry structures. It is based on the limit state concept used in conjunction with a partial factor method. For the design of new structures, EN 1996-1-1 is intended to be used, for direct application, together with ENs 1990, 1991, 1992, 1993, 1994, 1995, 1997, 1998 and 1999.

EN 1996-1-1 is intended for use by:

- committees drafting standards for structural design and related product, testing and execution standards;
- clients (e. g. for the formulation of their specific requirements on reliability levels and durability);
- designers and contractors; relevant authorities.

1.1.2 Scope of Part 1-1 of Eurocode 6

(1)P The basis for the design of buildings and civil engineering works in masonry is given in this Part 1-1 of Eurocode 6, which deals with unreinforced masonry and reinforced masonry where the reinforcement is added to provide ductility, strength or improve serviceability. The principles of the design of prestressed masonry and confined masonry are given, but application rules are not provided. This Part is not valid for masonry with a plan area of less than 0,04 m^2.

(2) For those types of structures not covered entirely, for new structural uses for established materials, for new materials, or where actions and other influences outside normal experience have to be resisted, the principles and application rules given in this EN may be applicable, but may need to be supplemented.

(3) Part 1-1 gives detailed rules which are mainly applicable to ordinary buildings. The applicability of these rules may be limited, for practical reasons or due to simplifications; any limits of applicability are given in the text where necessary.

(4)P The following subjects are dealt with in Part 1-1:

- section 1 : General
- section 2 : Basis of design
- section 3 : Materials
- section 4 : Durability
- section 5 : Structural analysis
- section 6 : Ultimate Limit States
- section 7 : Serviceability Limit States
- section 8 : Detailing
- section 9 : Execution.

(5)P Part 1-1 does not cover:

- resistance to fire (which is dealt with in EN 1996-1-2);
- particular aspects of special types of building (for example, dynamic effects on tall buildings);
- particular aspects of special types of civil engineering works (such as masonry bridges, dams, chimneys or liquid-retaining structures);
- particular aspects of special types of structures (such as arches or domes);
- masonry where gypsum, with or without cement, mortars are used;
- masonry where the units are not laid in a regular pattern of courses (rubble masonry);
- masonry reinforced with other materials than steel.

Scope of Part 1-2 of Eurocode 6

This Part deals with the design of masonry structures for the accidental situation of fire exposure and identifies differences from, or supplements to, normal temperature design. Only passive methods of fire protection are considered – active methods are not covered. It addresses the need to avoid premature collapse of the structure and to limit the spread of fire. It does not cover the use of reinforced masonry.

Scope of Part 2 of Eurocode 6

This Part gives the basic rules for the selection and execution of masonry to enable it to comply with the design assumptions of the other parts of EN 1996. It includes guidance on factors affecting performance and durability, storage and use of materials, site erection and protection and the assessment of the appearance of masonry.

Scope of Part 3 of Eurocode 6

This Part provides simplified calculation methods to facilitate the design of a range of common wall types under certain conditions of use. The rules are consistent with Part 1-1 but are more conservative in respect of the conditions and limitations of their use. The simplified rules are not applicable to design for accidental situations which should be designed in accordance with sub-clause 5.2 of Part 1-1.

1.5 Terms and definitions

1.5.1 General

(1) The terms and definitions given in EN 1990:2002, clause 1.5, apply to this EN 1996-1-1.

(2) The terms used in this EN 1996-1-1 are given the meanings contained in clauses 1.5.2 to 1.5.11, inclusive.

1.5.2 Terms relating to masonry

1.5.2.1
masonry
an assemblage of masonry units laid in a specified pattern and joined together with mortar

1.5.2.2
unreinforced masonry
masonry not containing sufficient reinforcement so as to be considered as reinforced masonry

1.5.2.3
reinforced masonry
masonry in which bars or mesh are embedded in mortar or concrete so that all the materials act together in resisting action effects

1.5.2.4
prestressed masonry
masonry in which internal compressive stresses have been intentionally induced by tensioned reinforcement

1.5.2.5
confined masonry
masonry provided with reinforced concrete or reinforced masonry confining elements in the vertical and horizontal direction

1.5.2.6
masonry bond
disposition of units in masonry in a regular pattern to achieve common action

1.5.3 Terms relating to strength of masonry

1.5.3.1
characteristic strength of masonry
value of the strength of masonry having a prescribed probability of 5 % of not being attained in a hypothetically unlimited test series. This value generally corresponds to a specified fractile of the assumed statistical distribution of the particular property of the material or product. A nominal value is used as the characteristic value in some circumstances

1.5.3.2
compressive strength of masonry
the strength of masonry in compression without the effects of platen restraint, slenderness or eccentricity of loading

1.5.3.3
shear strength of masonry
[AC1) the strength of masonry in shear subjected to shear forces (AC1]

1.5.3.4
flexural strength of masonry
the strength of masonry in bending

1.5.3.5
anchorage bond strength
the bond strength, per unit surface area, between reinforcement and concrete or mortar, when the reinforcement is subjected to tensile or compressive forces

1.5.3.6
adhesion
the effect of mortar developing a tensile or shear resistance at the contact surface of masonry units

1.5.4 Terms relating to masonry units

1.5.4.1
masonry unit
a preformed component, intended for use in masonry construction

1.5.4.2
groups 1, 2, 3 and 4 masonry units
group designations for masonry units, according to the percentage size and orientation of holes in the units when laid

1.5.4.3
bed face
the top or bottom surface of a masonry unit when laid as intended

1.5.4.4
frog
a depression, formed during manufacture, in one or both bed faces of a masonry unit

1.5.4.5
hole
a formed void which may or may not pass completely through a masonry unit

1.5.4.6
griphole
a formed void in a masonry unit to enable it to be more readily grasped and lifted with one or both hands or by machine

1.5.4.7
web
the solid material between the holes in a masonry unit

1.5.4.8
shell
the peripheral material between a hole and the face of a masonry unit

1.5.4.9
gross area
the area of a cross-section through the unit without reduction for the area of holes, voids and re-entrants

1.5.4.10
compressive strength of masonry units
the mean compressive strength of a specified number of masonry units (see EN 771-1 to EN 771-6)

1.5.4.11
normalized compressive strength of masonry units
the compressive strength of masonry units converted to the air dried compressive strength of an equivalent 100 mm wide x 100 mm high masonry unit (see EN 771-1 to EN 771-6)

1.5.5 Terms relating to mortar

1.5.5.1
masonry mortar
mixture of one or more inorganic binders, aggregates and water, and sometimes additions and/or admixtures, for bedding, jointing and pointing of masonry

1.5.5.2
general purpose masonry mortar
masonry mortar without special characteristics

1.5.5.3
thin layer masonry mortar
designed masonry mortar with a maximum aggregate size less than or equal to a prescribed figure

NOTE See note in 3.6.1.2 (2)

1.5.5.4
lightweight masonry mortar
[AC1) designed masonry mortar with a dry hardened density equal to or below 1300 kg/m^3 according to EN 998-2 (AC1]

1.5.5.5
designed masonry mortar
a mortar whose composition and manufacturing method is chosen in order to achieve specified properties (performance concept)

1.5.5.6
prescribed masonry mortar
mortar made in predetermined proportions, the properties of which are assumed from the stated proportions of the constituents (recipe concept)

1.5.5.7
factory made masonry mortar
mortar batched and mixed in a factory

1.5.5.8
semi-finished factory made masonry mortar
prebatched masonry mortar or a premixed lime and sand masonry mortar

1.5.5.9
prebatched masonry mortar
mortar whose constituents are wholly batched in a factory, supplied to the building site and mixed there according to the manufacturers' specification and conditions

1.5.5.10
premixed lime and sand masonry mortar
mortar whose constituents are wholly batched and mixed in a factory, supplied to the building site, where further constituents specified or provided by the factory are added (e.g. cement) and mixed with the lime and sand

1.5.5.11
site-made mortar
a mortar composed of individual constituents batched and mixed on the building site

1.5.5.12
compressive strength of mortar
the mean compressive strength of a specified number of mortar specimens after curing for 28 days

1.5.6 Terms relating to concrete infill

1.5.6.1
concrete infill
a concrete used to fill pre-formed cavities or voids in masonry

1.5.7 Terms relating to reinforcement

1.5.7.1
reinforcing steel
steel reinforcement for use in masonry

1.5.7.2
bed joint reinforcement
reinforcing steel that is prefabricated for building into a bed joint

1.5.7.3
prestressing steel
steel wires, bars or strands for use in masonry

1.5.8 Terms relating to ancillary components

1.5.8.1
damp proof course
a layer of sheeting, masonry units or other material used in masonry to resist the passage of water

1.5.8.2
wall tie
a device for connecting one leaf of a cavity wall across a cavity to another leaf or to a framed structure or backing wall

1.5.8.3
strap
a device for connecting masonry members to other adjacent components, such as floors and roofs

1.5.9 Terms relating to mortar joints

1.5.9.1
bed joint
a mortar layer between the bed faces of masonry units

1.5.9.2
perpend joint (head joint)
a mortar joint perpendicular to the bed joint and to the face of wall

1.5.9.3
longitudinal joint
a vertical mortar joint within the thickness of a wall, parallel to the face of the wall

1.5.9.4
thin layer joint
a joint made with thin layer mortar

1.5.9.5
jointing
the process of finishing a mortar joint as the work proceeds

1.5.9.6
pointing
the process of filling and finishing mortar joints where the surface of the joint has been raked out or left open for pointing

1.5.10 Terms relating to wall types

1.5.10.1
load-bearing wall
a wall primarily designed to carry an imposed load in addition to its own weight

1.5.10.2
single-leaf wall
a wall without a cavity or continuous vertical joint in its plane

1.5.10.3
cavity wall
a wall consisting of two parallel single-leaf walls, effectively tied together with wall ties or bed joint reinforcement. The space between the leaves is left as a continuous cavity or filled or partially filled with non-loadbearing thermal insulating material

NOTE A wall consisting of two leaves separated by a cavity, where one of the leaves is not contributing to the strength or stiffness of the other (possibly loadbearing) leaf, is to be regarded as a veneer wall.

1.5.10.4
double-leaf wall
a wall consisting of two parallel leaves with the longitudinal joint between filled solidly with mortar and securely tied together with wall ties so as to result in common action under load

1.5.10.5
grouted cavity wall
a wall consisting of two parallel leaves with the cavity filled with concrete or grout and securely tied together with wall ties or bed joint reinforcement so as to result in common action under load

1.5.10.6
faced wall
a wall with facing units bonded to backing units so as to result in common action under load

1.5.10.7
shell bedded wall
a wall in which the masonry units are bedded on two strips of mortar at the outside edges of the bed face of the units

1.5.10.8
veneer wall
a wall used as a facing but not bonded or contributing to the strength of the backing wall or framed structure

1.5.10.9
shear wall
a wall to resist lateral forces in its plane

1.5.10.10
stiffening wall
a wall set perpendicular to another wall to give it support against lateral forces or to resist buckling and so to provide stability to the building

1.5.10.11
non-loadbearing wall
a wall not considered to resist forces such that it can be removed without prejudicing the remaining integrity of the structure

1.5.11 Miscellaneous terms

1.5.11.1
chase
channel formed in masonry

1.5.11.2
recess
indentation formed in the face of a wall

1.5.11.3
grout
a pourable mixture of cement, sand and water for filling small voids or spaces

1.5.11.4
movement joint
a joint permitting free movement in the plane of the wall

1.6 Symbols

(1) Material-independent symbols are given in 1.6 of EN 1990.

(2) Material-dependent symbols used in this EN 1996-1-1 are:

Latin letters

a_1 Distance from the end of a wall to the nearest edge of a loaded area
a_x Distance from the face of a support to the cross-section being considered
A Loaded horizontal gross cross-sectional area of a wall
A_{ef} Effective area of bearing
A_s Cross-sectional area of steel reinforcement
A_{sw} Area of shear reinforcement
b Width of a section
b_c Width of the compression face midway between restraints
b_{ef} Effective width of a flanged member
[AC1⟩ $b_{ef,l}$ Effective width of a L-shaped flanged member
$b_{ef,t}$ Effective width of a T-shaped flanged member ⟨AC1]
c_{nom} Nominal concrete cover
d Effective depth of a beam
d_a Deflection of an arch under the design lateral load
d_c Largest dimension of the cross-section of a core in the direction of bending
e_c Additional eccentricity;
e_{he} Eccentricity at the top or bottom of a wall, resulting from horizontal loads
e_{hm} Eccentricity at the middle of a wall, resulting from horizontal loads
e_i Eccentricity at the top or the bottom of a wall
e_k Eccentricity due to creep
e_m Eccentricity due to loads
e_{mk} Eccentricity at the middle of the wall
E Short term secant modulus of elasticity of masonry
[AC1⟩ E_d Design value of the load applied to a reinforced masonry member ⟨AC1]
$E_{longterm}$ Long term modulus of elasticity of masonry
E_n Modulus of elasticity of member n
f_b Normalised mean compressive strength of a masonry unit
f_{bod} Design anchorage strength of reinforcing steel
f_{bok} Characteristic anchorage strength
f_{ck} Characteristic compressive strength of concrete infill
f_{cvk} Characteristic shear strength of concrete infill
f_d Design compressive strength of masonry in the direction being considered
f_k Characteristic compressive strength of masonry
f_m Compressive strength of masonry mortar
f_{vd} Design shear strength of masonry
f_{vk} Characteristic shear strength of masonry
f_{vko} Characteristic initial shear strength of masonry, under zero compressive stress
f_{vlt} Limit to the value of f_{vk}
f_{xd} Design flexural strength appropriate to the plane of bending
f_{xd1} Design flexural strength of masonry having the plane of failure parallel to the bed joints
$f_{xd1,app}$ Apparent design flexural strength of masonry having the plane of failure parallel to the bed joints
f_{xk1} Characteristic flexural strength of masonry having [AC1⟩ the plane of failure ⟨AC1] parallel to the bed joints
f_{xd2} Design flexural strength of masonry having the plane of failure perpendicular to the bed joints
$f_{xd2,app}$ Apparent design flexural strength of masonry having the plane of failure perpendicular to the bed joints
f_{xk2} Characteristic flexural strength of masonry having [AC1⟩ the plane of failure ⟨AC1] perpendicular to the bed joints
f_{yd} Design strength of reinforcing steel
f_{yk} Characteristic strength of reinforcing steel
F_d Design compressive or tensile resistance of a wall tie

g Total width of mortar strips
G Shear modulus of masonry
h Clear height of a masonry wall
h_i Clear height of masonry wall, i
h_{ef} Effective height of a wall
h_{tot} Total height of a structure from the top of the foundation, or a wall, or a core
h_c Height of a wall to the level of the load
I_j Second moment of area of member, j
k Ratio of the lateral load capacity of a vertically spanning wall to the lateral load capacity of the actual wall area, taking possible edge restraint into account
k_m Ratio of slab stiffness to wall stiffness
k_r Rotational stiffness of a restraint
K Constant used in the calculation of the compressive strength of masonry
l Length of wall (between other walls, between a wall and an opening, or between openings)
l_b Straight anchorage length
l_c Length of the compressed part of a wall
l_{cl} Clear length of an opening
l_{ef} Effective span of a masonry beam
l_{efm} Effective length of a bearing at mid height of a wall
l_r Clear distance between lateral restraints
l_a The length or the height of the wall between supports capable of resisting an arch thrust
M_{ad} Additional design moment
M_d Design bending moment at the bottom of a core
M_{Ed} Design value of the moment applied
M_{Edf} Design value of the moment below a floor
M_{Edu} Design value of the moment above the floor
AC1⟩ M_i End moment at node i ⟨AC1
M_{id} Design value of the bending moment at the top or the bottom of the wall
M_{md} Design value of the greatest moment at the middle of the height of the wall
M_{Rd} Design value of the moment of resistance
n Number of storeys
n_i Stiffness factor of members
n_t Number of wall ties or connectors per m^2 of wall
n_{tmin} Minimum number of wall ties or connectors per m^2 of wall
N Sum of the design vertical actions on a building
N_{ad} The maximum design arch thrust per unit length of wall
N_{id} Design value of the vertical load at the top or bottom of a wall or column
N_{md} Design value of the vertical load at the middle of the height of a wall or column
N_{Rd} Design value of the vertical resistance of a masonry wall or column
N_{Rdc} Design value of the vertical concentrated load resistance of a wall
N_{Ed} Design value of the vertical load
N_{Edf} Design value of the load out of a floor
N_{Edc} Design value of a concentrated vertical load
N_{Edu} Design value of the load above the floor
AC1⟩ *Text deleted* ⟨AC1
$q_{lat,d}$ Design lateral strength per unit area of wall
Q_d Design value of the total vertical load, in the part of a building stabilised by a core
r Arch rise
AC1⟩ R_e Yield strength of steel ⟨AC1
s Spacing of shear reinforcement
AC1⟩ *Text deleted* ⟨AC1
t Thickness of a wall
$t_{ch,h}$ Maximum depth of a horizontal chase or recess without calculation
$t_{ch,v}$ Maximum depth of a vertical chase or recess without calculation
t_i Thickness of wall, i
t_{ef} Effective thickness of a wall
t_f Thickness of a flange
t_{min} Minimum thickness of a wall
t_{ri} Thickness of the rib, i
V_{Ed} Design value of a shear load

V_{Rd}	Design value of the shear resistance
w_i	Uniformly distributed design load, *i*
W_{Ed}	Design lateral load per unit area
x	Depth of the neutral axis in a masonry beam
z	Lever arm
Z	Elastic section modulus of a unit height or length of the wall

Greek letters

α	Angle of shear reinforcement to the axis of the beam
α_t	Coefficient of thermal expansion of masonry
$\alpha_{1,2}$	Bending moment coefficients
β	Enhancement factor for concentrated loads
χ	Magnification factor for the shear resistance of reinforced walls
δ	Factor used in the determination of the normalised mean compressive strength of masonry units
$\varepsilon_{c\infty}$	Final creep strain of masonry
ε_{el}	Elastic strain of masonry
ε_{mu}	Limiting compressive strain in masonry
ε_{sy}	Yield stain of reinforcement
ϕ	Effective diameter of the reinforcing steel
ϕ_∞	Final creep coefficient of masonry
Φ	Reduction factor
Φ_{fl}	Reduction factor, taking the influence of the flexural strength into account
Φ_i	Reduction factor at the top or bottom of the wall
Φ_m	Reduction factor within the middle height of the wall
γ_M	Partial factor for materials, including uncertainties about geometry and modelling
η	Factor for use in calculating the out-of-plane eccentricity of loading on walls
λ_x	Depth of the compressed zone in a beam, when using a rectangular stress block
λ_c	Value of the slenderness ratio up to which eccentricities due to creep can be neglected
μ	Orthogonal ratio of the flexural strengths of masonry
ξ	Magnification factor for the rotational stiffness of the restraint of the structural element being considered
ρ_d	Dry density
ρ_n	Reduction factor
ρ_t	Stiffness coefficient
σ_d	Design compressive stress
υ	Angle of inclination to the vertical of the structure

3.6 Mechanical properties of masonry

3.6.1 Characteristic compressive strength of masonry

3.6.1.1 General

(1)P The characteristic compressive strength of masonry, f_k , shall be determined from results of tests on masonry specimens.

NOTE Test results may be obtained from tests carried out for the project, or be available from a database.

3.6.1.2 Characteristic compressive strength of masonry other than shell bedded masonry

(1) The characteristic compressive strength of masonry should be determined from either:

(i) results of tests in accordance with EN 1052-1 which tests may be carried out for the project or be available from tests previously carried out e.g. a database; the results of the tests should be expressed as a table, or in terms of equation (3.1)

$$f_k = K f_b^{\alpha} f_m^{\beta} \quad (3.1)$$

where:

f_k is the characteristic compressive strength of the masonry, in N/mm²
K is a constant and, where relevant, modified according to 3.6.1.2(3) AC1 and/or AC1 3.6.1.2(6)
α, β are constants
f_b is the normalised mean compressive strength of the units, in the direction of the applied action effect, in N/mm²
f_m is the compressive strength of the mortar, in N/mm²

Limitations on the use of equation (3.1) should be given in terms of f_b, f_m, the coefficient of variation of the test results, and the grouping of the units.

or

(ii) from (2) and (3), below.

NOTE The decision on which of methods (i) and (ii) is to be used in a country should be given in its National Annex. If (i) is used, tabulated values or the constants to be used in equation (3.1) and the limitations should be given in the National Annex.

This section deals with the compressive strength when a full mortar bed is employed. A shell bedded wall is a wall in which the masonry units are bedded on two strips of mortar at the outside edge of the bed face of the units.

The grouping of units (e.g. Group 1, Group 4) refers to a system of classifying units according to the volume and direction of any holes and perforations and the thicknesses of any web or shell. This is detailed in Table 3.1 of the Eurocode but the information will normally be provided by the manufacturer of the units. It should be noted that the information in Table 3.1 is provided to cover all the units available throughout Europe.

The normalized compressive strength of masonry units is the compressive strength of masonry units converted to the air dried compressive strength of an equivalent 100 mm wide by 100 mm high masonry unit. This takes into account the moisture condition of the specimens at the time of testing and the effect of platen restraint on the indicated strength of the specimens (which are usually whole masonry units and therefore have different height to thickness ratios when the size of the units used is changed).

Masonry mortars may be general purpose, thin layer or lightweight and may either be designed or prescribed. They are classified by their compressive strength e.g. M5 has a compressive strength of 5 N/mm^2. It is important to note that the specification of mortar for durability in a particular application is usually a key requirement and may require a higher specification mortar to be used than that which meets the basic requirement for strength.

NA.2.3.1 Mortars

The proportions of the prescribed constituents required to provide the stated "M" values for prescribed masonry mortars are given in Table NA.2.

Table NA.2 — Acceptable assumed equivalent mixes for prescribed masonry mortars

Compressive strength class[A)]	Prescribed mortars (proportion of materials by volume) (see Note)				Mortar designation
	Cement[B)] : lime : sand with or without air entrainment	Cement[B)] : sand with or without air entrainment	Masonry cement[C)] : sand	Masonry cement[D)] : sand	
M12	1 : 0 to ¼ : 3	1 : 3	Not suitable	Not suitable	(i)
M6	1 : ½ : 4 to 4½	1 : 3 to 4	1 : 2½ to 3½	1 : 3	(ii)
M4	1 : 1 : 5 to 6	1 : 5 to 6	1 : 4 to 5	1 : 3½ to 4	(iii)
M2	1 : 2 : 8 to 9	1 : 7 to 8	1 : 5½ to 6½	1 : 4½	(iv)

A) The number following "M" is the compressive strength at 28 days in N/mm^2
B) Cement or combinations of cement in accordance with NA.2.3.2, except masonry cements
C) Masonry cement in accordance with NA.2.3.2, (inorganic filler other than lime)
D) Masonry cement in accordance with NA.2.3.2 (lime)

NOTE When the sand portion is given as, for example, 5 to 6, the lower figure should be used with sands containing a higher proportion of fines whilst the higher figure should be used with sands containing a lower proportion of fines.

The design strength of masonry is the characteristic strength divided by the appropriate partial safety factor as shown in Table NA.2.1.

NA.2.1 Ultimate limit states [see BS EN 1996-1-1, 2.4.3(1)P]

The values for γ_M are given in Table NA.1.

Table NA.1 — Values of γ_M for ultimate limit states

	γ_M	
Class of execution control:	1[A)]	2[A)]
Material		
Masonry		
When in a state of direct or flexural compression		
Unreinforced masonry made with:		
units of category I	2,3[B)]	2,7[B)]
units of category II	2,6[B)]	3,0[B)]

Table NA.1 — Values of γ_M for ultimate limit states *(continued)*

Reinforced masonry made with:		
units of category I	2,0[B)]	[C)]
units of category II	2,3[B)]	[C)]
When in a state of flexural tension		
units of category I and II	2,3[B)]	2,7[B)]
When in a state of shear		
Unreinforced masonry made with:		
units of category I and II	2,5[B)]	2,5[B)]
Reinforced masonry made with:		
units of category I and II	2,0[B)]	[C)]
Steel and other components		
Anchorage of reinforcing steel	1,5[D)]	[C)]
Reinforcing steel and prestressing steel	1,15[D)]	[C)]
Ancillary components – wall ties	3,5[B)]	3,5[B)]
Ancillary components – straps	1,5[E)]	1,5[E)]
Lintels in accordance with EN 845-2	See NA to BS EN 845-2	See NA to BS EN 845-2

[A)] Class 1 of execution control should be assumed whenever the work is carried out following the recommendations for workmanship in BS EN 1996-2, including appropriate supervision and inspection, and in addition:

a) the specification, supervision and control ensure that the construction is compatible with the use of the appropriate partial safety factors given in BS EN 1996-1-1;

b) the mortar conforms to BS EN 998-2, if it is factory made mortar, or if it is site mixed mortar, preliminary compression strength tests carried out on the mortar to be used, in accordance with BS EN 1015-2 and BS EN 1015-11, indicate conformity to the strength requirements given in BS EN 1996-1-1 and regular testing of the mortar used on site, in accordance with BS EN 1015-2 and BS EN 1015-11, shows that the strength requirements of BS EN 1996-1-1 are being maintained.

Class 2 of execution control should be assumed whenever the work is carried out following the recommendations for workmanship in BS EN 1996-2, including appropriate supervision.

[B)] When considering the effects of misuse or accident these values may be halved.

[C)] Class 2 of execution control is not considered appropriate for reinforced masonry and should not be used. However, masonry wall panels reinforced with bed joint reinforcement used:

a) to enhance the lateral strength of the masonry panel;

b) to limit or control shrinkage or expansion of the masonry,

can be considered to be unreinforced masonry for the purpose of class of execution control and the unreinforced masonry direct or flexural compression γ_M values are appropriate for use.

[D)] When considering the effects of misuse or accident these values should be taken as 1,0.

[E)] For horizontal restraint straps, unless otherwise specified, the declared ultimate load capacity depends on there being a design compressive stress in the masonry of at least 0,4 N/mm^2. When a lower stress due to design loads may be acting, for example when autoclaved aerated concrete or lightweight aggregate concrete masonry is used, the manufacturer's advice should be sought and a partial safety factor of 3 should be used.

Categories I and II relate to the level of quality control employed by the unit manufacturer. Category I is the higher level and hence a more favourable partial safety factor may be employed.

The term masonry unit is used throughout the European Standards and replaces the use of descriptors such as brick and block.

NA.2.4 Characteristic compressive strength of masonry other than shell bedded [see BS EN 1996-1-1, 3.6.1.2(1)]

Option 3.6.1.2(1)(i) should be used, using Equation 3.1: $f_k = K f_b^{\alpha} f_m^{\beta}$

Table NA.4 — Values of *K* to be used with equation 3.1:

Masonry unit		General purpose mortar	Thin layer mortar (bed joint ≥ 0,5 mm and ≤ 3 mm)	Lightweight mortar of density	
				$600 \le \rho_d \le 800$ kg/m^3	$800 < \rho_d \le 1\,300$ kg/m^3
Clay	Group 1	0,50	0,75	0,30	0,40
	Group 2	0,40	0,70	0,25	0,30
	Group 3	A)	A)	A)	A)
	Group 4	A)	A)	A)	A)
Calcium silicate	Group 1	0,50	0,80	B)	B)
	Group 2	0,40	0,70	B)	B)
Aggregate concrete	Group 1	0,55	0,80	0,45	0,45
	Group 1C) (units laid flat)	0,50	0,70	0,40	0,40
	Group 2	0,52	0,76	0,45	0,45
	Group 3	A)	A)	A)	A)
	Group 4	A)	A)	A)	A)
Autoclaved aerated concrete	Group 1	0,55	0,80	0,45	0,45
Manufactured stone	Group 1	0,45	0,75	B)	B)
Dimensioned natural stone	Group 1	0,45	B)	B)	B)

A) Group 3 and 4 units have not traditionally been used in the UK, so no values are available.
B) These masonry unit and mortar combinations have not traditionally been used in the UK, so no values are available.
C) If Group 1 aggregate concrete units contain formed vertical voids, multiply *K* by (100-n) / 100, where n is the percentage of voids, maximum 25%.

Values of α, β for use with Equation 3.1 are as follows:

For general purpose mortar:	$\alpha = 0,7$ and $\beta = 0,3$
For lightweight mortar:	$\alpha = 0,7$ and $\beta = 0,3$
For thin layer mortar (in bed joints of thickness 0,5 mm to 3 mm):	
a) using clay units of Group 1, calcium silicate and aggregate concrete units of Group 1 and 2 and autoclaved concrete units of Group 1	$\alpha = 0,85$ and $\beta = 0$
b) using clay units of Group 2	$\alpha = 0,7$and $\beta = 0$

When using Equation 3.1 the following limitations apply:

- the masonry is detailed in accordance with EN 1996-1-1, section **8**;
- all bed joints and perpend joints satisfy the requirements of **8.1.5**(1) and all mortar pockets satisfy the requirements of **8.1.5**(3) so as to be considered as filled;
- f_b is not taken to be greater than:
  - 110 N/mm^2 when units are laid in general purpose mortar;
  - 50 N/mm^2 when units are laid in thin layer mortar;

  where f_b is derived from BS EN 772-1 when the load is applied in the normal orientation, i.e. perpendicular to the normal bed face.

NOTE f_b is the normalized strength of a unit; if concrete blocks are to be laid flat, then the normalized strength is still used for the design, even if that strength was obtained by testing blocks in the upright position.

- f_m is not taken to be greater than 2 f_b nor greater than:
  - 12 N/mm^2 when units are laid in general purpose mortar;
  - 10 N/mm^2 when units are laid in lightweight mortar;
- the coefficient of variation of the strength of the masonry units is not more than 25%;

For masonry made with general purpose mortar and where the thickness of the masonry is equal to the width or length of the unit, so that there is no mortar joint parallel to the face of the wall through all or any part of the length of the wall, K is obtained from Table NA.4.

For masonry made with general purpose mortar and where there is a mortar joint parallel to the face of the wall through all or any part of the length of the wall the value of K obtained from Table NA.4 is multiplied by 0,8.

For masonry made of general purpose mortar where Group 2 and Group 3 aggregate concrete units are used with the vertical cavities filled completely with concrete, the value of f_b should be obtained by considering the units to be Group 1 having a compressive strength corresponding to the compressive strength of the units or of the concrete infill, whichever is the lesser.

Where action effects are parallel to the direction of the bed joints, the characteristic compressive strength may be determined from Equation 3.1 with f_b, derived from BS EN 772-1, where the direction of application of the load to the test specimens is in the same direction as the direction of the action effect in the masonry, but with the factor, δ, as given in BS EN 772-1 taken to be no greater than 1,0. For Group 2 and 3 units, K should then be multiplied by 0,5.

When the perpend joints are unfilled, equation 3.1 may be used, with consideration of any horizontal actions that might be applied to, or be transmitted by, the masonry. See also **3.6.2**(4).

3.6.1.3 Characteristic compressive strength of shell bedded masonry

AC1 (1) The characteristic compressive strength of shell bedded masonry may also be obtained from 3.6.1.2 using the normalised mean compressive strength of the units f_b that is obtained for normal bedding (thus not obtained from tests on units tested in accordance with EN 772-1 for shell bedded units), provided that: AC1

- the width of each strip of mortar is 30 mm or greater;
- the thickness of the masonry is equal to the width or length of the masonry units so that there is no longitudinal mortar joint through all or part of the length of the wall;
- the ratio g/t is not less than 0,4;
- K is taken from 3.6.1.2(2) when g/t = 1,0 or K is taken as half of those values when g/t = 0,4, with intermediate values obtained by linear interpolation,

where:

g is the total width of the mortar strips;
t is the thickness of the wall.

(2) The characteristic compressive strength of shell bedded masonry AC1 *Text deleted* AC1 may be obtained from 3.6.1.2, provided that the normalised mean compressive strength of the units, f_b, used in the equation is that obtained from tests on units tested in accordance with EN 772-1 for shell bedded units.

3.6.2 Characteristic shear strength of masonry

(1)P The characteristic shear strength of masonry, f_{vk}, shall be determined from the results of tests on masonry.

NOTE Test results may be obtained from tests carried out for the project, or be available from a database.

(2) The characteristic initial shear strength of masonry, f_{vko}, should be determined from tests in accordance with EN 1052-3 or EN 1052-4.

(3) The characteristic shear strength of masonry, f_{vk}, using general purpose mortar in accordance with 3.2.2(2), or thin layer mortar in beds of thickness 0,5 mm to 3,0 mm, in accordance with 3.2.2(3), or lightweight mortar in accordance with 3.2.2(4) with all joints satisfying the requirements of 8.1.5 so as to be considered as filled, may be taken from equation (3.5)

$$f_{vk} = f_{vko} + 0,4\,\sigma_d \quad (3.5)$$

but not greater than $0,065 f_b$ or f_{vlt}

where:

f_{vko} is the characteristic initial shear strength, under zero compressive stress;
f_{vlt} is a limit to the value of f_{vk};
σ_d is the design compressive stress perpendicular to the shear in the member at the level under consideration, using the appropriate load combination based on the average vertical stress over the compressed part of the wall that is providing shear resistance;
f_b is the normalised compressive strength of the masonry units, as described in 3.1.2.1, for the direction of application of the load on the test specimens being perpendicular to the bed face.

NOTE The decision on whether to use 0,065 f_b or f_{vlt} in a country, and the values or derivation of f_{vlt} related to e.g. the tensile strength of the units and/or overlap in the masonry, if that option is chosen, may be found in its National Annex.

NA.2.5 Characteristic shear strength of masonry [see BS EN 1996-1-1, 3.6.2(3)]

The limit of f_{vk} should be taken as 0,065 f_b.

(4) The characteristic shear strength of masonry using general purpose mortar in accordance with 3.2.2(2), or thin layer mortar in accordance with 3.2.2(3), of thickness 0,5 mm to 3,0 mm, or lightweight mortar in accordance with 3.2.2(4), and having the perpend joints unfilled, but with adjacent faces of the masonry units closely abutted together, may be taken from equation (3.6)

$$f_{vk} = 0,5\, f_{vko} + 0,4\, \sigma_d \tag{3.6}$$

but not greater than 0,045f_b or f_{vlt}

where:

f_{vko} , f_{vlt} , σ_d and f_b are as defined in (3) above.

NOTE The decision on whether to use [AC1) 0,045 (AC1] f_b or f_{vlt} in a country, and the values or derivation of f_{vlt} related to e.g. the tensile strength of the units and/or overlap in the masonry, if that option is chosen, may be found in its National Annex.

NA.2.6 Characteristic shear strength of masonry [see BS EN 1996-1-1, 3.6.2(4)]

The limit of f_{vk} should be taken as 0,045 f_b.

(5) In shell bedded masonry, where the units are bedded on two or more equal strips of general purpose mortar, each at least 30 mm in width, two of which are at the outside edges of the bed face of the unit, f_{vk} may be taken from equation (3.7)

$$f_{vk} = \frac{g}{t}\, f_{vko} + 0,4\, \sigma_d \tag{3.7}$$

but not greater than would be obtained from (4) above.

where:

f_{vk} , σ_d and f_b are as defined in (3) above and:
g is the total width of the mortar strips;
t is the thickness of the wall.

(6) The initial shear strength of the masonry, f_{vko}, may be determined from either:

- the evaluation of a database on the results of tests on the initial shear strength of masonry,

or

- from the values given in Table 3.4, provided that general purpose mortars made in accordance with EN 1996-2 do not contain admixtures or additives.

NOTE The decision on which of the above two methods is to be used in a country may be found in its National Annex. When a country decides to determine its values of f_{vko} from a database, the values may be found in the National Annex.

NA.2.7 Characteristic shear strength of masonry [see BS EN 1996-1-1, 3.6.2(6)]

The characteristic initial shear strength f_{vko} should be taken from Table NA.5.

Table NA.5 — Values of the initial shear strength of masonry, f_{vko}

Masonry units	Strength class of general purpose mortar	f_{vko} (N/mm^2)		
		General purpose mortar	Thin layer mortar (bed joint ≤ 0,5 mm and ≥ 3 mm)	Lightweight mortar
Clay	M12	0,30	} 0,30	} 0,15
	M4 and M6	0,20		
	M2	0,10		
Calcium silicate	M12	0,20	} 0,40	} 0,15
	M4 and M6	0,15		
	M2	0,10		
Aggregate concrete, autoclaved aerated concrete, manufactured stone and dimensioned natural stone	M12	0,20	} 0,30	} 0,15
	M4 and M6	0,15		
	M2	0,10		

(7) The vertical shear resistance of the junction of two masonry walls may be obtained from suitable tests for a specific project or it may be taken from an evaluation of test data. In the absence of such data, the characteristic vertical shear resistance may be based on f_{vko}, where f_{vko} is the shear strength under zero compressive stress, as given in 3.6.2(2) and (6), provided that the connection between the walls is in accordance with 8.5.2.1.

3.6.3 Characteristic flexural strength of masonry

(1) In considering out-of plane bending, the following situations should be considered: flexural strength having a plane of failure parallel to the bedjoints, f_{xk1}; flexural strength having a plane of failure perpendicular to the bedjoints, f_{xk2} (see Figure 3.1).

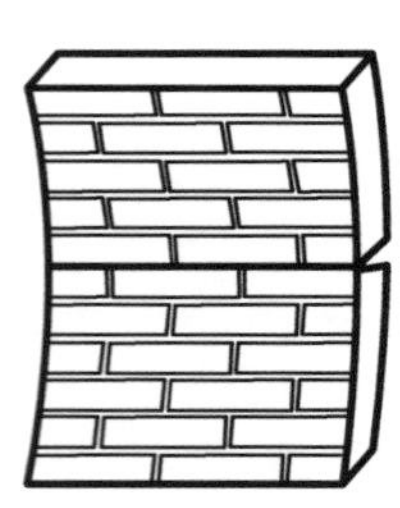

(a) Plane of failure parallel to bed joints, f_{xk1}

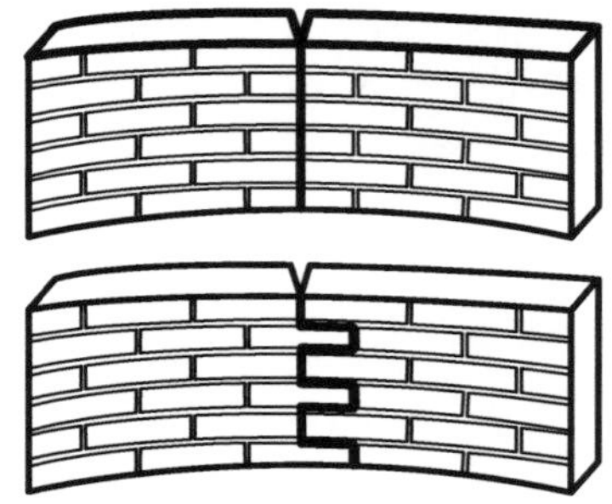

(b) Plane of failure perpendicular to bed joints, f_{xk2}

Figure 3.1 — Planes of failure of masonry in bending.

(2)P The characteristic flexural strength of masonry, f_{xk1} and f_{xk2}, shall be determined from the results of tests on masonry.

NOTE Tests results may be obtained from tests carried out for the project, or be available from a database.

(3) The characteristic flexural strength of masonry may be determined by tests in accordance with EN 1052-2, or it may be established from an evaluation of test data based on the flexural strengths of masonry obtained from appropriate combinations of units and mortar.

NOTE 1 Values of f_{xk1} and f_{xk2} to be used in a country may be found in its National Annex.

NOTE 2 Where test data are not available values of the characteristic flexural strength of masonry made with general purpose mortar, thin layer mortar or lightweight mortar, may be taken from the tables in this note, provided that thin layer mortar and lightweight mortars are M5, or stronger;

NOTE 3 For masonry made with autoclaved aerated concrete units laid in thin layer mortar, f_{xk1} and f_{xk2} values may be taken from the tables in this note or from the following equations:

$f_{xk1} = 0{,}035 f_b$, with filled and unfilled perpend joints
$f_{xk2} = 0{,}035 f_b$, with filled perpend joints or $0{,}025 f_b$, with unfilled perpend joints.

NA.2.8 Characteristic flexural strength of masonry [see BS EN 1996-1-1, 3.6.3(3)]

The values of f_{xk1} and f_{xk2} to be used for general purpose mortars are given in Table NA.6.

For thin layer mortars use the values given for M12 mortar.

For lightweight mortars use the values given for M2 mortar.

Table NA.6 — Characteristic flexural strength of masonry, f_{xk1} and f_{xk2}, in N/mm²

	Values of f_{xk1} Plane of failure parallel to bed joints			Values of f_{xk2} Plane of failure perpendicular to bed joints		
Mortar strength class:	M12	M6 and M4	M2	M12	M6 and M4	M2
Clay masonry units of groups 1 and 2 having a water absorption (see Note 1) of:						
less than 7%	0,7	0,5	0,4	2,0	1,5	1,2
between 7% and 12%	0,5	0,4	0,35	1,5	1,1	1,0
over 12%	0,4	0,3	0,25	1,1	0,9	0,8
Calcium silicate brick sized* masonry units	0,3		0,2	0,9		0,6
Aggregate concrete brick sized* masonry units	0,3		0,2	0,9		0,6
Aggregate concrete masonry units and manufactured stone of groups 1 and 2 and AAC masonry units used in walls of thickness up to 100 mm (see Note 2 and 3) of declared compressive strength:						
2,9				0,4		0,4
3,6	0,25		0,2	0,45		0,4
7,3				0,6		0,5
Aggregate concrete masonry units and manufactured stone of groups 1 and 2 and AAC masonry units used in walls of thickness of 250 mm or greater (see Note 2 and 3), of declared compressive strength:						
2,9				0,25		0,2
3,6	0,15		0,1	0,25		0,2
7,3				0,35		0,3
Aggregate concrete masonry units and manufactured stone of groups 1 and 2 and AAC masonry units used in walls of any thickness (see Note 2), of declared compressive strength:						
10,4	0,25		0,2	0,75		0.6
≥ 17,5				0,9 (see Note 4)		0,7 (see Note 4)

NOTE 1 Tests to determine the water absorption of clay masonry units are to be conducted in accordance with EN 772-7.

NOTE 2 The thickness should be taken to be the thickness of the wall, for a single-leaf wall, or the thickness of the leaf, for a cavity wall.

NOTE 3 Linear interpolation may be used to obtain the values of f_{xk1} and f_{xk2} for:

a) wall thicknesses greater than 100 mm and less than 250 mm;

b) compressive strengths between 2,9 N/mm² and 7,3 N/mm² in a wall of given thickness.

NOTE 4 When used with flexural strength in the parallel direction, assume the orthogonal ratio μ = 0,3.

* units not exceeding 337.5 mm × 225 mm × 112.5 mm

5.5 Analysis of structural members

5.5.1 Masonry walls subjected to vertical loading

5.5.1.1 General

(1) When analysing walls subjected to vertical loading, allowance in the design should be made for the following:

- vertical loads directly applied to the wall;
- second order effects;
- eccentricities calculated from a knowledge of the layout of the walls, the interaction of the floors and the stiffening walls;
- eccentricities resulting from construction deviations and differences in the material properties of individual components.

NOTE See EN 1996-2 for permitted construction deviations.

(2) The bending moments may be calculated from the material properties given in Section 3, the joint behaviour, and from the principles of structural mechanics.

NOTE A simplified method for calculating the bending moments in walls due to vertical loading is given in Annex C. Annex C(4) and C(5) may be used with any calculation, including linear elastic theory.

(3)P An initial eccentricity, e_{init}, shall be assumed for the full height of a wall to allow for construction imperfections.

(4) The initial eccentricity, e_{init}, may be assumed to be h_{ef} / 450, where h_{ef} is the effective height of the wall, calculated from 5.5.1.2.

5.5.1.2 Effective height of masonry walls

(1)P The effective height of a loadbearing wall shall be assessed taking account of the relative stiffness of the elements of structure connected to the wall and the efficiency of the connections.

(2) A wall may be stiffened by floors, or roofs, suitably placed cross walls, or any other similarly rigid structural elements to which the wall is connected.

(3) Walls may be considered as stiffened at a vertical edge if:

- cracking between the wall and its stiffening wall is not expected to occur i.e. both walls are made of materials with approximately similar deformation behaviour, are approximately evenly loaded, are erected simultaneously and bonded together and differential movement between the walls, for example, due to shrinkage, loading etc, is not expected

or

- the connection between a wall and its stiffening wall can resist tension and compression forces by anchors or ties or other suitable means.

(4) Stiffening walls should have a length of at least 1/5 of the clear height and have a thickness of at least 0,3 times the effective thickness of the wall to be stiffened.

(5) If the stiffening wall is interrupted by openings, the minimum length of the wall between openings, encompassing the stiffened wall, should be as shown in Figure 5.1, and the stiffening wall should extend a distance of at least 1/5 of the storey height beyond each opening.

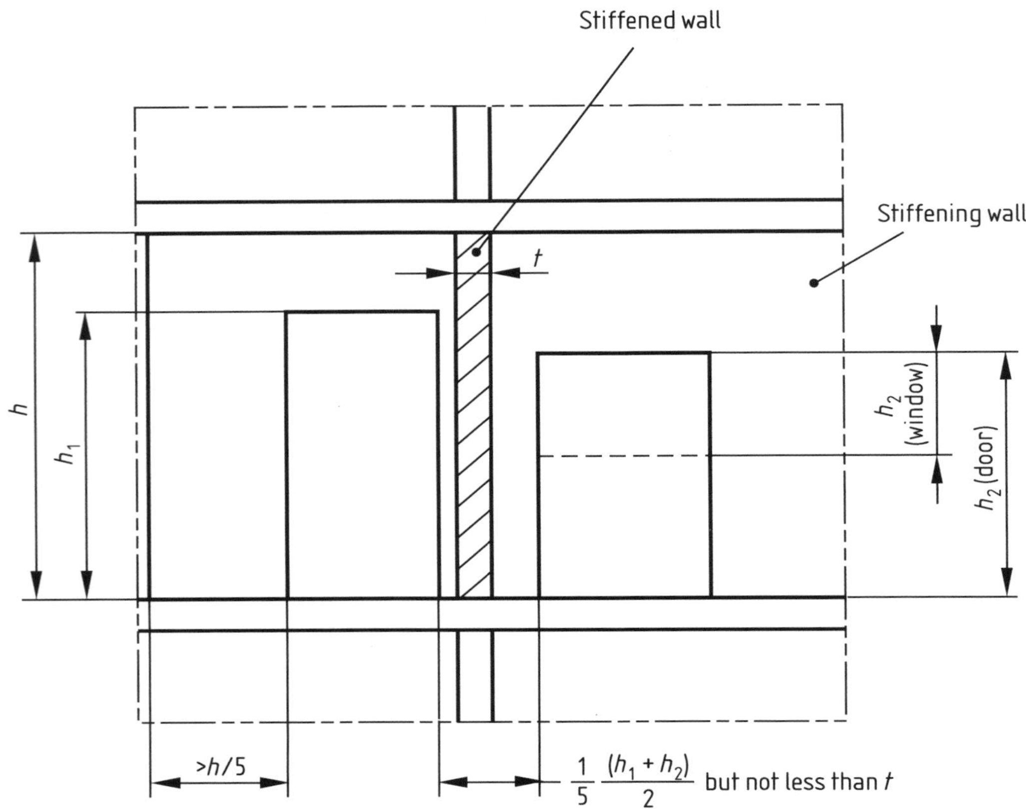

Figure 5.1 — Minimum length of stiffening wall with openings

(6) Walls may be stiffened by members other than masonry walls provided that such members have the equivalent stiffness of the masonry stiffening wall, described in paragraph (4) above, and they are connected to the stiffened wall with anchors or ties designed to resist the tension and compression forces that will develop.

(7) Walls stiffened on two vertical edges, with $l \geq 30\ t$, or walls stiffened on one vertical edge, with $l \geq 15\ t$, where l is the clear length of the wall and t is the thickness of the stiffened wall, should be treated as walls restrained at top and bottom only.

(8) If the stiffened wall is weakened by vertical chases and/or recesses, other than those allowed by 6.1.2(7), the reduced thickness of the wall should be used for t, or a free edge should be assumed at the position of the vertical chase or recess. A free edge should always be assumed when the thickness of the wall remaining after the vertical chase or recess has been formed is less than half the wall thickness.

(9) Walls with openings having a clear height of more than 1/4 of the clear height of the wall or a clear width of more than 1/4 of the wall length or an area of more than 1/10 of the total area of the wall, should be considered as having a free edge at the edge of the opening for the purposes of determining the effective height.

(10) The effective height of a wall should be taken as:

$$h_{ef} = \rho_n h \tag{5.2}$$

where:

h_{ef} is the effective height of the wall;
h is the clear storey height of the wall;
ρ_n is a reduction factor where n = 2, 3 or 4 depending on the edge restraint or stiffening of the wall.

(11) The reduction factor, ρ_n, may be assumed to be:

(i) For walls restrained at the top and bottom by reinforced concrete floors or roofs spanning from both sides at the same level or by a reinforced concrete floor spanning from one side only and having a bearing of at least 2/3 of the thickness of the wall:

$$\rho_2 = 0,75 \qquad (5.3)$$

unless the eccentricity of the load at the top of the wall is greater than 0,25 times the thickness of wall in which case

$$\rho_2 = 1,0 \qquad (5.4)$$

(ii) For walls restrained at the top and bottom by timber floors or roofs spanning from both sides at the same level or by a timber floor spanning from one side having a bearing of at least 2/3 the thickness of the wall but not less than 85 mm:

$$\rho_2 = 1,0 \qquad (5.5)$$

(iii) For walls restrained at the top and bottom and stiffened on one vertical edge (with one free vertical edge):

– when $h \leq 3,5\,l$,

$$\rho_3 = \frac{1}{1 + \left[\frac{\rho_2 h}{3 l}\right]^2} \rho_2 \qquad (5.6)$$

with ρ_2 from (i) or (ii) , whichever is appropriate, or

– when $h > 3,5\,l$,

$$\rho_3 = \frac{1,5\,l}{h} \geq 0,3 \qquad (5.7)$$

where:

l is the length of the wall.

NOTE Values for ρ_3 are shown in graphical form in Annex D.

(iv) For walls restrained at the top and bottom and stiffened on two vertical edges:

– when $h \leq 1,15\,l$, with ρ_2 from (i) or (ii), whichever is appropriate,

$$\rho_4 = \frac{1}{1 + \left[\frac{\rho_2 h}{l}\right]^2} \rho_2 \qquad (5.8)$$

or

– when $h > 1,15\,l$,

$$\rho_4 = \frac{0,5\,l}{h} \qquad (5.9)$$

where

l is the length of the wall.

NOTE Values for ρ_4 are shown in graphical form in Annex D.

5.5.1.3 Effective thickness of masonry walls

(1) The effective thickness, t_{ef}, of a single-leaf wall, a double-leaf wall, a faced wall, a shell bedded wall and a grouted cavity wall, as defined in 1.5.10, should be taken as the actual thickness of the wall, t.

(2) The effective thickness of a wall stiffened by piers should be obtained from equation (5.10):

$$t_{ef} = \rho_t t \tag{5.10}$$

where:

t_{ef} is the effective thickness;
ρ_t is a coefficient obtained from Table 5.1;
t is the thickness of the wall.

Table 5.1 — Stiffness coefficient, ρ_t, for walls stiffened by piers, see Figure 5.2

Ratio of pier spacing (centre to centre) to pier width	Ratio of AC1 pier depth AC1 to actual thickness of wall to which it is bonded		
	1	2	3
6	1,0	1,4	2,0
10	1,0	1,2	1,4
20	1,0	1,0	1,0
NOTE Linear interpolation between the values given in Table 5.1 is permissible.			

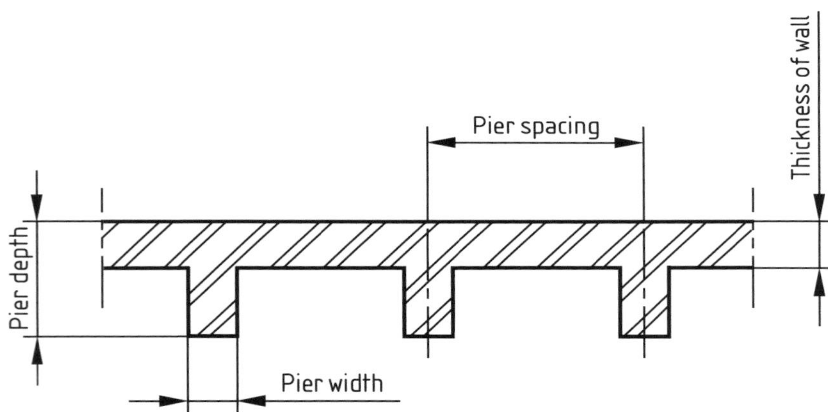

Figure 5.2 — Diagrammatic view of the definitions used in Table 5.1

(3) The effective thickness, t_{ef}, of a cavity wall in which both leaves are connected with wall ties in accordance with 6.5 should be determined using equation (5.11):

$$t_{ef} = \sqrt[3]{t_2^3 + k_{tef}\, t_1^3} \tag{5.11}$$

where:

t_1 , t_2 are the actual thicknesses of the leaves or their effective thicknesses, calculated from equation (5.10), when relevant and t_1 is the thickness of the outer or unloaded leaf and t_2 is the thickness of the inner or loaded leaf;

k_{tef} is a factor to allow for the relative E values of the leaves t_1 and t_2.

NOTE The value of k_{tef} to be used in a country may be found in its National Annex. The recommended value of k_{tef} (as defined as E_2 / E_1), should not be taken to be greater than 2.

> **NA.2.13 Effective thickness of masonry walls [see BS EN 1996-1-1, 5.5.1.3(3)]**
>
> The value for k_{tef} should be taken as 1.

(4) When only one leaf of a cavity wall is loaded, equation (5.11) may be used to calculate the effective thickness, provided that the wall ties have sufficient flexibility such that the loaded leaf is not affected adversely by the unloaded leaf. In calculating the effective thickness, the thickness of the unloaded leaf should not be taken to be greater than the thickness of the loaded leaf.

5.5.1.4 Slenderness ratio of masonry walls

(1)P The slenderness ratio of a masonry wall shall be obtained by dividing the value of the effective height, h_{ef} , by the value of the effective thickness, t_{ef} .

(2) The slenderness ratio of the masonry wall should not be greater than 27 when subjected to mainly vertical loading.

5.5.3 Masonry shear walls subjected to shear loading

(1) When analysing masonry walls subjected to shear loading, the elastic stiffness of the walls, including any flanges, should be used as the stiffness of the wall. For walls higher than twice their length, the effect of shear deformations on the stiffness can be neglected.

(2) An intersecting wall, or a portion of such a wall, may be considered to act as a flange to a shear wall provided that the connection of the shear wall to the flange is able to resist the corresponding shearing actions, and provided the flange will not buckle within the length assumed.

(3) The length of any intersecting wall, which may be considered to act as a flange (see Figure 5.6), is the thickness of the shear wall plus, on each side of it - where appropriate - the least of:

- $h_{tot}/5$, where h_{tot} is the overall height of the shear wall;
- half the distance between shear walls (l_s), when connected by the intersecting wall;
- the distance to the end of the wall;
- half the clear height (h);
- six times the thickness of the intersecting wall, t.

(4) In intersecting walls, openings with dimensions smaller than $h/4$ or $l/4$ may be disregarded. Openings with dimensions greater than $h/4$ or $l/4$ should be regarded as marking the end of the wall.

(5) If the floors can be idealised as rigid diaphragms, the horizontal forces may be distributed to the shear walls in proportion to their stiffness.

(6)P Where the plan arrangement of the shear walls is asymmetric, or for any other reason the horizontal force is eccentric to the overall stiffness centre of the structure, account shall be taken of the effect of the consequent rotation on the individual walls (torsional effects).

(7) If the floors are not sufficiently rigid when considered as horizontal diaphragms (for example, precast concrete units which are not inter-connected) horizontal forces to be resisted by the shear walls should be taken to be the forces from the floors to which they are directly connected, unless a semi rigid analysis is carried out.

(8) The maximum horizontal load on a shear wall may be reduced by up to 15 % provided that the load on the parallel shear walls is correspondingly increased.

(9) When deriving the relevant design load that assists shear resistance, the vertical load applied to slabs spanning in two directions may be distributed equally onto the supporting walls; in the case of floor or roof slabs spanning one way, a 45° spread of the load may be considered in deriving the axial load, at the lower storeys, on the walls not directly loaded.

(10) The distribution of shear stress along the compressed part of a wall may be assumed to be constant.

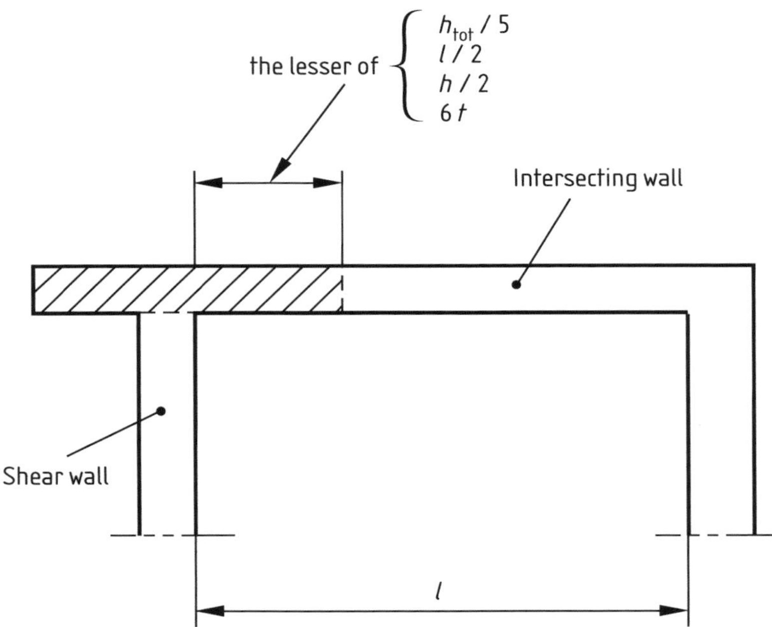

Figure 5.6 — Flange widths that can be assumed for shear walls

5.5.5 Masonry walls subjected to lateral loading

(1) When analysing masonry walls subjected to lateral loading, allowance should be made in the design for the following:

- the effect of damp proof courses;
- support conditions and continuity over supports.

(2) A faced wall should be analysed as a single-leaf wall constructed entirely of the units giving the lower flexural strength.

(3) A movement joint in a wall should be treated as an edge across which moment and shear may not be transmitted.

NOTE Some specialised anchors are designed to transmit moment and/or shear across a movement joint; their use is not covered in this standard.

(4) The reaction along an edge of a wall due to the load may be assumed to be uniformly distributed when designing the means of support. Restraint at a support may be provided by ties, by bonded masonry returns or by floors or roofs.

(5) Where laterally loaded walls are bonded (see 8.1.4) to vertically loaded walls, or where reinforced concrete floors bear onto them, the support may be considered as being continuous. A damp proof course should be considered as providing simple support. Where walls are connected to a vertically load bearing wall or other suitable structure by ties at the vertical edges, partial moment continuity at the vertical sides of the wall may be assumed, if the strength of the ties is verified to be sufficient.

(6) In the case of cavity walls, full continuity may be assumed even if only one leaf is continuously bonded across a support, provided that the cavity wall is provided with ties in accordance with 6.3.3. The load to be transmitted from a wall to its support may be taken by ties to one leaf only, provided that there is adequate connection between the two leaves (see 6.3.3) particularly at the vertical edges of the walls. In all other cases, partial continuity may be assumed.

(7) When the wall is supported along 3 or 4 edges, the calculation of the applied moment, M_{Edi}, may be taken as:

– when the plane of failure is parallel to the bed joints, i.e. in the f_{xk1} direction:

$$M_{Ed1} = \alpha_1 W_{Ed} l^2 \quad \text{per unit length of the wall} \qquad (5.17)$$

or,

– when the plane of failure is perpendicular to the bed joints, i.e. in the f_{xk2} direction:

$$M_{Ed2} = \alpha_2 W_{Ed} l^2 \quad \text{per unit height of the wall} \qquad (5.18)$$

where:

α_1, α_2 are bending moment coefficients taking account of the degree of fixity at the edges of the walls, the height to length ratio of the walls; they can be obtained from a suitable theory;
l is the length of the wall between supports;
W_{Ed} is the design lateral load per unit area.

NOTE Values of the bending coefficient α_1 and α_2 may be obtained from Annex E for single leaf walls with a thickness less than or equal to 250 mm , where $\alpha_1 = \mu\ \alpha_2$

where:

μ is the orthogonal ratio of the design flexural strengths of the masonry, f_{xd1}/f_{xd2}, see 3.6.3, or $f_{xd1,app}/f_{xd2}$, see [AC1) 6.3.1(4) (AC1] or $f_{xd1}/f_{xd2,app}$, see [AC1) 6.6.2(9) (AC1].

(8) The bending moment coefficient at a damp proof course may be taken as for an edge over which full continuity exists when the design vertical stress on the damp proof course equals or exceeds the design tensile stress caused by the moment arising due to the action.

(9) When the wall is supported only along its bottom and top edges, the applied moment may be calculated from normal engineering principles, taking into account any continuity.

[AC1) (10) In a laterally loaded panel or free standing wall built of masonry set in mortar designations M2 to M20, and designed in accordance with 6.3, the dimensions should be limited to avoid undue movements resulting from deflections, creep, shrinkage, temperature effects and cracking.

NOTE The limiting values may be obtained from Annex F. (AC1]

(11) When irregular shapes of walls, or those with substantial openings, are to be designed, an analysis, using a recognized method of obtaining bending moments in flat plates, for example, finite element method or yield line analogy may be used, taking into account the anisotropy of masonry when appropriate.

The design of walls to resist lateral wind loads is not carried out in those European countries where walls have traditionally been sufficiently thick to provide adequate transverse strength. This section of the code is derived from UK experience based on the tradition of constructing relatively thin walls.

It should be noted that this method of design is only appropriate when loads are distributed and of short duration. The method should not be used for seismic, impact or concentrated loads.

It is important that the designer assesses the kind of restraint offered to the panel by its supports and is satisfied that the supports are capable of resisting the forces transmitted to them by the panel. The edge restraint depends upon continuity over the support, the restraining influence of any vertical loading on the wall, the type of damp proof course (if any) and the adequacy of the connection to the supports. Also note the need for adequate ties between the leaves of cavity walls (see also 6.5).

6. Ultimate Limit State

6.1 Unreinforced masonry walls subjected to mainly vertical loading

6.1.1 General

(1)P The resistance of masonry walls to vertical loading shall be based on the geometry of the wall, the effect of the applied eccentricities and the material properties of the masonry.

(2) In calculating the vertical resistance of masonry walls, it may be assumed that:

- plane sections remain plane;
- the tensile strength of masonry perpendicular to bed joints is zero.

6.1.2 Verification of unreinforced masonry walls subjected to mainly vertical loading

6.1.2.1 General

(1)P At the ultimate limit state, the design value of the vertical load applied to a masonry wall, N_{Sd}, shall be less than or equal to the design value of the vertical resistance of the wall, N_{Rd}, such that:

$$N_{Ed} \leq N_{Rd} \tag{6.1}$$

(2) The design value of the vertical resistance of a single leaf wall per unit length, N_{Rd}, is given by:

$$N_{Rd} = \Phi \, t \, f_d \tag{6.2}$$

where:

Φ is the capacity reduction factor, Φ_i, at the top or bottom of the wall, or Φ_m , in the middle of the wall, as appropriate, allowing for the effects of slenderness and eccentricity of loading, obtained from 6.1.2.2;
t is the thickness of the wall;
f_d is the design compressive strength of the masonry, obtained from 2.4.1 and 3.6.1.

(3) Where the cross-sectional area of a wall is less than 0,1 m^2, the design compressive strength of the masonry, f_d, should be multiplied by the factor:

$$(0{,}7 + 3\,A) \tag{6.3}$$

where:

A is the loaded horizontal gross cross-sectional area of the wall, expressed in square metres.

(4) For cavity walls, each leaf should be verified separately, using the plan area of the loaded leaf and the slenderness ratio based upon the effective thickness of the cavity wall, calculated according to equation (5.11).

(5) A faced wall should be designed in the same manner as a single-leaf wall constructed entirely of the weaker units, using the value of K, from Table 3.3, appropriate to a wall with a longitudinal mortar joint.

(6) A double-leaf wall, tied together according to clause 6.5 may be designed as a single-leaf wall, if both leaves have a load of similar magnitude, or, alternatively, as a cavity wall.

(7) When chases or recesses are outside the limits given in clause 8.6, the effect on loadbearing capacity should be taken into account as follows:

- vertical chases or recesses should be treated either as a wall end or, alternatively, the residual thickness of the wall should be used in the calculations of the design vertical load resistance;

– horizontal or inclined chases should be treated by verifying the strength of the wall at the chase position, taking account of the load eccentricity.

NOTE As a general guide the reduction in vertical loadbearing capacity may be taken to be proportional to the reduction in cross-sectional area due to any vertical chase or recess, provided that the reduction in area does not exceed 25 %.

With cavity walls the load carried by each leaf should be assessed and the design vertical load resistance of each leaf verified using equation (5.11). When only one leaf of a cavity wall is loaded the loadbearing capacity should be based on the horizontal cross-sectional area of the leaf alone but using the effective thickness of the leaf to determine the slenderness ratio.

6.1.2.2 Reduction factor for slenderness and eccentricity

(1) The value of the reduction factor for slenderness and eccentricity, Φ, may be based on a rectangular stress block as follows:

(i) At the top or bottom of the wall (Φ_i)

$$\Phi_i = 1 - 2\frac{e_i}{t} \tag{6.4}$$

where:

e_i is the eccentricity at the top or the bottom of the wall, as appropriate, calculated using equation (6.5):

$$e_i = \frac{M_{id}}{N_{id}} + e_{he} + e_{init} \geq 0,05\,t \tag{6.5}$$

M_{id} is the design value of the bending moment at the top or the bottom of the wall resulting from the eccentricity of the floor load at the support, analysed according to 5.5.1 (see Figure 6.1);

N_{id} is the design value of the vertical load at the top or bottom of the wall;

e_{he} is the eccentricity at the top or bottom of the wall, if any, resulting from horizontal loads (for example, wind);

AC1⟩ e_{init} is the initial eccentricity with a sign that increases the absolute value of e_i (see 5.5.1.1); ⟨AC1

t is the thickness of the wall.

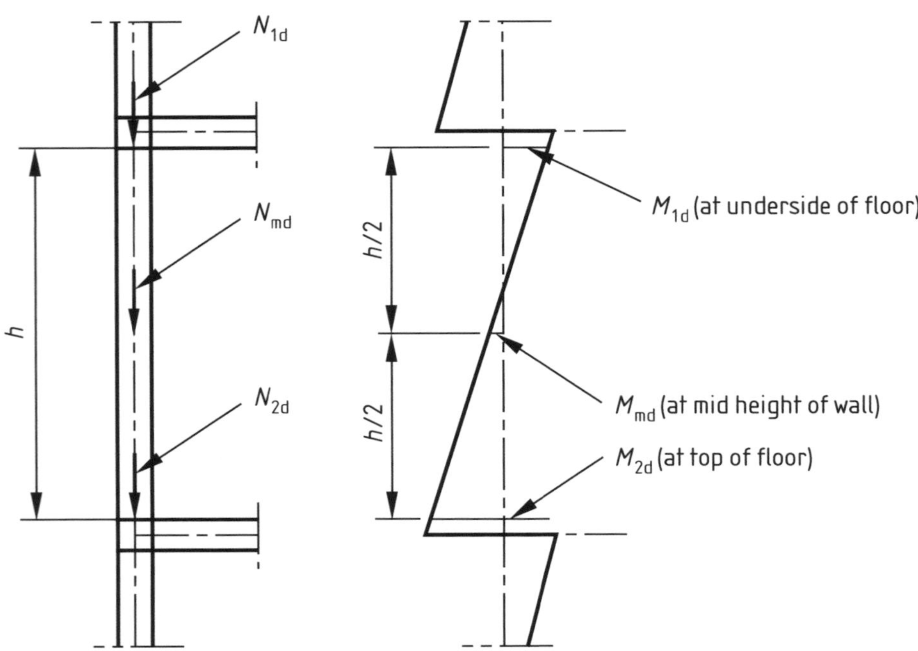

Figure 6.1 — Moments from calculation of eccentricities

(ii) In the middle of the wall height (Φ_m)

AC1 By using a simplification of the general principles given in 6.1.1, the reduction factor within the middle height of the wall, Φ_m , may be determined using e_{mk}, where: AC1

e_{mk} is the eccentricity at the middle height of the wall, calculated using equations (6.6) and (6.7):

$$e_{mk} = e_m + e_k \geq 0,05\,t \tag{6.6}$$

AC1 $$e_m = \frac{M_{md}}{N_{md}} + e_{hm} + e_{init} \tag{6.7}$$ AC1

e_m is the eccentricity due to loads;
M_{md} is the design value of the greatest moment at the middle of the height of the wall resulting from the moments at the top and bottom of the wall (see Figure 6.1), including any load applied eccentrically to the face of the wall (e.g. brackets);
N_{md} is the design value of the vertical load at the middle height of the wall, including any load applied eccentrically to the face of the wall (e.g. brackets);
e_{hm} is the eccentricity at mid-height resulting from horizontal loads (for example, wind);

NOTE The inclusion of e_{hm} depends on the load combination being used for the verification; its sign relative to that of M_{md} / N_{md} should be taken into account.

AC1 e_{init} is the initial eccentricity with a sign that increases the absolute value of e_m (see 5.5.1.1); AC1
h_{ef} is the effective height, obtained from 5.5.1.2 for the appropriate restraint or stiffening condition;
t_{ef} is the effective thickness of the wall, obtained from 5.5.1.3;
e_k is the eccentricity due to creep, calculated from equation (6.8):

$$e_k = 0,002\,\phi_\infty \frac{h_{ef}}{t_{ef}} \sqrt{t\,e_m} \tag{6.8}$$

ϕ_∞ is the final creep coefficient (see note under 3.7.4(2))

AC1 NOTE Φ_m may be determined from Annex G, using e_{mk} as expressed above. AC1

The requirement is to evaluate the capacity reduction factor at both the top and bottom of the wall as well as at the mid height of the wall and use the least favourable value when determining the load capacity of the wall. It will often be easier to use the graphical method given in Annex G for evaluating the reduction factor at mid- height rather than use the equation which is shown.

(2) For walls having a slenderness ratio of λ_c or less, the creep eccentricity, e_k, may be taken as zero.

NOTE The value of λ_c to be used in a country may be found in its National Annex, the recommended value of λ_c is 15. The country can make a distinction for different types of masonry related to the national choices made on the final creep coefficient.

NA.2.14 Slenderness ratio γ_c below which creep may be ignored [see BS EN 1996-1-1, 6.1.2.2(2)]

The value for γ_c should be taken as 27.

The note under 3.7.4(2) contains the following information:

A range of values for the deformation properties of masonry is given below. The values to be used in the UK may be found in Table NA.7

Table NA.7 — Range of coefficients of creep, moisture expansion or shrinkage, and thermal properties of masonry

Type of masonry unit	Final creep coefficient[A)] ϕ_∞	Long term moisture expansion or shrinkage[B)] mm/m	Coefficient of thermal expansion, α_t, 10^{-6}/K
Clay	1,5	0,5	6
Calcium silicate	1,5	−0,2	10
Dense aggregate concrete and manufactured stone	1,5	−0,2	10
Lightweight aggregate concrete	1,5	−0,4	10
Autoclaved aerated concrete	1,5	−0,2	10
Natural stone	normally very low	0,1	10

A) The final creep coefficient $\phi_\infty = \varepsilon_{c\infty} / \varepsilon_{el}$, where $\varepsilon_{c\infty}$ is the final creep strain and $\varepsilon_{el} = \sigma / E$.
B) Where the long term value of moisture expansion or shrinkage is shown as a negative number it indicates shortening and as a positive number it indicates expansion.

6.1.3 Walls subjected to concentrated loads

(1)P The design value of a concentrated vertical load, N_{Edc}, applied to a masonry wall, shall be less than or equal to the design value of the vertical concentrated load resistance of the wall, N_{Rdc}, such that

$$N_{Edc} \leq N_{Rdc} \tag{6.9}$$

(2) When a wall, built with Group 1 masonry units and detailed in accordance with Section 8, other than a shell bedded wall, is subjected to a concentrated load, the design value of the vertical load resistance of the wall is given by:

$$N_{Rdc} = \beta A_b f_d \tag{6.10}$$

where:

$$\beta = \left(1 + 0,3\frac{a_1}{h_c}\right)\left(1,5 - 1,1\frac{A_b}{A_{ef}}\right) \tag{6.11}$$

which should not be less than 1,0 nor taken to be greater than:

$1,25 + \frac{a_1}{2 h_c}$ or 1,5 whichever is the lesser

where:

- β is an enhancement factor for concentrated loads;
- a_1 is the distance from the end of the wall to the nearer edge of the loaded area (see Figure 6.2);
- h_c is the height of the wall to the level of the load;
- A_b is the loaded area;
- A_{ef} is the effective area of bearing, i.e. $l_{efm} \cdot t$;

l_{efm} is the effective length of the bearing as determined at the mid height of the wall or pier (see Figure 6.2);
t is the thickness of the wall, taking into account the depth of recesses in joints greater than 5 mm;
A_b/A_{ef} is not to be taken greater than 0,45.

NOTE Values for the enhancement factor for β are shown in graphical form in Annex H.

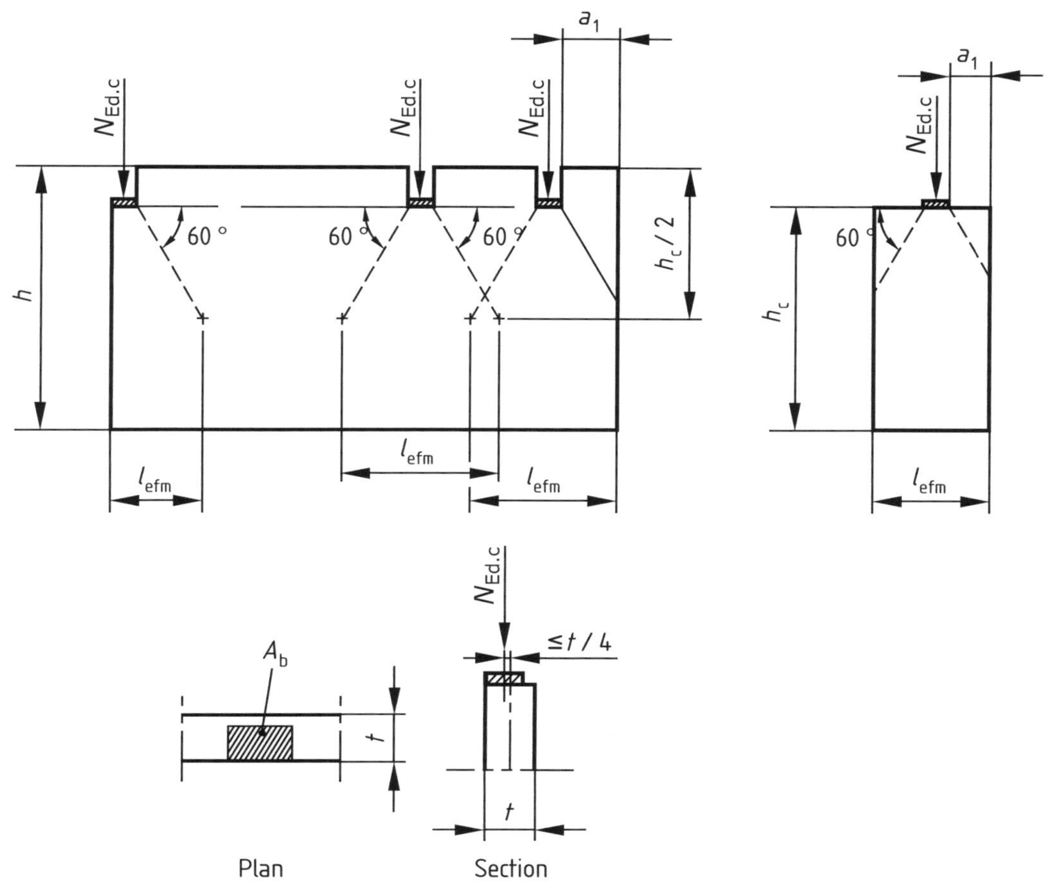

Figure 6.2 — Walls subjected to concentrated load

(3) For walls built with Groups 2, 3 and Group 4 masonry units and when shell bedding is used, it should be verified that, locally under the bearing of a concentrated load, the design compressive stress does not exceed the design compressive strength of masonry, f_d (i.e. β is taken to be AC1 1,0). AC1

(4) The eccentricity of the load from the centre line of the wall should not be greater than $t/4$ (see Figure 6.2).

(5) In all cases, the requirements of 6.1.2.1 should be met at the middle height of the wall below the bearings, including the effects of any other superimposed vertical loading, particularly for the case where concentrated loads are sufficiently close together for their effective lengths to overlap.

(6) The concentrated load should bear on a Group 1 unit or other solid material of length equal to the required bearing length plus a length on each side of the bearing based on a 60° spread of load to the base of the solid material; for an end bearing the additional length is required on one side only.

(7) Where the concentrated load is applied through a spreader beam of adequate stiffness and of width equal to the thickness of the wall, height greater than 200 mm and length greater than three times the bearing length of the load, the design value of the compressive stress beneath the concentrated load should not exceed 1,5 f_d.

In cases where only a small central area of a pier is loaded the masonry beneath the loaded area is in a state of triaxial stress which enhances the ultimate strength compared to the situation which is obtained with uniform loading. A similar enhancement may also be found when only a short length of wall is loaded.

6.2 Unreinforced masonry walls subjected to shear loading

(1)P At the ultimate limit state the design value of the shear load applied to the masonry wall, V_{Ed}, shall be less than or equal to the design value of the shear resistance of the wall, V_{Rd}, such that :

$$V_{Ed} \leq V_{Rd} \tag{6.12}$$

(2) The design value of the shear resistance is given by:

$$V_{Rd} = f_{vd}\, t\, l_c \tag{6.13}$$

where:

f_{vd} is the design value of the shear strength of masonry, obtained from 2.4.1 and 3.6.2, based on the average of the vertical stresses over the compressed part of the wall that is providing the shear resistance;

t is the thickness of the wall resisting the shear;

l_c is the length of the compressed part of the wall, ignoring any part of the wall that is in tension.

(3) The length of the compressed part of the wall, l_c, should be calculated assuming a linear stress distribution of the compressive stresses, and taking into account any openings, chases or recesses; any portion of the wall subjected to vertical tensile stresses should not be used in calculating the area of the wall to resist shear.

(4)P The connections between shear walls and flanges of intersecting walls shall be verified for vertical shear.

(5) The length of the compressed part of the wall should be verified for the vertical loading applied to it and the vertical load effect of the shear loads.

Horizontal forces such as wind loads are transferred by the walls carrying them to floors (acting as diaphragms) and other walls acting as buttresses and are ultimately transferred to the foundations. The buttressing walls need to be verified by using the characteristic shear strength over the length of the wall deemed to be in compression. There could be tension at the base of the wall, close to the supported wall, and this area should be excluded from the calculation.

6.3 Unreinforced masonry walls subjected to lateral loading

6.3.1 General

(1)P At the ultimate limit state, the design value of the moment applied to the masonry wall, M_{Ed} (see 5.5.5), shall be less than or equal to the design value of the moment of resistance of the wall, M_{Rd}, such that:

$$M_{Ed} \leq M_{Rd} \tag{6.14}$$

(2) The orthogonal strength ratio, μ, of the masonry should be taken into account in the design.

(3) The design value of the lateral moment of resistance of a masonry wall, M_{Rd}, per unit height or length, is given by:

$$M_{Rd} = f_{xd}\, Z \tag{6.15}$$

where:

f_{xd} is the design flexural strength appropriate to the plane of bending, obtained from 3.6.3, 6.3.1(4) or 6.6.2 (9);
Z is the elastic section modulus of unit height or length of the wall.

(4) When a vertical load is present, the favourable effect of the vertical stress may be taken into account either by:

(i) using the apparent flexural strength, $f_{xd1,app}$, given by equation (6.16), the orthogonal ratio used in (2) above being modified accordingly.

$$f_{xd1,app} = f_{xd1} + \sigma_d \tag{6.16}$$

where:

f_{xd1} is the design flexural strength of masonry with the plane of failure parallel to the bed joints, see 3.6.3;
σ_d is the design value of the vertical stress on the wall, not taken to be greater than $0,2f_d$

or

(ii) by calculating the resistance of the wall using formula (6.2) in which Φ is replaced by Φ_{fl}, taking into account the flexural strength, f_{xd1}.

NOTE This part does not include a method of calculating Φ_{fl} including flexural strength.

(5) In assessing the section modulus of a pier in a wall, the outstanding length of flange from the face of the pier should be taken as the lesser of:

- $h/10$ for walls spanning vertically between restraints;
- $h/5$ for cantilever walls;
- half the clear distance between piers;

where:

h is the clear height of the wall.

(6) In a cavity wall, the design lateral load per unit area, W_{Ed}, may be apportioned between the two leaves provided that the wall ties, or other connectors between the leaves, are capable of transmitting the actions to which the cavity wall is subjected. The apportionment between the two leaves may be in proportion either to their strength (i.e. using M_{Rd}), or the stiffness of each leaf. When using the stiffness, each leaf should then be verified for its proportion of M_{Ed}.

(7) If a wall is weakened by chases or recesses outside the limits given in clause 8.6, this weakening should be taken into account when determining the load bearing capacity by using the reduced thickness of the wall at the chase or recess position.

In respect of (6) above in the UK the apportionment of the design lateral load, per unit area, between the two leaves is carried out in proportion to their strength.

It should be noted that Clause 7.2 (5) indicates that the serviceability requirements for laterally loaded panels will be met if the dimensions are limited in accordance with Annex F.

6.3.2 Walls arching between supports

(1)P At the ultimate limit state, the design lateral load effect due to arch action in a wall shall be less than or equal to the design load resistance under an arch action and the design strength of the supports for the arch shall be greater than the effect of the design lateral load.

(2) A masonry wall built solidly between supports capable of resisting an arch thrust may be designed assuming that a horizontal or vertical arch develops within the thickness of the wall.

(3) Analysis may be based on a three-pin arch, when the bearing of the arch thrust at the supports and at the central hinge should be assumed as 0,1 times the thickness of the wall, as indicated on Figure 6.3. If chases or recesses occur near the thrust-lines of the arch, their effect on the strength of the masonry should be taken into account.

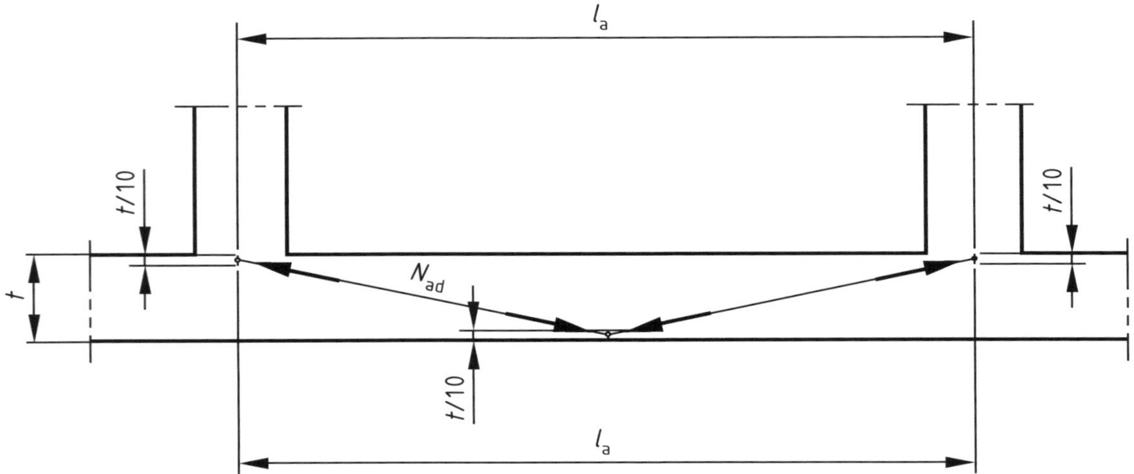

Figure 6.3 — Arch assumed for resisting lateral loads (diagrammatic)

(4) The arch thrust should be assessed from knowledge of the applied lateral load, the strength of the masonry in compression, the effectiveness of the junction between the wall and the support resisting the thrust and the elastic and time dependent shortening of the wall. The arch thrust may be provided by a vertical load.

(5) The arch rise, r, is given by equation (6.17):

$$r = 0,9\,t - d_a \tag{6.17}$$

where:

t is the thickness of the wall, taking into account the reduction in thickness resulting from recessed joints;
d_a is the deflection of the arch under the design lateral load; it may be taken to be zero for walls having a length to thickness ratio of 25 or less.

(6) The maximum design arch thrust per unit length of wall, N_{ad}, may be obtained from equation (6.18):

$$N_{ad} = 1,5\,f_d \frac{t}{10} \tag{6.18}$$

and where the lateral deflection is small, the design lateral strength is given by:

$$q_{lat,d} = f_d \left(\frac{t}{l_a}\right)^2 \tag{6.19}$$

where:

N_{ad} is the design arch thrust;
$q_{lat,d}$ is the design lateral strength per unit area of wall;
t is the thickness of the wall;

f_d is the design compressive strength of the masonry in the direction of the arch thrust, obtained from clause 3.6.1;

l_a is the length or the height of the wall between supports capable of resisting the arch thrust

provided that:

- any damp proof course or other plane of low frictional resistance in the wall can transmit the relevant horizontal forces;
- the design value of the stress due to vertical load is not less than 0,1 N/mm^2;
- the slenderness ratio AC1 in the considered direction AC1 does not exceed 20.

Arching action should only be assumed in situations where the wall is firmly restrained within its plane, for example such as would occur when the wall spanned between substantial buttresses.

6.3.3 Walls subjected to wind loading

(1) Walls subjected to wind loading should be designed using 5.5.5, 6.3.1 and 6.3.2, as relevant.

6.3.4 Walls subjected to lateral loading from earth and water

(1) Walls subject to lateral earth pressure with or without vertical loads, should be designed using 5.5.5, 6.1.2, 6.3.1 and 6.3.2, as relevant.

NOTE 1 The flexural strength of masonry f_{xk1} should not be used in the design of walls subjected to lateral earth pressure.

NOTE 2 A simplified method for designing basement walls subjected to lateral earth pressure is given in EN 1996-3.

6.3.5 Walls subjected to lateral loading from accidental situations

(1) Walls subjected to horizontal accidental loads, other than those resulting from seismic actions (for example, gas explosions), may be designed in accordance with 5.5.5, 6.1.2, 6.3.1, and 6.3.2, as relevant.

6.4 Unreinforced masonry walls subjected to combined vertical and lateral loading

6.4.1 General

(1) Unreinforced masonry walls that are subjected to both vertical and lateral loading may be verified by using any one of the methods given in 6.4.2, 6.4.3 or 6.4.4, as appropriate.

6.4.2 Method using Φ factor

(1) By using the relevant value of the eccentricity due to horizontal actions, AC1 e_{he} AC1 or e_{hm}, according to 6.1.2.2(1) (i) or (ii), a slenderness reduction factor, Φ, that takes into account the combined vertical and horizontal loading, can be obtained, using equations (6.5) and (6.7), for use in equation (6.2).

6.4.3 Method using apparent flexural strength

(1) 6.3.1 allows the design flexural strength of masonry, f_{xd1}, to be increased by the permanent vertical load to an apparent flexural strength, $f_{xd1.app}$, for use with the verification given in that part.

6.4.4 Method using equivalent bending moment coefficients

(1) Equivalent bending moments may be obtained from a combination of 6.4.2 and 6.4.3, to allow a combined calculation of vertical and horizontal loading.

NOTE Annex I gives a method of modifying the bending moment coefficient, α, as described in 5.5.5, to allow for both vertical and horizontal loads.

6.5 Ties

(1)P For calculation of the structural resistance of ties, the combination of the following shall be taken into account:

- differential movement between the connected structural members, typically faced wall and backing leaf, e.g. due to temperature differences, changes of moisture and actions;
- horizontal wind action;
- force due to interaction of leaves in cavity walls.

(2)P In determining the structural resistance of the ties, account shall be taken of any deviations from straightness and to any impairment of the material including the risk of brittle failure due to the successive deformations to which they are subjected during and after the execution.

(3)P Where walls, especially cavity walls, are subjected to lateral wind loads, the wall ties connecting the two leaves shall be capable of distributing the wind loads from the loaded leaf to the other leaf, backing wall or support.

(4) The minimum number of wall ties per unit area, n_t, should be obtained from equation (6.20):

$$n_t \geq \frac{W_{Ed}}{F_d} \tag{6.20}$$

but not less than according to 8.5.2.2

where:

W_{Ed} is the design value of the horizontal load, per unit area, to be transferred;
F_d is the design compressive or tensile resistance of a wall tie, as appropriate to the design condition.

NOTE 1 EN 845-1 requires that a manufacturer declares the strength of the ties; the declared value should be divided by γ_M to obtain the design value.

NOTE 2 The selection of wall ties should allow differential movement to take place between the leaves, without causing damage.

(5) In the case of a veneer wall, W_{Ed}, should be calculated on the basis that the wall ties are required to transmit all the design horizontal wind load acting on the wall to the backing structure.

8. Detailing

8.1 Masonry details

8.1.1 Masonry materials

(1)P Masonry units shall be suitable for the type of masonry, its location and its durability requirements. Mortar, concrete infill and reinforcement shall be appropriate to the type of unit and the durability requirements.

[AC1] (2) Masonry mortars for use in reinforced masonry, other than bed joint reinforced masonry, should not have a compressive strength, f_m, less than 4 N/mm^2, and for use in bed joint reinforced masonry, not less than 2 N/mm^2. [AC1]

8.1.2 Minimum thickness of wall

(1)P The minimum thickness of a wall shall be that required to give a robust wall.

(2) The minimum thickness, t_{min}, of a loadbearing wall should satisfy the outcome of the calculations according to this standard.

NOTE The value of t_{min} to be used in a Country may be found in its National Annex. The recommended value equals the outcome of the calculations.

NA.2.15 Minimum thickness of wall [see BS EN 1996-1-1, 8.1.2(2)]

The value for the minimum thickness, t_{min}, of a loadbearing wall should be taken as:

- 90 mm for a single leaf wall; and
- 75 mm for the leaves of a cavity wall.

8.1.3 Minimum area of wall

(1)P A load-bearing wall shall have a minimum net area on plan of 0,04 m^2, after allowing for any chases or recesses.

8.1.4 Bonding of masonry

8.1.4.1 Manufactured units

(1)P Masonry units shall be bonded together with mortar in accordance with proven practice.

(2)P Masonry units in an unreinforced masonry wall shall be overlapped on alternate courses so that the wall acts as a single structural element.

(3) In unreinforced masonry, masonry units less than or equal to a height of 250 mm should overlap by a length equal to at least 0,4 times the height of the unit or 40 mm, whichever is the greater (see Figure 8.1). For units greater than 250 mm high, the overlap should be the greater of 0,2 times the height of the unit or 100 mm. At corners or junctions, the overlap of the units should not be less than the thickness of the units if this would be less than the requirements given above; cut units should be used to achieve the specified overlap in the remainder of the wall.

NOTE The length of walls and the size of openings and piers preferably should suit the dimensions of the units so as to avoid excessive cutting.

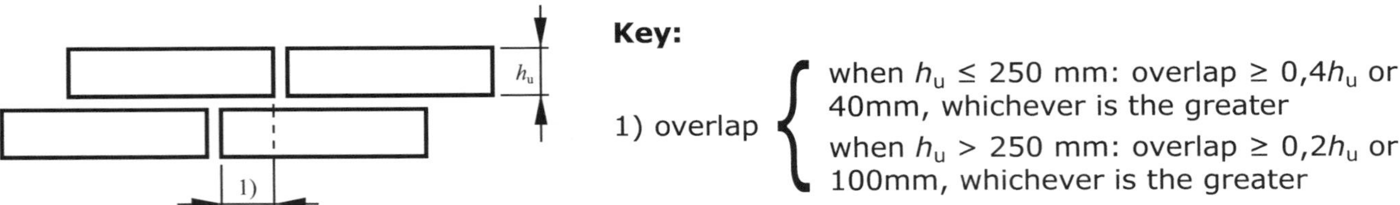

Figure 8.1 — Overlap of masonry units

(4) Bonding arrangements not meeting the minimum overlap requirements may be used in reinforced masonry where experience or experimental data indicate that they are satisfactory.

NOTE When a wall is reinforced, the degree of overlap can be determined as part of the design of the reinforcement.

(5) Where non-loadbearing walls abut loadbearing walls, allowance for differential deformation due to creep and shrinkage should be taken into account. When such walls are not bonded together, they should be tied together with suitable connectors allowing for differential deformations.

(6) The differential deformation behaviour of materials should be taken into account if different materials are to be rigidly connected together.

The requirements for bonding should be noted carefully to ensure that the proposed structure can be designed in accordance with the Eurocode. Where a bonding pattern is used that does not conform (such as vertical stack bonding which is sometimes used for aesthetic reasons) the designer will need to specify a significant inclusion of bed joint reinforcement or take other measures to verify that the wall will be adequate.

8.1.4.2 Dimensioned natural stone units

(1) Sedimentary and metamorphosed sedimentary natural stone should normally be specified to be laid with its bedding planes horizontal or near horizontal.

(2) Adjacent natural stone masonry facing units should overlap by a distance equal to at least 0,25 times the dimension of the smaller unit, with a minimum of 40 mm, unless other measures are taken to ensure adequate strength.

(3) In walls where the masonry units do not extend through the thickness of the wall, bonding units with a length equal to between 0,6 and 0,7 times the thickness of the wall, should be built at a spacing not exceeding 1 m, both vertically and horizontally. Such masonry units should have a height not less than 0,3 times their length.

8.1.5 Mortar joints

(1) Bed joints and perpend joints made with general purpose and lightweight mortars should have [AC1) an actual thickness (AC1] not less than 6 mm nor more than 15 mm, and bed and perpend joints made with thin layer mortars should have [AC1) an actual thickness (AC1] not less than 0,5 mm nor more than 3 mm.

NOTE Joints of thickness between 3 mm and 6 mm may be constructed if the mortars have been specially developed for the particular use, when the design may be based on the use of general purpose mortar.

(2) Bed joints should be horizontal unless the designer specifies otherwise.

(3) When units that rely on mortar pockets are used, perpend joints can be considered to be filled if mortar is provided to the full height of the joint over a minimum of 40 % of the width of the unit. Perpend joints in reinforced masonry subject to bending and shear across the joints should be fully filled with mortar.

The practice of specifying that the vertical perpend joints can be considered filled as long as a minimum of 40 % of the width of the unit is filled is new to the UK and needs to be treated with caution. In areas of severe exposure to wind driven rain the designer may wish to tighten the specification for exposed walls. Separating walls between dwellings usually have to provide a high level of sound insulation which would be degraded if the mortar joints are not fully filled with mortar.

8.1.6 Bearings under concentrated loads

(1) Concentrated loads should bear on a wall a minimum length of 90 mm or such distance as is required from calculations according to 6.1.3, whichever is the greater.

8.5 Connection of walls

8.5.1 Connection of walls to floors and roofs

British Standards have historically given extensive details to ensure the adequacy of connections and it is hoped that this guidance will continue to be available in some form.

8.5.1.1 General

(1)P Where walls are assumed to be restrained by floors or roofs, the walls shall be connected to the floors or roofs so as to provide for the transfer of the design lateral loads to the bracing elements.

(2) Transfer of lateral loads to the bracing elements should be made by the floor or roof structure, for example, reinforced or precast concrete or timber joists incorporating boarding, provided the floor or roof structure is capable of developing diaphragm action, or by a ring beam capable of transferring the resulting shear and bending action effects. Either the frictional resistance of the bearing of structural members on masonry walls, or metal straps of suitable end fixing, should be capable of resisting the transfer loads.

(3)P Where a floor or roof bears on a wall, the bearing length shall be sufficient to provide the required bearing capacity and shear resistance, allowing for manufacturing and erection tolerances.

(4) The minimum bearing length of floors or roofs on walls should be as required by calculation.

8.5.1.2 Connection by straps

(1)P Where straps are used they shall be capable of transferring the lateral loads between the wall and the restraining structural element.

(2) When the surcharge on the wall is negligible, for example, at a gable wall/roof junction, special consideration is necessary to ensure that the connection between the straps and the wall will be effective.

(3) The spacing of straps between walls and floors or roofs should be not greater than 2 m for buildings up to 4 storeys high, and 1,25 m for higher buildings.

8.5.1.3 Connection by frictional resistance

(1)P Where concrete floors, roofs or ring beams bear directly on a wall, the frictional resistance shall be capable of transferring the lateral loads.

8.5.1.4 Ring ties and ring beams

(1) When the transfer of lateral loads to the bracing elements is to be achieved by the use of ring beams, or ring ties, they should be placed in every floor level or directly below. The ring ties may consist of reinforced concrete, reinforced masonry, steel or wood and should be able to support a design tensile force of 45 kN.

(2) When the ring ties are not continuous, additional measures should be undertaken to ensure continuity.

(3) Ring ties made of reinforced concrete should contain at least two reinforcing steel bars of at least 150 mm^2. The laps should be designed in accordance with EN 1992-1-1 and staggered, if possible. Parallel continuous reinforcement may be considered with their full cross-section provided that they are situated in floors or window lintels at a distance of not more than 0,5 m from the middle of the wall and floor, respectively.

(4) If floors without diaphragm action are used, or sliding layers are put under the floor bearings, the horizontal stiffening of the walls should be ensured by ring beams or statically equivalent measures.

8.5.2 Connection between walls

8.5.2.1 General

(1)P Intersecting loadbearing walls shall be joined together so that the required vertical and lateral loads can be transferred between them.

(2) The joint at the intersection of walls should be made either by:

- masonry bond (see 8.1.4), or
- connectors or reinforcement extending into each wall.

(3) Intersecting loadbearing walls should be erected simultaneously.

8.5.2.2 Cavity and veneer walls

(1)P The two leaves of a cavity wall shall be effectively tied together.

(2) Wall ties connecting together the two leaves of a cavity wall should be not less than the number calculated according to 6.5, where relevant, nor less than n_{tmin} per m^2.

NOTE 1 The requirements for the use of wall ties are given in EN 1996-2.

NOTE 2 When connecting elements, for example, prefabricated bed joint reinforcement, are used to connect two leaves of a wall together, each tying element should be treated as a wall tie.

NOTE 3 The value of n_{tmin} for use in a country may be found in its National Annex; the recommended value is 2.

NA.2.16 Cavity walls [see BS EN 1996-1-1, 8.5.2.2(2)]

The value for n_{tmin} should be taken as 2,5.

8.5.2.3 Double-leaf walls

(1)P The two leaves of a double-leaf wall shall be effectively tied together.

(2) Wall ties connecting the two leaves of a double-leaf wall, calculated according to [AC1) 6.5(4) (AC1], should have a sufficient cross-sectional area with not less than *j* connectors per square metre of the double-leaf wall, and be evenly distributed.

NOTE 1 Some forms of prefabricated bed joint reinforcement can also function as ties between the two leaves of a double-leaf wall (see EN 845-3).

NOTE 2 The value of *j* for use in a country may be found in its National Annex; the recommended value is 2.

NA.2.17 Double-leaf walls [see BS EN 1996-1-1, 8.5.2.3(2)]

The value for j, for double leaf walls, should be taken as 2,5.

8.6 Chases and recesses on walls

8.6.1 General

(1)P Chases and recesses shall not impair the stability of the wall.

(2) Chases and recesses should not pass through lintels or other structural items built into a wall nor should they be allowed in reinforced masonry members unless specifically allowed for by the designer.

(3) In cavity walls, the provision of chases and recesses should be considered separately for each leaf.

8.6.2 Vertical chases and recesses

(1) The reduction in vertical load, shear and flexural resistance resulting from vertical chases and recesses may be neglected if such vertical chases and recesses are not deeper than $t_{ch,v}$; the depth of the recess or chase should include the depth of any hole reached when forming the recess or chase. If these limits are exceeded, the vertical load, shear and flexural resistance should be checked by calculation with the masonry section reduced by the extent of the chases or recesses.

NOTE The value of $t_{ch,v}$ for use in a Country may be found in its National Annex.

NA.2.18 Vertical chases and recesses [see BS EN 1996-1-1, 8.6.2(1)]

The values for the maximum depth of vertical chases and recesses allowed without calculation, $t_{ch,v}$, are given in Table NA.11.

Table NA.11 – Value of $t_{ch,v}$, the maximum depth of a vertical chase or recess allowed without calculation

Thickness of single leaf wall or loaded leaf of a cavity wall	Chases and recesses formed after construction of masonry		Chases and recesses formed during construction of masonry	
	$t_{ch,v}$	Maximum width	$t_{ch,v}$ should never be so great as to result in the remaining wall thickness being less than:	Maximum width
mm	mm	mm	mm	mm
75 – 89	30	75	60	300
90 – 115	30	100	70	300
116 – 175	30	125	90	300
176 – 225	30	150	140	300
226 – 300	30	175	175	300
> 300	30	200	215	300

NOTE 1 The maximum depth of the recess or chase should include the depth of any hole reached when forming the recess or chase.

NOTE 2 Vertical chases which do not extend more than one third of the storey height above floor level may have a depth up to 80 mm and a width up to 120 mm, if the thickness of the wall is 225 mm or more.

NOTE 3 The horizontal distance between adjacent chases or between a chase and a recess or an opening should not be less than 225 mm.

NOTE 4 The horizontal distance between any two adjacent recesses, whether they occur on the same side or on opposite sides of the wall, or between a recess and an opening, should not be less than twice the width of the wider of the two recesses.

NOTE 5 The cumulative width of vertical chases and recesses should not exceed 0,13 times the length of the wall.

8.6.3 Horizontal and inclined chases

(1) Any horizontal and inclined chases should be positioned within one eighth of the clear height of the wall, above or below a floor. The total depth, including the depth of any hole reached when forming the chase, should be less than AC1 $t_{ch,h}$ AC1 providing that the eccentricity in the region of the chase is less than t/3. If this limit is exceeded, the vertical load, shear and flexural resistance should be checked by calculation taking the reduced cross section into account.

NOTE The value of AC1 $t_{ch,h}$ AC1 for use in a Country may be found in its National Annex. The values given in the Table below are recommended.

NA.2.19 Horizontal or inclined chases [see BS EN 1996-1-1, 8.6.3(1)]

The values for the maximum depth of a horizontal or inclined chase allowed without calculation, $t_{ch,h}$, are given in Table NA.12.

Table NA.12 – Value of $t_{ch,h}$, the maximum depth of a horizontal or inclined chase allowed without calculation

Thickness of solid wall or loaded leaf of a cavity wall mm	$t_{ch,h}$	
	Unlimited length mm	Length ≤ 1 250 mm mm
75 – 84	0	0
85 – 115	0	0
116 – 175	0	15
176 – 225	10	20
226 – 300	15	25
Over 300	20	30

NOTE 1 The maximum depth of the chase should include the depth of any hole reached when forming the chase.

NOTE 2 The horizontal distance between the end of a chase and an opening should not be less than 500 mm.

NOTE 3 The horizontal distance between adjacent chases of limited length, whether they occur on the same side or on opposite sides of the wall, should be not less than twice the length of the longest chase.

NOTE 4 In walls of thickness greater than 175 mm, the permitted depth of the chase may be increased by 10 mm if the chase is machine cut accurately to the required depth. If machine cuts are used, chases up to 10 mm deep may be cut in both sides of walls of thickness not less than 225 mm.

NOTE 5 The width of chase should not exceed half the residual thickness of the wall.

8.7 Damp proof courses

(1)P Damp proof courses shall be capable of transferring the horizontal and vertical design loads without suffering or causing damage; they shall have sufficient surface frictional resistance to prevent unintended movement of the masonry resting on them.

8.8 Thermal and long term movement

(1)P Allowance shall be made for the effects of movements such that the performance of the masonry is not affected adversely.

NOTE Information on the allowance for movement in masonry will be found in EN 1996-2.

NA.3 Decisions on the status of the informative annexes

BS EN 1996-1-1 informative Annexes A, B, C, D, E, F, G, H, I and J may be used.

Annex E
(informative)
Bending moment coefficients, AC1 α_2 AC1, in single leaf laterally loaded wall panels of thickness less than or equal to 250 mm

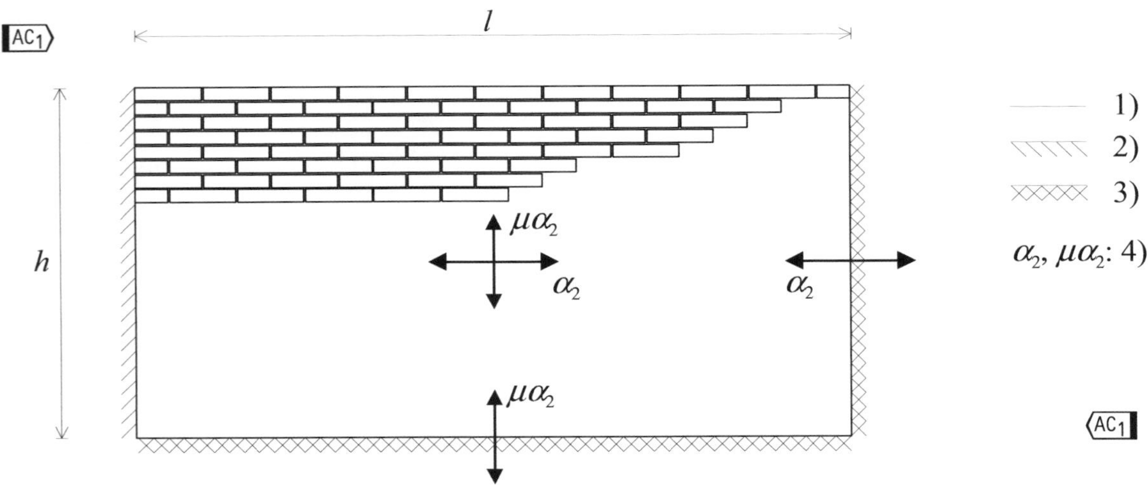

Key

1) free edge
2) simply supported edge
3) fully restrained/continuous edge
AC1 4) moment coefficients in the indicated directions AC1

Figure E1 — Key to support conditions used in tables

Wall support condition

A

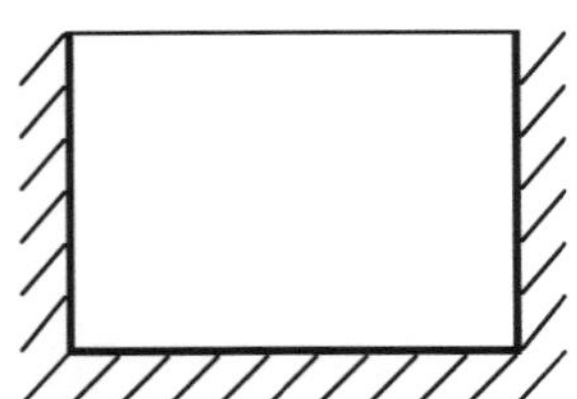

μ	h/l							
	0,30	**0,50**	**0,75**	**1,00**	**1,25**	**1,50**	**1,75**	**2,00**
1,00	0,031	0,045	0,059	0,072	0,079	0,085	0,090	0,094
0,90	0,032	0,047	0,061	0,073	0,081	0,087	0,092	0,095
0,80	0,034	0,049	0,064	0,075	0,083	0,089	0,093	0,097
0,70	0,035	0,051	0,066	0,077	0,085	0,091	0,095	0,098
0,60	0,038	0,053	0,069	0,080	0,088	0,093	0,097	0,100
0,50	0,040	0,056	0,073	0,083	0,090	0,095	0,099	0,102
0,40	0,043	0,061	0,077	0,087	0,093	0,098	0,101	0,104
0,35	0,045	0,064	0,080	0,089	0,095	0,100	0,103	0,105
0,30	0,048	0,067	0,082	0,091	0,097	0,101	0,104	0,107
0,25	0,050	0,071	0,085	0,094	0,099	0,103	0,106	0,109
0,20	0,054	0,075	0,089	0,097	0,102	0,105	0,108	0,111
0,15	0,060	0,080	0,093	0,100	0,104	0,108	0,110	0,113
0,10	0,069	0,087	0,098	0,104	0,108	0,111	0,113	0,115
0,05	0,082	0,097	0,105	0,110	0,113	0,115	0,116	0,117

Wall support condition

B

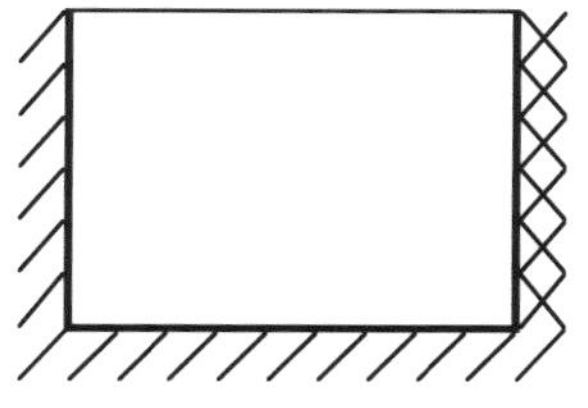

μ	h/l							
	0,30	**0,50**	**0,75**	**1,00**	**1,25**	**1,50**	**1,75**	**2,00**
1,00	0,024	0,035	0,046	0,053	0,059	0,062	0,065	0,068
0,90	0,025	0,036	0,047	0,055	0,060	0,063	0,066	0,068
0,80	0,027	0,037	0,049	0,056	0,061	0,065	0,067	0,069
0,70	0,028	0,039	0,051	0,058	0,062	0,066	0,068	0,070
0,60	0,030	0,042	0,053	0,059	0,064	0,067	0,069	0,071
0,50	0,031	0,044	0,055	0,061	0,066	0,069	0,071	0,072
0,40	0,034	0,047	0,057	0,063	0,067	0,070	0,072	0,074
0,35	0,035	0,049	0,059	0,065	0,068	0,071	0,073	0,074
0,30	0,037	0,051	0,061	0,066	0,070	0,072	0,074	0,075
0,25	0,039	0,053	0,062	0,068	0,071	0,073	0,075	0,077
0,20	0,043	0,056	0,065	0,069	0,072	0,074	0,076	0,078
0,15	0,047	0,059	0,067	0,071	0,074	0,076	0,077	0,079
0,10	0,052	0,063	0,070	0,074	0,076	0,078	0,079	0,080
0,05	0,060	0,069	0,074	0,077	0,079	0,080	0,081	0,082

Wall support condition

C

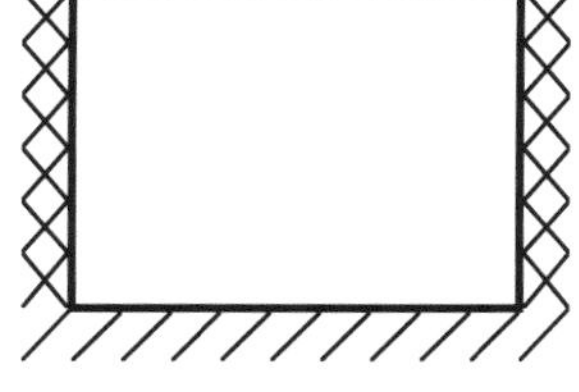

μ	h/l							
	0,30	**0,50**	**0,75**	**1,00**	**1,25**	**1,50**	**1,75**	**2,00**
1,00	0,020	0,028	0,037	0,042	0,045	0,048	0,050	0,051
0,90	0,021	0,029	0,038	0,043	0,046	0,048	0,050	0,052
0,80	0,022	0,031	0,039	0,043	0,047	0,049	0,051	0,052
0,70	0,023	0,032	0,040	0,044	0,048	0,050	0,051	0,053
0,60	0,024	0,034	0,041	0,046	0,049	0,051	0,052	0,053
0,50	0,025	0,035	0,043	0,047	0,050	0,052	0,053	0,054
0,40	0,027	0,038	0,044	0,048	0,051	0,053	0,054	0,055
0,35	0,029	0,039	0,045	0,049	0,052	0,053	0,054	0,055
0,30	0,030	0,040	0,046	0,050	0,052	0,054	0,055	0,056
0,25	0,032	0,042	0,048	0,051	0,053	0,054	0,056	0,057
0,20	0,034	0,043	0,049	0,052	0,054	0,055	0,056	0,058
0,15	0,037	0,046	0,051	0,053	0,055	0,056	0,057	0,059
0,10	0,041	0,048	0,053	0,055	0,056	0,057	0,058	0,059
0,05	0,046	0,052	0,055	0,057	0,058	0,059	0,059	0,060

Wall support condition

D

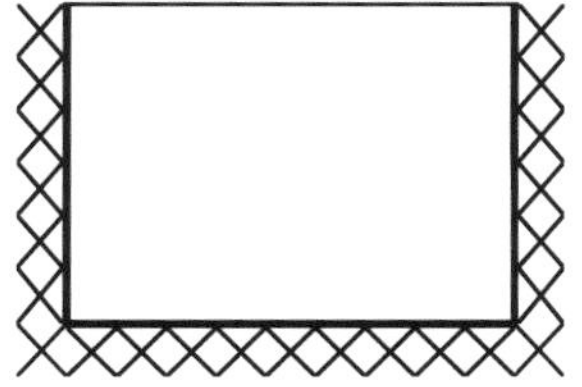

μ	h/l							
	0,30	**0,50**	**0,75**	**1,00**	**1,25**	**1,50**	**1,75**	**2,00**
1,00	0,013	0,021	0,029	0,035	0,040	0,043	0,045	0,047
0,90	0,014	0,022	0,031	0,036	0,040	0,043	0,046	0,048
0,80	0,015	0,023	0,032	0,038	0,041	0,044	0,047	0,048
0,70	0,016	0,025	0,033	0,039	0,043	0,045	0,047	0,049
0,60	0,017	0,026	0,035	0,040	0,044	0,046	0,048	0,050
0,50	0,018	0,028	0,037	0,042	0,045	0,048	0,050	0,051
0,40	0,020	0,031	0,039	0,043	0,047	0,049	0,051	0,052
0,35	0,022	0,032	0,040	0,044	0,048	0,050	0,051	0,053
0,30	0,023	0,034	0,041	0,046	0,049	0,051	0,052	0,053
0,25	0,025	0,035	0,043	0,047	0,050	0,052	0,053	0,054
0,20	0,027	0,038	0,044	0,048	0,051	0,053	0,054	0,055
0,15	0,030	0,040	0,046	0,050	0,052	0,054	0,055	0,056
0,10	0,034	0,043	0,049	0,052	0,054	0,055	0,056	0,057
0,05	0,041	0,048	0,053	0,055	0,056	0,057	0,058	0,059

Wall support condition

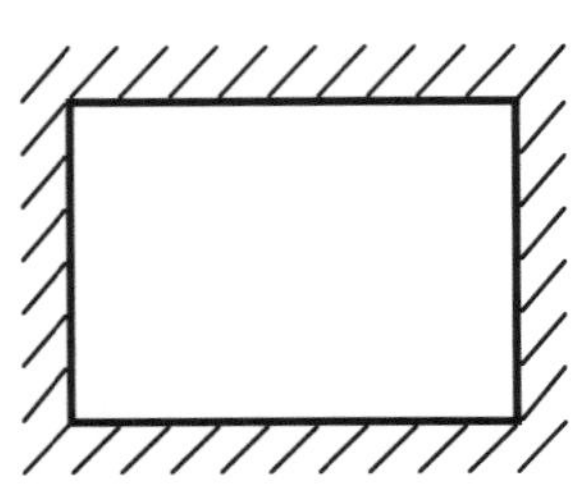

μ	h/l							
	0,30	**0,50**	**0,75**	**1,00**	**1,25**	**1,50**	**1,75**	**2,00**
1,00	0,008	0,018	0,030	0,042	0,051	0,059	0,066	0,071
0,90	0,009	0,019	0,032	0,044	0,054	0,062	0,068	0,074
0,80	0,010	0,021	0,035	0,046	0,056	0,064	0,071	0,076
0,70	0,011	0,023	0,037	0,049	0,059	0,067	0,073	0,078
0,60	0,012	0,025	0,040	0,053	0,062	0,070	0,076	0,081
0,50	0,014	0,028	0,044	0,057	0,066	0,074	0,080	0,085
0,40	0,017	0,032	0,049	0,062	0,071	0,078	0,084	0,088
0,35	0,018	0,035	0,052	0,064	0,074	0,081	0,086	0,090
0,30	0,020	0,038	0,055	0,068	0,077	0,083	0,089	0,093
0,25	0,023	0,042	0,059	0,071	0,080	0,087	0,091	0,096
0,20	0,026	0,046	0,064	0,076	0,084	0,090	0,095	0,099
0,15	0,032	0,053	0,070	0,081	0,089	0,094	0,098	0,103
0,10	0,039	0,062	0,078	0,088	0,095	0,100	0,103	0,106
0,05	0,054	0,076	0,090	0,098	0,103	0,107	0,109	0,110

Wall support condition

F

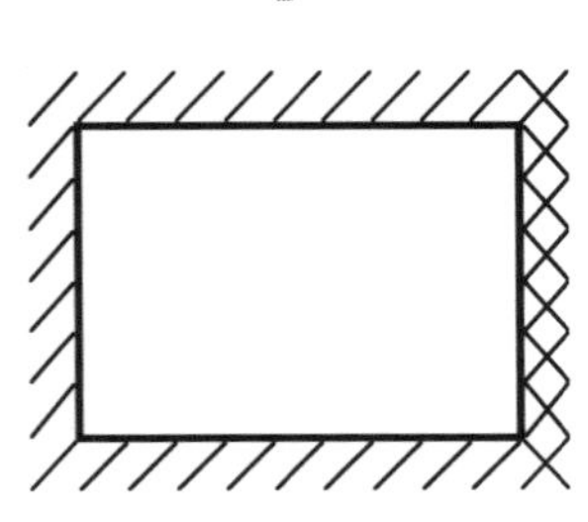

μ	h/l							
	0,30	**0,50**	**0,75**	**1,00**	**1,25**	**1,50**	**1,75**	**2,00**
1,00	0,008	0,016	0,026	0,034	0,041	0,046	0,051	0,054
0,90	0,008	0,017	0,027	0,036	0,042	0,048	0,052	0,055
0,80	0,009	0,018	0,029	0,037	0,044	0,049	0,054	0,057
0,70	0,010	0,020	0,031	0,039	0,046	0,051	0,055	0,058
0,60	0,011	0,022	0,033	0,042	0,048	0,053	0,057	0,060
0,50	0,013	0,024	0,036	0,044	0,051	0,056	0,059	0,062
0,40	0,015	0,027	0,039	0,048	0,054	0,058	0,062	0,064
0,35	0,016	0,029	0,041	0,050	0,055	0,060	0,063	0,066
0,30	0,018	0,031	0,044	0,052	0,057	0,062	0,065	0,067
0,25	0,020	0,034	0,046	0,054	0,060	0,063	0,066	0,069
0,20	0,023	0,037	0,049	0,057	0,062	0,066	0,068	0,070
0,15	0,027	0,042	0,053	0,060	0,065	0,068	0,070	0,072
0,10	0,032	0,048	0,058	0,064	0,068	0,071	0,073	0,074
0,05	0,043	0,057	0,066	0,070	0,073	0,075	0,077	0,078

Wall support condition

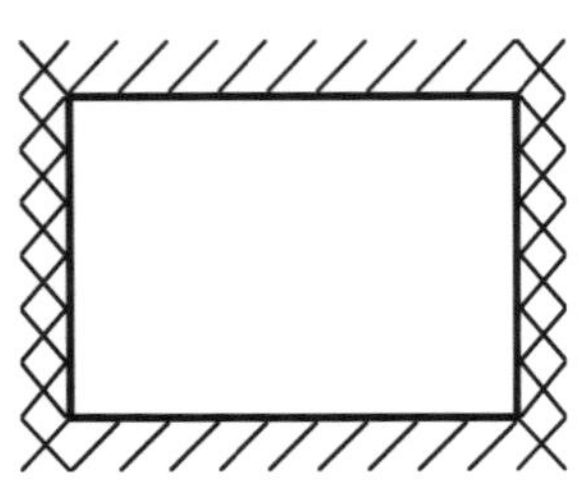

μ	h/l							
	0,30	**0,50**	**0,75**	**1,00**	**1,25**	**1,50**	**1,75**	**2,00**
1,00	0,007	0,014	0,022	0,028	0,033	0,037	0,040	0,042
0,90	0,008	0,015	0,023	0,029	0,034	0,038	0,041	0,043
0,80	0,008	0,016	0,024	0,031	0,035	0,039	0,042	0,044
0,70	0,009	0,017	0,026	0,032	0,037	0,040	0,043	0,045
0,60	0,010	0,019	0,028	0,034	0,038	0,042	0,044	0,046
0,50	0,011	0,021	0,030	0,036	0,040	0,043	0,046	0,048
0,40	0,013	0,023	0,032	0,038	0,042	0,045	0,047	0,049
0,35	0,014	0,025	0,033	0,039	0,043	0,046	0,048	0,050
0,30	0,016	0,026	0,035	0,041	0,044	0,047	0,049	0,051
0,25	0,018	0,028	0,037	0,042	0,046	0,048	0,050	0,052
0,20	0,020	0,031	0,039	0,044	0,047	0,050	0,052	0,054
0,15	0,023	0,034	0,042	0,046	0,049	0,051	0,053	0,055
0,10	0,027	0,038	0,045	0,049	0,052	0,053	0,055	0,057
0,05	0,035	0,044	0,050	0,053	0,055	0,056	0,057	0,058

Wall support condition

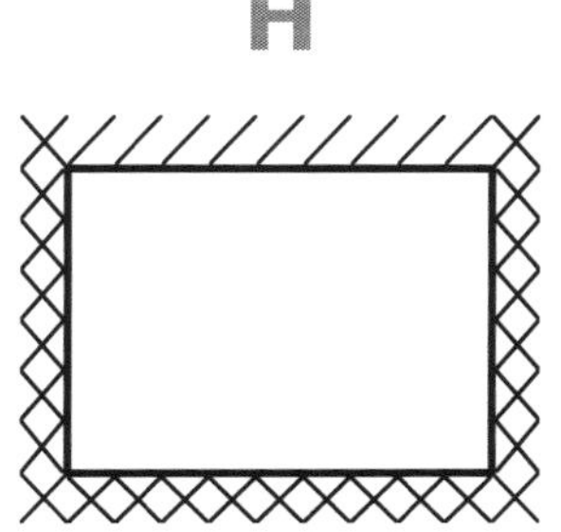

μ	h/l							
	0,30	**0,50**	**0,75**	**1,00**	**1,25**	**1,50**	**1,75**	**2,00**
1,00	0,005	0,011	0,018	0,024	0,029	0,033	0,036	0,039
0,90	0,006	0,012	0,019	0,025	0,030	0,034	0,037	0,040
0,80	0,006	0,013	0,020	0,027	0,032	0,035	0,038	0,041
0,70	0,007	0,014	0,022	0,028	0,033	0,037	0,040	0,042
0,60	0,008	0,015	0,024	0,030	0,035	0,038	0,041	0,043
0,50	0,009	0,017	0,025	0,032	0,036	0,040	0,043	0,045
0,40	0,010	0,019	0,028	0,034	0,039	0,042	0,045	0,047
0,35	0,011	0,021	0,029	0,036	0,040	0,043	0,046	0,047
0,30	0,013	0,022	0,031	0,037	0,041	0,044	0,047	0,049
0,25	0,014	0,024	0,033	0,039	0,043	0,046	0,048	0,051
0,20	0,016	0,027	0,035	0,041	0,045	0,047	0,049	0,052
0,15	0,019	0,030	0,038	0,043	0,047	0,049	0,051	0,053
0,10	0,023	0,034	0,042	0,047	0,050	0,052	0,053	0,054
0,05	0,031	0,041	0,047	0,051	0,053	0,055	0,056	0,056

Wall support condition

μ	h/l							
	0,30	**0,50**	**0,75**	**1,00**	**1,25**	**1,50**	**1,75**	**2,00**
1,00	0,004	0,009	0,015	0,021	0,026	0,030	0,033	0,036
0,90	0,004	0,010	0,016	0,022	0,027	0,031	0,034	0,037
0,80	0,005	0,010	0,017	0,023	0,028	0,032	0,035	0,038
0,70	0,005	0,011	0,019	0,025	0,030	0,033	0,037	0,039
0,60	0,006	0,013	0,020	0,026	0,031	0,035	0,038	0,041
0,50	0,007	0,014	0,022	0,028	0,033	0,037	0,040	0,042
0,40	0,008	0,016	0,024	0,031	0,035	0,039	0,042	0,044
0,35	0,009	0,017	0,026	0,032	0,037	0,040	0,043	0,045
0,30	0,010	0,019	0,028	0,034	0,038	0,042	0,044	0,046
0,25	0,011	0,021	0,030	0,036	0,040	0,043	0,046	0,048
0,20	0,013	0,023	0,032	0,038	0,042	0,045	0,047	0,050
0,15	0,016	0,026	0,035	0,041	0,044	0,047	0,049	0,051
0,10	0,020	0,031	0,039	0,044	0,047	0,050	0,052	0,054
0,05	0,027	0,038	0,045	0,049	0,052	0,053	0,055	0,056

Wall support condition

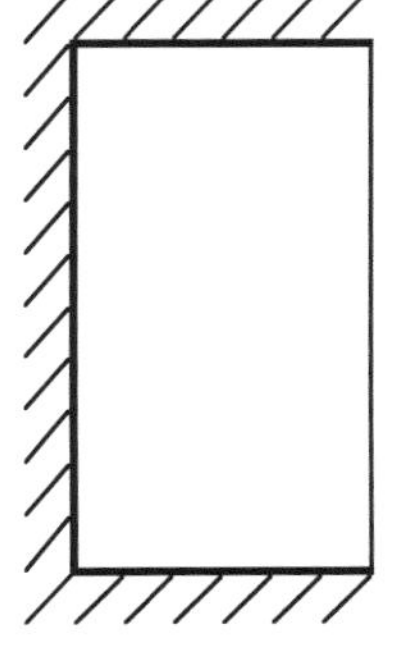

μ	h/l							
	0,30	**0,50**	**0,75**	**1,00**	**1,25**	**1,50**	**1,75**	**2,00**
1,00	0,009	0,023	0,046	0,071	0,096	0,122	0,151	0,180
0,90	0,010	0,026	0,050	0,076	0,103	0,131	0,162	0,193
0,80	0,012	0,028	0,054	0,083	0,111	0,142	0,175	0,208
0,70	0,013	0,032	0,060	0,091	0,121	0,156	0,191	0,227
0,60	0,015	0,036	0,067	0,100	0,135	0,173	0,211	0,250
0,50	0,018	0,042	0,077	0,113	0,153	0,195	0,237	0,280
0,40	0,021	0,050	0,090	0,131	0,177	0,225	0,272	0,321
0,35	0,024	0,055	0,098	0,144	0,194	0,244	0,296	0,347
0,30	0,027	0,062	0,108	0,160	0,214	0,269	0,325	0,381
0,25	0,032	0,071	0,122	0,180	0,240	0,300	0,362	0,428
0,20	0,038	0,083	0,142	0,208	0,276	0,344	0,413	0,488
0,15	0,048	0,100	0,173	0,250	0,329	0,408	0,488	0,570
0,10	0,065	0,131	0,224	0,321	0,418	0,515	0,613	0,698
0,05	0,106	0,208	0,344	0,482	0,620	0,759	0,898	0,959

Wall support condition

K

μ	h/l							
	0,30	**0,50**	**0,75**	**1,00**	**1,25**	**1,50**	**1,75**	**2,00**
1,00	0,009	0,021	0,038	0,056	0,074	0,091	0,108	0,123
0,90	0,010	0,023	0,041	0,060	0,079	0,097	0,113	0,129
0,80	0,011	0,025	0,045	0,065	0,084	0,103	0,120	0,136
0,70	0,012	0,028	0,049	0,070	0,091	0,110	0,128	0,145
0,60	0,014	0,031	0,054	0,077	0,099	0,119	0,138	0,155
0,50	0,016	0,035	0,061	0,085	0,109	0,130	0,149	0,167
0,40	0,019	0,041	0,069	0,097	0,121	0,144	0,164	0,182
0,35	0,021	0,045	0,075	0,104	0,129	0,152	0,173	0,191
0,30	0,024	0,050	0,082	0,112	0,139	0,162	0,183	0,202
0,25	0,028	0,056	0,091	0,123	0,150	0,174	0,196	0,217
0,20	0,033	0,064	0,103	0,136	0,165	0,190	0,211	0,234
0,15	0,040	0,077	0,119	0,155	0,184	0,210	0,231	0,253
0,10	0,053	0,096	0,144	0,182	0,213	0,238	0,260	0,279
0,05	0,080	0,136	0,190	0,230	0,260	0,286	0,306	0,317

Wall support condition

L

μ	h/l							
	0,30	**0,50**	**0,75**	**1,00**	**1,25**	**1,50**	**1,75**	**2,00**
1,00	0,006	0,015	0,029	0,044	0,059	0,073	0,088	0,102
0,90	0,007	0,017	0,032	0,047	0,063	0,078	0,093	0,107
0,80	0,008	0,018	0,034	0,051	0,067	0,084	0,099	0,114
0,70	0,009	0,021	0,038	0,056	0,073	0,090	0,106	0,122
0,60	0,010	0,023	0,042	0,061	0,080	0,098	0,115	0,131
0,50	0,012	0,027	0,048	0,068	0,089	0,108	0,126	0,142
0,40	0,014	0,032	0,055	0,078	0,100	0,121	0,139	0,157
0,35	0,016	0,035	0,060	0,084	0,108	0,129	0,148	0,165
0,30	0,018	0,039	0,066	0,092	0,116	0,138	0,158	0,176
0,25	0,021	0,044	0,073	0,101	0,127	0,150	0,170	0,190
0,20	0,025	0,052	0,084	0,114	0,141	0,165	0,185	0,206
0,15	0,031	0,061	0,098	0,131	0,159	0,184	0,205	0,226
0,10	0,041	0,078	0,121	0,156	0,186	0,212	0,233	0,252
0,05	0,064	0,114	0,164	0,204	0,235	0,260	0,281	0,292

Annex F
(informative)
Limiting height and length to thickness ratios for walls under the serviceability limit state

(1) Notwithstanding the ability of a wall to satisfy the ultimate limit state, which must be verified, its size should be limited to that which results from use of figures F.1, F.2 or F.3, depending on the restraint conditions as shown on the figures, where his is the clear height of the wall, l is the length of the wall and t is the thickness of the wall; for cavity wall use t_{ef} in place of t.

(2) Where walls are restrained at the top but not at the ends, h should be limited to 30 t.

(3) This annex is valid when the thickness of the wall, or one leaf of a cavity wall, is not less than 100 mm.

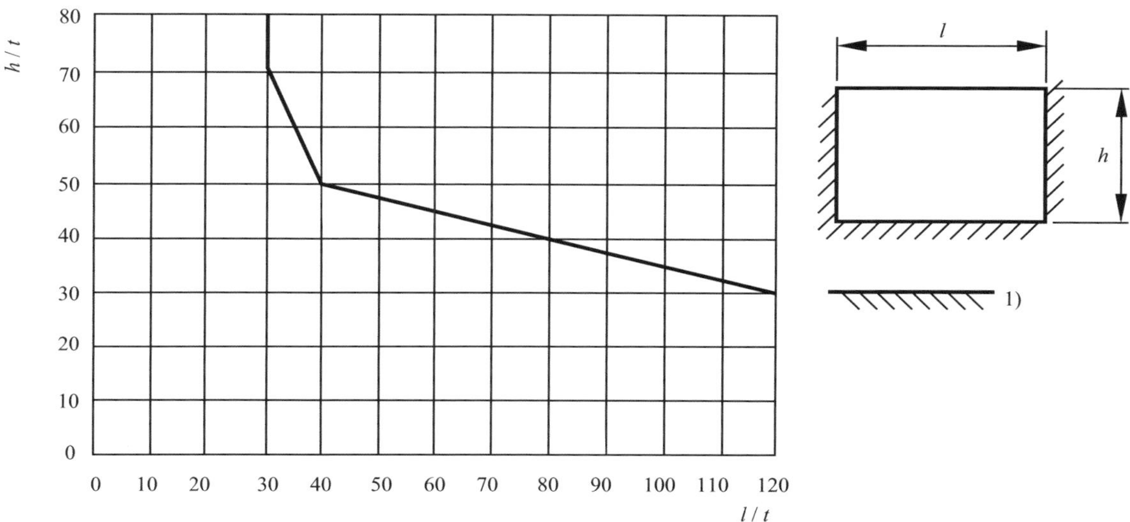

Key

1) simply supported or with full continuity

Figure F.1 — Limiting height and length to thickness ratios of walls restrained on all four edges

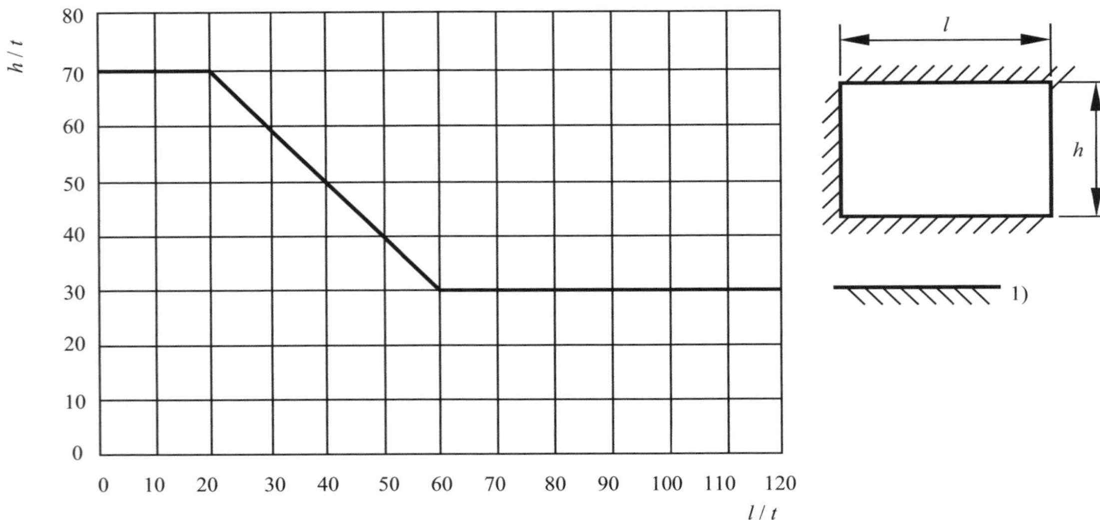

Key

1) simply supported or with full continuity

Figure F.2 — Limiting height and length to thickness ratios of walls restrained at the bottom, the top and one vertical edge

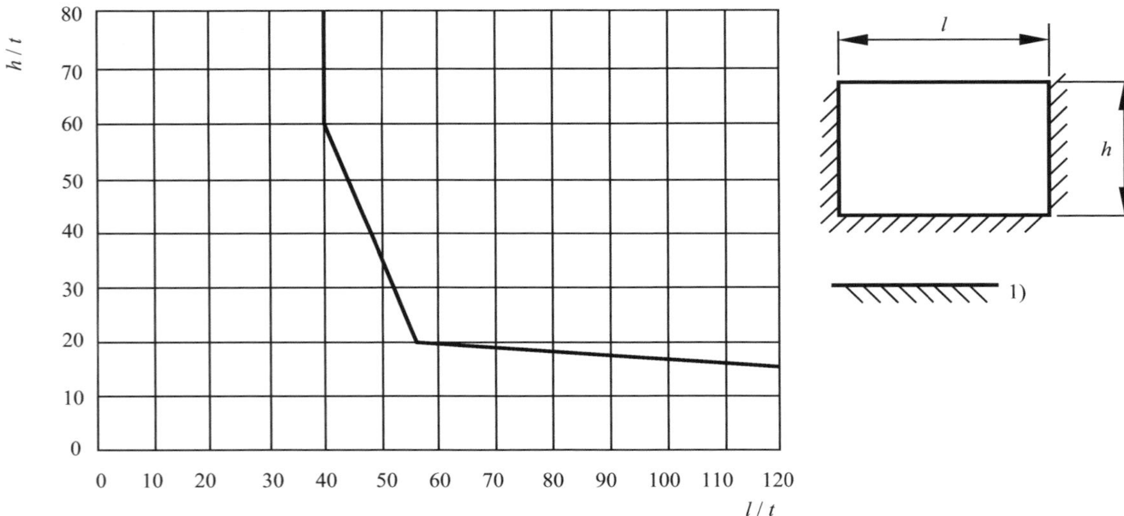

Key

1) simply supported or with full continuity

Figure F.3 — Limiting height and length to thickness ratios of walls restrained at the edges, the bottom, but not the top

Annex G (informative) Reduction factor for slenderness and eccentricity

(1) In the middle of the wall height, by using a simplification of the general principles given in 6.1.1, the reduction factor, Φ_m, taking into account the slenderness of the wall and the eccentricity of loading, for any modulus of elasticity E and characteristic compressive strength of unreinforced masonry f_k, may be estimated from:

AC1 $$\Phi_m = A_1 e^{-\frac{u^2}{2}} \quad \text{(G.1)}$$ AC1

where:

$$A_1 = 1 - 2\frac{e_{mk}}{t} \quad \text{(G.2)}$$

$$u = \frac{\lambda - 0,063}{0,73 - 1,17\frac{e_{mk}}{t}} \quad \text{(G.3)}$$

where:

$$\lambda = \frac{h_{ef}}{t_{ef}}\sqrt{\frac{f_k}{E}} \quad \text{(G.4)}$$

and e_{mk}, h_{ef}, t and t_{ef} are as defined in 6.1.2.2, and e is the base of natural logarithms.

(2) For $E = 1000\, f_k$ equations (G.3) becomes:

$$u = \frac{\frac{h_{ef}}{t_{ef}} - 2}{23 - 37\frac{e_{mk}}{t}} \quad \text{(G.5)}$$

and for $E = 700\, f_k$:

$$u = \frac{\frac{h_{ef}}{t_{ef}} - 1,67}{19,3 - 31\frac{e_{mk}}{t}} \quad \text{(G.6)}$$

(3) The values of Φ_m derived from equation (G.5) and (G.6) are represented in graphical form in Figure G.1 and G.2.

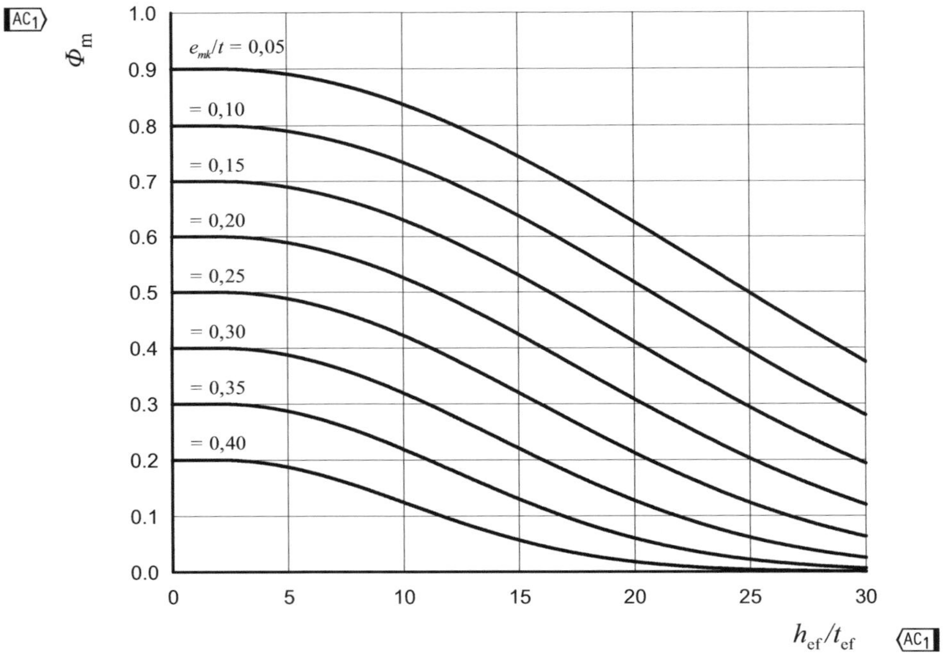

Figure G.1 — Values of Φ_m against slenderness ratio for different eccentricities, based on an E of 1000 f_k

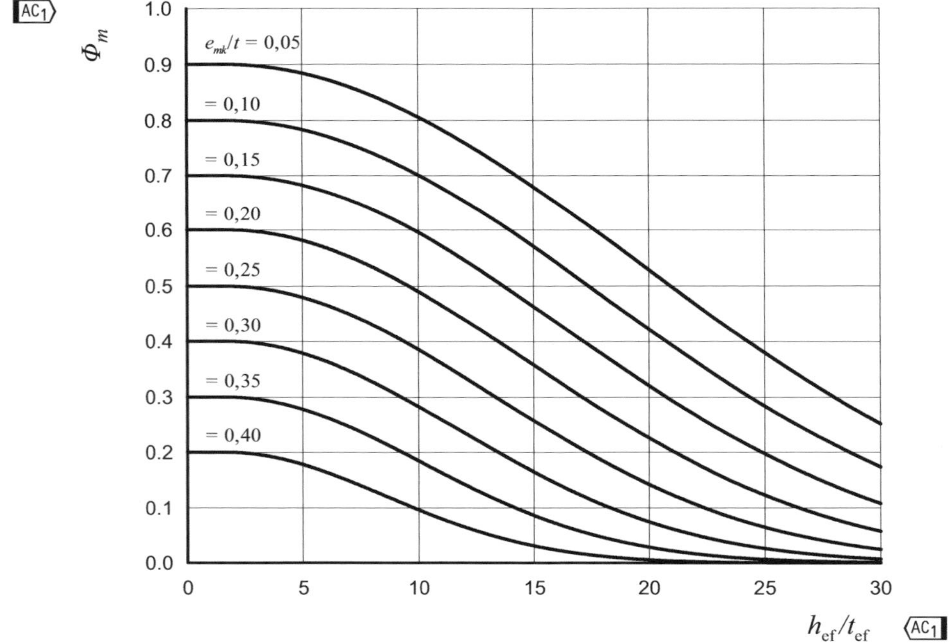

Figure G.2 — Values of Φ_m against slenderness ratio for different eccentricities, based on an E of 700 f_k

Bibliography

BS 3892-1, *Pulverized-fuel ash – Part 1: Specification for pulverized-fuel ash for use with Portland cement*

BS 4027, *Specification for sulfate-resisting Portland cement*

BS 6699, *Specification for ground granulated blastfurnace slag for use with Portland cement*

BS 7979, *Specification for limestone fines for use with Portland cement*

BS 8500 (all parts), *Concrete – Complementary British Standard to BS EN 206-1*

BS EN 197-1:2000, *Cement – Part 1: Composition, specifications and conformity criteria for common cements*

BS EN 206-1, *Concrete – Part 1: Specification, performance, production and conformity*

BS EN 413-1, *Masonry cement – Part 1: Composition, specifications and conformity criteria*

BS EN 450-1, *Fly ash for concrete – Part 1: Definition, specifications and conformity criteria*

BS EN 459-1, *Building lime – Part 1: Definitions, specifications and conformity criteria*

BS EN 772-1, *Methods of test for masonry units – Part 1: Determination of compressive strength*

BS EN 845-2, *Specification for ancillary components for masonry – Part 2: Lintels*

BS EN 845-3, *Specification for ancillary components for masonry – Part 3: Bed joint reinforcement of steel meshwork*

BS EN 934-3, *Admixtures for concrete, mortar and grout – Admixtures for masonry mortar – Part 3: Definitions, requirements, conformity, marking and labelling*

BS EN 998-2, *Specification for mortar for masonry – Part 2: Masonry mortar*

BS EN 1015-2, *Methods of test for mortar for masonry – Part 2: Bulk sampling of mortars and preparation of test mortars*

BS EN 1015-11, *Methods of test for mortar for masonry – Part 11: Determination of flexural and compressive strength of hardened mortar*

BS EN 1996-2, *Eurocode 6 – Design of masonry structures – Part 2: Design considerations, selection of materials and execution of masonry*

BS EN 10088 (all parts), *Stainless steels*

BS EN 12878, *Pigments for the colouring of building materials based on cement and/or lime – Specifications and methods of test*

BS EN 13139, *Aggregates for mortar*

BS EN ISO 1461, *Hot dip galvanized coatings on fabricated iron and steel articles – Specifications and test methods*

NA.4 References to non-contradictory complementary information

PD XXXX: 200Y, TITLE, [a standard comprising complementary and non-contradictory material taken from BS 5628-1, BS 5628-2 and BS 5628-3][1)]

Morton J. *Designers' guide to EN 1996-1-1 Eurocode 6: Design of masonry structures – Common rules for reinforced and unreinforced masonry structures*[1)]. London: Thomas Telford Ltd.

Manual for the design of masonry buildings structures to Eurocode 6[1)] London: Institution of Structural Engineers

EUROCODE 6 HANDBOOK[1)] London: Department of Communities and Local Government

Eurocode for Masonry, BS EN 1996: Guidance and Worked Examples[1)] Surrey: British Masonry Society

[1)] In preparation.

Useful references

1. Institution of Structural Engineers. Manual for the design of plain masonry in building structures to Eurocode 6, London, 2008.
2. International Masonry Society. Eurocode for Masonry EN 1996-1-1 and EN 1996-2 Guidance and worked examples, Penkhull, 2009.
3. ROBERTS, J.J & BROOKER, O. How to design masonry structures using Eurocode 6. 1. Introduction to Eurocode 6. Camberley, The Concrete Centre, 2007.
4. ROBERTS, J.J & BROOKER, O. How to design masonry structures using Eurocode 6. 2. Vertical resistance. Camberley, The Concrete Centre, 2007.
5. ROBERTS, J.J & BROOKER, O. How to design masonry structures using Eurocode 6. 3. Lateral resistance. Camberley, The Concrete Centre, 2007.
6. ROBERTS, J.J., TOVEY, A.K. & FRIED, A.N. Concrete Masonry Designer's Handbook, London, Spon Press, 2001.
7. www.eurocode6.org

Chapter 7 — Extracts from Eurocode 7: Geotechnical design

The extracts in this chapter are taken from EN 1997-1:2004 (incorporating corrigendum February 2009), *Eurocode 7: Geotechnical design — Part 1: General rules*.

Text altered by CEN corrigendum February 2009 is indicated in the text by $\text{AC}_1\rangle$ $\langle\text{AC}_1$.

The National Annex extracts are taken from NA to BS EN 1997-1:2004 (incorporating Corrigendum No. 1), *UK National Annex to Eurocode 7: Geotechnical design – Part 1: General rules.*

EN 1997 covers the geotechnical design of civil engineering works. As with all the sections of the code, EN 1997 seeks to provide a unifying framework for design that can be used across the European Community. Unlike other structural materials, the design of geotechnical structures traditionally has not been considered using limit state principles. Various codes have attempted to consider limit state design for structures involving soils (e.g. BS 8002, *Code of practice for earth retaining structures*) but there has never been a unified limit state approach to cover all geotechnical works and their interface with other structural materials. As the adoption of limit state principles in geotechnical engineering is not widespread across the European Community, it has led to significant differences in how these principles need to be applied. Under the regulations governing the adoption of the European codes, each country is allowed to provide a National Annex that describes how the code should be applied to the country under consideration. Typically this might involve providing separate sets of partial factors to reflect the practices in the country.

This chapter considers the major clauses of EN 1997-1 and provides commentary to clarify the meaning of the clauses. All clauses included in this chapter are highlighted in bold in the full contents list from the code below. EN 1997-1 provides very useful check lists for design which have not been repeated in this chapter but which are extremely valuable for both the experienced designer and young engineer alike.

In EN 1997-1 providing separate sets of partial factors to reflect the practices in the country is taken one stage further by introducing three Design Approaches: DA1 is the design method adopted in the UK and in six other European Countries; DA2 will be adopted in about nine European countries; DA3 is preferred by about three European countries. All three approaches are contained within the body of EN 1997-1, but in this guide all examples will use DA1.

The full list of contents of EN 1997-1 follows, and is given for reference purposes. (Bold items are covered in this chapter.)

3	**Geotechnical data**
3.1	**General**
3.2	Geotechnical investigations
3.3	Evaluation of geotechnical parameters
3.4	Ground Investigation Report
4	**Supervision of construction, monitoring and maintenance**
4.1	**General**
4.2	Supervision
4.3	Checking ground conditions
4.4	Checking construction
4.5	Monitoring
4.6	Maintenance
5	**Fill, dewatering, ground improvement and reinforcement**
5.1	General
5.2	**Fundamental requirements**
5.3	**Fill construction**
5.4	**Dewatering**
5.5	**Ground improvement and reinforcement**
6	**Spread foundations**
6.1	General
6.2	**Limit states**
6.3	**Actions and design situations**
6.4	**Design and construction considerations**
6.5	**Ultimate limit state design**
6.6	**Serviceability limit state design**
6.7	Foundations on rock; additional design considerations
6.8	Structural design of spread foundations
6.9	Preparation of the subsoil
7	**Pile foundations**
7.1	General
7.2	**Limit states**
7.3	**Actions and design situations**
7.4	**Design methods and design considerations**
7.5	**Pile load tests**
7.6	**Axially loaded piles**
7.7	**Transversely loaded piles**
7.8	**Structural design of piles**
7.9	**Supervision of construction**
8	**Anchorages**
8.1	**General**
8.2	**Limit states**
8.3	**Design situations and actions**
8.4	**Design and construction considerations**
8.5	**Ultimate limit state design**
8.6	Serviceability limit state design
8.7	Suitability tests
8.8	Acceptance tests
8.9	Supervision and monitoring
9	**Retaining structures**
9.1	**General**
9.2	**Limit states**
9.3	**Actions, geometrical data and design situations**
9.4	**Design and construction considerations**
9.5	**Determination of earth pressures**
9.6	**Water pressures**
9.7	**Ultimate limit state design**
9.8	**Serviceability limit state design**
10	**Hydraulic failure**
10.1	**General**
10.2	**Failure by uplift**
10.3	**Failure by heave**

1. General

The Scope for EN 1997 has not been given in full; only selected extracts from it have been included in this guide.

1.1 Scope

1.1.1 Scope of EN 1997

(2) EN 1997 is intended to be applied to the geotechnical aspects of the design of buildings and civil engineering works. It is subdivided into various separate parts (see 1.1.2 and 1.1.3).

(3) EN 1997 is concerned with the requirements for strength, stability, serviceability and durability of structures. Other requirements, e.g. concerning thermal or sound insulation, are not considered.

1.1.3 Further Parts of EN 1997

(1) EN 1997-1 is supplemented by EN 1997-2 that provides requirements and rules for the performance and evaluation of field and laboratory testing.

General principles are contained in EN 1990 and EN 1991 (see Chapters 0 and 1). EN 1997-1 adopts these principles and definitions and the reader should refer to Chapters 0 and 1 for an understanding of the topics. EN 1997-2 is not covered in this guide.

1.5 Definitions

1.5.2 Definitions specific for EN 1997-1

1.5.2.1
geotechnical action
action transmitted to the structure by the ground, fill, standing water or ground-water

NOTE Definition taken from EN 1990:2002.

1.5.2.2
comparable experience
documented or other clearly established information related to the ground being considered in design, involving the same types of soil and rock and for which similar geotechnical behaviour is expected, and involving similar structures. Information gained locally is considered to be particularly relevant

1.5.2.3
ground
soil, rock and fill in place prior to the execution of the construction works

1.5.2.4
structure
organized combination of connected parts, including fill placed during execution of the construction works, designed to carry loads and provide adequate rigidity

NOTE Definition derived from EN 1990:2002.

1.5.2.5
derived value
value of a geotechnical parameter obtained by theory, correlation or empiricism from test results

1.5.2.6
stiffness
material resistance against deformation

1.5.2.7
resistance
capacity of a component, or cross-section of a component of a structure to withstand actions without mechanical failure e.g. resistance of the ground, bending resistance, buckling resistance, tensile resistance

NOTE Definition derived from EN 1990:2002.

1.6 Symbols

(1) For the purpose of EN 1997-1 the following symbols apply.

Latin letters

[AC1⟩ A' Effective base area ($A' = B' \times L'$) ⟨AC1]
A_b Base area under pile
A_c Total base area under compression
$A_{s;i}$ Pile shaft surface area in layer i
a_d Design value of geometrical data
a_{nom} Nominal value of geometrical data
Δa Change made to nominal geometrical data for particular design purposes
[AC1⟩ B ⟨AC1] Width of a foundation
b' Effective width of a foundation
C_d Limiting design value of the [AC1⟩ relevant serviceability criterion ⟨AC1]
c Cohesion intercept
c' Cohesion intercept in terms of effective stress
c_u Undrained shear strength
$c_{u;d}$ Design value of undrained shear strength
d Embedment depth
E_d Design value of the effect of actions
$E_{stb;d}$ Design value of the effect of stabilizing actions
$E_{dst;d}$ Design value of the effect of destabilizing actions
$F_{c;d}$ Design axial compression load on a pile or a group of piles
F_d Design value of an action
F_k Characteristic value of an action
F_{rep} Representative value of an action
$F_{t;d}$ Design axial tensile load on a tensile pile or a group of tensile piles
$F_{tr;d}$ Design value of the transverse load on a pile or a pile foundation
$G_{dst;d}$ Design value of the destabilizing permanent actions for uplift verification
$G_{stb;d}$ Design value of the stabilizing permanent vertical actions for uplift verification
$G'_{stb;d}$ Design value of the stabilizing permanent vertical actions for heave verification (submerged weight)
H Horizontal load, or component of total action acting parallel to the foundation base
H_d Design value of H
h Height of a wall
h Water level for hydraulic heave
h' Height of a soil prism for verifying hydraulic heave
$h_{w;k}$ Characteristic value of the hydrostatic water head at the bottom of a soil prism
K_0 Coefficient of earth pressure at rest
$K_{0;\beta}$ Coefficient of earth pressure at rest for a retained earth surface inclined at angle β to the horizontal
k Ratio $\delta_d / \varphi_{cv;d}$
[AC1⟩ L ⟨AC1] Foundation length
l' Effective foundation length
n Number of e.g. piles or test profiles
P Load on an anchorage
P_d Design value of P
P_p Proof load in a suitability test of a grouted anchorage
$Q_{dst;d}$ Design value of the destabilizing variable vertical actions for uplift verification
[AC1⟩ $q_{b;k}$ Characteristic value of unit base resistance ⟨AC1]
[AC1⟩ $q_{s;i;k}$ Characteristic value of unit shaft resistance in stratum i ⟨AC1]
[AC1⟩ q_u Unconfined compressive strength ⟨AC1]

R_a Anchorage pull-out resistance
$R_{a;d}$ Design value of R_a
$R_{a;k}$ Characteristic value of R_a
$R_{b;cal}$ Pile base resistance, calculated from ground test results, at the ultimate limit state
$R_{b;d}$ Design value of the base resistance of a pile
$R_{b;k}$ Characteristic value of the base resistance of a pile
R_c Compressive resistance of the ground against a pile, at the ultimate limit state
$R_{c;cal}$ Calculated value of R_c
$R_{c;d}$ Design value of R_c
$R_{c;k}$ Characteristic value of R_c
$R_{c;m}$ Measured value of R_c in one or several pile load tests
R_d Design value of the resistance to an action
$R_{p;d}$ Design value of the resisting force caused by earth pressure on the side of a foundation
$R_{s;d}$ Design value of the shaft resistance of a pile
$R_{s;cal}$ Ultimate shaft friction, calculated using ground parameters from test results
$R_{s;k}$ Characteristic value of the shaft resistance of a pile
R_t Ultimate tensile resistance of an isolated pile
$R_{t;d}$ Design value of the tensile resistance of a pile or of a group of piles, or of the structural tensile resistance of an anchorage
$R_{t;k}$ Characteristic value of the tensile resistance of a pile or a pile group
$R_{t;m}$ Measured tensile resistance of an isolated pile in one or several pile load tests
R_{tr} Resistance of a pile to transverse loads
$R_{tr;d}$ Design resistance of transversally loaded pile
$S_{dst;d}$ Design value of the destabilizing seepage force in the ground
$S_{dst;k}$ Characteristic value of the destabilizing seepage force in the ground
s Settlement
s_0 Immediate settlement
s_1 Settlement caused by consolidation
s_2 Settlement caused by creep (secondary settlement)
T_d Design value of total shearing resistance that develops around a block of ground in which a group of tension piles is placed, or on the part of the structure in contact with the ground
u Pore-water pressure
$u_{dst;d}$ Design value of destabilizing total pore-water pressure
V Vertical load, or component of the total action acting normal to the foundation base
V_d Design value of V
V'_d Design value of the effective vertical action or component of the total action acting normal to the foundation base
$V_{dst;d}$ Design value of the destabilizing vertical action on a structure
$V_{dst;k}$ Characteristic value of the destabilizing vertical action on a structure
X_d Design value of a material property
X_k Characteristic value of a material property
z Vertical distance

Greek letters

α Inclination of a foundation base to the horizontal
β Slope angle of the ground behind a wall (upward positive)
δ Structure-ground interface friction angle
δ_d Design value of δ
γ Weight density
γ' Effective weight density
γ_a Partial factor for anchorages
$\gamma_{a;p}$ Partial factor for permanent anchorages
$\gamma_{a;t}$ Partial factor for temporary anchorages
γ_b Partial factor for the base resistance of a pile
$\gamma_{c'}$ Partial factor for the effective cohesion
γ_{cu} Partial factor for the undrained shear strength
γ_E Partial factor for the effect of an action
γ_f Partial factor for actions, which takes account of the possibility of unfavourable deviations of the action values from the representative values
γ_F Partial factor for an action

γ_G Partial factor for a permanent action
$\gamma_{G;dst}$ Partial factor for a permanent destabilizing action
$\gamma_{G;stb}$ Partial factor for a permanent stabilizing action
γ_m Partial factor for a soil parameter (material property)
$\gamma_{m;i}$ Partial factor for a soil parameter in stratum *i*
γ_M Partial factor for a soil parameter (material property), also accounting for model uncertainties
γ_Q Partial factor for a variable action
γ_{qu} Partial factor for unconfined strength
γ_R Partial factor for a resistance
$\gamma_{R;d}$ Partial factor for uncertainty in a resistance model
AC1 $\gamma_{R;e}$ Partial factor for passive earth resistance AC1
$\gamma_{R;h}$ Partial factor for sliding resistance
$\gamma_{R;v}$ Partial factor for bearing resistance
γ_s Partial factor for shaft resistance of a pile
$\gamma_{S;d}$ Partial factor for uncertainties in modelling the effects of actions
AC1 $\gamma_{Q;dst}$ Partial factor for a variable destabilizing action AC1
AC1 $\gamma_{Q;stb}$ Partial factor for a variable stabilizing action AC1
$\gamma_{s;t}$ Partial factor for tensile resistance of a pile
γ_t Partial factor for total resistance of a pile
γ_w Weight density of water
$\gamma_{\varphi'}$ Partial factor for the angle of shearing resistance (tan φ')
γ_γ Partial factor for weight density
θ Direction angle of H
ξ Correlation factor depending on the number of piles tested or of profiles of tests
ξ_a Correlation factor for anchorages
ξ_1; ξ_2 Correlation factors to evaluate the results of static pile load tests
ξ_3; ξ_4 Correlation factors to derive the pile resistance from ground investigation results, not being pile load tests
ξ_5; ξ_6 Correlation factors to derive the pile resistance from dynamic impact tests
ψ Factor for converting the characteristic value to the representative value
$\sigma_{stb;d}$ Design value of stabilizing total vertical stress
$\sigma'_{h;0}$ Horizontal component of effective earth pressure at rest
$\sigma(z)$ Stress normal to a wall at depth z
$\tau(z)$ Stress tangential to a wall at depth z
φ' Angle of shearing resistance in terms of effective stress
φ_{cv} Critical state angle of shearing resistance
$\varphi_{cv;d}$ Design value of φ_{cv}
φ'_d Design value of φ'

Abbreviations

CFA Continuous flight auger piles
OCR Over-consolidation ratio

NOTE 1 The symbols commonly used in all Eurocodes are defined in EN 1990:2002.

NOTE 2 The notation of the symbols used is based on ISO 3898:1997.

(2) For geotechnical calculations, the following units or their multiples are recommended:

— force kN
— mass kg
— moment kNm
— mass density kg/m^3
— weight density kN/m^3
— stress, pressure, strength and stiffness kPa
— coefficient of permeability m/s
— coefficient of consolidation m^2/s

"Weight density" is a new term for what has traditionally been known in the UK as "unit weight".

2. Basis of geotechnical design

2.1 Design requirements

(2) When defining the design situations and the limit states, the following factors should be considered:

- site conditions with respect to overall stability and ground movements;
- nature and size of the structure and its elements, including any special requirements such as the design life;
- conditions with regard to its surroundings (e.g. neighbouring structures, traffic, utilities, vegetation, hazardous chemicals);
- ground conditions;
- ground-water conditions;
- regional seismicity;
- influence of the environment (hydrology, surface water, subsidence, seasonal changes of temperature and moisture).

(3) Limit states can occur either in the ground or in the structure or by combined failure in the structure and the ground.

(4) Limit states should be verified by one or a combination of the following:

- use of calculations as described in 2.4;
- adoption of prescriptive measures, as described in 2.5;
- experimental models and load tests, as described in 2.6;
- an observational method, as described in 2.7.

(8)P In order to establish minimum requirements for the extent and content of geotechnical investigations, calculations and construction control checks, the complexity of each geotechnical design shall be identified together with the associated risks. In particular, a distinction shall be made between:

- light and simple structures and small earthworks for which it is possible to ensure that the minimum requirements will be satisfied by experience and qualitative geotechnical investigations, with negligible risk;
- other geotechnical structures.

NOTE The manner in which these minimum requirements are satisfied may be given in the National Annex.

Subclauses 2.1(10) to (21) of EN 1997-1 introduce the concept of geotechnical categories (GCs), which may be used to establish design requirements. GC1 includes small and relatively simple structures for which routine methods of foundation design and construction may be used. GC2 covers conventional types of structure and foundation with no exceptional risk or difficult loading conditions – such as spread foundations, rafts, pile foundations and walls – which should be designed using quantitative geotechnical data and analysis, but with routine procedures for field and laboratory testing. GC3 includes structures or parts of structures that are not in GC1 or 2 and should normally be designed using alternative provisions to those given in EN 1997.

2.2 Design situations

(1)P Both short-term and long-term design situations shall be considered.

Subclause 2.2(2) lists over twenty aspects that should be considered when specifying design situations and provides a useful checklist to enable competent design.

2.3 Durability

(1)P At the geotechnical design stage, the significance of environmental conditions shall be assessed in relation to durability and to enable provisions to be made for the protection or adequate resistance of the materials.

Subclauses 2.3(2) and (3) highlight particular durability issues with construction materials in the ground.

2.4 Geotechnical design by calculation

2.4.1 General

(2) It should be considered that knowledge of the ground conditions depends on the extent and quality of the geotechnical investigations. Such knowledge and the control of workmanship are usually more significant to fulfilling the fundamental requirements than is precision in the calculation models and partial factors.

Subclause 2.4.1(2) is key to geotechnical design. The variability of geotechnical materials is such that accurate prediction of behaviour is extremely difficult. This should be borne in mind when considering the detail of this Eurocode.

Subclauses 2.4.1(3) to (15) outline the principles on which geotechnical design by calculation should be carried out.

2.4.2 Actions

An important test of what is or is not a geotechnical action is the question: "is it a known quantity before a calculation is performed?" If the answer is yes, it is an action.

Subclauses 2.4.2(1) to (9) describe those things that constitute actions in geotechnical engineering and matters that require consideration. In particular, 2.4.2(4) lists things that should be considered for inclusion in the design as actions.

2.4.3 Ground properties

(1)P Properties of soil and rock masses, as quantified for design calculations by geotechnical parameters, shall be obtained from test results, either directly or through correlation, theory or empiricism, and from other relevant data.

EN 1997-1 requires geotechnical parameters to be established with regard to relevant published data, local and general experience, results of neighbouring field trials, correlations between test results, and deterioration of properties during the design life of the structure. Subclauses 2.4.3(3) to (6) give guidance on how geotechnical parameters should be considered in design.

2.4.4 Geometrical data

(1)P The level and slope of the ground surface, water levels, levels of interfaces between strata, excavation levels and the dimensions of the geotechnical structure shall be treated as geometrical data.

2.4.5 Characteristic values

2.4.5.2 Characteristic values of geotechnical parameters

(1)P The selection of characteristic values for geotechnical parameters shall be based on derived values resulting from laboratory and field tests, complemented by well-established experience.

(2)P The characteristic value of a geotechnical parameter shall be selected as a cautious estimate of the value affecting the occurrence of the limit state.

The term "characteristic value" is defined in EN 1990 as the value of a material property which will give the most conservative design in 95 per cent of cases. Typically, the characteristic value is a low value (e.g. for the strength of the material); but in some situations, it is a high value (e.g. for the weight of the material). Because it is extremely difficult in geotechnical design to define material properties to specified percentiles, clause 2.4.5.2(2)P of EN 1997-1 redefines the meaning of "characteristic value" as a cautious estimate of the relevant material property, where 'relevant' refers, among other things, to the property of the in situ material (e.g. not of a sample).

(12)P When using standard tables of characteristic values related to soil investigation parameters, the characteristic value shall be selected as a very cautious value.

Selection of geotechnical parameters should allow for geology, existing knowledge, the extent of field and laboratory investigation, and the ability of the structure to redistribute loads. EN 1997-2 provides guidance on obtaining derived values from laboratory and field tests. It is rare that sufficient data is gathered in a site investigation for statistical methods to be used. However, clause 2.4.5.2(11) indicates what the characteristic value represents, should sufficient data be available.

2.4.5.3 Characteristic values of geometrical data

(2) Characteristic values of levels of ground and dimensions of geotechnical structures or elements should usually be nominal values.

The nominal value is that value of the geometrical data which is typical for the element under consideration, e.g. the nominal diameter of a bored-cast-in-place pile may be 600 mm but it is recognized that this will vary both above and below this value.

2.4.6 Design values

2.4.6.1 Design values of actions

(2)P The design value of an action (F_d) shall either be assessed directly or shall be derived from representative values using the following equation:

$$F_d = \gamma_F F_{rep} \qquad (2.1a)$$

with

$$F_{rep} = \psi \cdot F_k \qquad (2.1b)$$

In equation (2.1a), F_d is the design value of an action, F_{rep} its representative value, and γ_F a partial factor for that action. In equation (2.1b), F_k is the characteristic value of the action and ψ is a factor (applied to variable and accidental actions only) for converting characteristic to representative values.

Values of γ_F for buildings taken from Table NA.A1.2 of the National Annex to EN 1990 and Tables A.NA.15 and 17 of the National Annex to EN 1997-1 are given in the table below (some values differ from EN 1997-1). Different partial factors are given in the National Annex for bridges. The different limit states (EQU, STR/GEO, etc) are explained in clause 2.4.7.1.

Partial factors on actions for buildings for different limit states:

Duration of action	Effect of action	Symbol γ_F	Limit state/partial factor set				
			EQU	STR/GEO		UPL	HYD
				A1	A2		
Permanent	Unfavourable	$\gamma_{G;dst}$	1,1	1,35	1,0	1,1	1,35
	Favourable	$\gamma_{G;stb}$	0,9	1,0	1,0	0,9	0,9
Variable	Unfavourable	$\gamma_{Q;dst}$	1,5	1,5	1,3	1,5	1,5

Unfavourable actions (with the subscript "dst" above) are those which destabilize the structure and favourable actions (subscript "stb") are those which stabilize the structure. Favourable variable actions are omitted from the table above because they are deliberately ignored in EN 1997-1 (i.e. $\gamma_{Q;stb} = 0$).

Example (using limit state STR/GEO partial factor set A1)
If the representative vertical load (F_{rep}) on a footing is 100 kN, then the design vertical load (F_d) would be 100 x 1.35 = 135 kN.

Values of ψ are given in EN 1990. For those geotechnical situations that involve a single variable action, ψ = 1, i.e. the representative and characteristic values of an action are the same. When there is more than one variable action ψ < 1.0 on the non-leading action.

2.4.6.2 Design values of geotechnical parameters

(1)P Design values of geotechnical parameters (X_d) shall either be derived from characteristic values using the following equation:

$$X_d = X_k / \gamma_M \quad (2.2)$$

or shall be assessed directly.

In equation (2.2), X_d is the design value of a material property, X_k its characteristic value, and γ_M a partial factor for that material property. Values of γ_M from Annex A of the National Annex to BS EN 1997-1 are given in the table below (some values differ from EN 1997-1). The different limit states (EQU, STR/GEO, etc.) are explained in clause 2.4.7.1.

Partial factors on material properties for different limit states:

Soil parameter	Symbol γ_M	Limit state/partial factor set				
		EQU	STR/GEO		UPL	HYD
			M1	M2		
Angle of shearing resistance	$\gamma_{\phi'}$	1,1*	1,0*	1,25*	1,25*	–
Effective cohesion	$\gamma_{c'}$	1,1	1,0	1,25	1,25	–
Undrained shear strength	γ_{cu}	1,2	1,0	1,4	1,4	–
Unconfined strength	γ_{qu}	1,2	1,0	1,4	1,4	–
Weight density	γ_{γ}	1,0	1,0	1,0	–	–
Tensile pile resistance	$\gamma_{s;t}$	–	–	–	see NOTE	–
Anchorage	γ_R	–	–	–	1,4**	–

*Applied to tan φ' not φ'
**Larger values should be used for non-prestressed anchorages

NOTE Pile design should conform to A.3.3.2 and A.3.3.3 of the National Annex to EN 1997-1.

Example 1 (using limit state STR/GEO partial factor set M2)
If the characteristic undrained shear strength (c_{uk}) of a clay is 80 kPa, then its design strength (c_{ud}) is 80 ÷ 1.4 = 57 kPa.

Example 2 (using limit state STR/GEO partial factor set M2)
If the characteristic angle of shearing resistance (φ'_k) of a clay is 23°, then its design value (φ'_d) is $\tan^{-1}((\tan 23°) \div 1.25) = 18.8°$.
Note: $\gamma_{\varphi'}$ is applied to $\tan \varphi'$ not φ'.

2.4.6.3 Design values of geometrical data

(1) The partial action and material factors (γ_F and γ_M) include an allowance for minor variations in geometrical data and, in such cases, no further safety margin on the geometrical data should be required.

(2)P In cases where deviations in the geometrical data have a significant effect on the reliability of a structure, design values of geometrical data (a_d) shall either be assessed directly or be derived from nominal values using the following equation (see 6.3.4 of EN 1990:2002):

$$a_d = a_{nom} \pm \Delta a \qquad (2.3)$$

for which values of Δa are given in 6.5.4(2) and 9.3.2.2.

In equation (2.3), a_d is the design value of geometrical data, a_{nom} its nominal value, and Δa is a safety margin for the data. Values of Δa are typically zero, except where explicitly given in EN 1997-1 (e.g. for spread foundations and retaining structures – see 9.3.2.2).

2.4.7 Ultimate Limit States

2.4.7.1 General

(1)P Where relevant, it shall be verified that the following limit states are not exceeded:

- loss of equilibrium of the structure or the ground, considered as a rigid body, in which the strengths of structural materials and the ground are insignificant in providing resistance (EQU);
- internal failure or excessive deformation of the structure or structural elements, including e.g. footings, piles or basement walls, in which the strength of structural materials is significant in providing resistance (STR);
- failure or excessive deformation of the ground, in which the strength of soil or rock is significant in providing resistance (GEO);
- loss of equilibrium of the structure or the ground due to uplift by water pressure (buoyancy) or other vertical actions (UPL);
- hydraulic heave, internal erosion and piping in the ground caused by hydraulic gradients (HYD).

NOTE Limit state GEO is often critical to the sizing of structural elements involved in foundations or retaining structures and sometimes to the strength of structural elements.

All limit states should be satisfied but it is typically the case that one of the states will dominate the design. In particular EQU is rarely critical except in the case of potential overturning, e.g. toppling failures in rock slopes, overturning of gravity retaining walls, and footings subject to high lateral loads relative to vertical loads. Typically either GEO or STR is found to be most critical.

Subclauses 2.4.7.1(2) to (6) give situations where the provided partial factors may be varied to account for particular situations.

2.4.7.2 Verification of static equilibrium

(1)P When considering a limit state of static equilibrium or of overall displacements of the structure or ground (EQU), it shall be verified that:

$$E_{dst;d} \leq E_{stb;d} + T_d \tag{2.4}$$

with

$$E_{dst;d} = E\left\{\gamma_F F_{rep}; X_k / \gamma_M; a_d\right\}_{dst} \tag{2.4a}$$

and

$$E_{stb;d} = E\left\{\gamma_F F_{rep}; X_k / \gamma_M; a_d\right\}_{stb} \tag{2.4b}$$

In equation (2.4), E_d is the design value of the effect of actions, with the subscripts "dst" and "stb" denote destabilizing and stabilizing effects respectively, and T_d is the design total resistance that develops on the part of the structure in contact with the ground. E_d is a function of the design actions (F_d), design material properties (X_d), and design geometry (a_d) defined above (see clauses 2.4.6.1 to 2.4.6.3).

This and the following clause of EN 1997-1 introduce the term "effect of actions" to represent resultant effects such as overturning moments and forces, bending moments and shear forces, bearing pressures, etc.

Example
In the design of a gravity retaining wall, the overturning moment about the toe of the wall due to destabilizing forces ($E_{dst;d}$) is calculated to be 1500 kNm and the resistance provided by the part of the structure in contact with the ground (T_d) is 100 kNm. Limit state EQU requires the designer to verify that the restoring moment about the toe due to stabilizing forces ($E_{stb;d}$) is greater than or equal to 1400 kNm (1500 kNm ≥ 1400 + 100 kNm).

2.4.7.3 Verification of resistance for structural and ground limit states in persistent and transient situations

2.4.7.3.1 General

(1)P When considering a limit state of rupture or excessive deformation of a structural element or section of the ground (STR and GEO), it shall be verified that:

$$E_d \leq R_d \tag{2.5}$$

In equation (2.5), E_d is the design value of the effect of actions and R_d the design value of the resistance to those actions.

Example 1
In the design of a gravity retaining wall, the bending moment induced in the stem of the wall (E_d) is calculated to be 2000 kNm. Limit state STR requires the designer to verify that the bending resistance of the wall stem (R_d) is greater than or equal to 2000 kNm.

Example 2
In the same design, the horizontal sliding force on the base of the wall (E_d) is calculated to be 500 kN. Limit state GEO requires the designer to verify that the sliding resistance of the ground beneath the wall base (R_d) is greater than or equal to 500 kN.

2.4.7.3.2 Design effects of actions

(1) Partial factors on actions may be applied either to the actions themselves (F_{rep}) or to their effects (E):

$$E_d = E\left\{\gamma_f F_{rep}\,;\, X_k / \gamma_M\,;\, a_d\right\} \qquad (2.6a)$$

or

$$E_d = \gamma_E E\left\{F_{rep}\,;\, X_k / \gamma_M\,;\, a_d\right\} \qquad (2.6b)$$

In equation (2.6a), the partial factor γ_F is applied to representative actions before calculating the effect of those actions. In equation (2.6b), the effect of actions is calculated using representative actions and then multiplied by γ_E. Values of γ_F and γ_E given in EN 1997-1 are identical.

Which of equations (2.6a) and (2.6b) is used is a matter of national preference. In the UK, equation (2.6a) is generally preferred.

Examples of the calculation of E_d are provided in the commentary to Sections 6 to 9.

2.4.7.3.3 Design resistances

(1) Partial factors may be applied either to ground properties (X) or resistances (R) or to both, as follows:

$$R_d = R\left\{\gamma_F F_{rep}\,;\, X_k / \gamma_M\,;\, a_d\right\} \qquad (2.7a)$$

or

$$R_d = R\left\{\gamma_F F_{rep}\,;\, X_k\,;\, a_d\right\} / \gamma_R \qquad (2.7b)$$

or

$$R_d = R\left\{\gamma_F F_{rep}\,;\, X_k / \gamma_M\,;\, a_d\right\} / \gamma_R \qquad (2.7c)$$

NOTE In design procedures where the effects of actions are factored, the partial factor for actions γ_F = 1,0 (see also B.3(6)).

(2)P The partial factors, defined in A.3.3.1(1)P, A.3.3.2(1)P, A.3.3.4(1)P, A.3.3.5(1)P and A.3.3.6(1)P shall be used in equations (2.7a, b, and c).

NOTE The values of the partial factors may be set by the National Annex. Tables A.5, A.6, A.7, A.8, A.12, A.13 and A.14 give the recommended values.

In equations (2.7b) and (2.7c), γ_R is a partial factor for resistance and the other symbols are as defined earlier. When equation (2.6b) is used to calculate the effects of actions, the value of γ_F to be used in equations (2.7a), (2.7b) and (2.7c) is 1.0.

Which of equations (2.7a), (2.7b), and (2.7c) is used depends on the type of structure being verified and is a matter of national preference. In the UK, equations (2.7a) and (2.7b) are generally preferred.

Examples of the calculation of R_d are provided in the commentary to Sections 6 to 9.

2.4.7.3.4 Design Approaches

2.4.7.3.4.1 General

(1)P The manner in which equations (2.6) and (2.7) are applied shall be determined using one of three Design Approaches.

NOTE 1 The way to use equations (2.6) and (2.7) and the particular Design Approach to be used may be given in the National Annex.

NOTE 2 Further clarification of the Design Approaches is provided in Annex B.

NOTE 3 The partial factors in Annex A to be used in equations (2.6) and (2.7) are grouped in sets denoted by *A* (for actions or effects of actions), *M* (for soil parameters) and *R* (for resistances). They are selected according to the Design Approach used.

The Design Approaches were introduced in EN 1997-1 to accommodate differences in design procedures across Europe.

NA.2 The procedure to be used when alternative procedures are given in EN 1997-1:2004

National choice is permitted in the use of a Design Approach for the STR and GEO limit states (see BS EN 1997-1:2004, 2.4.7.3.4.1(1)P). As indicated in Table NA.1, only Design Approach 1 is to be used in the UK.

2.4.7.3.4.2 Design Approach 1

(1)P Except for the design of axially loaded piles and anchors, it shall be verified that a limit state of rupture or excessive deformation will not occur with either of the following combinations of sets of partial factors:

Combination 1: *A1* "+" *M1* "+" *R1*
Combination 2: *A2* "+" *M2* "+" *R1*

where "+" implies: "to be combined with".

NOTE In Combinations 1 and 2, partial factors are applied to actions and to ground strength parameters.

(2)P For the design of axially loaded piles and anchors, it shall be verified that a limit state of rupture or excessive deformation will not occur with either of the following combinations of sets of partial factors:

Combination 1: *A1* "+" *M1* "+" *R1*
Combination 2: *A2* "+" (*M1 or M2*) "+" *R4*

NOTE 1 In Combination 1, partial factors are applied to actions and to ground strength parameters. In Combination 2, partial factors are applied to actions, to ground resistances and sometimes to ground strength parameters.

NOTE 2 In Combination 2, set *M1* is used for calculating resistances of piles or anchors and set *M2* for calculating unfavourable actions on piles owing e.g. to negative skin friction or transverse loading.

(3) If it is obvious that one of the two combinations governs the design, calculations for the other combination need not be carried out. However, different combinations may be critical to different aspects of the same design.

This application rule only applies to Design Approach 1 (DA1), in which two combinations of sets of partial factors should be considered. It allows one of the combinations to be omitted if the other obviously governs the design.

2.4.7.4 Verification procedure and partial factors for uplift

(1)P Verification for uplift (UPL) shall be carried out by checking that the design value of the combination of destabilising permanent and variable vertical actions ($V_{dst;d}$) is less than or equal to the sum of the design value of the stabilising permanent vertical actions ($G_{stb;d}$) and of the design value of any additional resistance to uplift (R_d):

$$V_{dst;d} \leq G_{stb;d} + R_d \qquad (2.8)$$

where

$$V_{dst;d} = G_{dst;d} + Q_{dst;d}$$

In equation (2.8), $V_{dst;d}$ is the destabilizing design vertical action, $G_{stb;d}$ is the stabilizing design permanent vertical action, and R_d is the design value of any additional resistance to uplift. $V_{dst,d}$ is made up of permanent (G) and variable (Q) components. Any stabilizing variable action is ignored.

Example
A footing is subject to a representative variable uplift characteristic force, $Q_{dst;rep}$ = 100 kN and a representative permanent uplift force, $G_{dst;rep}$ = 500 kN. The total representative stabilizing force ($G_{stb;rep}$) is 800 kN. Assume R_d = 0 kN.

$Q_{dst;d} = Q_{dst;rep} \times \gamma_{Q;dst} = 100 \times 1.5 = 150$ kN
$G_{dst;d} = G_{dst;rep} \times \gamma_{G;dst} = 500 \times 1.0 = 500$ kN

Therefore:

$V_{dst;d} = 500 + 150 = 650$ kN
$G_{stb;d} = G_{stb;rep} \times \gamma_{G;stb} = 800 \times 0.9 = 720$ kN

and equation (2.8) is satisfied.

2.4.7.5 Verification of resistance to failure by heave due to seepage of water in the ground

(1)P When considering a limit state of failure due to heave by seepage of water in the ground (HYD, see 10.3), it shall be verified, for every relevant soil column, that the design value of the destabilising total pore water pressure ($u_{dst;d}$) at the bottom of the column, or the design value of the seepage force ($S_{dst;d}$) in the column is less than or equal to the stabilising total vertical stress ($\sigma_{stb;d}$) at the bottom of the column, or the submerged weight ($G'_{stb;d}$) of the same column:

$$u_{dst;d} \leq \sigma_{stb;d} \qquad (2.9a)$$

$$S_{dst;d} \leq G'_{std;d} \qquad (2.9b)$$

In equation (2.9a), $u_{dst;d}$ is the design value of the destabilizing total pore-water pressure at the bottom of the soil column and $\sigma_{stb;d}$ is the corresponding stabilizing total vertical stress. In equation (2.9b), $S_{dst;d}$ is the design value of the seepage force in the soil column and $G'_{stb;d}$ is the submerged weight of that column.

Example
The characteristic values of pore pressure and total vertical stress are 60 kPa and 80 kPa respectively. The design stabilizing vertical total stress is:

$\sigma_{stb;d} = \sigma_{stb;k} \times \gamma_{G;stb} = 80 \times 0.9 = 72$ kPa

The design destabilizing total pore pressure is:

$u_{dst;d} = u_{dst;k} \times \gamma_{G;dst} = 60 \times 1.35 = 81$ kPa

In this case $u_{dst;d}$ is not less than $\sigma_{stb;d}$ and therefore equation (2.9a) is not satisfied.

2.4.8 Serviceability limit states

(1)P Verification for serviceability limit states in the ground or in a structural section, element or connection, shall either require that:

$$E_d \leq C_d \qquad (2.10)$$

or be done through the method given in 2.4.8(4).

In equation (2.10), E_d is the design value of the effect of actions and C_d the limiting design value of the effect of an action. Values of partial factors for serviceability limit states are normally equal to 1.0.

Example
A 1.2 m wide strip footing founded on a uniform clay, with characteristic undrained strength c_u = 120 kPa and coefficient of volume compressibility m_v = 0,0001 m^2/kN, is subject to a representative vertical action V = 240 kN. Considering an effective consolidating layer 3 m thick with an average increase in stress of 75 kPa gives a consolidation settlement:

$s_1 = 75 \times 0{,}0001 \times 3 = 22{,}5$ mm

If the immediate settlement s_0 = 5 mm and the creep settlement s_2 = 0, then the total settlement is:

$s = s_0 + s_1 + s_2 = 27{,}5$ mm

Thus E_d = 27,5 mm needs to be less than or equal to C_d, the design settlement limit, in order to meet the serviceability limit state. All partial safety factors on actions, materials, and resistances are 1,0 in the calculation of settlement.

(4) It may be verified that a sufficiently low fraction of the ground strength is mobilised to keep deformations within the required serviceability limits, provided this simplified approach is restricted to design situations where:

— a value of the deformation is not required to check the serviceability limit state;
— established comparable experience exists with similar ground, structures and application method.

Example
For the above example using the approach outlined in Annex D of EN 1997-1, the ultimate bearing capacity with an overburden pressure q = 15 kPa is:

$R/A' = 5{,}14c_u + q = 5{,}14 \times 120 + 15 = 631$ kPa

The ratio of the resistance to the representative vertical action for a footing with effective area A' = 1,2 m^2/m is then:

$R/V = 631 \times 1{,}2/240 = 3{,}16$

For R to exceed V, the undrained strength would need to be reduced to below 36 kPa (i.e. to less than 30% of its actual value). Therefore in accordance with 6.6.2(16), calculations for settlement are not required.

2.4.9 Limiting values for movements of foundations

(1)P In foundation design, limiting values shall be established for the foundation movements.

NOTE Permitted foundation movements may be set by the National Annex.

Subclauses 2.4.9(3) and (4) list things that should be considered when selecting design values for limiting movements and deformations and calculating differential settlement. In practice, it is difficult to establish limiting values for foundation movements (which is perhaps why EN 1997-1 gives little practical guidance on this matter).

2.5 Design by prescriptive measures

(1) In design situations where calculation models are not available or not necessary, exceeding limit states may be avoided by the use of prescriptive measures. These involve conventional and generally conservative rules in the design, and attention to specification and control of materials, workmanship, protection and maintenance procedures.

NOTE Reference to such conventional and generally conservative rules may be given in the National Annex.

(2) Design by prescriptive measures may be used where comparable experience, as defined in 1.5.2.2, makes design calculations unnecessary. It may also be used to ensure durability against frost action and chemical or biological attack, for which direct calculations are not generally appropriate.

2.6 Load tests and tests on experimental models

(1)P When the results of load tests or tests on large or small scale models are used to justify a design, or in order to complement one of the other alternatives mentioned in 2.1(4), the following features shall be considered and allowed for:

- differences in the ground conditions between the test and the actual construction;
- time effects, especially if the duration of the test is much less than the duration of loading of the actual construction;
- scale effects, especially if small models are used. The effects of stress levels shall be considered, together with the effects of particle size.

(2) Tests may be carried out on a sample of the actual construction or on full scale or smaller scale models.

2.7 Observational method

(1) When prediction of geotechnical behaviour is difficult, it can be appropriate to apply the approach known as "the observational method", in which the design is reviewed during construction.

Subclauses 2.7(2) to (5) give specific guidance for use of the observational method. Further guidance on this method is available in the geotechnical literature.

2.8 Geotechnical Design Report

(1)P The assumptions, data, methods of calculation and results of the verification of safety and serviceability shall be recorded in a Geotechnical Design Report.

Subclauses 2.8(2) to (6) give detailed guidance as to the contents of the Geotechnical Design Report (GDR). Although few clauses covering the GDR have been reproduced in this Guide, the GDR is a key feature of EN 1997 and is mentioned throughout the Eurocode.

3 Geotechnical data

3.1 General

(1)P Careful collection, recording and interpretation of geotechnical information shall always be made. This information shall include geology, geomorphology, seismicity, hydrology and history of the site. Indications of the variability of the ground shall be taken into account.

(2)P Geotechnical investigations shall be planned taking into account the construction and performance requirements of the proposed structure. The scope of geotechnical investigations shall be continuously reviewed as new information is obtained during execution of the work.

(3)P Routine field investigations and laboratory testing shall be carried out and reported generally in accordance with internationally recognized standards and recommendations. Deviations from these standards and additional test requirements shall be reported.

Section 3 contains essential information on the collection of geotechnical data and should be consulted when designing appropriate geotechnical investigations, evaluating geotechnical parameters, assessing rock parameters and assessing in-situ tests. It also contains detailed requirements for the Ground Investigation Report, which forms part of the Geotechnical Design Report. Section 3 makes several references to EN 1997-2.

4 Supervision of construction, monitoring and maintenance

4.1 General

(1)P To ensure the safety and quality of a structure, the following shall be undertaken, as appropriate:

- the construction processes and workmanship shall be supervised;
- the performance of the structure shall be monitored during and after construction;
- the structure shall be adequately maintained.

Section 4 provides useful guidance on the execution of geotechnical works, highlighting factors that need to be considered to ensure safe construction and satisfactory working performance.

5 Fill, dewatering, ground improvement and reinforcement

5.2 Fundamental requirements

(1)P Fill and dewatered, improved or reinforced ground shall be capable of sustaining the actions arising from its function and from its environment.

(2)P These fundamental requirements shall also be satisfied for the ground on which the fill is placed.

5.3 Fill construction

5.3.1 Principles

(1)P When designing fill constructions it shall be considered that the adequacy of the fill depends on the following:

- good material handling properties,
- adequate engineering properties after compaction.

5.3.2 Selection of fill material

(1)P The criteria for specifying material as suitable for use as fill shall be based on achieving adequate strength, stiffness, durability and permeability after compaction. These criteria shall take account of the purpose of the fill and the requirements of any structure to be placed on it.

Subclause 5.3.2(3)P lists aspects that should be taken into account when specifying a fill material.

5.3.3 Selection of procedures for fill placement and compaction

(1)P Compaction criteria shall be established for each zone or layer of fill, related to its purpose and performance requirements.

Subclause 5.3.3(3)P lists things that should be considered when specifying the compaction procedure. 5.3.4 provides useful guidance on the requirements for checking fill.

5.4 Dewatering

(1)P Any scheme for removing water from the ground or for lowering the water pressure shall be based on the results of a geotechnical or hydrogeological investigation.

Subclause 5.4(4) lists conditions that should be considered in the dewatering scheme.

(5)P The effectiveness of dewatering shall be checked by monitoring the ground-water level, the pore-water pressures and the ground movements, as necessary. Data shall be reviewed and interpreted frequently to determine the effects of dewatering on the ground conditions and on the behaviour of nearby structures.

5.5 Ground improvement and reinforcement

(1)P A geotechnical investigation of the initial ground conditions shall be carried out before any ground improvement or reinforcement method is chosen or used.

(3)P The effectiveness of the ground improvement shall be checked against the acceptance criteria by determining the induced changes in the appropriate ground properties.

Subclause 5.5(2)P lists factors that should be taken into account when designing the ground improvement method.

6. Spread foundations

6.2 Limit states

(1)P The following limit states shall be considered and an appropriate list shall be compiled:

- loss of overall stability;
- bearing resistance failure, punching failure, squeezing;
- failure by sliding;
- combined failure in the ground and in the structure;
- structural failure due to foundation movement;
- excessive settlements;
- excessive heave due to swelling, frost and other causes;
- unacceptable vibrations.

6.3 Actions and design situations

(3) If structural stiffness is significant, an analysis of the interaction between the structure and the ground should be performed in order to determine the distribution of actions.

6.4 Design and construction considerations

(5)P One of the following design methods shall be used for spread foundations:

- a direct method, in which separate analyses are carried out for each limit state. When checking against an ultimate limit state, the calculation shall model as closely as possible the failure mechanism which is envisaged. When checking against a serviceability limit state, a settlement calculation shall be used;
- an indirect method using comparable experience and the results of field or laboratory measurements or observations, and chosen in relation to serviceability limit state loads so as to satisfy the requirements of all relevant limit states;
- a prescriptive method in which a presumed bearing resistance is used (see 2.5).

Subclause 6.4(1)P lists things that should be considered when choosing the depth of a spread foundation.

A sample indirect method for estimating bearing resistance is given in Annex E of EN 1997-1. A sample method for deriving presumed bearing resistance for spread foundations on rock is given in Annex G.

6.5 Ultimate limit state design

6.5.1 Overall stability

(1)P Overall stability, with or without the foundations, shall be checked particularly in the following situations:

- near or on a natural or man-made slope;
- near an excavation or a retaining wall;
- near a river, a canal, a lake, a reservoir or the sea shore;
- near mine workings or buried structures.

6.5.2 Bearing resistance

6.5.2.1 General

(1)P The following inequality shall be satisfied for all ultimate limit states:

$$V_d \leq R_d \qquad (6.1)$$

In equation (6.1), V_d is the design value of vertical load (or component of the total action) acting normal to the foundation base and R_d is the design resistance to that load. Equation (6.1) is a special form of equation (2.5) (see clause 2.4.7.3.1(1)P), in which E_d is replaced by V_d.

(3)P V_d shall include the weight of the foundation, the weight of any backfill material and all earth pressures, either favourable or unfavourable. Water pressures not caused by the foundation load should be included as actions.

Example (using analytical method from Annex D of EN 1997-1)
A 1.2 m wide strip footing founded on a uniform clay, with properties γ = 20 kN/m³, φ' = 23°, c' = 5 kPa, and c_u = 40 kPa, subjects the ground to a representative vertical bearing pressure (action) = 160 kPa, which includes the weight of the foundation and any soil on it. The water table is below the zone of influence of the footing and the base of the footing is 0.75 m below ground level.

Undrained (short term)

$R_d/A' = (\pi + 2)c_u b_c s_c i_c + q = (\pi + 2)c_u + q$

Base, shape and load inclination factors are all 1,0 for a strip footing.

DA1 combination 1

Using partial factor sets A1 + M1 + R1, only set A1 has values other than 1,0. Partial factor γ_G = 1,35.

R_d/A' = 5,14 x 40 + 0,75 x 20 = 220,6 kPa
$V_d/A' = F_{rep}\gamma_G$ = 160 x 1,35 = 216 kPa
$V_d \leq R_d$ and thus combination 1 is satisfied

DA1 combination 2

Using partial factor sets A2 + M2 + R1, only set M2 has values other than 1,0. Partial factor γ_{cu} = 1,4.

$R_d/A' = (\pi + 2)\ c_u/\gamma_{cu} + q$ = 5,14 x 40/1,4 + 0,75 x 20 = 161,9 kPa
V_d/A' = 160 x 1,0 = 160 kPa
$V_d \leq R_d$ and thus combination 2 is satisfied

Drained (long term)

$R_d/A' = c'N_c b_c s_c i_c + qN_q b_q s_q i_q + 0{,}5\gamma BN_\gamma b_\gamma s_\gamma i_\gamma$
$R_d/A' = cN_c + qN_q + 0{,}5\gamma BN_\gamma$

where N_c, N_q, and N_γ are functions of φ'. Formulae for these coefficients are given in Annex D of EN 1997-1. Base, shape, and load inclination factors are all 1,0 for a strip footing.

DA1 combination 1

Partial factor γ_G = 1,35.

The bearing capacity factors are obtained using the design value of ϕ:

$\varphi'_d = \tan^{-1}(\tan 23°/1{,}0) = 23°$
$N_c = 18$, $N_q = 8{,}66$, $N_\gamma = 6{,}5$

Thus:

$R_d/A' = 5 \times 18 + 15 \times 8,66 + 0,5 \times 20 \times 1,2 \times 6,5 = 297,9$ kPa
$V_d/A' = F_{rep}\gamma_G = 160 \times 1,35 = 216$ kPa
$V_d \leq R_d$ and thus combination 1 is satisfied

DA1 combination 2

Partial factors $\gamma_{c'} = \gamma_{\varphi'} = 1,25$

The bearing capacity factors are obtained using the design value of ϕ:

$\varphi'_d = \tan^{-1}(\tan 23°/1,25) = 18,76°$
$N_c = 13,72$, $N_q = 5,66$, $N_\gamma = 3,17$

Thus:

$R_d/A' = (c'/\gamma_{c'})N_c + q'N_q + 0.5\gamma BN_\gamma$
$R_d/A' = 5/1,25 \times 13,72 + 15 \times 5,66 + 0,5 \times 20 \times 1,2 \times 3,17 = 177,8$ kPa
$V_d/A' = 160 \times 1,0 = 160$ kPa
$V_d \leq R_d$ and thus combination 2 is satisfied

6.5.2.2 Analytical method

(1) A commonly recognized analytical method should be used.

NOTE The sample analytical calculation for bearing resistance given in Annex D may be used.

The sample analytical method given in Annex D is just one of several that are available. It should be noted that the method has several omissions from the usually accepted formulations of bearing capacity (particularly, there are no depth or ground inclinations factors. Any generally acceptable method may be used.

(2)P An analytical evaluation of the short-term and long-term values of R_d shall be considered, particularly in fine-grained soils.

(5) Where a strong formation underlies a weak formation, the bearing resistance may be calculated using the shear strength parameters of the weak formation. For the reverse situation, punching failure should be checked.

6.5.3 Sliding resistance

(1)P Where the loading is not normal to the foundation base, foundations shall be checked against failure by sliding on the base.

(2)P The following inequality shall be satisfied:

$$H_d \leq R_d + R_{p;d} \qquad (6.2)$$

In equation (6.2), H_d is the design value of horizontal load or component of the total action acting parallel to the foundation base, R_d is the design resistance to that load, and $R_{p;d}$ is the design value of the resisting force caused by earth pressure on the side of the foundation. H_d should include any active earth forces imposed on the foundation.

(8)P For drained conditions, the design shear resistance, R_d, shall be calculated either by factoring the ground properties or the ground resistance, as follows:

$$R_d = V'_d \tan \delta_d \qquad (6.3a)$$

or

$$R_d = (V'_d \tan \delta_k) / \gamma_{R;h} \qquad (6.3b)$$

NOTE In design procedures where the effects of actions are factored, the partial factor for the actions (γ_F) is 1,0 and $V'_d = V'_k$ in equation (6.3b).

In equation (6.3), V'_d is the design value of the effective vertical action or component of the effective action acting normal to the foundation base, and δ_d is the design structure-soil interface friction angle. The design friction angle δ_d may be assumed to be equal to the effective design critical state angle of shearing resistance, $\varphi'_{cv;d}$, for cast-in-situ concrete foundations and equal to 2/3 $\varphi'_{cv;d}$ for smooth precast foundations. Any effective cohesion c' should be neglected.

Example
For the 1,2 m wide footing above, assuming, $\varphi'_{cv;d} = 23°$

R_d = 160 x 1,2 x tan 23° = 81,5 kN/m

Thus to satisfy the limit state the horizontal design action, H_d should be less than 81,5 kN.

(11)P For undrained conditions, the design shearing resistance, R_d, shall be calculated either by factoring the ground properties or the ground resistance, as follows:

AC1⟩ $R_d = A c_{u;d}$ ⟨AC1 (6.4a)

or

AC1⟩ $R_d = (A c_{u;k}) / \gamma_{R;h}$ ⟨AC1 (6.4b)

In equations (6.4a) and (6.4b), A is the total base area under compression and $c_{u;d}$ is the design undrained shear strength of the soil.

Example
For the example above the design resistance R_d would be 1,2 x 40/1,4 = 34,3 kN/m. Thus to satisfy the limit state the horizontal design action, H_d, should be less than 34,3 kN/m.

(12)P If it is possible for water or air to reach the interface between a foundation and an undrained clay subgrade, the following check shall be made:

$$R_d \leq 0.4\, V_d \qquad (6.5)$$

In equation (6.5), V_d is the design value of the total vertical action or component of the total action acting normal to the foundation base.

Example
For the example above the design resistance R_d would be 0,4 x 160 = 64 kN/m. Thus to satisfy the limit state the horizontal design action, H_d, should still be less than 34,3 kN/m as equation (6.4a) gives a lower value.

6.5.4 Loads with large eccentricities

(1)P Special precautions shall be taken where the eccentricity of loading exceeds 1/3 of the width of a rectangular footing or 0,6 of the radius of a circular footing.

Such precautions include:

- careful review of the design values of actions in accordance with 2.4.2;
- designing the location of the foundation edge by taking into account the magnitude of construction tolerances.

Note that this is not the traditional "middle third" rule (in which the eccentricity should be less than 1/6th of the footing width).

6.6 Serviceability limit state design

6.6.1 General

(1)P Account shall be taken of displacements caused by actions on the foundation, such as those listed in 2.4.2(4).

(3)P For soft clays, settlement calculations shall always be carried out.

(6) Calculations of settlements should not be regarded as accurate. They merely provide an approximate indication.

(7)P Foundation displacements shall be considered both in terms of displacement of the entire foundation and differential displacements of parts of the foundation.

(8)P The effect of neighbouring foundations and fills shall be taken into account when calculating the stress increase in the ground and its influence on ground compressibility.

6.6.2 Settlement

(1)P Calculations of settlements shall include both immediate and delayed settlement.

(2) The following three components of settlement should be considered for partially or fully saturated soils:

- s_0: immediate settlement; for fully-saturated soil due to shear deformation at constant volume, and for partially-saturated soil due to both shear deformation and volume reduction;
- s_1: settlement caused by consolidation;
- s_2: settlement caused by creep.

Subclauses 6.6.2(3) to (16) contain guidance on the appropriate considerations for the assessment of settlement.

Example
See Example 1 of commentary on 2.4.8.

6.6.3 Heave

(1)P The following causes of heave shall be distinguished:

- reduction of effective stress;
- volume expansion of partly saturated soil;
- heave due to constant volume conditions in fully saturated soil, caused by settlement of an adjacent structure.

(2)P Calculations of heave shall include both immediate and delayed heave.

6.6.4 Vibration analysis

(1)P Foundations for structures subjected to vibrations or to vibrating loads shall be designed to ensure that vibrations will not cause excessive settlements.

Subclauses 6.7, 6.8 and 6.9 contain additional considerations of foundations on rock, of the structural design of spread foundations and of the preparation of the subsoil.

7 Pile foundations

7.2 Limit states

(1)P The following limit states shall be considered and an appropriate list shall be compiled:

- loss of overall stability;
- bearing resistance failure of the pile foundation;
- uplift or insufficient tensile resistance of the pile foundation;
- failure in the ground due to transverse loading of the pile foundation;
- structural failure of the pile in compression, tension, bending, buckling or shear;
- combined failure in the ground and in the pile foundation;
- combined failure in the ground and in the structure;
- excessive settlement;
- excessive heave;
- excessive lateral movement;
- unacceptable vibrations.

7.3 Actions and design situations

7.3.2 Actions due to ground displacement

7.3.2.1 General

(1)P Ground in which piles are located may be subject to displacement caused by consolidation, swelling, adjacent loads, creeping soil, landslides or earthquakes. Consideration shall be given to these phenomena as they can affect the piles by causing downdrag (negative skin friction), heave, stretching, transverse loading and displacement.

(3)P One of the two following approaches shall be adopted for design:

- the ground displacement is treated as an action. An interaction analysis is then carried out to determine the forces, displacements and strains in the pile;
- an upper bound to the force which the ground could transmit to the pile shall be introduced as the design action. Evaluation of this force shall take account of the strength of the soil and the source of the load, represented by the weight or compression of the moving soil or the magnitude of disturbing actions.

7.3.2.2 Downdrag (negative skin friction)

(1)P If ultimate limit state design calculations are carried out with the downdrag load as an action, its value shall be the maximum which could be generated by the downward movement of the ground relative to the pile.

7.3.2.3 Heave

(1)P In considering the effect of heave, or upward loads which may be generated along the pile shaft, the movement of the ground shall generally be treated as an action.

7.3.2.4 Transverse loading

(1)P Consideration shall be given to transverse actions originating from ground movements around a pile.

Subclause 7.3.2.4(2) lists things that may result in transverse actions.

7.4 Design methods and design considerations

7.4.1 Design methods

(1)P The design shall be based on one of the following approaches:

- the results of static load tests which have been demonstrated, by means of calculations or otherwise, to be consistent with other relevant experience;
- empirical or analytical calculation methods whose validity has been demonstrated by static load tests in comparable situations;
- the results of dynamic load tests whose validity has been demonstrated by static load tests in comparable situations;
- the observed performance of a comparable pile foundation, provided that this approach is supported by the results of site investigation and ground testing.

7.4.2 Design considerations

(1)P The behaviour of individual piles and pile groups and the stiffness and strength of the structure connecting the piles shall be considered.

Subclauses 7.4.2(4) and (5) list things that should be taken into account when choosing the type of pile and pile material.

7.5 Pile load tests

7.5.1 General

(1)P Pile load tests shall be carried out in the following situations:

- when using a type of pile or installation method for which there is no comparable experience;
- when the piles have not been tested under comparable soil and loading conditions;
- when the piles will be subject to loading for which theory and experience do not provide sufficient confidence in the design. The pile testing procedure shall then provide loading similar to the anticipated loading;
- when observations during the process of installation indicate pile behaviour that deviates strongly and unfavourably from the behaviour anticipated on the basis of the site investigation or experience, and when additional ground investigations do not clarify the reasons for this deviation.

Subclauses 7.5.1 to 7.5.5 provide guidance for pile load tests. Further guidance is contained in EN 1536 and EN 12699.

7.6 Axially loaded piles

7.6.1 General

7.6.1.1 Limit state design

(1)P The design shall demonstrate that exceeding the following limit states is sufficiently improbable:

- ultimate limit states of compressive or tensile resistance failure of a single pile;
- ultimate limit states of compressive or tensile resistance failure of the pile foundation as a whole;
- ultimate limit states of collapse or severe damage to a supported structure caused by excessive displacement or differential displacements of the pile foundation;
- serviceability limit states in the supported structure caused by displacement of the piles.

7.6.2 Compressive ground resistance

7.6.2.1 General

(1)P To demonstrate that the pile foundation will support the design load with adequate safety against compressive failure, the following inequality shall be satisfied for all ultimate limit state load cases and load combinations:

$$F_{c;d} \leq R_{c;d} \tag{7.1}$$

In equation (7.1), $F_{c;d}$ is the design axial compression load on a pile or pile group and $R_{c;d}$ is the design value of the compressive resistance of the ground against that pile or group. Equation (7.1) is a specific form of equation (2.5), with $F_{c;d}$ replacing E_d.

(3)P For piles in groups, two failure mechanisms shall be taken into account:

- compressive resistance failure of the piles individually;
- compressive resistance failure of the piles and the soil contained between them acting as a block.

The design resistance shall be taken as the lower value caused by these two mechanisms.

Subclauses 7.6.2.1(4) to (13) provide further guidance on things to be considered in axial design of piles.

7.6.2.2 Ultimate compressive resistance from static load tests

(8)P For structures, which do not exhibit capacity to transfer loads from "weak" piles to "strong" piles, as a minimum, the following equation shall be satisfied:

$$R_{c;k} = \text{Min}\left\{(R_{c;m})_{\text{mean}} / \xi_1 ; (R_{c;m})_{\text{min}} / \xi_2\right\} \tag{7.2}$$

where ξ_1 and ξ_2 are correlation factors related to the number of piles tested and are applied to the mean $(R_{c;m})_{mean}$ and the lowest $(R_{c;m})_{min}$ of $R_{c;m}$ respectively.

NOTE The values of the correlation factors may be set by the National Annex. The recommended values are given in Table A.9.

In equation (7.2), $R_{c;k}$ is the characteristic value of the compressive resistance of the ground against a pile, $R_{c;m}$ is the measured value of the compressive resistance of the pile in one or several pile load tests and ξ is a correlation factor related to the number of piles tested. Values of ξ from the National Annex to BS EN 1997-1 are given in NA.2 (these values differ from those given in EN 1997-1 Annex A).

A.3.3.3 Correlation factors for pile foundations

Table A.NA.9

Correlation factors (ξ) to derive characteristic values of the resistance of axially loaded piles from static pile load tests (n – number of tested piles)

ξ **for** n **=**	**1**	**2**	**3**	**4**	**≥ 5**
ξ_1	1,55	1,47	1,42	1,38	1,35
ξ_2	1,55	1,35	1,23	1,15	1,08
NOTE For structures having sufficient stiffness and strength to transfer loads from "weak" to "strong" piles, values of ξ_1 and ξ_2 may be divided by 1,1, provided that ξ_1 is never less than 1,0, see EN 1997-1 7.6.2.2(9).					

Example
The measured load in three static load tests on identical piles at a site were 250 kN, 280 kN, and 298 kN. The mean resistance $R_{c;m}$ was therefore 276 kN, and the characteristic resistance $R_{c;k}$ is calculated as the lesser of 276 / 1,42 = 194 kN and 250 / 1,23 = 203 kN, i.e. 194 kN.

(12) The characteristic compressive resistance of the ground, $R_{c;k}$, may be derived from the characteristic values of the base resistance, $R_{b;k}$, and of the shaft resistance, $R_{s;k}$, such that:

$$R_{c;k} = R_{b;k} + R_{s;k} \qquad (7.3)$$

In equation (7.3), $R_{b;k}$ is the characteristic value of the base resistance of a pile and $R_{s;k}$ is the characteristic value of its shaft resistance. It is assumed that the two components can be identified from the pile tests carried out.

Example
For the example above the characteristic compressive resistance ($R_{c;k}$) is 194 kN. From test measurements or from an understanding of the ground properties the characteristic base resistance of the pile ($R_{b;k}$) is assumed to be 160 kN and its characteristic shaft resistance ($R_{s;k}$) is 34 kN.

(14)P The design resistance, $R_{c;d}$, shall be derived from either:

$$R_{c;d} = R_{c;k} / \gamma_t \qquad (7.4)$$

or

$$R_{c;d} = R_{b;k} / \gamma_b + R_{s;k} / \gamma_s \qquad (7.5)$$

NOTE The values of the partial factors may be set by the National Annex. The recommended values for persistent and transient situations are given in Tables A.6, A.7 and A.8.

In equation (7.4), $R_{c;k}$ is the characteristic value of the compressive resistance of the pile and γ_t is a partial factor on that resistance.

In equation (7.5), $R_{b;k}$ is the characteristic base resistance of the pile, $R_{s;k}$ is its characteristic shaft resistance, γ_b is a partial factor on the base resistance and γ_s is a partial factor on the shaft resistance.

Values of γ from the National Annex to BS EN 1997-1 are given below. Please note that these values differ significantly from those given in EN 1997-1 Annex A. With these factors, equation (7.4) always gives design resistances equal to or lower than equation (7.5).

Partial factors for piles in compression

Resistance	**Symbol**	**Partial factor set for different pile types**				
		R1	**R4**			
			Without load tests*		**With load tests***	
		All types	**Bored & CFA**	**Driven**	**Bored & CFA**	**Driven**
Base	γ_b	1,0	2,0	1,7	1,7	1,5
Shaft	γ_s		1,6	1,5	1,4	1,3
Total	γ_t		2,0	1,7	1,7	1,5

* The lower values of γ_b, γ_s, and γ_t in R4 may be adopted if serviceability is verified by load tests (preliminary and/or working) carried out on more than 1% of the constructed piles to loads not less than 1,5 times the representative load for which they are designed, or if settlement at the serviceability limit state is of no concern.

Example (using equation 7.4)
If the characteristic base resistance ($R_{b;k}$) of a bored pile is 160 kN and its characteristic shaft resistance ($R_{s;k}$) is 34 kN, then its design resistance ($R_{c;d}$) when using partial factor set R4 without test loads is (160 kN + 34 kN) / 2,0 = 97 kN and no verification of serviceability is required.

If load tests are performed to verify serviceability, then the design resistance at the ultimate limit state can be increased to $R_{c;d}$ = (160 kN + 34 kN) / 1,7 = 114 kN.

Example (using equation 7.5)
Using the same values of characteristic resistance as the example above, then the pile's design resistance ($R_{c;d}$) when using partial factor set R4 without test loads is 160 kN / 2,0 + 34 kN / 1,6 = 101 kN and no verification of serviceability is required.

If load tests are performed to verify serviceability, then the design resistance at the ultimate limit state can be increased to $R_{c;d}$ = 160 kN / 1,7 + 34 kN / 1,4 = 118 kN.

7.6.2.3 Ultimate compressive resistance from ground test results

Subclauses 7.6.2.3(3) and (4) give equations for calculating the design compressive resistance of a pile from ground test results. These equations are identical to equation (7.5) above. Values of γ are also as given above.

Subclause 7.6.2.3(5)P gives an equation for calculating the characteristic compressive resistance of a pile from ground test results that is similar to equation (7.2), with the subscripts "m" (for measured) replaced with "cal" (for calculated). The corresponding values of ξ from the National Annex to BS EN 1997-1 are given in NA.2 (these values differ from those given in EN 1997-1 Annex A).

A.3.3.3 Correlation factors for pile foundations

Table A.NA.10

Correlation factors (ξ) to derive characteristic values of the resistance of axially loaded piles from ground test results (n – the number of profiles of tests)

ξ **for** n =	**1**	**2**	**3**	**4**	**5**	**7**	**10**
ξ_3	1,55	1,47	1,42	1,38	1,36	1,33	1,30
ξ_4	1,55	1,39	1,33	1,29	1,26	1,20	1,15

NOTE For structures having sufficient stiffness and strength to transfer loads from "weak" to "strong" piles, values of ξ_3 and ξ_4 may be divided by 1,1, provided that ξ_3 is never less than 1,0, see EN 1997-1 7.6.2.3(7).

Values of ξ_3 and ξ_4 may be reduced by a factor of 1,15 if the pile resistance is verified by a maintained load test to failure.

Example

Consider a 15 m long x 0,6 m diameter CFA pile in a uniform clay. Ground test results from one borehole suggests the clay's weight density γ = 20 kN/m^3 and undrained strength c_u = 80 kPa, while those from another borehole suggest γ = 20 kN/m^3 and c_u = 95 kPa.

The calculated base resistance of the pile from borehole 1 is (assuming a bearing capacity factor N_c = 9);

$$R_{b;cal} = A_b(N_c c_u + \sigma_v) = (\pi \times 0{,}6^2/4) \times (9 \times 80 + 15 \times 20) = 288 \text{ kN}$$

and from borehole 2:

$$R_{b;cal} = (\pi \times 0{,}6^2/4) \times (9 \times 95 + 15 \times 20) = 327 \text{ kN}$$

Hence the characteristic base resistance is the lesser of:

$$R_{b;k} = (R_{b;cal})_{mean}/\xi_3 = (288 + 327) / (2 \times 1{,}47) = 209 \text{ kN}$$

and:

$$R_{b;k} = (R_{b;cal})_{min}/\xi_4 = 288 / 1{,}39 = 207 \text{ kN}$$

The calculated shaft resistance of the pile from borehole 1 is (assuming an adhesion factor a = 0,6):

$$R_{s;cal} = A_s a\, c_u = (\pi \times 15 \times 0{,}6) \times 0{,}6 \times 80 = 1357 \text{ kN}$$

and from borehole 2:

$R_{s;cal} = (\pi \times 15 \times 0,6) \times 0,6 \times 95 = 1611$ kN

Hence the characteristic shaft resistance is the lesser of:

$R_{s;k} = (R_{s;cal})_{mean}/\xi_3 = (1357 + 1611) / (2 \times 1,47) = 1009$ kN

and:

$R_{s;k} = (R_{s;cal})_{min}/\xi_4 = 1357 / 1,39 = 976$ kN

The design resistance is therefore (from equation (7.5), using Design Approach 1 (DA1), combination 2, with partial factor sets A1 + M1 + R4):

$R_{c;d} = R_{b;k}/\gamma_b + R_{s;k}/\gamma_s = 207 / 2,0 + 976 / 1,6 = 103,5 + 610 = 714$ kN

If a static pile load test is performed to verify serviceability, then the ultimate design resistance may be increased by 1,15 (since ξ_3 and ξ_4 are reduced by 1,15). Hence:

$R_{c;d} = 714 \text{ kN} \times 1,15 = 821$ kN

(8) The characteristic values may be obtained by calculating:

$$R_{b;k} = A_b\, q_{b;k} \quad \text{and} \quad R_{s;k} = \sum_i A_{s;i} \cdot q_{s;i;k} \qquad (7.9)$$

where $q_{b;k}$ and $q_{s;i;k}$ are characteristic values of base resistance and shaft friction in the various strata, obtained from values of ground parameters.

This procedure, based on characteristic values for each layer obtained directly from ground parameters, more closely represents existing UK design practice than the earlier procedure involving correlation factors.

NOTE If this alternative procedure is applied, the values of the partial factors γ_b and γ_s recommended in Annex A may need to be corrected by a model factor larger than 1,0. The value of the model factor may be set by the National Annex.

The National Annex to BS EN 1997-1 recommends that a model factor $\gamma_{Rd} = 1,4$ is used in conjunction with expression 7.9 to obtain characteristic base and shaft resistances, unless preliminary static pile load tests are performed to establish the load vs displacement behaviour of the piles up to the ultimate limit state, in which case γ_{Rd} may be reduced to 1,2. The correlation and model factors given in the National Annex to BS EN 1997-1 have been chosen to give roughly comparable design resistances whichever procedure is used.

Example
Consider the 15 m long x 0,6 m diameter CFA pile from the previous example. Consideration of the ground test results from both boreholes leads to a characteristic strength $c_{uk} = 85$ kPa being selected for the design of the piles.

The calculated base resistance (assuming $N_c = 9$) is;

$R_{b;k} = (A_b\, q_{bk}) / \gamma_{Rd} = A_b(N_c\, c_{uk} / \gamma_{cu} + \sigma_v) / \gamma_{Rd}$
$= (\pi \times 0,6^2/4) \times (9 \times 85 / 1,0 + 15 \times 20) / 1,4 = 215$ kN

The calculated shaft resistance (assuming a = 0,6) is:

$R_{s;k} = \Sigma(A_b\, q_{sk}) / \gamma_{Rd} = A_s\, \alpha\, c_{uk} / (\gamma_{cu}\, \gamma_{Rd})$
$= (\pi \times 15 \times 0{,}6) \times 0{,}6 \times 85 / (1.0 \times 1.4) = 1030$ kN

The design resistance is therefore (from equation 7.5, using Design Approach 1 (DA1), combination 2, with partial factor sets A1 + M1 + R4):

$R_{c;d} = R_{b;k} / \gamma_b + R_{s;k} / \gamma_s = 215 / 2{,}0 + 1030 / 1{,}6 = 107{,}5 + 643{,}8 = 751$ kN

If a static pile load test is performed to verify serviceability, then the ultimate design resistance may be increased by the ratio 1,4 / 1,2 = 1,17 (since γ_{Rd} is reduced from 1.4 to 1.2). Hence:

$R_{c;d} = 751$ kN x 1,4 / 1,2 = 876 kN

7.6.2.4 Ultimate compressive resistance from dynamic impact tests

7.6.2.5 Ultimate compressive resistance by applying pile driving formulae

7.6.2.6 Ultimate compressive resistance from wave equation analysis

Subclauses 7.6.2.4, 7.6.2.5, and 7.6.2.6 cover the application of dynamic impact tests, pile driving formulae and wave equation analysis to the assessment of pile axial capacity.

7.6.3 Ground tensile resistance

7.6.3.1 General

(1)P The design of piles in tension shall be consistent with the design rules given in 7.6.2, where applicable. Design rules that are specific for foundations involving piles in tension are presented below.

(2)P To verify that the foundation will support the design load with adequate safety against a failure in tension, the following inequality shall be satisfied for all ultimate limit state load cases and load combinations:

$$F_{t;d} \leq R_{t;d} \tag{7.12}$$

In equation (7.12), $F_{t;d}$ is the design axial tension load on a pile or pile group and $R_{t;d}$ is the design value of the tensile resistance of the ground against that pile. Equation (7.12) is a specific form of equation (2.5), with $F_{t;d}$ replacing E_d.

(3)P For tension piles, two failure mechanisms shall be considered:

- pull-out of the piles from the ground mass;
- uplift of the block of ground containing the piles.

Subclause 7.6.3.2 contains further considerations for the design of piles in tension including a useful diagram to indicate potentially loading mechanisms.

7.6.3.2 Ultimate tensile resistance from pile load tests

(2)P The design tensile resistance, $R_{t;d}$, shall be derived from:

$$R_{t;d} = R_{t;k} / \gamma_{s;t} \tag{7.13}$$

NOTE The values of the partial factors may be set by the National Annex. The recommended values for persistent and transient situations are given in Tables A.6, A.7 and A.8.

In equation (7.13), $R_{t;k}$ is the characteristic value of the tensile resistance of the pile and $\gamma_{s;t}$ is a partial factor on that resistance.

Values of γ from the National Annex to BS EN 1997-1 are given below. (Note that these values differ significantly from those given in EN 1997-1 Annex A.) The values of γ are the same for driven, bored and continuous flight auger (CFA) piles.

Partial factors for piles in tension:

Resistance	Symbol	Partial factor set		
		R1	R4	
			Without load tests*	With load tests*
Shaft	$\gamma_{s;t}$	1,0	2,0	1,7
* See note to table given in commentary to clause 7.6.2.2(14)P				

Example
If the characteristic tensile resistance ($R_{t;k}$) of a driven pile is 265 kN, then its design resistance ($R_{t;d}$) when using partial factor set R4 without load tests is 265 kN / 2,0 = 132,5 kN and no verification of serviceability is required.

If load tests are performed to verify serviceability, then the design resistance at the ultimate limit state can be increased to $R_{t;d}$ = 265 kN / 1,7 = 155,9 kN.

Subclause 7.6.3.2(5)P gives an equation for determining the characteristic tensile resistance of a pile from pile load tests that is similar to equation (7.2). The corresponding values of ξ from the National Annex to BS EN 1997-1 are as given in the commentary to 7.6.2.2.

7.6.3.3 Ultimate tensile resistance from ground test results

Subclause 7.6.3.3(3)P gives an equation for calculating the design tensile resistance of a pile from ground test results that is identical to equation (7.13). Values of γ are as given in the table in the commentary to 7.6.3.2.

Subclause 7.6.3.3(4)P gives an equation for determining the characteristic tensile resistance of a pile from ground test results that is similar to equation (7.2), with the subscripts "m" (for measured) replaced by "cal" (for calculated). The corresponding values of ξ from the National Annex to BS EN 1997-1 are as given in the commentary to 7.6.2.3.

7.6.4 Vertical displacements of pile foundations (serviceability of supported structure)

7.6.4.1 General

(2) When calculating the vertical displacements of a pile foundation, the uncertainties involved in the calculation model and in determining the relevant ground properties should be taken into account. Hence it should not be overlooked that in most cases calculations will provide only an approximate estimate of the displacements of the pile foundation.

7.7 Transversely loaded piles

7.7.1 General

(2)P To demonstrate that a pile will support the design transverse load with adequate safety against failure, the following inequality shall be satisfied for all ultimate limit state load cases and load combinations:

$$F_{tr;d} \leq R_{tr;d} \qquad (7.19)$$

In equation (7.19), $F_{tr;d}$ is the design transverse load on a pile or pile group and $R_{tr;d}$ is the design resistance of that pile or group. Equation (7.19) is a specific form of equation (2.5), with $F_{tr;d}$ replacing E_d.

(3) One of the following failure mechanisms should be considered:

- for short piles, rotation or translation as a rigid body;
- for long slender piles, bending failure of the pile, accompanied by local yielding and displacement of the soil near the top of the pile.

7.7.3 Transverse load resistance from ground test results and pile strength parameters

(1)P The transverse resistance of a pile or pile group shall be calculated using a compatible set of structural effects of actions, ground reactions and displacements.

(2)P The analysis of a transversely loaded pile shall include the possibility of structural failure of the pile in the ground, in accordance with 7.8.

7.7.4 Transverse displacement

(1)P The assessment of the transverse displacement of a pile foundation shall take into account:

- the stiffness of the ground and its variation with strain level;
- the flexural stiffness of the individual piles;
- the moment fixity of the piles at the connection with the structure;
- the group effect;
- the effect of load reversals or of cyclic loading.

7.8 Structural design of piles

(1)P Piles shall be verified against structural failure in accordance with 2.4.6.4.

Subclause 7.8 contains further guidance on the structural design of piles.

7.9 Supervision of construction

Subclause 7.9 lists things that need to be recorded during pile construction and makes reference to other codes relating to the satisfactory installation and performance of piles.

8 Anchorages

8.1 General

8.1.1 Scope

(2)P This Section is applicable to:

- pre-stressed anchorages consisting of an anchor head, a tendon free length and a tendon bond length bonded to the ground by grout;
- non pre-stressed anchorages consisting of an anchor head, a tendon free length and a restraint such as a fixed anchor length bonded to the ground by grout, a deadman anchorage, a screw anchor or a rock bolt.

AC1 (3)P This Section does not apply to soil nails. AC1

8.2 Limit states

(1)P The following limit states shall be considered for anchorages, both individually and in combination:

- structural failure of the tendon or anchor head, caused by the applied stresses;
- distortion or corrosion of the anchor head;
- for grouted anchors, failure at the interface between the body of grout and the ground;
- for grouted anchors, failure of the bond between the steel tendon and the grout;
- for deadman anchorages, failure by insufficient resistance of the deadman;
- loss of anchorage force by excessive displacements of the anchor head or by creep and relaxation;
- failure or excessive deformation of parts of the structure due to the applied anchorage force;
- loss of overall stability of the retained ground and the retaining structure;
- interaction of groups of anchorages with the ground and adjoining structures.

8.3 Design situations and actions

Subclause 8.3(1)P lists things that should be considered when selecting design situations for anchorages.

8.4 Design and construction considerations

(1)P The design of the anchorage and the specification for its execution shall take into account any adverse effects of tensile stresses transmitted to ground beyond the vicinity of the anchorage.

Subclauses 8.4(2) to (15) provide guidance on the practical aspects of design and construction of anchorages, with particular reference to European execution standards.

8.5 Ultimate limit state design

8.5.1 Design of the anchorage

(1)P The design value, $R_{a;d}$, of the pull-out resistance, R_a, of an anchorage shall fulfil the limit condition:

$$P_d \leq R_{a;d} \tag{8.1}$$

In equation (8.1), P_d is the design value of the load on an anchorage and $R_{a;d}$ is the design value of the pull-out resistance of that anchorage. Equation (8.1) is a specific form of equation (2.5), with P_d replacing E_d.

8.5.2 Design values of pull-out resistance determined from the results of tests

(1)P The design value of the pull-out resistance shall be derived from the characteristic value using the equation:

$$R_{a;d} = R_{a;k} / \gamma_a \qquad (8.2)$$

NOTE The partial factor, γ_a, takes into account unfavourable deviations of the pull-out resistance of the anchorage.

In equation (8.2), $R_{a;k}$ is the characteristic value of the pull-out resistance of the anchorage and γ_a is a partial factor on that resistance.

Values of γ from the National Annex to BS EN 1997-1 are given below. The values of γ are the same for temporary and permanent anchorages.

Partial factors for pre-stressed anchorages

Resistance	Symbol	Partial factor set	
		R1	R4
Temporary	$\gamma_{a;t}$	1,1	1,1
Permanent	$\gamma_{a;p}$		

Example
If the characteristic tensile resistance ($R_{a;k}$) of an anchorage is 95 kN, then its design resistance ($R_{a;d}$) when using partial factor set R4 is 95 kN/1,1 = 86 kN.

8.5.4 Design value of the structural resistance of the anchorage

(1)P The structural design of the anchorage shall satisfy the following inequality:

$$R_{a;d} \leq R_{t;d} \qquad (8.3)$$

In equation (8.3), $R_{a;d}$ is the design value of the pull-out resistance of an anchorage and $R_{t;d}$ is the design value of the structural tensile resistance of that anchorage.

8.5.5 Design value of the anchorage load

(1)P The design value of the anchorage load, P_d, shall be derived from the design of the retained structure as the maximum value of

- the ultimate limit state force applied by the retained structure, and if relevant
- the serviceability limit state force applied by the retained structure.

Clauses 8.6 to 8.9 contain further aspects of anchorage design relating to serviceability limit states, suitability tests, acceptance tests and supervision and monitoring.

9 Retaining structures

9.1 General

9.1.1 Scope

(1)P The provisions of this Section shall apply to structures which retain ground comprising soil, rock or backfill and water. Material is retained if it is kept at a slope steeper than it would eventually adopt if no structure were present. Retaining structures include all types of wall and support systems in which structural elements have forces imposed by the retained material.

9.1.2 Definitions

(1) In considering the design of retaining structures the following three main types should be distinguished:

- gravity walls
- embedded walls
- composite retaining structures

Subclause 9.1.2 contains detailed descriptions of these types of wall.

9.2 Limit states

(1)P A list shall be compiled of limit states to be considered. As a minimum the following limit states shall be considered for all types of retaining structure:

- loss of overall stability;
- failure of a structural element such as a wall, anchorage, wale or strut or failure of the connection between such elements;
- combined failure in the ground and in the structural element;
- failure by hydraulic heave and piping;
- movement of the retaining structure which may cause collapse or affect the appearance or efficient use of the structure or nearby structures or services which rely on it;
- unacceptable leakage through or beneath the wall;
- unacceptable transport of soil particles through or beneath the wall;
- unacceptable change in the ground-water regime.

(2)P In addition, the following limit states shall be considered for gravity walls and for composite retaining structures:

- bearing resistance failure of the soil below the base;
- failure by sliding at the base;
- failure by toppling;

and for embedded walls:

- failure by rotation or translation of the wall or parts thereof;
- failure by lack of vertical equilibrium.

9.3 Actions, geometrical data and design situations

9.3.1 Actions

9.3.1.3 Surcharges

(1)P Determination of design values for surcharges shall take account of the presence, on or near the surface of the retained ground, of, for example, nearby buildings, parked or moving vehicles or cranes, stored material, goods and containers.

EN 1997-1 does not provide minimum values for surcharge.

Subclauses 9.3.1.4 to 9.3.1.8 consider the actions resulting from weight of water, waves and ice, seepage, collision and temperature.

9.3.2 Geometrical data

9.3.2.2 Ground surfaces

(2) In ultimate limit state calculations in which the stability of a retaining wall depends on the ground resistance in front of the structure, the level of the resisting soil should be lowered below the nominally expected level by an amount Δa. The value of Δa should be selected taking into account the degree of site control over the level of the surface. With a normal degree of control, the following should be applied:

- for a cantilever wall, Δa should equal 10 % of the wall height above excavation level, limited to a maximum of 0,5 m;
- for a supported wall, Δa should equal 10 % of the distance between the lowest support and the excavation level, limited to a maximum of 0,5 m.

This is one of the few areas where the Eurocode recommends use of a safety margin on geometrical data.

9.3.2.3 Water levels

(1)P The selection of design or characteristic values for the positions of free water and phreatic surfaces shall be made on the basis of data for the hydraulic and hydrogeological conditions at the site.

(3)P The possibility shall be considered of adverse water pressures due to the presence of perched or artesian water tables.

9.3.3 Design situations

Subclause 9.3.3(1)P lists items that should be considered in design situations for retaining structures.

9.4 Design and construction considerations

9.4.1 General

(2)P It shall be demonstrated that vertical equilibrium can be achieved for the assumed pressure distributions and actions on the wall.

Subclauses 9.4.1(3) to (7) provide general guidance for designers and 9.4.1(8)P lists items that should be considered in the design of retaining structures.

9.4.2 Drainage systems

(1)P If the safety and serviceability of the designed structure depend on the successful performance of a drainage system, the consequences of its failure shall be considered, having regard for both safety and cost of repair. One of the following conditions (or a combination of them) shall apply:

- a maintenance programme for the drainage system shall be specified and the design shall allow access for this purpose;
- it shall be demonstrated both by comparable experience and by assessment of any water discharge, that the drainage system will operate adequately without maintenance.

9.5 Determination of earth pressures

9.5.1 General

(1)P Determination of earth pressures shall take account of the acceptable mode and amount of any movement and strain which may occur at the limit state under consideration.

(3)P Calculations of the magnitudes of earth pressures and directions of forces resulting from them shall take account of:

- the surcharge on and slope of the ground surface;
- the inclination of the wall to the vertical;
- the water tables and the seepage forces in the ground;
- the amount and direction of the movement of the wall relative to the ground;
- the horizontal as well as vertical equilibrium for the entire retaining structure;
- the shear strength and weight density of the ground;
- the rigidity of the wall and the supporting system;
- the wall roughness.

> Subclauses 9.5.1(4) to (12) provide further guidance on the relevant parameters and factors to be considered in determining the earth pressure.

9.5.2 At rest values of earth pressure

(1)P When no movement of the wall relative to the ground takes place, the earth pressure shall be calculated from the at rest state of stress. The determination of the at rest state shall take account of the stress history of the ground.

(2) For normally consolidated soil, at rest conditions should normally be assumed in the ground behind a retaining structure if the movement of the structure is less than $5\times10^{-4}\times h$.

(3) For a horizontal ground surface, the at rest earth pressure coefficient, K_0, should be determined from:

$$K_0 = (1 - \sin\varphi') \times \sqrt{\text{OCR}} \qquad (9.1)$$

This formula should not be used for very high values of OCR.

> In equation (9.1), φ' is the soil's angle of shearing resistance in terms of effective stress and OCR is the over-consolidation ratio of the soil. The formula is not reliable for OCRs greater than 10.

(4) If the ground slopes upwards from the wall at an angle $\beta \leq \varphi'$ to the horizontal, the horizontal component of the effective earth pressure $\sigma'_{h;0}$ may be related to the effective overburden pressure q' by the ratio $K_{0;\beta}$, where

$$K_{0;\beta} = K_0 (1 + \sin\beta) \qquad (9.2)$$

The direction of the resulting force should then be assumed to be parallel to the ground surface.

> In equation (9.2), β is the slope angle of the ground behind the wall and K_0 is as defined in equation (9.1).

9.5.4 Intermediate values of earth pressure

(1)P Intermediate values of earth pressure occur if the wall movements are insufficient to mobilize the limiting values. The determination of the intermediate values of earth pressure shall take account of the amount of wall movement and its direction relative to the ground.

NOTE Annex C, figure C.3, gives a diagram, which may be used for the determination of the mobilised passive earth pressure.

9.6 Water pressures

(1)P Determination of characteristic and design water pressures shall take account of water levels both above and in the ground.

AC1⟩ (3) ⟨AC1 For structures retaining earth of medium or low permeability (silts and clays), water pressures AC1⟩ should normally ⟨AC1 be assumed to act behind the wall. Unless a reliable drainage system is installed (see 9.4.2(1)P) or infiltration is prevented, the values of water pressures AC1⟩ should normally ⟨AC1 correspond to a water table at the surface of the retained material.

(5)P Where no special drainage or flow prevention measures are taken, the possible effects of water-filled tension or shrinkage cracks shall be considered.

9.7 Ultimate limit state design

9.7.1 General

(6)P For fine grained soils, both short- and long-term behaviour shall be considered.

(7)P For walls subject to differential water pressures, safety against failure due to hydraulic heave and piping shall be checked.

> Subclause 9.7.1(7)P is one of the few examples of a formal requirement for the designer to satisfy the HYD limit state.

9.7.2 Overall stability

(2) As a minimum, limit modes of the types illustrated in Figure 9.1 should be considered, taking progressive failure and liquefaction into account as relevant.

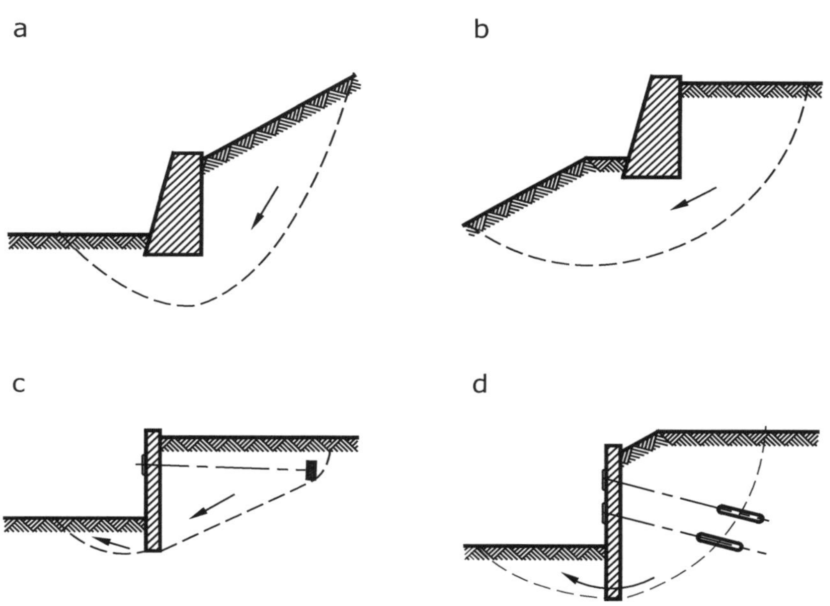

Figure 9.1 — Examples of limit modes for overall stability of retaining structures

9.7.3 Foundation failure of gravity walls

(2) As a minimum, limit modes of the types illustrated in Figure 9.2 should be considered.

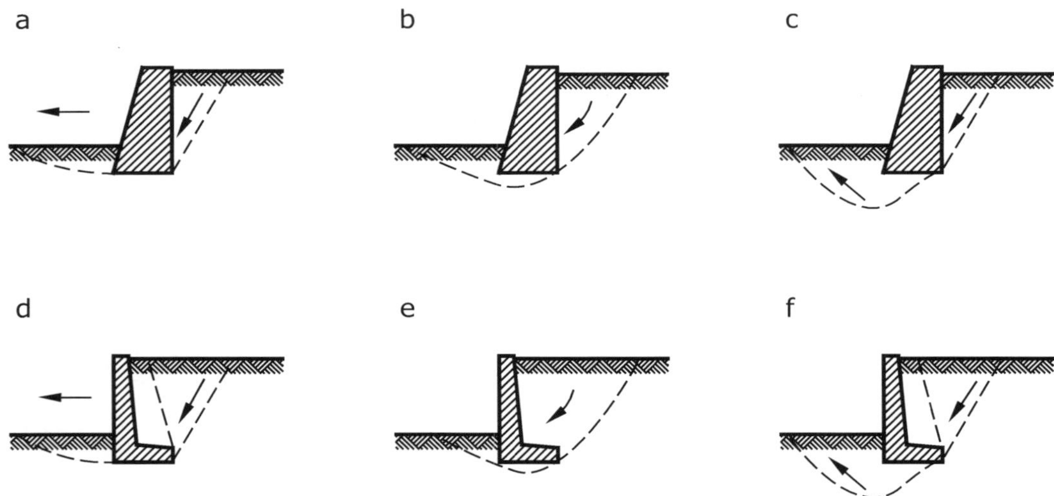

Figure 9.2 — Examples of limit modes for foundation failures of gravity walls

9.7.4 Rotational failure of embedded walls

(1)P It shall be demonstrated by equilibrium calculations that embedded walls have sufficient penetration into the ground to prevent rotational failure.

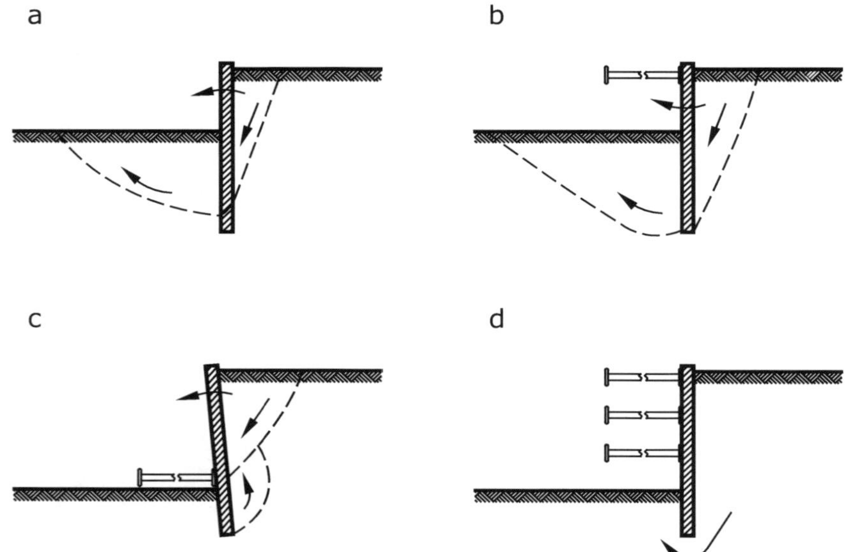

Figure 9.3 — Examples of limit modes for rotational failures of embedded walls

(2) As a minimum, limit modes of the types illustrated in Figure 9.3 should be considered.

9.7.5 Vertical failure of embedded walls

(1)P It shall be demonstrated that vertical equilibrium can be achieved using the design soil strengths or resistances and design vertical forces on the wall.

(2) As a minimum, the limit mode of the type illustrated in Figure 9.4 should be considered.

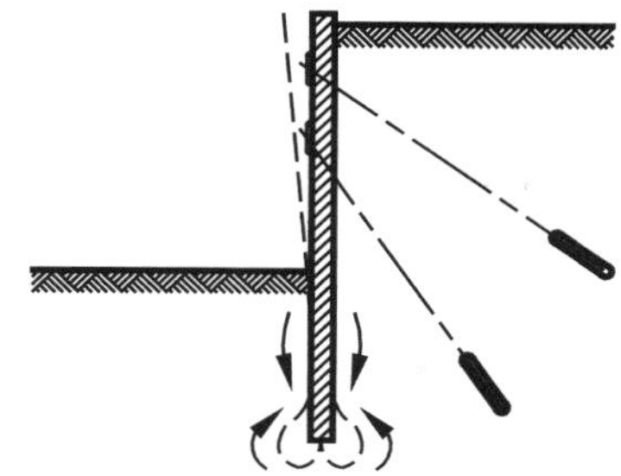

Figure 9.4 — Example of a limit mode for vertical failure of embedded walls

9.7.6 Structural design of retaining structures

(1)P Retaining structures, including their supporting structural elements such as anchorages and props, shall be verified against structural failure in accordance with 2.4 and EN 1992, EN 1993, EN 1995 and EN 1996.

(2) As a minimum, limit modes of the types illustrated in Figure 9.5 should be considered.

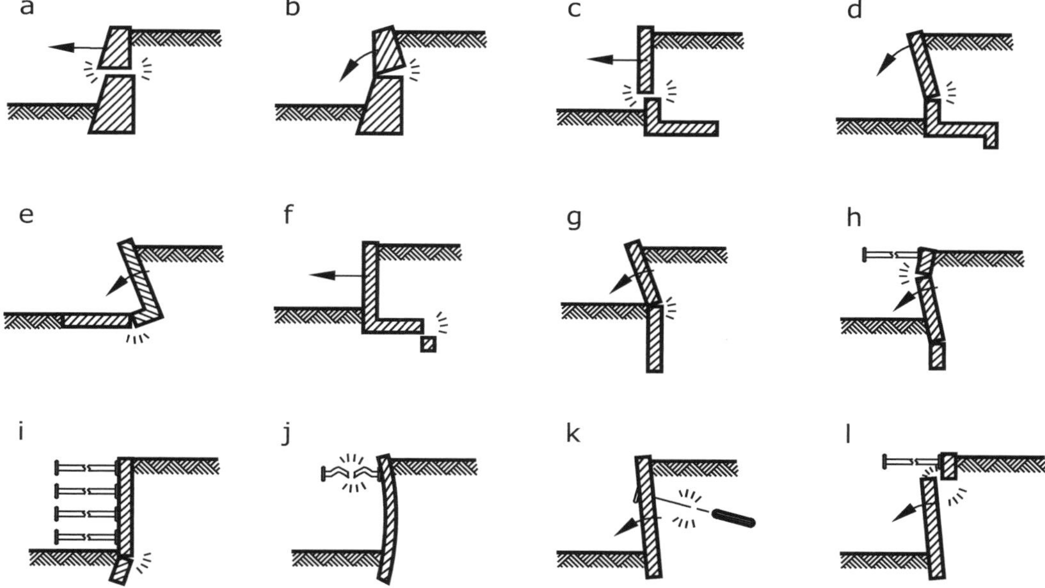

Figure 9.5 — Examples of limit modes for structural failure of retaining structures

9.7.7 Failure by pull-out of anchorages

(1)P It shall be demonstrated that equilibrium can be achieved without pull-out failure of ground anchorages.

(3) As a minimum, limit modes of the types illustrated in Figure 9.6 (a, b) should be considered.

(4) For deadman anchors, the failure mode illustrated in Figure 9.6 (c) should also be considered.

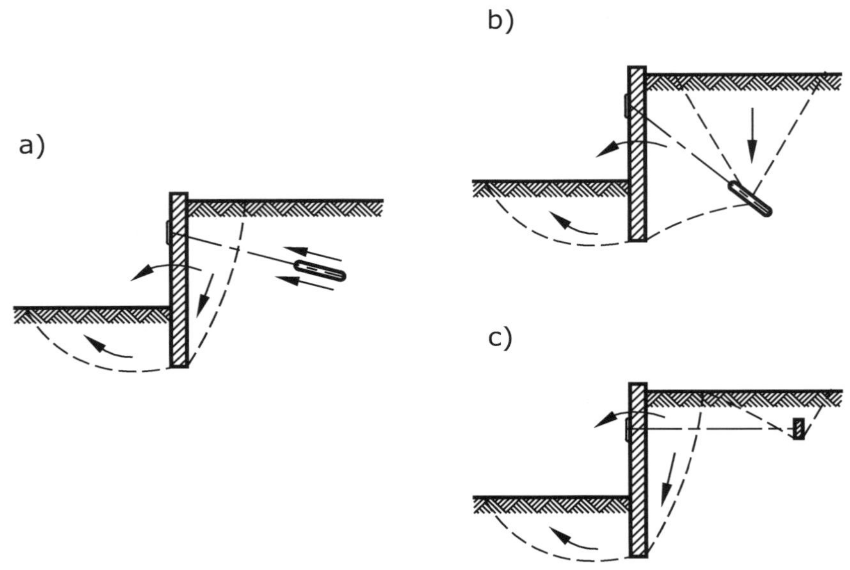

Figure 9.6 — Examples of limit modes for failure by pull-out of anchors

9.8 Serviceability limit state design

9.8.1 General

AC1 (2) AC1 The assessment of design values of earth pressures should take account of the initial stress, stiffness and strength of the ground and the stiffness of the structural elements.

AC1 (3) AC1 The design values of earth pressures should be derived taking account of the allowable deformation of the structure at its serviceability limit state. These pressures AC1 need AC1 not necessarily be limiting values.

9.8.2 Displacements

(2)P A cautious estimate of the distortion and displacement of retaining walls, and the effects on supported structures and services, shall always be made on the basis of comparable experience. This estimate shall include the effects of construction of the wall. The design may be justified by checking that the estimated displacements do not exceed the limiting values.

Subclauses 9.8.2(3) to (9) provide further guidance on establishing relevant displacements for consideration of the serviceability limit state.

10 Hydraulic failure

10.1 General

(1)P The provisions of this Section apply to four modes of ground failure induced by pore-water pressure or pore-water seepage, which shall be checked, as relevant:

- failure by uplift (buoyancy);
- failure by heave;
- failure by internal erosion;
- failure by piping.

NOTE 1 Buoyancy occurs when pore-water pressure under a structure or a low permeability ground layer becomes larger than the mean overburden pressure (due to the structure and/or the overlying ground layer).

NOTE 2 Failure by heave occurs when upwards seepage forces act against the weight of the soil, reducing the vertical effective stress to zero. Soil particles are then lifted away by the vertical water flow and failure occurs (boiling).

NOTE 3 Failure by internal erosion is produced by the transport of soil particles within a soil stratum, at the interface of soil strata, or at the interface between the soil and a structure. This may finally result in regressive erosion, leading to collapse of the soil structure.

NOTE 4 Failure by piping is a particular form of failure, for example of a reservoir, by internal erosion, where erosion begins at the surface, then regresses until a pipe-shaped discharge tunnel is formed in the soil mass or between the soil and a foundation or at the interface between cohesive and non-cohesive soil strata. Failure occurs as soon as the upstream end of the eroded tunnel reaches the bottom of the reservoir.

NOTE 5 The conditions for hydraulic failure of the ground can be expressed in terms of total stress and pore-water pressure or in terms of effective stresses and hydraulic gradient. Total stress analysis is applied to failure by uplift. For failure by heave, both total and effective stresses are applied. Conditions are put on hydraulic gradients in order to control internal erosion and piping.

(2) In situations where the pore-water pressure is hydrostatic (negligible hydraulic gradient) it is not required to check other than failure by uplift.

Subclauses 10.1(3) to (6) provide guidance on and measures for avoiding the above causes of failure.

10.2 Failure by uplift

(1)P The stability of a structure or of a low permeability ground layer against uplift shall be checked by comparing the permanent stabilizing actions (for example, weight and side friction) to the permanent and variable destabilizing actions from water and, possibly, other sources. Examples of situations where uplift stability shall be checked are given in Figure 7.1 and Figure 10.1.

The following text has been adapted from 10.2(2):

The design should be checked against failure by uplift using inequality (2.8) of 2.4.7.4. In this inequality, the design value of the vertical component of the stabilizing permanent actions ($G_{stb;d}$) is the sum of, for example, the weight of the structure (or ground layer), any friction forces (T) in Figure 10.1, and any anchor forces.

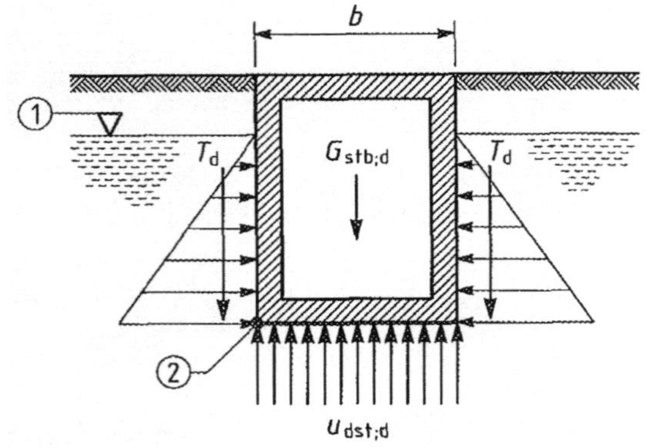

a) Uplift of a buried hollow structure

1 AC1 groundwater table AC1
2 water tight surface

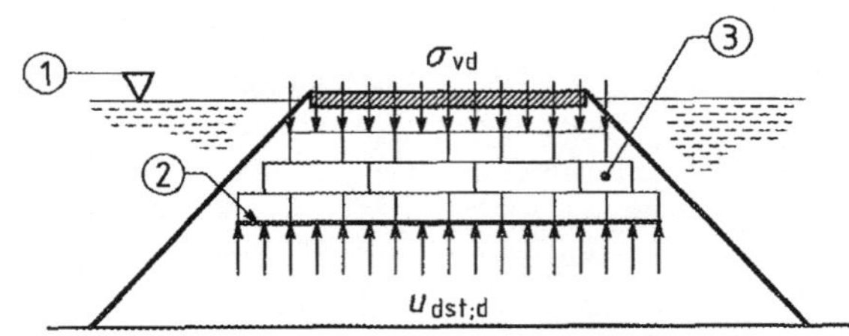

b) Uplift of a lightweight embankment during flood

1 AC1 groundwater table AC1
2 water tight surface
3 light weight embankment material

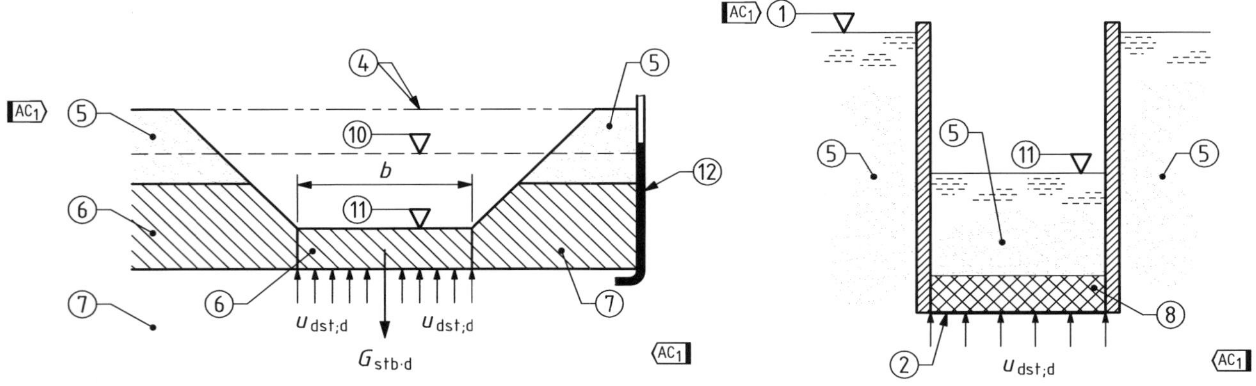

c) Uplift of the bottom of an excavation

4 former ground surface
5 sand
6 clay
7 gravel
AC1 10 groundwater level before the excavation
11 groundwater level in the excavation
12 piezometric level at the base of the clay layer AC1

d) Execution of a slab below water level

1 AC1 groundwater table AC1
2 water tight surface
5 sand
AC1 *Text deleted* AC1
8 injected sand
AC1 11 groundwater level in the excavation AC1

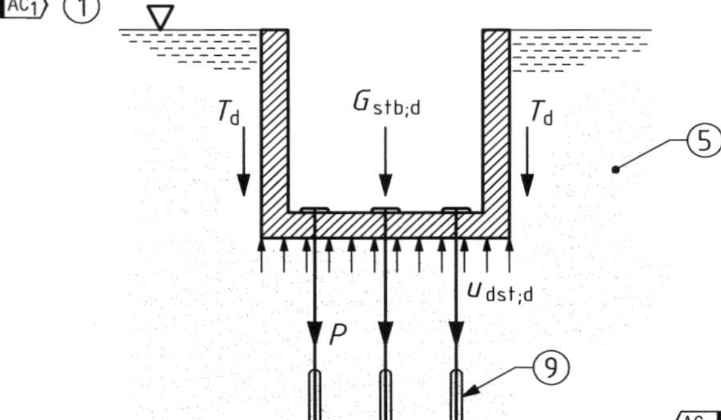

e) Structure anchored to resist uplift

1 AC1 groundwater table AC1
5 sand
9 anchorage

Figure 10.1 — Examples of situations where uplift might be critical

10.3 Failure by heave

(1)P The stability of soil against heave shall be checked by verifying either equation (2.9a) or equation (2.9b) for every relevant soil column. Equation (2.9a) expresses the condition for stability in terms of pore-water pressures and total stresses.

Equation (2.9b) expresses the same condition in terms of seepage forces and submerged weights. An example of situations where heave shall be checked is given in Figure 10.2.

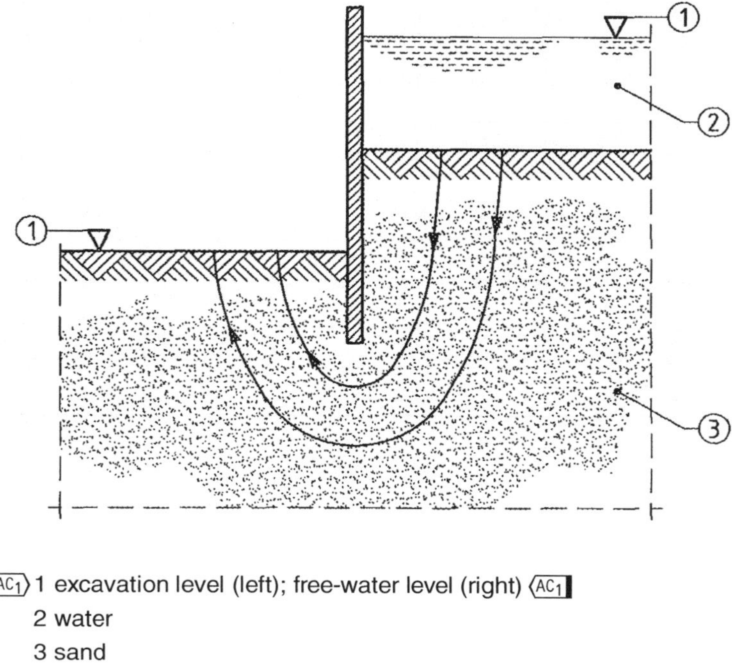

AC1⟩ 1 excavation level (left); free-water level (right) ⟨AC1

2 water

3 sand

Figure 10.2 — Example of situation where heave might be critical

10.4 Internal erosion

Subclause 10.4 provides guidance on avoiding internal erosion of the ground by the adoption of suitable drainage filters.

10.5 Failure by piping

(1)P Where prevailing hydraulic and soil conditions can lead to the occurrence of piping (see Figure 10.3) and where piping endangers the stability or serviceability of the hydraulic structure, prescriptive measures shall be taken to prevent the onset of the piping process, either by the application of filters or by taking structural measures to control or to block the ground-water flow.

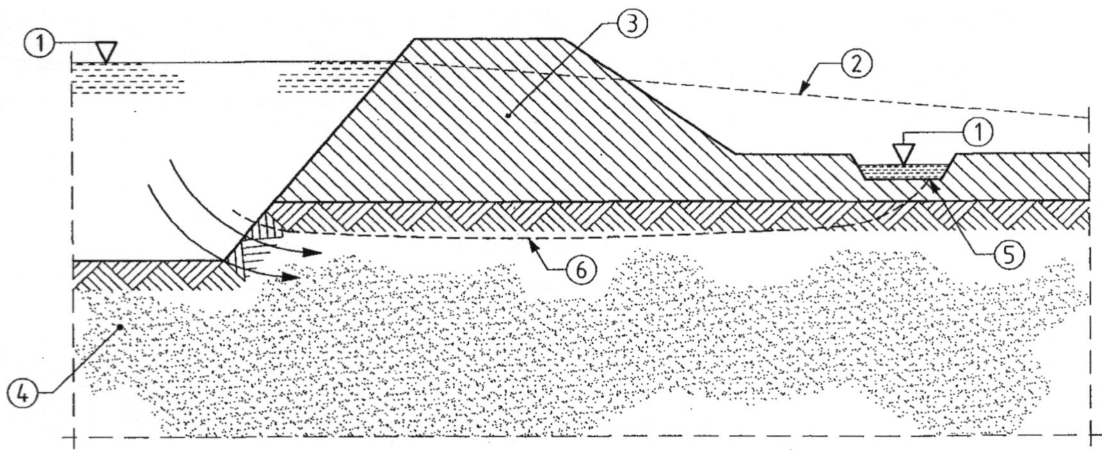

[AC1⟩ 1 free-water level ⟨AC1]

2 piezometric level in the permeable subsoil

3 low permeability soil

4 permeable subsoil

5 possible well; starting point for pipe

6 possible pipe

Figure 10.3 — Example of conditions that may cause piping

11 Overall stability

11.2 Limit states

(1)P All possible limit states for the particular ground shall be considered in order to fulfil the fundamental requirements of stability, limited deformations, durability and limitations in movements of nearby structures or services.

(2) Some possible limit states are listed below:

- loss of overall stability of the ground and associated structures;
- excessive movements in the ground due to shear deformations, settlement, vibration or heave;
- damage or loss of serviceability in neighbouring structures, roads or services due to movements in the ground.

11.3 Actions and design situations

Subclause 11.3(2)P lists the circumstances whose effects should be taken into account when determining overall stability.

(3)P In ultimate limit states, design free water and ground-water levels, or their combination, shall be selected from available hydrological data and in situ observations to give the most unfavourable conditions that could occur in the design situation being considered. The possibility of failure of drains, filters or seals shall be considered.

Subclauses 11.3(4) to (6) provide further guidance on the importance of water pressures in the checking of overall stability.

11.4 Design and construction considerations

Subclauses 11.4(1) to (11) provide guidance on the factors and situations to be considered in the checking of overall stability.

11.5 Ultimate limit state design

11.5.1 Stability analysis for slopes

(1)P The overall stability of slopes including existing, affected or planned structures shall be verified in ultimate limit states (GEO and STR) with design values of actions, resistances and strengths, where the partial factors defined in A.3.1(1)P, A.3.2(1)P and A.3.3.6(1)P shall be used.

NOTE The values of the partial factors may be set by the National Annex. The recommended values for persistent and transient situations are given in Tables A.3, A.4 and A.14.

Values of γ from the National Annex of BS EN 1997-1 are given below.

Partial factors for slopes and overall stability

Resistance	**Symbol**	**Partial factor set**	
		R1	**R4**
Earth	$\gamma_{R;e}$	1,0	1,0*

*Not explicitly stated in EN 1997-1

Example
Consider an infinite slope in a uniform sand, whose planar surface is oriented at an angle β = 30° to the horizontal. The soil has characteristic properties γ = 20 kN/m^3, c = 0 kPa, and φ = 38°.

Design Approach 1 (DA1), combination 1

Using partial factor sets A1 + M1 + R1, only set A1 has values other than 1,0.

Partial factor $\gamma_{G;dst}$ = 1,35.

The force acting down the slope, on a plane parallel to the ground surface at a depth d = 1 m below it, is:

$G_{k;dst} = \gamma \times d \times \sin\beta = 20 \times 1 \times \sin 30° = 10$ kPa
$G_{d;dst} = \gamma_{G;dst} \times G_{k;dst} = 1,35 \times 10 = 13,5$ kPa

The resisting force on the same plane is:

$R_d = \gamma \times d \times \cos\beta \times \tan\varphi'_d = 20 \times 1 \times \cos 30° \times \tan 38° = 13,53$ kPa

Thus $R_d \geq G_d$ and the slope is safe.

Design Approach 1 (DA1), combination 2

Using partial factor sets A2 + M2 + R1, only set M2 has values other than 1,0.

Partial factor $\gamma_{\varphi'}$ = 1,25.

The design force acting down the slope is now:

$G_{d;dst} = G_{k;dst} = 10$ kPa

The resisting force on the same plane is now:

$R_d = \gamma \times d \times \cos\beta \times \tan\varphi'_d = 20 \times 1 \times \cos 30° \times (\tan 38°/1,25) = 10,8$ kPa

Thus $R_d \geq G_d$ and the slope is safe.

Subclauses 11.5.1(2) to (13) provide guidance on the selection of failure modes and calculation models.

11.5.2 Slopes and cuts in rock masses

(1)P The stability of slopes and cuts in rock masses shall be checked against translational and rotational modes of failure involving isolated rock blocks or large portions of the rock mass, and also against rock falls. Particular attention shall be given to the pressure caused by blocked seepage water in joints and fissures.

Subclauses 11.5.2(2) to (10) provide further guidance and matters for consideration when analysing rock slopes.

11.5.3 Stability of excavations

(1)P The overall stability of the ground close to an excavation, including excavation spoil and existing structures, roads and services shall be checked (see Section 9).

(2)P The stability of the bottom of an excavation shall be checked in relation to the design pore-water pressure in the ground. For the analysis of hydraulic failure see Section 10.

(3)P Heave of the bottom of deep excavations due to unloading shall be considered.

11.6 Serviceability limit state design

(1)P The design shall show that the deformation of the ground will not cause a serviceability limit state in structures and infrastructure on or near the particular ground.

Subclauses 11.6(2) and (3) provide additional matters that can be considered in relation to the serviceability limit state. 11.7 covers monitoring requirements.

12 Embankments

12.2 Limit states

(2) The following limit states should be checked:

- loss of overall site stability;
- failure in the embankment slope or crest;
- failure caused by internal erosion;
- failure caused by surface erosion or scour;
- deformations in the embankment leading to loss of serviceability, e.g. excessive settlements or cracks;
- settlements and creep displacements leading to damages or loss of serviceability in nearby structures or utilities;
- excessive deformations in transition zones, e.g. the access embankment of a bridge abutment;
- loss of serviceability of traffic areas by climatic influences such as freezing and thawing or extreme drying;
- creep in slopes during the freezing and thawing period;
- degradation of base coarse material due to high traffic loads;
- deformations caused by hydraulic actions;
- changes of environmental conditions such as pollution of surface or ground-water, noise or vibrations.

12.3 Actions and design situations

Subclauses 12.3(1) to (8) list the design situations that should be taken into account and make particular reference to the treatment of water levels, thus highlighting the importance of water pressures in the analysis and design of embankments.

12.4 Design and construction considerations

(1)P Embankments shall be designed taking into account experience with embankments on similar ground and made of similar fill material.

Subclause 12.4(1)P highlights the value of past experience when designing geotechnical structures. Subclauses 12.4(2) to (13) list the things that should be considered when assessing the foundation level for an embankment and other factors that should be taken into account.

12.5 Ultimate limit state design

(1)P In analysing the stability of part or all of an embankment, all possible failure modes shall be considered, as stated in Section 11.

Subclauses 12.5(2) to (7) highlight matters that should be taken into account when considering the ultimate limit state.

12.6 Serviceability limit state design

(1)P The design shall show that the deformation of the embankment will not cause a serviceability limit state in the embankment or in structures, roads or services sited on, in or near the embankment.

12.7 Supervision and monitoring

Subclauses 12.7(2) to (5) list the situations in which monitoring should be applied to embankments and what records of that monitoring programme should be made.

Chapter 8 — Extracts from Eurocode 8: Design of structures for earthquake resistance

The extracts in this chapter are taken from EN 1998-1:2004 (incorporating corrigendum July 2009), *Eurocode 8: Design of structures for earthquake resistance — Part 1: General rules, seismic actions and rules for buildings*.

Text altered by CEN corrigendum July 2009 is indicated in the text by [AC1) (AC1].

The National Annex extracts are taken from NA to BS EN 1998-1:2004, *UK National Annex to Eurocode 8: Design of structures for earthquake resistance - Part 1: General rules, seismic actions and rules for buildings*

EN 1998, *Eurocode 8: Design of structures for earthquake resistance*, comprises the following Parts (the items in bold are covered in this chapter).

EN 1998-1, General rules, seismic actions and rules for buildings
EN 1998-2, Bridges
EN 1998-3, Assessment and retrofitting of buildings
EN 1998-4, Silos, tanks and pipelines
EN 1998-5, Foundations, retaining structures and geotechnical aspects
EN 1998-6, Towers, masts and chimneys

This chapter aims to introduce the principles of seismic design to EN 1998-1 in conjunction with the other non-seismic Eurocodes such as EN 1992 and EN 1993. Therefore Sections 1 to 4, for the seismic actions and performance requirements for buildings, are extensively covered whereas Sections 5 to 9, for material-specific detailed design, are drastically summarized.

The full list of contents of EN 1998-1 follows, and is given for reference purposes. (Bold items are covered in this chapter.)

1.6.7 Further symbols used in Section 8 of EN 1998-1
1.6.8 Further symbols used in Section 9 of EN 1998-1
1.6.9 Further symbols used in Section 10 of EN 1998-1
1.7 S.I. units
2 Performance requirements and compliance criteria
2.1 Fundamental requirements
2.2 Compliance criteria
2.2.1 General
2.2.2 Ultimate limit state
2.2.3 Damage limitation state
2.2.4 Specific measures
2.2.4.1 Design
2.2.4.2 Foundations
2.2.4.3 Quality system plan
3 Ground conditions and seismic action
3.1 Ground conditions
3.1.1 General
3.1.2 Identification of ground types
3.2 Seismic action
3.2.1 Seismic zones
3.2.2 Basic representation of the seismic action
3.2.2.1 General
3.2.2.2 Horizontal elastic response spectrum
3.2.2.3 Vertical elastic response spectrum
3.2.2.4 Design ground displacement
3.2.2.5 Design spectrum for elastic analysis
3.2.3 Alternative representations of the seismic action
3.2.3.1 Time-history representation
3.2.3.2 Spatial model of the seismic action
3.2.4 Combinations of the seismic action with other actions
4 Design of buildings
4.1 General
4.1.1 Scope
4.2 Characteristics of earthquake resistant buildings
4.2.1 Basic principles of conceptual design
4.2.1.1 Structural simplicity
4.2.1.2 Uniformity, symmetry and redundancy
4.2.1.3 Bi-directional resistance and stiffness
4.2.1.4 Torsional resistance and stiffness
4.2.1.5 Diaphragmatic behaviour at storey level
4.2.1.6 Adequate foundation
4.2.2 Primary and secondary seismic members
4.2.3 Criteria for structural regularity
4.2.3.1 General
4.2.3.2 Criteria for regularity in plan
4.2.3.3 Criteria for regularity in elevation
4.2.4 Combination coefficients for variable actions
4.2.5 Importance classes and importance factors
4.3 Structural analysis
4.3.1 Modelling
4.3.2 Accidental torsional effects
4.3.3 Methods of analysis
4.3.3.1 General
4.3.3.2 Lateral force method of analysis
4.3.3.3 Modal response spectrum analysis
4.3.3.4 Non-linear methods
4.3.3.5 Combination of the effects of the components of the seismic action

1 General

1.1 Scope

1.1.1 Scope of EN 1998

(1) P EN 1998 applies to the design and construction of buildings and civil engineering works in seismic regions. Its purpose is to ensure that in the event of earthquakes:

- human lives are protected;
- damage is limited; and
- structures important for civil protection remain operational.

NOTE The random nature of the seismic events and the limited resources available to counter their effects are such as to make the attainment of these goals only partially possible and only measurable in probabilistic terms. The extent of the protection that can be provided to different categories of buildings, which is only measurable in probabilistic terms, is a matter of optimal allocation of resources and is therefore expected to vary from country to country, depending on the relative importance of the seismic risk with respect to risks of other origin and on the global economic resources.

(2) P Special structures, such as nuclear power plants, offshore structures and large dams, are beyond the scope of EN 1998.

(3) P EN 1998 contains only those provisions that, in addition to the provisions of the other relevant Eurocodes, must be observed for the design of structures in seismic regions. It complements in this respect the other Eurocodes.

1.1.2 Scope of EN 1998-1

Part 1 specifies general rules, performance requirements, details of the seismic hazard and action, analysis procedures and general concepts that are applicable not only for the seismic design of buildings but also for all the other Parts of EN 1998. Part 1 also includes specific rules for the detailed design of concrete, steel, composite steel-concrete, timber, masonry and base isolated structures.

(1) EN 1998-1 applies to the design of buildings and civil engineering works in seismic regions. It is subdivided in 10 Sections, some of which are specifically devoted to the design of buildings.

(2) Section 2 of EN 1998-1 contains the basic performance requirements and compliance criteria applicable to buildings and civil engineering works in seismic regions.

(3) Section 3 of EN 1998-1 gives the rules for the representation of seismic actions and for their combination with other actions. Certain types of structures, dealt with in EN 1998-2 to EN 1998-6, need complementing rules that are given in those Parts.

(4) Section 4 of EN 1998-1 contains general design rules relevant specifically to buildings.

(5) Sections 5 to 9 of EN 1998-1 contain specific rules for various structural materials and elements, relevant specifically to buildings as follows:

Section 5: Specific rules for concrete buildings;
Section 6: Specific rules for steel buildings;
Section 7: Specific rules for composite steel-concrete buildings;
Section 8: Specific rules for timber buildings;
Section 9: Specific rules for masonry buildings.

(6) Section 10 contains the fundamental requirements and other relevant aspects of design and safety related to base isolation of structures and specifically to base isolation of buildings.

NOTE Specific rules for isolation of bridges are developed in EN 1998-2.

(7) Annex C contains additional elements related to the seismic design of slab reinforcement in stell-concrete composite beams at beam-column joints in moment resisting frames.

NOTE Informative Annex A and informative Annex B contain additional elements related to the elastic displacement response spectrum and to target displacement for pushover analysis.

The scopes of the other Parts of Eurocode 8 are summarized as follows:

Scope of EN 1998-2

Within the framework of the general requirements set forth in Part 1, this Part contains design principles, criteria and application rules applicable to the seismic design of bridges. Part 2 primarily covers the seismic design of bridges in which the horizontal seismic actions are mainly resisted at either the abutments or through bending of the piers i.e. bridges composed of vertical or near vertical pier systems supporting the traffic deck superstructure. It can also be applied to special bridges such as arch, portal or tied, and cable-stayed bridges. Suspension, moveable or extreme configuration bridges are not fully covered. Timber and floating bridges are not included. Finally, a clause on seismic isolation is included.

Scope of EN 1998-3

This Part covers the repair and strengthening of buildings and, where applicable, monuments, considering commonly used structural materials (concrete, steel, masonry and timber). Part 3 provides criteria for the evaluation of the seismic performance of existing individual structures, the approach in selecting necessary corrective measures and criteria for the design of the repair/strengthening measures (i.e. conception, structural analysis including intervention measures, final dimensioning of structural parts and their connections to existing structural elements).

Scope of EN 1998-4

This Part provides basic rules for the seismic design of the structural aspects of integrated facilities composed of pipeline systems and of storage tanks of different types and destinations, as well as for independent items, such as single water towers serving a specific purpose or groups of silos enclosing granular materials, etc. Part 4 may also be used as a basis for evaluating the amount of strengthening needed by existing facilities to bring them up to present standards. In applying this Part, there is no restriction on the size, structural type and other functional characteristics of these structures and for some types of tanks and silos, detailed methods of assessment and verification rules are included.

Scope of EN 1998-5

This Part establishes the requirements, criteria and rules for siting and foundation soil. Part 5 covers the design of different foundation systems, earth retaining structures and soil-structure interaction under seismic actions. As such it complements the rules of Eurocode 7, which do not cover the special requirements of seismic design. The provisions in Part 5 generally apply to buildings (Part 1), bridges (Part 2), silos, tanks and pipelines (Part 4) and towers, masts and chimneys (Part 6).

Scope of EN 1998-6

This Part establishes requirements, criteria and rules for the seismic design of tall slender structures: towers, including bell-towers and intake towers, masts, industrial chimneys and lighthouses. Different provisions apply to reinforced concrete and to steel structures. Requirements are set up for non-structural elements, such as the lining material of an industrial chimney. Part 6 is not applicable to cooling towers, offshore structures and masonry chimneys.

1.5 Terms and definitions

1.5.1 Terms common to all Eurocodes

(1) The terms and definitions given in EN 1990:2002, 1.5 apply.

AC1) 1.5.2 Further terms used in EN 1998-1 (AC1

(1) The following terms are used in EN 1998 with the following meanings:

1.5.2.1
behaviour factor
factor used for design purposes to reduce the forces obtained from a linear analysis, in order to account for the non-linear response of a structure, associated with the material, the structural system and the design procedures

1.5.2.2
AC1) **capacity design** (AC1
design method in which elements of the structural system are chosen and suitably designed and detailed for energy dissipation under severe deformations while all other structural elements are provided with sufficient strength so that the chosen means of energy dissipation can be maintained

1.5.2.3
dissipative structure
structure which is able to dissipate energy by means of ductile hysteretic behaviour and/or by other mechanisms

1.5.2.4
dissipative zones
predetermined parts of a dissipative structure where the dissipative capabilities are mainly located

NOTE 1 These are also called critical regions.

1.5.2.5
dynamically independent unit
structure or part of a structure which is directly subjected to the ground motion and whose response is not affected by the response of adjacent units or structures

1.5.2.6
importance factor
factor that relates to the consequences of a structural failure

1.5.2.7
non-dissipative structure
structure designed for a particular seismic design situation without taking into account the non-linear material behaviour

1.5.2.8
non-structural element
architectural, mechanical or electrical element, system and component which, whether due to lack of strength or to the way it is connected to the structure, is not considered in the seismic design as a load carrying element

1.5.2.9
primary seismic members
members considered as part of the structural system that resists the seismic action, modelled in the analysis for the seismic design situation and fully designed and detailed for earthquake resistance in accordance with the rules of EN 1998

1.5.2.10
secondary seismic members
members which are not considered as part of the seismic action resisting system and whose strength and stiffness against seismic actions is neglected

NOTE 2 They are not required to comply with all the rules of EN 1998, but are designed and detailed to maintain support of gravity loads when subjected to the displacements caused by the seismic design situation.

1.6 Symbols

1.6.1 General

(1) The symbols indicated in EN 1990:2002, 1.6 apply. For the material-dependent symbols, as well as for symbols not specifically related to earthquakes, the provisions of the relevant Eurocodes apply.

(2) Further symbols, used in connection with seismic actions, are defined in the text where they occur, for ease of use. However, in addition, the most frequently occurring symbols used in EN 1998-1 are listed and defined in 1.6.2 and 1.6.3.

1.6.2 Further symbols used in Sections 2 and 3 of EN 1998-1

A_{Ed}	Design value of seismic action (= $\gamma_I . A_{Ek}$)
A_{Ek}	Characteristic value of the seismic action for the reference return period
E_d	Design value of action effects
N_{SPT}	Blow-count of Standard Penetration Test
P_{NCR}	Reference probability of exceedance in 50 years of the reference seismic action for the no-collapse requirement
Q	Variable action
$S_e(T)$	Elastic horizontal ground acceleration response spectrum also called "elastic response spectrum". At T=0, the spectral acceleration given by this spectrum equals the design ground acceleration on type A ground multiplied by the soil factor S
$S_{ve}(T)$	Elastic vertical ground acceleration response spectrum
$S_{De}(T)$	Elastic displacement response spectrum
[AC1> $S_d(T)$	Design spectrum (for elastic analysis) <AC1]
S	Soil factor
T	Vibration period of a linear single degree of freedom system
T_s	Duration of the stationary part of the seismic motion
T_{NCR}	Reference return period of the reference seismic action for the no-collapse requirement
a_{gR}	Reference peak ground acceleration on type A ground
a_g	Design ground acceleration on type A ground
a_{vg}	Design ground acceleration in the vertical direction
c_u	Undrained shear strength of soil
d_g	Design ground displacement
g	Acceleration of gravity
q	Behaviour factor
$v_{s,30}$	Average value of propagation velocity of S waves in the upper 30 m of the soil profile at shear strain of 10^{-5} or less
γ_I	Importance factor
η	Damping correction factor
ξ	Viscous damping ratio (in per cent)
$\psi_{2,i}$	Combination coefficient for the quasi-permanent value of a variable action i
$\psi_{E,i}$	Combination coefficient for a variable action i, to be used when determining the effects of the design seismic action

1.6.3 Further symbols used in Section 4 of EN 1998-1

E_E	Effect of the seismic action
E_{Edx}, E_{Edy}	Design values of the action effects due to the horizontal components (x and y) of the seismic action
E_{Edz}	Design value of the action effects due to the vertical component of the seismic action
F_i	Horizontal seismic force at storey i
F_a	Horizontal seismic force acting on a non-structural element (appendage)
F_b	Base shear force
H	Building height from the foundation or from the top of a rigid basement
L_{max}, L_{min}	Larger and smaller in plan dimension of the building measured in orthogonal directions
R_d	Design value of resistance
S_a	Seismic coefficient of non-structural elements
T_1	Fundamental period of vibration of a building
T_a	Fundamental period of vibration of a non-structural element (appendage)
W_a	Weight of a non-structural element (appendage)
d	Displacement
d_r	Design interstorey drift
e_a	Accidental eccentricity of the mass of one storey from its nominal location
h	Interstorey height
m_i	Mass of storey i
n	Number of storeys above the foundation or the top of a rigid basement
q_a	Behaviour factor of a non-structural element (appendage)
q_d	Displacement behaviour factor
s_i	Displacement of mass m_i in the fundamental mode shape of a building
z_i	Height of mass m_i above the level of application of the seismic action
α	Ratio of the design ground acceleration to the acceleration of gravity
γ_a	Importance factor of a non-structural element (appendage)
γ_d	Overstrength factor for diaphragms
θ	Interstorey drift sensitivity coefficient

Further terms and symbols for Sections 5 to 9 are defined in the text where they occur, for ease of use.

2 Performance requirements and compliance criteria

2.1 Fundamental requirements

(1)P Structures in seismic regions shall be designed and constructed in such a way, that the following requirements are met, each with an adequate degree of reliability.

- No-collapse requirement.

  The structure shall be designed and constructed to withstand the design seismic action defined in Section 3 without local or global collapse, thus retaining its structural integrity and a residual load bearing capacity after the seismic events. The design seismic action is expressed in terms of: a) the reference seismic action associated with a reference probability of exceedance, P_{NCR}, in 50 years or a reference return period, T_{NCR}, and b) the importance factor γ_I (see EN 1990:2002 and (2)P and (3)P of this clause) to take into account reliability differentiation.

NOTE 1 The values to be ascribed to P_{NCR} or to T_{NCR} for use in a country may be found in its National Annex of this document. The recommended values are P_{NCR} =10 % and T_{NCR} = 475 years.

NOTE 2 The value of the probability of exceedance, P_R, in T_L years of a specific level of the seismic action is related to the mean return period, T_R, of this level of the seismic action in accordance with the expression $T_R = -T_L / \ln(1- P_R)$. So for a given T_L, the seismic action may equivalently be specified either via its mean return period, T_R, or its probability of exceedance, P_R in T_L years.

- Damage limitation requirement.

Table NA.1, 2.1(1)P UK decision

In the absence of a project-specific assessment, adopt a return period T_{NCR} of 2500 years. Further guidance is given in PD 6698.

  The structure shall be designed and constructed to withstand a seismic action having a larger probability of occurrence than the design seismic action, without the occurrence of damage and the associated limitations of use, the costs of which would be disproportionately high in comparison with the costs of the structure itself. The seismic action to be taken into account for the damage limitation requirement has a probability of exceedance, P_{DLR}, in 10 years and a return period, T_{DLR}. In the absence of more precise information, the reduction factor applied on the design seismic action in accordance with 4.4.3.2(2) may be used to obtain the seismic action for the verification of the damage limitation requirement.

NOTE 3 The values to be ascribed to P_{DLR} or to T_{DLR} for use in a country may be found in its National Annex of this document. The recommended values are P_{DLR} =10 % and T_{DLR} = 95 years.

Table NA.1, 2.1(1)P UK decision

In the absence of a project-specific assessment, adopt the recommended values. Further guidance is given in PD 6698.

(2) P Target reliabilities for the no-collapse requirement and for the damage limitation requirement are established by the National Authorities for different types of buildings or civil engineering works on the basis of the consequences of failure.

(3)P Reliability differentiation is implemented by classifying structures into different importance classes. An importance factor γ_I is assigned to each importance class. Wherever feasible this factor should be derived so as to correspond to a higher or lower value of the return period of the seismic event (with regard to the reference return period) as appropriate for the design of the specific category of structures (see 3.2.1(3)).

(4) The different levels of reliability are obtained by multiplying the reference seismic action or, when using linear analysis, the corresponding action effects by this importance factor. Detailed guidance on the importance classes and the corresponding importance factors is given in the relevant Parts of EN 1998.

NOTE At most sites the annual rate of exceedance, $H(a_{gR})$, of the reference peak ground acceleration a_{gR} may be taken to vary with a_{gR} as: $H(a_{gR}) \sim k_0\ a_{gR}^{-k}$, with the value of the exponent k depending on seismicity, but being generally of the order of 3. Then, if the seismic action is defined in terms of the reference peak ground acceleration a_{gR}, the value of the importance factor γ_I multiplying the reference seismic action to achieve the same probability of exceedance in T_L years as in the T_{LR} years for which the reference seismic action is defined, may be computed as $\gamma_I \sim (T_{LR}/T_L)^{-1/k}$. Alternatively, the value of the importance factor γ_I that needs to multiply the reference seismic action to achieve a value of the probability of exceeding the seismic action, P_L, in T_L years other than the reference probability of exceedance P_{LR}, over the same T_L years, may be estimated as $\gamma_I \sim (P_L/P_{LR})^{-1/k}$.

2.2 Compliance criteria

2.2.1 General

(1)P In order to satisfy the fundamental requirements in 2.1 the following limit states shall be checked (see 2.2.2 and 2.2.3):

- ultimate limit states;
- damage limitation states;

Ultimate limit states are those associated with collapse or with other forms of structural failure which might endanger the safety of people.

Damage limitation states are those associated with damage occurrence, corresponding to states beyond which specified service requirements are no longer met.

EN 1998 adopts a one-level design philosophy in which only the ultimate limit states are required to be satisfied explicitly. The damage limitation states are achieved by limiting the overall deformations of the structure.

(2)P In order to limit the uncertainties and to promote a good behaviour of structures under seismic actions more severe than the design seismic action, a number of pertinent specific measures shall also be taken (see 2.2.4).

(3) For well defined categories of structures in cases of low seismicity (see 3.2.1(4)), the fundamental requirements may be satisfied through the application of rules simpler than those given in the relevant parts of EN 1998.

(4) In cases of very low seismicity, the provisions of EN 1998 need not be observed (see 3.2.1(5) and the notes therein for the definition of cases of very low seismicity).

2.2.2 Ultimate limit state

(1)P It shall be verified that the structural system has the resistance and energy-dissipation capacity specified in the relevant Parts of EN 1998.

(2) The resistance and energy-dissipation capacity to be assigned to the structure are related to the extent to which its non-linear response is to be exploited. In operational terms such balance between resistance and energy-dissipation capacity is characterized by the values of the behaviour factor q and the associated ductility classification, which are given in the relevant Parts of EN 1998. As a limiting case, for the design of structures classified as low dissipative, no account is taken of any hysteretic energy dissipation and the behaviour factor may not be taken, in general, as being greater than the value of 1,5 considered to account for overstrengths. For steel or composite steel-concrete buildings, the limiting value of the q factor may be taken

as being between 1,5 and 2 (see Note 1 of Table 6.1 or Note 1 of Table 7.1, respectively). For dissipative structures the behaviour factor is taken as being greater than these limiting values accounting for the hysteretic energy dissipation that mainly occurs in specifically designed zones, called dissipative zones or critical zones.

NOTE The value of the behaviour factor q should be limited by the limit state of dynamic stability of the structure and by the damage due to low-cycle fatigue of structural details (especially connections). The most AC1) unfavourable limiting condition should be applied (AC1 when the values of the q factor are determined. The values of the q factor given in the various Parts of EN 1998 are deemed to conform to this requirement.

(3)P The structure as a whole shall be checked to ensure that it is stable under the design seismic action. Both overturning and sliding stability shall be taken into account. Specific rules for checking the overturning of structures are given in the relevant Parts of EN 1998.

(4)P It shall be verified that both the foundation elements and the foundation soil are able to resist the action effects resulting from the response of the superstructure without substantial permanent deformations. In determining the reactions, due consideration shall be given to the actual resistance that can be developed by the structural element transmitting the actions.

(5)P In the analysis the possible influence of second order effects on the values of the action effects shall be taken into account.

(6)P It shall be verified that under the design seismic action the behaviour of non-structural elements does not present risks to persons and does not have a detrimental effect on the response of the structural elements. For buildings, specific rules are given in 4.3.5 and 4.3.6.

2.2.3 Damage limitation state

(1)P An adequate degree of reliability against unacceptable damage shall be ensured by satisfying the deformation limits or other relevant limits defined in the relevant Parts of EN 1998.

(2)P In structures important for civil protection the structural system shall be verified to ensure that it has sufficient resistance and stiffness to maintain the function of the vital services in the facilities for seismic events associated with an appropriate return period.

2.2.4 Specific measures

2.2.4.1 Design

(1) To the extent possible, structures should have simple and regular forms both in plan and elevation, (see 4.2.3). If necessary this may be realised by subdividing the structure by joints into dynamically independent units.

(2)P In order to ensure an overall dissipative and ductile behaviour, brittle failure or the premature formation of unstable mechanisms shall be avoided. To this end, where required in the relevant Parts of EN 1998, resort shall be made to the capacity design procedure, which is used to obtain the hierarchy of resistance of the various structural components and failure modes necessary for ensuring a suitable plastic mechanism and for avoiding brittle failure modes.

(3)P Since the seismic performance of a structure is largely dependent on the behaviour of its critical regions or elements, the detailing of the structure in general and of these regions or elements in particular, shall be such as to maintain the capacity to transmit the necessary forces and to dissipate energy under cyclic conditions. To this end, the detailing of connections between structural elements and of regions where non-linear behaviour is foreseeable should receive special care in design.

(4)P The analysis shall be based on an adequate structural model, which, when necessary, shall take into account the influence of soil deformability and of non-structural elements and other aspects, such as the presence of adjacent structures.

2.2.4.2 Foundations

(1)P The stiffness of the foundations shall be adequate for transmitting the actions received from the superstructure to the ground as uniformly as possible.

(2) With the exception of bridges, only one foundation type should in general be used for the same structure, unless the latter consists of dynamically independent units.

3 Ground conditions and seismic action

3.1 Ground conditions

3.1.1 General

(1)P Appropriate investigations shall be carried out in order to identify the ground conditions in accordance with the types given in 3.1.2.

(4) Depending on the importance class of the structure and the particular conditions of the project, ground investigations and/or geological studies should be performed to determine the seismic action.

NOTE The conditions under which ground investigations additional to those necessary for design for non-seismic actions may be omitted and default ground classification may be used may be specified in the National Annex.

Table NA.1, 3.1.1(4) UK decision

The need for additional ground investigations should be established on a site-specific basis. Further guidance is given in PD 6698.

3.1.2 Identification of ground types

(1) Ground types A, B, C, D, and E, described by the stratigraphic profiles and parameters given in Table 3.1 and described hereafter, may be used to account for the influence of local ground conditions on the seismic action. This may also be done by additionally considering the influence of deep geology on the seismic action.

NOTE The ground classification scheme accounting for deep geology for use in a country may be specified in its National Annex, including the values of the parameters S, T_B, T_C and T_D defining the horizontal and vertical elastic response spectra in accordance with 3.2.2.2 and 3.2.2.3.

Table NA.1, 3.1.2(1) UK decision

There is no requirement to account for deep geology. Further guidance is given in PD 6698.

Table 3.1 — Ground types

Ground type	Description of stratigraphic profile	Parameters		
		$v_{s,30}$ (m/s)	N_{SPT} (blows/30cm)	c_u (kPa)
A	Rock or other rock-like geological formation, including at most 5 m of weaker material at the surface.	> 800	–	–
B	Deposits of very dense sand, gravel, or very stiff clay, at least several tens of metres in thickness, characterised by a gradual increase of mechanical properties with depth.	360 – 800	> 50	> 250
C	Deep deposits of dense or medium-dense sand, gravel or stiff clay with thickness from several tens to many hundreds of metres.	180 – 360	15 – 50	70 – 250

D	Deposits of loose-to-medium cohesionless soil (with or without some soft cohesive layers), or of predominantly soft-to-firm cohesive soil.	< 180	< 15	< 70
E	A soil profile consisting of a surface alluvium layer with v_s values of type C or D and thickness varying between about 5 m and 20 m, underlain by stiffer material with $v_s > 800$ m/s.			
S_1	Deposits consisting, or containing a layer at least 10 m thick, of soft clays/silts with a high plasticity index (PI > 40) and high water content	< 100 (indicative)	–	10 – 20
S_2	Deposits of liquefiable soils, of sensitive clays, or any other soil profile not included in types A – E or S_1			

(2) The site shall be classified according to the value of the average shear wave velocity, $v_{s,30}$, if this is available. Otherwise the value of N_{SPT} shall be used.

3.2 Seismic action

3.2.1 Seismic zones

(1) P For the purpose of EN 1998, national territories shall be subdivided by the National Authorities into seismic zones, depending on the local hazard. By definition, the hazard within each zone is assumed to be constant.

(2) For most of the applications of EN 1998, the hazard is described in terms of a single parameter, i.e. the value of the reference peak ground acceleration on type A ground, a_{gR}. Additional parameters required for specific types of structures are given in the relevant Parts of EN 1998.

NOTE The reference peak ground acceleration on type A ground, a_{gR}, for use in a country or parts of a country, may be derived from zonation maps found in its National Annex.

(3) The reference peak ground acceleration, chosen by the National Authorities for each seismic zone, corresponds to the reference return period T_{NCR} of the seismic action for the no-collapse requirement (or equivalently the reference probability of exceedance in 50 years, P_{NCR}) chosen by the National Authorities (see 2.1(1) P). An importance factor γ_I equal to 1,0 is assigned to this reference return period. For return periods other than the reference (see importance classes in 2.1(3) P and (4)), the design ground acceleration on type A ground a_g is equal to a_{gR} times the importance factor γ_I ($a_g = \gamma_I \cdot a_{gR}$). (See Note to 2.1(4)).

Table NA.1, 3.2.1(1), (2) and (3) UK decision

In the absence of a project-specific assessment, adopt the reference ground accelerations for a return period T_{NCR} of 2 500 years given by the seismic contour map in PD 6698.

(4) In cases of low seismicity, reduced or simplified seismic design procedures for certain types or categories of structures may be used.

NOTE The selection of the categories of structures, ground types and seismic zones in a country for which the provisions of low seismicity apply may be found in its National Annex. It is recommended to consider as low seismicity cases either those in which the design ground acceleration on type A ground, a_g, is not greater than 0,08 g (0,78 m/s^2), or those where the product $a_g \cdot S$ is not greater than 0,1 g (0,98 m/s^2). The selection of whether the value of a_g, or that of the product $a_g \cdot S$ will be used in a country to define the threshold for low seismicity cases, may be found in its National Annex.

Table NA.1, 3.2.1(4) UK decision
$a_g \leq 2$ m/s^2 (for T_{NCR} = 2 500 years)

(5) P In cases of very low seismicity, the provisions of EN 1998 need not be observed.

NOTE The selection of the categories of structures, ground types and seismic zones in a country for which the EN 1998 provisions need not be observed (cases of very low seismicity) may be found in its National Annex. It is recommended to consider as very low seismicity cases either those in which the design ground acceleration on type A ground, a_g, is not greater than 0,04 g (0,39 m/s^2), or those where the product $a_g \cdot S$ is not greater than 0,05 g (0,49 m/s^2). The selection of whether the value of a_g, or that of the product $a_g \cdot S$ will be used in a country to define the threshold for very low seismicity cases, can be found in its National Annex.

Table NA.1, 3.2.1(5) UK decision
$a_g \leq 1.8$ m/s^2 (for T_{NCR} = 2 500 years)

3.2.2 Basic representation of the seismic action

3.2.2.1 General

(1) P Within the scope of EN 1998 the earthquake motion at a given point on the surface is represented by an elastic ground acceleration response spectrum, henceforth called an "elastic response spectrum".

(2) The shape of the elastic response spectrum is taken as being the same for the two levels of seismic action introduced in 2.1(1) P and 2.2.1(1) P for the no-collapse requirement (ultimate limit state – design seismic action) and for the damage limitation requirement.

(3) P The horizontal seismic action is described by two orthogonal components considered as being independent and represented by the same response spectrum.

(4) For the three components of the seismic action, one or more alternative shapes of response spectra may be adopted, depending on the seismic sources and the earthquake magnitudes generated from them.

NOTE 1 The selection of the shape of the elastic response spectrum to be used in a country or part of a country may be found in its National Annex.

NOTE 2 In selecting the appropriate shape of the spectrum, consideration should be given to the magnitude of earthquakes that contribute most to the seismic hazard defined for the purpose of probabilistic hazard assessment, rather than on conservative upper limits (e.g. the Maximum Credible Earthquake) defined for that purpose.

Recommended shapes are described in the Note of 3.2.2.2 (2) P.

3.2.2.2 Horizontal elastic response spectrum

(1) P For the horizontal components of the seismic action, the elastic response spectrum $S_e(T)$ is defined by the following expressions (see Figure 3.1):

$$0 \leq T \leq T_B : S_e(T) = a_g \cdot S \cdot \left[1 + \frac{T}{T_B} \cdot (\eta \cdot 2,5 - 1)\right] \quad (3.2)$$

$$T_B \leq T \leq T_C : S_e(T) = a_g \cdot S \cdot \eta \cdot 2,5 \quad (3.3)$$

$$T_C \leq T \leq T_D : S_e(T) = a_g \cdot S \cdot \eta \cdot 2,5\left[\frac{T_C}{T}\right] \qquad (3.4)$$

$$T_D \leq T \leq 4s : S_e(T) = a_g \cdot S \cdot \eta \cdot 2,5\left[\frac{T_C T_D}{T^2}\right] \qquad (3.5)$$

where

$S_e(T)$ is the elastic response spectrum;
T is the vibration period of a linear single-degree-of-freedom system;
a_g is the design ground acceleration on type A ground ($a_g = \gamma_I \cdot a_{gR}$);
T_B is the lower limit of the period of the constant spectral acceleration branch;
T_C is the upper limit of the period of the constant spectral acceleration branch;
T_D is the value defining the beginning of the constant displacement response range of the spectrum;
S is the soil factor;
η is the damping correction factor with a reference value of $\eta = 1$ for 5 % viscous damping, see (3) of this clause.

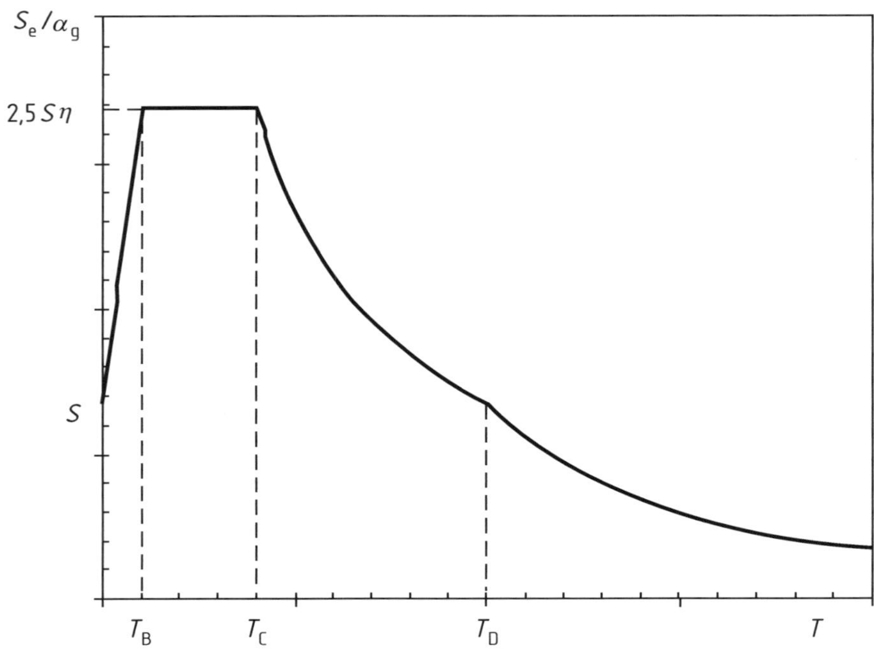

Figure 3.1 — Shape of the elastic response spectrum

(2) P The values of the periods T_B, T_C and T_D and of the soil factor S describing the shape of the elastic response spectrum depend on the ground type.

NOTE 1 The values to be ascribed to T_B, T_C, T_D and S for each ground type and type (shape) of spectrum to be used in a country may be found in its National Annex. If deep geology is not accounted for (see 3.1.2(1)), the recommended choice is the use of two types of spectra: Type 1 and Type 2. If the earthquakes that contribute most to the seismic hazard defined for the site for the purpose of probabilistic hazard assessment have a surface-wave magnitude, M_s, not greater than 5,5, it is recommended that the Type 2 spectrum is adopted. For the five ground types A, B, C, D and E the recommended values of the parameters S, T_B, T_C and T_D are given in Table 3.2 for the Type 1 spectrum and in Table 3.3 for the Type 2 spectrum. Figure 3.2 and Figure 3.3 show the shapes of the recommended Type 1 and Type 2 spectra, respectively, normalised by a_g, for 5% damping. Different spectra may be defined in the National Annex, if deep geology is accounted for.

Table NA.1, 3.2.2.2(1)P UK decision

In the absence of site-specific information, the recommended values for Type 2 earthquakes may be used, but see also PD 6698.

Table 3.2 — Values of the parameters describing the Type 1 elastic response spectrum

Ground type	S	T_B (s)	T_C (s)	T_D (s)
A	1,0	0,15	0,4	2,0
B	1,2	0,15	0,5	2,0
C	1,15	0,20	0,6	2,0
D	1,35	0,20	0,8	2,0
E	1,4	0,15	0,5	2,0

Table 3.3 — Values of the parameters describing the recommended Type 2 elastic response spectrum

Ground type	S	T_B (s)	T_C (s)	T_D (s)
A	1,0	0,05	0,25	1,2
B	1,35	0,05	0,25	1,2
C	1,5	0,10	0,25	1,2
D	1,8	0,10	0,30	1,2
E	1,6	0,05	0,25	1,2

(3) The value of the damping correction factor η may be determined by the expression:

$$\eta = \sqrt{10 / (5 + \xi)} \geq 0,55 \tag{3.6}$$

where

ξ is the viscous damping ratio of the structure, expressed as a percentage.

3.2.2.3 Vertical elastic response spectrum

(1) P The vertical component of the seismic action shall be represented by an elastic response spectrum, $S_{ve}(T)$, derived using expressions (3.8)-(3.11).

$$0 \leq T \leq T_B : S_{ve}(T) = a_{vg} \cdot \left[1 + \frac{T}{T_B} \cdot (\eta \cdot 3,0 - 1)\right] \tag{3.8}$$

$$T_B \leq T \leq T_C : S_{ve}(T) = a_{vg} \cdot \eta \cdot 3,0 \tag{3.9}$$

$$T_C \leq T \leq T_D : S_{ve}(T) = a_{vg} \cdot \eta \cdot 3,0 \left[\frac{T_C}{T}\right] \tag{3.10}$$

$$T_D \leq T \leq 4\mathrm{s} : S_{ve}(T) = a_{vg} \cdot \eta \cdot 3,0 \left[\frac{T_C \cdot T_D}{T^2}\right] \tag{3.11}$$

NOTE The values to be ascribed to T_B, T_C, T_D and a_{vg} for each type (shape) of vertical spectrum to be used in a country may be found in its National Annex. The recommended choice is the use of two types of vertical spectra: Type 1 and Type 2. As for the spectra defining the horizontal components of the seismic action, if the earthquakes that contribute most to the seismic hazard defined for the site for the purpose of probabilistic hazard assessment have a surface-wave magnitude, M_s, not greater than 5,5, it is recommended that the Type 2 spectrum is adopted.

For the five ground types A, B, C, D and E the recommended values of the parameters describing the vertical spectra are given in Table 3.4. These recommended values do not apply for special ground types S_1 and S_2.

Table NA.1, 3.2.2.3(1)P UK decision

In the absence of site-specific information, the recommended values for Type 2 earthquakes may be used, but see also PD 6698.

Table 3.4 — Recommended values of parameters describing the vertical elastic response spectrum

Spectrum	a_{vg}/a_g	T_B (s)	T_C (s)	T_D (s)
Type 1	0,90	0,05	0,15	1,0
Type 2	0,45	0,05	0,15	1,0

3.2.2.4 Design ground displacement

(1) Unless special studies based on the available information indicate otherwise, the value of the design ground displacement d_g may be estimated by means of the following expression:

$$d_g = 0,025 \cdot a_g \cdot S \cdot T_C \cdot T_D \qquad (3.12)$$

with a_g, S, T_C and T_D as defined in 3.2.2.2.

3.2.2.5 Design spectrum for elastic analysis

(1) The capacity of structural systems to resist seismic actions in the non-linear range generally permits their design to resist seismic forces smaller than those corresponding to a linear elastic response.

(2) To avoid explicit inelastic structural analysis in design, the capacity of the structure to dissipate energy, through mainly ductile behaviour of its elements and/or other mechanisms, is taken into account by performing an elastic analysis based on a response spectrum reduced with respect to the elastic one, henceforth called a "design spectrum". This reduction is accomplished by introducing the behaviour factor q.

(3)P The behaviour factor q is an approximation of the ratio of the seismic forces that the structure would experience if its response was completely elastic with 5 % viscous damping, to the seismic forces that may be used in the design, with a conventional elastic analysis model, still ensuring a satisfactory response of the structure. The value of the behaviour factor q, which also account for the influence of the viscous damping being different from 5 %, are given for various materials and structural systems according to the relevant ductility classes in the various Parts of EN 1998. The value of the behaviour factor q may be different in different horizontal directions of the structure, although the ductility classification shall be the same in all directions.

(4) P For the horizontal components of the seismic action the design spectrum, $S_d(T)$, shall be defined by the following expressions:

$$0 \le T \le T_B : S_d(T) = a_g \cdot S \cdot \left[\frac{2}{3} + \frac{T}{T_B} \cdot \left(\frac{2,5}{q} - \frac{2}{3}\right)\right] \qquad (3.13)$$

$$T_B \le T \le T_C : S_d(T) = a_g \cdot S \cdot \frac{2,5}{q} \qquad (3.14)$$

$$T_C \leq T \leq T_D : S_d(T) \begin{cases} = a_g \cdot S \cdot \frac{2,5}{q} \cdot \left[\frac{T_C}{T}\right] \\ \geq \beta \cdot a_g \end{cases} \tag{3.15}$$

$$T_D \leq T : S_d(T) \begin{cases} = a_g \cdot S \cdot \frac{2,5}{q} \cdot \left[\frac{T_C T_D}{T^2}\right] \\ \geq \beta \cdot a_g \end{cases} \tag{3.16}$$

where

a_g, S, T_C and T_D	are as defined in 3.2.2.2;
$S_d(T)$	is the design spectrum;
q	is the behaviour factor;
β	is the lower bound factor for the horizontal design spectrum.

NOTE The value to be ascribed to β for use in a country can be found in its National Annex. The recommended value for β is 0,2.

Table NA.1, 3.2.2.5(4) UK decision

Use the recommended value.

(5) For the vertical component of the seismic action the design spectrum is given by expressions (3.13) to (3.16), with the design ground acceleration in the vertical direction, a_{vg} replacing a_g, S taken as being equal to 1,0 and the other parameters as defined in 3.2.2.3.

(6) For the vertical component of the seismic action a behaviour factor q equal to 1,5 should generally be adopted for all materials and structural systems.

(7) The adoption of values for q greater than 1,5 in the vertical direction shall be justified through an appropriate analysis.

(8) P The design spectrum as defined above is not sufficient for the design of structures with base-isolation or energy-dissipation systems.

3.2.4 Combinations of the seismic action with other actions

(1) P The design value E_d of the effects of actions in the seismic design situation shall be determined in accordance with EN 1990:2002, 6.4.3.4.

(2) P The inertial effects of the design seismic action shall be evaluated by taking into account the presence of the masses associated with all gravity loads appearing in the following combination of actions:

$$\Sigma G_{k,j} \text{"+"} \Sigma \psi_{E,i} \cdot Q_{k,i} \tag{3.17}$$

where

$\psi_{E,i}$ is the combination coefficient for variable action i (see 4.2.4).

(3) The combination coefficients $\psi_{E,i}$ take into account the likelihood of the loads $Q_{k,i}$ not being present over the entire structure during the earthquake. These coefficients may also account for a reduced participation of masses in the motion of the structure due to the non-rigid connection between them.

4 Design of buildings

4.2 Characteristics of earthquake resistant buildings

4.2.1 Basic principles of conceptual design

(1) P In seismic regions the aspect of seismic hazard shall be taken into account in the early stages of the conceptual design of a building, thus enabling the achievement of a structural system which, within acceptable costs, satisfies the fundamental requirements, specified in 2.1.

(2) The guiding principles governing this conceptual design are:

- structural simplicity;
- uniformity, symmetry and redundancy;
- bi-directional resistance and stiffness;
- torsional resistance and stiffness;
- diaphragmatic behaviour at storey level;
- adequate foundation.

The guiding principles are generally satisfied in structures with properties such as: clear and direct load paths for the transmission of the seismic forces, even and/or symmetrical distribution of structural elements in plan and elevation, similar resistance and stiffness in both main horizontal directions, adequate torsional stiffness, sufficient in-plane stiffness of the floors (diaphragm action) and similar types and depths of foundations.

4.2.3 Criteria for structural regularity

4.2.3.1 General

(1) P For the purpose of seismic design, building structures are categorized into being regular or non-regular.

NOTE In building structures consisting of more than one dynamically independent units, the categorisation and the relevant criteria in 4.2.3 refer to the individual dynamically independent units. In such structures, "individual dynamically independent unit" is meant for "building" in 4.2.3.

(2) This distinction has implications for the following aspects of the seismic design:

- the structural model, which can be either a simplified planar model or a spatial model;
- the method of analysis, which can be either a simplified response spectrum analysis (lateral force procedure) or a modal one;
- the value of the behaviour factor q which shall be decreased for buildings non-regular in elevation (see 4.2.3.3).

(3) P With regard to the implications of structural regularity on analysis and design, separate consideration is given to the regularity characteristics of the building in plan and in elevation (Table 4.1).

(4) Criteria describing regularity in plan and in elevation are given in 4.2.3.2 and 4.2.3.3. Rules concerning modelling and analysis are given in 4.3.

(5) P The regularity criteria given in 4.2.3.2 and 4.2.3.3 should be taken as necessary conditions. It shall be verified that the assumed regularity of the building structure is not impaired by other characteristics, not included in these criteria.

(6) The reference values of the behaviour factors are given in Sections 5 to 9.

(7) For non-regular in elevation buildings the decreased values of the behaviour factor are given by the reference values multiplied by 0,8.

Table 4.1 — Consequences of structural regularity on seismic analysis and design

Regularity		Allowed simplification		Behaviour factor
Plan	Elevation	Model	Linear-elastic analysis	(for linear analysis)
Yes	Yes	Planar	Lateral force[a]	Reference value
Yes	No	Planar	Modal	Decreased value
No	Yes	Spatial[b]	Lateral force[a]	Reference value
No	No	Spatial	Modal	Decreased value

[a] If the condition of 4.3.3.2.1(2)a is also met.
[b] Under the specific conditions given in 4.3.3.1(8) a separate planar model may be used in each horizontal direction, in accordance with 4.3.3.1(8).

4.2.3.2 Criteria for regularity in plan

(1)P For a building to be categorised as being regular in plan, it shall satisfy all the conditions listed in the following paragraphs.

(2) With respect to the lateral stiffness and mass distribution, the building structure shall be approximately symmetrical in plan with respect to two orthogonal axes.

(3) The plan configuration shall be compact, i.e., each floor shall be delimited by a polygonal convex line. If in plan set-backs (re-entrant corners or edge recesses) exist, regularity in plan may still be considered as being satisfied, provided that these set-backs do not affect the floor in-plan stiffness and that, for each set-back, the area between the outline of the floor and a convex polygonal line enveloping the floor does not exceed 5% of the floor area.

(4) The in-plan stiffness of the floors shall be sufficiently large in comparison with the lateral stiffness of the vertical structural elements, so that the deformation of the floor shall have a small effect on the distribution of the forces among the vertical structural elements. In this respect, the L, C, H, I and X plan shapes should be carefully examined, notably as concerns the stiffness of the lateral branches, which should be comparable to that of the central part, in order to satisfy the rigid diaphragm condition. The application of this paragraph should be considered for the global behaviour of the building.

(5) The slenderness $\lambda = L_{max}/L_{min}$ of the building in plan shall be not higher than 4, where L_{max} and L_{min} are respectively the larger and smaller in plan dimension of the building, measured in orthogonal directions.

(6) At each level and for each direction of analysis x and y, the structural eccentricity e_o and the torsional radius r shall be in accordance with the two conditions below, which are expressed for the direction of analysis y:

$$e_{ox} \leq 0,30 \cdot r_x \quad (4.1a)$$

$$r_x \geq l_s \quad (4.1b)$$

where

e_{ox} is the distance between the centre of stiffness and the centre of mass, measured along the x direction, which is normal to the direction of analysis considered;

r_x is the square root of the ratio of the torsional stiffness to the lateral stiffness in the y direction ("torsional radius"); and

l_s is the radius of gyration of the floor mass in plan (square root of the ratio of (a) the polar moment of inertia of the floor mass in plan with respect to the centre of mass of the floor to (b) the floor mass).

The definitions of centre of stiffness and torsional radius r are provided in (7) to (9) of this clause.

(7) In single storey buildings the centre of stiffness is defined as the centre of the lateral stiffness of all primary seismic members. The torsional radius r is defined as the square root of the ratio of the global torsional stiffness with respect to the centre of lateral stiffness, to the global lateral stiffness, in one direction, taking into account all of the primary seismic members in this direction.

(8) In multi-storey buildings only approximate definitions of the centre of stiffness and of the torsional radius are possible. A simplified definition, for the classification of structural regularity in plan and for the approximate analysis of torsional effects, is possible if the following two conditions are satisfied:

a) all lateral load-resisting systems, such as cores, structural walls, or frames, run without interruption from the foundations to the top of the building;

b) the deflected shapes of the individual systems under horizontal loads are not very different. This condition may be considered satisfied in the case of frame systems and wall systems. In general, this condition is not satisfied in dual systems.

NOTE The National Annex can include reference to documents that might provide definitions of the centre of stiffness and of the torsional radius in multi-storey buildings, both for those that meet the conditions (a) and (b) of paragraph (8), and for those that do not.

Table NA.1, 4.2.3.2(8) UK decision

Any appropriate method may be used. Further guidance is given in PD 6698.

(9) In frames and in systems of slender walls with prevailing flexural deformations, the positions of the centres of stiffness and the torsional radius of all the storeys may be calculated as those of the moments of inertia of the cross-sections of the vertical elements. If, in addition to flexural deformations, shear deformations are also significant, they may be accounted for by using an equivalent moment of inertia of the cross-section.

4.2.3.3 Criteria for regularity in elevation

(1)P For a building to be categorised as being regular in elevation, it shall satisfy all the conditions listed in the following paragraphs.

(2) All lateral load-resisting systems, such as cores, structural walls or frames, shall run without interruption from their foundations to the top of the building or, if setbacks at different heights are present, to the top of the relevant zone of the building.

(3) Both the lateral stiffness and the mass of the individual storeys shall remain constant or reduce gradually, without abrupt changes, from the base to the top of a particular building.

(4) In framed buildings the ratio of the actual storey resistance to the resistance required by the analysis should not vary disproportionately between adjacent storeys. Within this context the special aspects of masonry infilled frames are treated in 4.3.6.3.2.

(5) When setbacks are present, the following additional conditions apply:

a) for gradual setbacks preserving axial symmetry, the setback at any floor shall be not greater than 20 % of the previous plan dimension in the direction of the setback (see Figure 4.1.a and Figure 4.1.b);

b) for a single setback within the lower 15 % of the total height of the main structural system, the setback shall be not greater than 50 % of the previous plan dimension (see Figure 4.1.c). In this case the structure of the base zone within the vertically projected perimeter of the upper storeys should be designed to resist at least 75 % of the horizontal shear forces that would develop in that zone in a similar building without the base enlargement;

c) if the setbacks do not preserve symmetry, in each face the sum of the setbacks at all storeys shall be not greater than 30 % of the plan dimension at the ground floor above the foundations or above the top of a rigid basement, and the individual setbacks shall be not greater than 10 % of the previous plan dimension (see Figure 4.1.d).

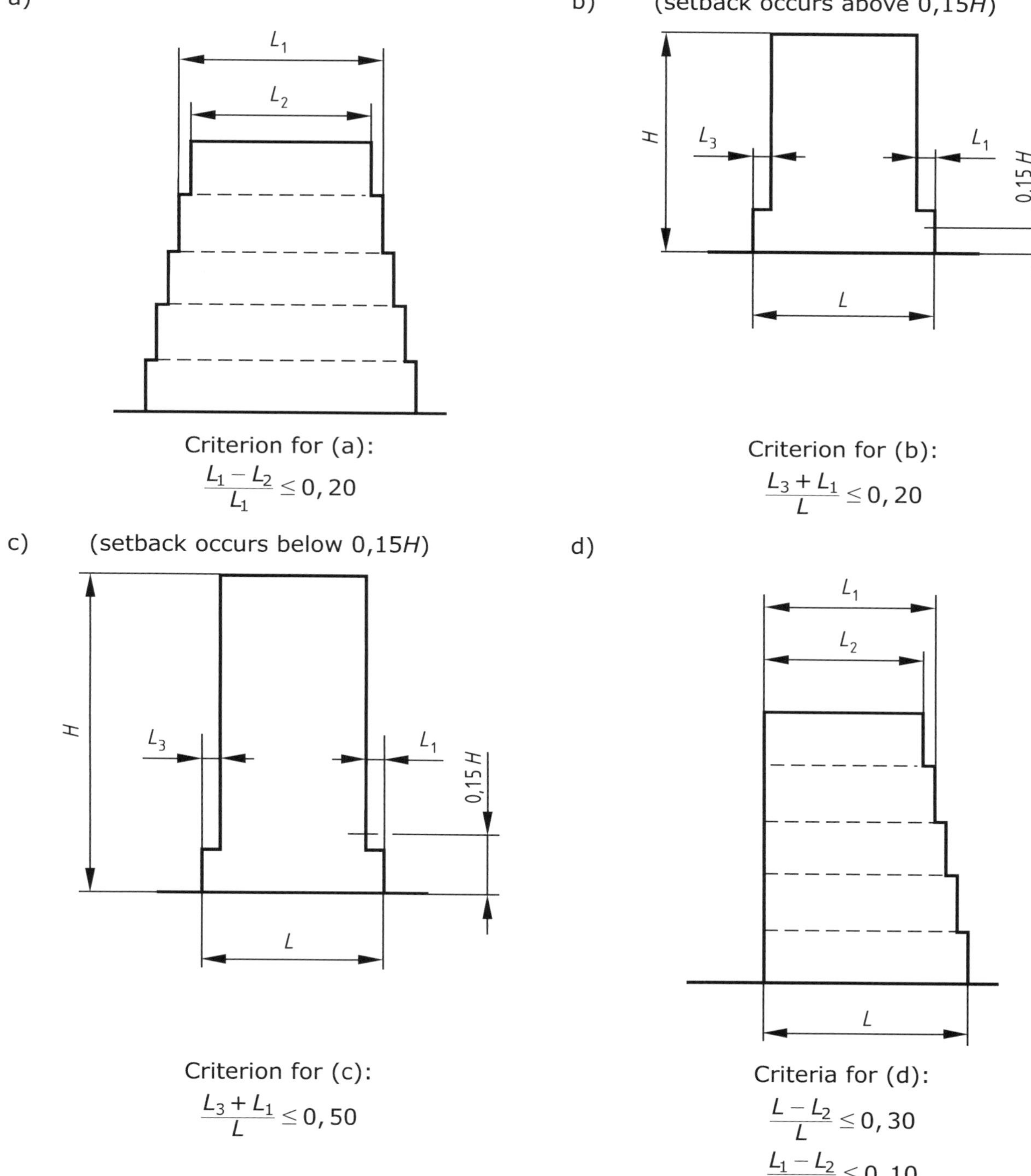

Figure 4.1 — Criteria for regularity of buildings with setbacks

4.2.4 Combination coefficients for variable actions

(1)P The combination coefficients ψ_{2i} (for the quasi-permanent value of q variable action i) for the design of buildings (see 3.2.4) shall be those given in EN 1990:2002 Annex A1.

(2)P The combination coefficients ψ_{Ei} introduced in 3.2.4(2) P for the calculation of the effects of the seismic actions shall be computed from the following expression:

$$\psi_{Ei} = \varphi \cdot \psi_{2i} \quad (4.2)$$

NOTE The values to be ascribed to φ for use in a country may be found in its National Annex. The recommended values for φ are listed in Table 4.2.

Table NA.1, 4.2.4(2)P UK decision

Use the recommended values. Storeys occupied by different tenants may be considered as independently occupied.

Table 4.2 — Values of φ for calculating ψ_{Ei}

Type of variable action	Storey	φ
Categories A-C*	Roof	1,0
	Storeys with correlated occupancies	0,8
	Independently occupied storeys	0,5
Categories D-F* and Archives		1,0

* Categories as defined in EN 1991-1-1:2002.

4.2.5 Importance classes and importance factors

(1)P Buildings are classified in 4 importance classes, depending on the consequences of collapse for human life, on their importance for public safety and civil protection in the immediate post-earthquake period, and on the social and economic consequences of collapse.

(2)P The importance classes are characterized by different importance factors γ_I as described in 2.1(3)P.

(3) The importance factor γ_I = 1,0 is associated with a seismic event having the reference return period indicated in 3.2.1(3).

(4) The definitions of the importance classes are given in Table 4.3.

Table 4.3 — Importance classes for buildings

Importance class	Buildings
I	Buildings of minor importance for public safety, e.g. agricultural buildings, etc.
II	Ordinary buildings, not belonging to the other categories.
III	Buildings whose seismic resistance is of importance in view of the consequences associated with a collapse, e.g. schools, assembly halls, cultural institutions etc.
IV	Buildings whose integrity during earthquakes is of vital importance for civil protection, e.g. hospitals, fire stations, power plants, etc.

NOTE Importance Classes I, II and III or IV correspond roughly to consequence classes CC1, CC2 and CC3, respectively, defined in EN1990:2002, Annex B.

(5)P The value of γ_I for importance class II shall be, by definition, equal to 1,0.

NOTE The values to be ascribed to γ_I for use in a country may be found in its National Annex. The values of γ_I may be different for the various seismic zones of the country, depending on the seismic hazard conditions and on public safety considerations (see Note to 2.1(4)). The recommended values of γ_I for importance classes I, III and IV are equal to 0,8, 1,2 and 1,4, respectively.

Table NA.1, 4.2.5(5)P UK decision

Where a value for the reference return period T_{NCR} of 2 500 years has been adopted for CC3 structures, γ_I=1 should be assumed. Where T_{NCR} has been assessed on a project-specific basis, γ_I should also be chosen on a project-specific basis. Further guidance is given in PD 6698.

4.3 Structural analysis

4.3.1 Modelling

(1)P The model of the building shall adequately represent the distribution of stiffness and mass in it so that all significant deformation shapes and inertia forces are properly accounted for under the seismic action considered. In the case of non-linear analysis, the model shall also adequately represent the distribution of strength.

(2) The model should also account for the contribution of joint regions to the deformability of the building, e.g. the end zones in beams or columns of frame type structures. Non-structural elements, which may influence the response of the primary seismic structure, should also be accounted for.

(3) In general the structure may be considered to consist of a number of vertical and lateral load resisting systems, connected by horizontal diaphragms.

(4) When the floor diaphragms of the building may be taken as being rigid in their planes, the masses and the moments of inertia of each floor may be lumped at the centre of gravity.

NOTE The diaphragm is taken as being rigid, if, when it is modelled with its actual in-plane flexibility, its horizontal displacements nowhere exceed those resulting from the rigid diaphragm assumption by more than 10% of the corresponding absolute horizontal displacements in the seismic design situation.

(5) For buildings conforming to the criteria for regularity in plan (see 4.2.3.2) or with the conditions presented in 4.3.3.1(8), the analysis may be performed using two planar models, one for each main direction.

(6) In concrete buildings, in composite steel-concrete buildings and in masonry buildings the stiffness of the load bearing elements should, in general, be evaluated taking into account the effect of cracking. Such stiffness should correspond to the initiation of yielding of the reinforcement.

(7) Unless a more accurate analysis of the cracked elements is performed, the elastic flexural and shear stiffness properties of concrete and masonry elements may be taken to be equal to one-half of the corresponding stiffness of the uncracked elements.

(8) Infill walls which contribute significantly to the lateral stiffness and resistance of the building should be taken into account. See 4.3.6 for masonry infills of concrete, steel or composite frames.

(9)P The deformability of the foundation shall be taken into account in the model, whenever it may have an adverse overall influence on the structural response.

NOTE Foundation deformability (including the soil-structure interaction) may always be taken into account, including the cases in which it has beneficial effects.

(10)P The masses shall be calculated from the gravity loads appearing in the combination of actions indicated in 3.2.4. The combination coefficients ψ_{Ei} are given in 4.2.4(2)P.

4.3.2 Accidental torsional effects

(1)P In order to account for uncertainties in the location of masses and in the spatial variation of the seismic motion, the calculated centre of mass at each floor *i* shall be considered as being displaced from its nominal location in each direction by an accidental eccentricity:

$$e_{ai} = \pm 0,05 \cdot L_i \tag{4.3}$$

where

e_{ai} is the accidental eccentricity of storey mass *i* from its nominal location, applied in the same direction at all floors;

L_i is the floor-dimension perpendicular to the direction of the seismic action.

4.3.3 Methods of analysis

4.3.3.1 General

(1) Within the scope of Section 4, the seismic effects and the effects of the other actions included in the seismic design situation may be determined on the basis of the linear-elastic behaviour of the structure.

(2)P The reference method for determining the seismic effects shall be the modal response spectrum analysis, using a linear-elastic model of the structure and the design spectrum given in 3.2.2.5.

(3) Depending on the structural characteristics of the building one of the following two types of linear-elastic analysis may be used:

a) the "lateral force method of analysis" for buildings meeting the conditions given in 4.3.3.2;

b) the "modal response spectrum analysis" which is applicable to all types of buildings (see 4.3.3.3).

(4) As an alternative to a linear method, a non-linear method may also be used, such as:

c) non-linear static (pushover) analysis;

d) non-linear time history (dynamic) analysis,

provided that the conditions specified in (5) and (6) of this subclause and in 4.3.3.4 are satisfied.

NOTE For base isolated buildings the conditions under which the linear methods a) and b) or the nonlinear ones c) and d), may be used are given in Section 10. For non-base-isolated buildings, the linear methods of 4.3.3.1(3) may always be used, as specified in 4.3.3.2.1. The choice of whether the nonlinear methods of 4.3.3.1(4) may also be applied to non-base-isolated buildings in a particular country will be found in its National Annex. The National Annex may also include reference to complementary information about member deformation capacities and the associated partial factors to be used in the Ultimate Limit State verifications in accordance with 4.4.2.2(5).

In the UK, no supplementary advice is given.

(5) Non-linear analyses should be properly substantiated with respect to the seismic input, the constitutive model used, the method of interpreting the results of the analysis and the requirements to be met.

(6) Non-base-isolated structures designed on the basis of non-linear pushover analysis without using the behaviour factor q (see 4.3.3.4.2.1(1) d), should satisfy 4.4.2.2(5), as well as the rules of Sections 5 to 9 for dissipative structures.

(7) Linear-elastic analysis may be performed using two planar models, one for each main horizontal direction, if the criteria for regularity in plan are satisfied (see 4.2.3.2).

(8) Depending on the importance class of the building, linear-elastic analysis may be performed using two planar models, one for each main horizontal direction, even if the criteria for regularity in plan in 4.2.3.2 are not satisfied, provided that all of the following special regularity conditions are met:

a) the building shall have well-distributed and relatively rigid cladding and partitions;

b) the building height shall not exceed 10 m;

c) the in-plane stiffness of the floors shall be large enough in comparison with the lateral stiffness of the vertical structural elements, so that rigid diaphragm behaviour may be assumed.

d) the centres of lateral stiffness and mass shall be each approximately on a vertical line and, in the two horizontal directions of analysis, satisfy the conditions: $r_x^2 > l_s^2 + e_{ox}^2$, $r_y^2 > l_s^2 + e_{oy}^2$, where the radius of gyration l_s, the torsional radii r_x and r_y and the natural eccentricities e_{ox} and e_{oy} are defined as in 4.2.3.2(6).

NOTE The value of the importance factor, γ_I, below which the simplification of the analysis according to 4.3.3.1(8) is allowed in a country, may be found in its National Annex.

Table NA.1, 4.3.3.1(8) UK decision

3D (spatial) analysis models are recommended for all consequence class CC3 buildings.

(9) In buildings satisfying all the conditions of (8) of this clause with the exception of d), linear-elastic analysis using two planar models, one for each main horizontal direction, may also be performed, but in such cases all seismic action effects resulting from the analysis should be multiplied by 1,25.

(10)P Buildings not conforming to the criteria in (7) to (9) of this clause shall be analysed using a spatial model.

(11)P Whenever a spatial model is used, the design seismic action shall be applied along all relevant horizontal directions (with regard to the structural layout of the building) and their orthogonal horizontal directions. For buildings with resisting elements in two perpendicular directions these two directions shall be considered as the relevant ones.

4.3.3.2 Lateral force method of analysis

4.3.3.2.1 General

(1)P This type of analysis may be applied to buildings whose response is not significantly affected by contributions from modes of vibration higher than the fundamental mode in each principal direction.

(2) The requirement in (1)P of this clause is deemed to be satisfied in buildings which fulfil both of the two following conditions.

a) They have fundamental periods of vibration T_1 in the two main directions which are smaller than the following values

$$T_1 \leq \begin{cases} 4 \cdot T_C \\ 2,0\ \text{s} \end{cases} \qquad (4.4)$$

where T_C is defined in 3.2.2.2;

b) they meet the criteria for regularity in elevation given in 4.2.3.3.

4.3.3.2.2 Base shear force

(1)P The seismic base shear force F_b, for each horizontal direction in which the building is analysed, shall be determined using the following expression:

$$F_b = S_d(T_1) \cdot m \cdot \lambda \quad (4.5)$$

where

$S_d(T_1)$ is the ordinate of the design spectrum (see 3.2.2.5) at period T_1;
T_1 is the fundamental period of vibration of the building for lateral motion in the direction considered;
m is the total mass of the building, above the foundation or above the top of a rigid basement, computed in accordance with 3.2.4(2);
λ is the correction factor, the value of which is equal to λ = 0,85 if $T_1 \leq 2T_C$ and the building has more than two storeys, or λ = 1,0 otherwise.

NOTE The factor λ accounts for the fact that in buildings with at least three storeys and translational degrees of freedom in each horizontal direction, the effective modal mass of the 1st (fundamental) mode is smaller, on average by 15%, than the total building mass.

(2) AC1 For the determination of the fundamental period of vibration T_1 AC1 of the building, expressions based on methods of structural dynamics (for example the Rayleigh method) may be used.

(3) For buildings with heights of up to 40 m the value of T_1 (in s) may be approximated by the following expression:

$$T_1 = C_t \cdot H^{3/4} \quad (4.6)$$

where

C_t is 0,085 for moment resistant space steel frames, 0,075 for moment resistant space concrete frames and for eccentrically braced steel frames and 0,050 for all other structures;
H is the height of the building, in m, from the foundation or from the top of a rigid basement.

(4) Alternatively, for structures with concrete or masonry shear walls the value C_t in expression (4.6) may be taken as being

$$C_t = 0,075 / \sqrt{A_c} \quad (4.7)$$

where

AC1 $$A_c = \Sigma \left[A_i \cdot \left(0,2 + (l_{wi} / H)^2\right) \right] \quad (4.8)$$ AC1

and

A_c is the total effective area of the shear walls in the first storey of the building, in m^2;
A_i is the effective cross-sectional area of the shear wall i in the first storey of the building, in m^2;
H is as in (3) of this subclause;
l_{wi} is the length of the shear wall i in the first storey in the direction parallel to the applied forces, in m, with the restriction that l_{wi}/H shall not exceed 0,9.

(5) Alternatively, the estimation of T_1 (in s) may be made by the following expression:

$$T_1 = 2 \cdot \sqrt{d} \quad (4.9)$$

where

d is the lateral elastic displacement of the top of the building, in m, due to the gravity loads applied in the horizontal direction.

4.3.3.2.3 Distribution of the horizontal seismic forces

(1) The fundamental mode shapes in the horizontal directions of analysis of the building may be calculated using methods of structural dynamics or may be approximated by horizontal displacements increasing linearly along the height of the building.

(2)P The seismic action effects shall be determined by applying, to the two planar models, horizontal forces F_i to all storeys.

$$F_i = F_b \cdot \frac{s_i \cdot m_i}{\Sigma s_j \cdot m_j} \qquad (4.10)$$

where

F_i is the horizontal force acting on storey i;
F_b is the seismic base shear in accordance with expression (4.5);
s_i, s_j are the displacements of masses m_i, m_j in the fundamental mode shape;
m_i, m_j are the storey masses computed in accordance with 3.2.4(2).

(3) When the fundamental mode shape is approximated by horizontal displacements increasing linearly along the height, the horizontal forces F_i shall be taken as being given by:

$$F_i = F_b \cdot \frac{z_i \cdot m_i}{\Sigma z_j \cdot m_j} \qquad (4.11)$$

where

z_i, z_j are the heights of the masses m_i m_j above the level of application of the seismic action (foundation or top of a rigid basement).

(4)P The horizontal forces F_i determined according to this clause shall be distributed to the lateral load resisting system assuming the floors are rigid in their plane.

4.3.3.2.4 Torsional effects

(1) If the lateral stiffness and mass are symmetrically distributed in plan and unless the accidental eccentricity of 4.3.2(1)P is taken into account by a more exact method (e.g. that of 4.3.3.3.3(1)), the accidental torsional effects may be accounted for by multiplying the action effects in the individual load resisting elements resulting from the application of 4.3.3.2.3(4) by a factor δ given by

$$\delta = 1 + 0,6 \cdot \frac{x}{L_e} \qquad (4.12)$$

where

x is the distance of the element under consideration from the centre of mass of the building in plan, measured perpendicularly to the direction of the seismic action considered;
L_e is the distance between the two outermost lateral load-resisting elements, measured perpendicularly to the direction of the seismic action considered.

(2) If the analysis is performed using two planar models, one for each main horizontal direction, torsional effects may be determined by doubling the accidental eccentricity e_{ai} of expression (4.3) and applying (1) of this subclause with factor 0,6 in expression (4.12) increased to 1,2.

4.3.3.3 Modal response spectrum analysis

4.3.3.3.1 General

(1)P This type of analysis shall be applied to buildings which do not satisfy the conditions given in 4.3.3.2.1(2) for applying the lateral force method of analysis.

(2)P The response of all modes of vibration contributing significantly to the global response shall be taken into account.

> The combination of modal responses (see 4.3.3.3.2 of EN 1998-1) may be carried out using the square root of the sum of the squares (SRSS) rule.

4.3.3.3.3 Torsional effects

(1) Whenever a spatial model is used for the analysis, the accidental torsional effects referred in 4.3.2(1) P may be determined as the envelope of the effects resulting from the application of static loadings, consisting of sets of torsional moments M_{ai} about the vertical axis of each storey *i*:

$$M_{ai} = e_{ai} \cdot F_i \qquad (4.17)$$

where

M_{ai} is the torsional moment applied at storey *i* about its vertical axis;
e_{ai} is the accidental eccentricity of storey mass *i* in accordance with expression (4.3) for all relevant directions;
F_i is the horizontal force acting on storey *i*, as derived in 4.3.3.2.3 for all relevant directions.

(2) The effects of the loadings in accordance with (1) should be taken into account with positive and negative signs (the same sign for all storeys).

(3) Whenever two separate planar models are used for the analysis, the torsional effects may be accounted for by applying the rules of 4.3.3.2.4(2) to the action effects computed in accordance with 4.3.3.3.2.

> The modal response spectrum analysis is the reference design method in EN 1998-1 and the use of non-linear methods (subclause 4.3.3.4 of EN 1998-1) is only recommended for evaluating structural performance.

4.3.3.5 Combination of the effects of the components of the seismic action

4.3.3.5.1 Horizontal components of the seismic action

(1)P In general the horizontal components of the seismic action (see 3.2.2.1(3)) shall be considered as acting simultaneously.

(2) The combination of the horizontal components of the seismic action may be accounted for as follows.

a) The structural response to each component shall be evaluated separately, using the combination rules for modal responses given in 4.3.3.3.2.

b) The maximum value of each action effect on the structure due to the two horizontal components of the seismic action may then be estimated by the square root of the sum of the squared values of the action effect due to each horizontal component.

c) The rule b) generally gives a safe side estimate of the probable values of other action effects simultaneous with the maximum value obtained as in b). More accurate models may be used for the estimation of the probable simultaneous values of more than one action effect due to the two horizontal components of the seismic action.

(3) As an alternative to b) and c) of (2) of this subclause, the action effects due to the combination of the horizontal components of the seismic action may be computed using both of the two following combinations:

a) E_{Edx} "+" $0,30\,E_{\text{Edy}}$ (4.18)

b) $0,30\,E_{\text{Edx}}$ "+" E_{Edy} (4.19)

where

"+" implies "to be combined with";
E_{Edx} represents the action effects due to the application of the seismic action along the chosen horizontal axis x of the structure;
E_{Edy} represents the action effects due to the application of the same seismic action along the orthogonal horizontal axis y of the structure.

(4) If the structural system or the regularity classification of the building in elevation is different in different horizontal directions, the value of the behaviour factor q may also be different.

(5)P The sign of each component in the above combinations shall be taken as being the most unfavourable for the particular action effect under consideration.

The vertical component of the seismic action is usually ignored except in certain cases as specified in 4.3.3.5.2 of EN 1998-1.

4.3.4 Displacement calculation

(1)P If linear analysis is performed the displacements induced by the design seismic action shall be calculated on the basis of the elastic deformations of the structural system by means of the following simplified expression:

$$d_s = q_d\, d_e \tag{4.23}$$

where

d_s is the displacement of a point of the structural system induced by the design seismic action;
q_d is the displacement behaviour factor, assumed equal to q unless otherwise specified;
d_e is the displacement of the same point of the structural system, as determined by a linear analysis based on the design response spectrum in accordance with 3.2.2.5.

The value of d_s does not need to be larger than the value derived from the elastic spectrum.

NOTE In general q_d is larger than q if the fundamental period of the structure is less than T_C (see Figure B.2).

4.4 Safety verifications

4.4.1 General

(1)P For the safety verifications the relevant limit states (see 4.4.2 and 4.4.3 below) and specific measures (see 2.2.4) shall be considered.

(2) For buildings of importance classes other than IV (see Table 4.3) the verifications prescribed in 4.4.2 and 4.4.3 may be considered satisfied if both of the following two conditions are met.

a) The total base shear due to the seismic design situation calculated with a behaviour factor equal to the value applicable to low-dissipative structures (see 2.2.2(2)) is less than that due to the other relevant action combinations for which the building is designed on the basis of a linear elastic analysis. This requirement relates to the shear force over the entire structure at the base level of the building (foundation or top of a rigid basement).

b) The specific measures described in 2.2.4 are taken into account, with the exception of the provisions in 2.2.4.1(2)-(3).

4.4.2 Ultimate limit state

4.4.2.1 General

(1)P The no-collapse requirement (ultimate limit state) under the seismic design situation is considered to have been met if the following conditions regarding resistance, ductility, equilibrium, foundation stability and seismic joints are met.

4.4.2.2 Resistance condition

(1)P The following relation shall be satisfied for all structural elements including connections and the relevant non-structural elements:

$$E_d \leq R_d \qquad (4.27)$$

where

E_d is the design value of the action effect, due to the seismic design situation (see EN 1990:2002 (6.4.3.4), including, if necessary, second order effects (see (2) of this subclause). Redistribution of bending moments in accordance with EN 1992-1-1:2004, [AC1) EN 1993-1-1:2005 (AC1] and EN 1994-1-1:2004 is permitted;

R_d is the corresponding design resistance of the element, calculated in accordance with the rules specific to the material used (in terms of the characteristic values of material properties f_k and partial factor γ_M) and in accordance with the mechanical models which relate to the specific type of structural system, as given in Sections 5 to 9 of this document and in other relevant Eurocode documents.

(2) Second-order effects (P-Δ effects) need not be taken into account if the following condition is fulfilled in all storeys:

$$\theta = \frac{P_{tot} \cdot d_r}{V_{tot} \cdot h} \leq 0,10 \qquad (4.28)$$

where

θ is the interstorey drift sensitivity coefficient;

P_{tot} is the total gravity load at and above the storey considered in the seismic design situation;

d_r is the design interstorey drift, evaluated as the difference of the average lateral displacements d_s at the top and bottom of the storey under consideration and calculated in accordance with 4.3.4;

V_{tot} is the total seismic storey shear; and

h is the interstorey height.

(3) If $0,1 < \theta < 0,2$, the second-order effects may approximately be taken into account by multiplying the relevant seismic action effects by a factor equal to $1/(1 - \theta)$.

(4)P The value of the coefficient θ shall not exceed 0,3.

4.4.2.3 Global and local ductility condition

(1)P It shall be verified that both the structural elements and the structure as a whole possess adequate ductility, taking into account the expected exploitation of ductility, which depends on the selected system and the behaviour factor.

(2)P Specific material related requirements, as defined in Sections 5 to 9, shall be satisfied, including, when indicated, capacity design provisions in order to obtain the hierarchy of resistance of the various structural components necessary for ensuring the intended configuration of plastic hinges and for avoiding brittle failure modes.

(3)P In multi-storey buildings formation of a soft storey plastic mechanism shall be prevented, as such a mechanism might entail excessive local ductility demands in the columns of the soft storey.

(4) Unless otherwise specified in Sections 5 to 8, to satisfy the requirement of (3)P, in frame buildings, including frame-equivalent ones as defined in 5.1.2(1), with two or more storeys, the following condition should be satisfied at all joints of primary or secondary seismic beams with primary seismic columns:

$$\sum M_{Rc} \geq 1,3 \sum M_{Rb} \qquad (4.29)$$

where:

$\sum M_{Rc}$ is the sum of the design values of the moments of resistance of the columns framing the joint. The minimum value of column moments of resistance within the range of column axial forces produced by the seismic design situation should be used in expression (4.29); and

$\sum M_{Rb}$ is the sum of the design values of the moments of resistance of the beams framing the joint. When partial strength connections are used, the moments of resistance of these connections are taken into account in the calculation of $\sum M_{Rb}$.

NOTE A rigorous interpretation of expression (4.29) requires calculation of the moments at the centre of the joint. These moments correspond to development of the design values of the moments of resistance of the columns or beams at the outside faces of the joint, plus a suitable allowance for moments due to shears at the joint faces. However, the loss in accuracy is minor and the simplification achieved is considerable if the shear allowance is neglected. This approximation is then deemed to be acceptable.

(5) Expression (4.29) should be satisfied in two orthogonal vertical planes of bending, which, in buildings with frames arranged in two orthogonal directions, are defined by these two directions. It should be satisfied for both directions (positive and negative) of action of the beam moments around the joint, with the column moments always opposing the beam moments. If the structural system is a frame or equivalent to a frame in only one of the two main horizontal directions of the structural system, then expression (4.29) should be satisfied just within the vertical plane through that direction.

(6) The rules of (4) and (5) of this subclause are waived at the top level of multi-storey buildings.

(7) Capacity design rules to avoid brittle failure modes are given in Sections 5 to 7.

4.4.2.4 Equilibrium condition

(1)P The building structure shall be stable – including overturning or sliding – in the seismic design situation specified in EN 1990:2002, 6.4.3.4.

(2) In special cases the equilibrium may be verified by means of energy balance methods, or by geometrically non-linear methods with the seismic action defined as described in 3.2.3.1.

4.4.2.5 Resistance of horizontal diaphragms

(1)P Diaphragms and bracings in horizontal planes shall be able to transmit, with sufficient overstrength, the effects of the design seismic action to the various lateral load-resisting systems to which they are connected.

(2) The requirement specified in (1)P of this clause is considered to be satisfied if for the relevant resistance verifications the seismic action effects in the diaphragm obtained from the analysis are multiplied by an overstrength factor γ_d greater than 1,0.

NOTE The values to be ascribed to γ_d for use in a country may be found in its National Annex. The recommended value for brittle failure modes, such as in shear in concrete diaphragms is 1,3, and for ductile failure modes is 1,1.

Table NA.1, 4.4.2.5(2) UK decision
Use the recommended values.

4.4.2.6 Resistance of foundations

(1)P The foundation system shall conform to EN 1998-5:2004, Section 5 and to EN 1997-1:2004.

(2)P The action effects for the foundation elements shall be derived on the basis of capacity design considerations accounting for the development of possible overstrength, but they need not exceed the action effects corresponding to the response of the structure under the seismic design situation inherent to the assumption of an elastic behaviour (q = 1,0).

(3) If the action effects for the foundation have been determined using the value of the behaviour factor q applicable to low-dissipative structures (see 2.2.2(2)), no capacity design considerations in accordance with (2)P are required.

4.4.2.7 Seismic joint condition

(1)P Buildings shall be protected from earthquake-induced pounding from adjacent structures or between structurally independent units of the same building.

4.4.3 Damage limitation

4.4.3.1 General

(1) The "damage limitation requirement" is considered to have been satisfied, if, under a seismic action having a larger probability of occurrence than the design seismic action corresponding to the no-collapse requirement in accordance with 2.1(1)P and 3.2.1(3), the interstorey drifts are limited in accordance with 4.4.3.2.

(2) Additional damage limitation verification might be required in the case of buildings important for civil protection or containing sensitive equipment.

4.4.3.2 Limitation of interstorey drift

(1) Unless otherwise specified in Sections 5 to 9, the following limits shall be observed:

a) for buildings having non-structural elements of brittle materials attached to the structure:

$$d_r \nu \leq 0,005\, h; \tag{4.31}$$

b) for buildings having ductile non-structural elements:

$$d_r \nu \leq 0,0075\, h; \tag{4.32}$$

c) for buildings having non-structural elements fixed in a way so as not to interfere with structural deformations, or without non-structural elements:

$$d_r \nu \leq 0,010\, h \tag{4.33}$$

where

d_r is the design interstorey drift as defined in 4.4.2.2 (2);
h is the storey height;
ν is the reduction factor which takes into account the lower return period of the seismic action associated with the damage limitation requirement.

(2) The value of the reduction factor ν may also depend on the importance class of the building. Implicit in its use is the assumption that the elastic response spectrum of the seismic action under which the "damage limitation requirement" should be met (see 3.2.2.1(1)P) has the same shape as the elastic response spectrum of the design seismic action corresponding to the "AC1 no-collapse requirement AC1" in accordance with 2.1(1)P and 3.2.1(3).

NOTE The values to be ascribed to ν for use in a country may be found in its National Annex. The recommended values are ν=0,4 for importance classes III and IV and ν= 0,5 for importance classes I and II.

Table NA.1, 4.4.3.2(2) UK decision

In consequence class CC3 buildings, storey drifts should be checked against the specified limits using the recommended values of reduction factor ν.

5 Specific rules for concrete buildings

5.2 Design concepts

5.2.1 Energy dissipation capacity and ductility classes

(1)P The design of earthquake resistant concrete buildings shall provide the structure with an adequate energy dissipation capacity without substantial reduction of its overall resistance against horizontal and vertical loading. To this end, the requirements and criteria of Section 2 apply. In the seismic design situation, adequate resistance of all structural elements shall be provided and non-linear deformations in critical regions should be commensurate with the overall ductility assumed in calculations.

(2)P Concrete buildings may alternatively be designed for low dissipation capacity and low ductility, by applying only the rules of EN 1992-1-1:2004 for the seismic design situation, and neglecting the specific provisions given in this clause, provided the requirements set forth in 5.3 are met. For buildings which are not base-isolated (see Section 10), design with this alternative, termed ductility class L (low), is recommended only in low seismicity cases (see 3.2.1(4)).

(3)P Earthquake resistant concrete buildings other than those to which (2)P of this clause applies, shall be designed to provide energy dissipation capacity and an overall ductile behaviour. Overall ductile behaviour is ensured if the ductility demand involves globally a large volume of the structure spread to different elements and locations of all its storeys. To this end ductile modes of failure (e.g. flexure) should precede brittle failure modes (e.g. shear) with sufficient reliability.

(4)P Concrete buildings designed in accordance with (3)P of this clause, are classified in two ductility classes DCM (medium ductility) and DCH (high ductility), depending on the hysteretic dissipation capacity. Both classes correspond to buildings designed, dimensioned and detailed in accordance with specific earthquake resistant provisions, enabling the structure to develop stable mechanisms associated with large dissipation of hysteretic energy under repeated reversed loading, without suffering brittle failures.

(5)P To provide the appropriate amount of ductility in ductility classes M and H, specific provisions for all structural elements shall be satisfied in each class (see 5.4 - 5.6). In correspondence with the different available ductility in the two ductility classes, different values of the behaviour factor q are used for each class (see 5.2.2.2).

NOTE Geographical limitations on the use of ductility classes M and H in a country may be found in its National Annex.

Table NA.1, 5.2.1(5) UK decision

There are no geographical limitations.

In DCM and DCH concrete buildings the behaviour factor q (see 5.2.2 of EN 1998-1) is linked, directly or indirectly, to the ductility demands on members and connections, hence to the corresponding design criteria (see 5.2.3.2 to 5.2.3.7 of EN 1998-1). The latter are deemed satisfied if the design and detailing rules of 5.4 to 5.7 of EN 1998-1 are observed.

5.3 Design to EN 1992-1-1

5.3.1 General

(1) Seismic design for low ductility (ductility class L), following EN 1992-1-1:2004 without any additional requirements other than those of 5.3.2, is recommended only for low seismicity cases (see 3.2.1(4)).

5.3.2 Materials

(1)P In primary seismic elements (see 4.2.2), reinforcing steel of class B or C of EN 1992-1-1:2004, Table C.1 shall be used.

5.3.3 Behaviour factor

(1) A behaviour factor q of up to 1,5 may be used in deriving the seismic actions, regardless of the structural system and the regularity in elevation.

6 Specific rules for steel buildings

6.1.2 Design concepts

(1)P Earthquake resistant steel buildings shall be designed according to one of the following concepts (see Table 6.1):

- Concept a) Low-dissipative structural behaviour;
- Concept b) Dissipative structural behaviour.

Table 6.1 — Design concepts, structural ductility classes and range of reference values of the behaviour factors

Design concept	Structural ductility class	Range of the reference values of the behaviour factor q
Concept a) Low dissipative structural behaviour	DCL (Low)	≤ 1,5 - 2
Concept b) Dissipative structural behaviour	DCM (Medium)	≤ 4 also limited by the values of Table 6.2
	DCH (High)	only limited by the values of Table 6.2

NOTE 1 The value ascribed to the upper limit of q for low dissipative behaviour, within the range of Table 6.1, for use in a country may be found in its National Annex. The recommended value of the upper limit of q for low-dissipative behaviour is 1,5.

NOTE 2 The National Annex of a particular country may give limitations on the choice of the design concept and of the ductility class which are permissible within that country.

Table NA.1, 6.1.2(1) UK decision

Upper limit of q for low-dissipative structural behaviour concept is 2. Further guidance is given in PD 6698.

No limitations on structural behaviour concept. Further guidance is given in PD 6698.

No geographical limitations. Further guidance is given in PD 6698.

(2) P In concept a) the action effects may be calculated on the basis of an elastic global analysis without taking into account a significant non-linear material behaviour. When using the design spectrum defined in 3.2.2.5, the reference value of the behaviour factor q may be taken between 1,5 and 2 (see Note 1 to (1) of this clause). In the case of irregularity in elevation the behaviour factor q should be corrected as indicated in 4.2.3.1(7) but it need not be taken as being smaller than 1,5.

(3) In concept a), if the upper limit of the reference value of q is taken as being larger than 1,5, the primary seismic members of the structure should be of cross-sectional classes 1, 2 or 3.

(4) In concept a), the resistance of the members and of the connections should be evaluated according to EN 1993 without any additional requirements. For buildings which are not seismically isolated (see Section 10), design in accordance with concept a) is recommended only for low seismicity cases (see 3.2.1(4)).

(5)P In concept b) the capability of parts of the structure (dissipative zones) to resist earthquake actions through inelastic behaviour is taken into account. When using the design spectrum defined in 3.2.2.5, the reference value of behaviour factor q may be taken as being greater than the upper limit value established in Table 6.1 and in Note 1 to (1) of this clause for low dissipative structural behaviour. The upper limit value of q depends on the Ductility Class and the structural type (see 6.3). When adopting this concept b), the requirements given in 6.2 to 6.11 should be fulfilled.

(6)P Structures designed to concept b) shall belong to structural ductility classes DCM or DCH. These classes correspond to increased ability of the structure to dissipate energy in plastic mechanisms. Depending on the ductility class, specific requirements in one or more of the following aspects shall be met: class of steel sections and rotational capacity of connections.

In DCM and DCH steel buildings the behaviour factor q (see EN 1998-1, 6.3) is linked, directly or indirectly, to the ductility demands on members and connections, hence to the corresponding design criteria and/or detailing rules (see EN 1998-1, 6.5 to 6.10).

7 Specific rules for composite steel-concrete buildings

7.1.2 Design concepts

(1)P Earthquake resistant composite buildings shall be designed according to one of the following concepts (see Table 7.1):

- Concept a) Low-dissipative structural behaviour;
- Concept b) Dissipative structural behaviour with composite dissipative zones;
- Concept c) Dissipative structural behaviour with steel dissipative zones.

Table 7.1 — Design concepts, structural ductility classes and range of reference values of the behaviour factors

Design concept	Structural ductility class	Range of the reference values of the behaviour factor q
Concept a) Low-dissipative structural behaviour	DCL (Low)	≤ 1,5 - 2
Concepts b) or c) Dissipative structural behaviour	DCM (Medium)	≤ 4 also limited by the values of Table 7.2
	DCH (High)	only limited by the values of Table 7.2

NOTE 1 The value ascribed to the upper limit of q for low dissipative behaviour, within the range of Table 7.1, for use in a country may be found in its National Annex to this document. The recommended value of the upper limit of q for low-dissipative behaviour is 1,5.

NOTE 2 The National Annex of a particular country may give limitations on the choice of the design concept and of the ductility class which are permissible within that country.

Table NA.1, 7.1.2(1) UK decision

Use the value of 2 for the upper limit of q for low-dissipative structural behaviour concept.

There are no limitations on structural behaviour concept and no geographical limitations.

(2)P In concept a), the action effects may be calculated on the basis of an elastic analysis without taking into account non-linear material behaviour but considering the reduction in the moment of inertia due to the cracking of concrete in part of the beam spans, in accordance with the general structural analysis rules defined in 7.4 and to the specific rules defined in 7.7 to 7.11 related to each structural type. When using the design spectrum defined in 3.2.2.5, the upper limit of the reference value of the behaviour factor q is taken as being between 1,5 and 2 (see Note 1 to (1) of this clause). In case of irregularity in elevation the upper limit value of the behaviour factor q should be corrected as indicated in 4.2.3.1(7) but it need not be taken as being smaller than 1,5.

(3) In concept a) the resistance of the members and of the connections should be evaluated in accordance with EN 1993 and EN 1994 without any additional requirements. For buildings which are not base-isolated (see Section 10), design to concept a) is recommended only for low seismicity cases (see 3.2.1(4)).

(4) In concepts b) and c), the capability of parts of the structure (dissipative zones) to resist earthquake actions through inelastic behaviour is taken into account. When using the design response spectrum defined in 3.2.2.5, the upper limit of the reference value of the behaviour factor q is taken as being greater than the upper value established in Table 7.1 and in Note 1 to (1) of this clause for low dissipative structural behaviour. The upper limit value of q depends on the ductility class and the structural type (see **7.3**). When adopting concepts b) or c) the requirements given in 7.2 to 7.12 should be fulfilled.

(5)P In concept c), structures are not meant to take advantage of composite behaviour in dissipative zones; the application of concept c) is conditioned by a strict compliance to measures that prevent involvement of the concrete in the resistance of dissipative zones. In concept c) the composite structure is designed in accordance with EN 1994-1:2004 under non-seismic loads and in accordance with Section 6 to resist earthquake action. The measures preventing involvement of the concrete are given in 7.7.5.

(6)P The design rules for dissipative composite structures (concept b) aim at the development of reliable local plastic mechanisms (dissipative zones) in the structure and of a reliable global plastic mechanism dissipating as much energy as possible under the design earthquake action. For each structural element or each structural type considered in this Section, rules allowing this general design objective to be achieved are given in 7.5 to 7.11 with reference to what is called the specific criteria. These criteria aim at the development of a global mechanical behaviour for which design provisions can be given.

(7)P Structures designed in accordance with concept b), shall belong to structural ductility classes DCM and DCH. These classes correspond to an increased ability of the structure to dissipate energy through plastic mechanisms. A structure belonging to a given ductility class shall meet specific requirements in one or more of the following aspects: class of steel sections, rotational capacity of connections and detailing.

In DCM and DCH buildings the behaviour factor q (see 7.3) is linked, directly or indirectly, to the ductility demands on members and connections, hence to the corresponding design criteria and/or detailing rules (see 7.5 to 7.11).

8 Specific rules for timber buildings

8.1.3 Design concepts

(1)P Earthquake-resistant timber buildings shall be designed in accordance with one of the following concepts:

a) dissipative structural behaviour;

b) low-dissipative structural behaviour.

(2) In concept a) the capability of parts of the structure (dissipative zones) to resist earthquake actions out of their elastic range is taken into account. When using the design spectrum defined in 3.2.2.5, the behaviour factor q is taken as being greater than 1,5. The value of q depends on the ductility class (see 8.3).

(3)P Structures designed in accordance with concept a) shall belong to structural ductility classes M or H. A structure belonging to a given ductility class shall meet specific requirements in one or more of the following aspects: structural type, type and rotational ductility capacity of connections.

(4)P Dissipative zones shall be located in joints and connections, whereas the timber members themselves shall be regarded as behaving elastically.

(5) The properties of dissipative zones shall be determined by tests either on single joints, on whole structures or on parts thereof in accordance with prEN 12512.

(6) In concept b) the action effects are calculated on the basis of an elastic global analysis without taking into account non-linear material behaviour. When using the design spectrum defined in 3.2.2.5, the behaviour factor q should not be taken greater than 1,5. The resistance of the members and connections should be [AC1) calculated in accordance with EN 1995-1-1:2004 (AC1] without any additional requirements. This concept is termed ductility class L (low) and is appropriate only for certain structural types (see Table 8.1).

8.3 Ductility classes and behaviour factors

(1)P Depending on their ductile behaviour and energy dissipation capacity under seismic actions, timber buildings shall be assigned to one of the three ductility classes L, M or H as given in Table 8.1, where the corresponding limit values of the behaviour factors are also given.

NOTE Geographical limitations on the use of ductility classes M and H in a country may be found in its National Annex.

Table NA.1, 8.3(1) UK decision

No geographical limits.

(2) If the building is non-regular in elevation (see 4.2.3.3) the q values listed in Table 8.1 should be reduced by 20 % but need not be taken less than q = 1,5 (see 4.2.3.1(7) and Table 4.1).

In DCM and DCH timber buildings the behaviour factor q (see 8.3) is linked to the ductility demands on members and connections, hence to the corresponding detailing rules (see 8.5).

Table 8.1 — Design concept, structural types and behaviour factors for the three ductility classes.

Design concept and ductility class	q	Examples of structures
Low capacity to dissipate energy - DCL	1,5	Cantilevers; beams; arches with two or three pinned joints; trusses joined with connectors.
Medium capacity to dissipate energy - DCM	2	Glued wall panels with glued diaphragms, connected with nails and bolts; trusses with dowelled and bolted joints; mixed structures consisting of timber framing (resisting the horizontal forces) and non-load bearing infill.
	2,5	Hyperstatic portal frames with dowelled and bolted joints (see 8.1.3(3)P).
High capacity to dissipate energy - DCH	3	Nailed wall panels with glued diaphragms, connected with nails and bolts; trusses with nailed joints.
	4	Hyperstatic portal frames with dowelled and bolted joints (see 8.1.3(3)P).
	5	Nailed wall panels with nailed diaphragms, connected with nails and bolts.

9 Specific rules for masonry buildings

9.2 Materials and bonding patterns

9.2.1 Types of masonry units

(1) Masonry units should have sufficient robustness in order to avoid local brittle failure.

NOTE The National Annex may select the type of masonry units from EN 1996-1:2004 Table 3.1 that satisfy (1).

Table NA.1, 9.2.1(1) UK decision
Any type of masonry unit listed in BS EN 1996-1-1:2005, Table 3.1, is acceptable.

9.2.2 Minimum strength of masonry units

(1) Except in cases of low seismicity, the normalised compressive strength of masonry units, derived in accordance with EN 772-1, should be not less than the minimum values as follows:

- normal to the bed face: $f_{b,min}$;
- parallel to the bed face in the plane of the wall: $f_{bh,min}$.

NOTE The values ascribed to $f_{b,min}$ and $f_{b,min}$ for use in a country may be found in its National Annex. The recommended values are $f_{b,min}$ = 5 N/mm^2 and $f_{bh,min}$ = 2 N/mm^2.

Table NA.1, 9.2.2(1) UK decision
Use the minimum values given in BS EN 1996-1-1:2005.

9.2.3 Mortar

(1) A minimum strength is required for mortar, $f_{m,min}$ which generally exceeds the minimum specified in EN 1996.

NOTE The value ascribed to $f_{m,min}$ for use in a country may be found in its National Annex. The recommended value is $f_{m,min}$ = 5 N/mm^2 for unreinforced or confined masonry and $f_{m,min}$ = 10 N/mm^2 for reinforced masonry.

Table NA.1, 9.2.3(1) UK decision
Use the minimum values given in BS EN 1996-1-1:2005.

9.2.4 Masonry bond

(1) There are three alternative classes of perpend joints:

a) joints fully grouted with mortar;

b) ungrouted joints;

c) ungrouted joints with mechanical interlocking between masonry units.

NOTE The National Annex will specify which ones among the three classes above will be allowed to be used in a country or parts of the country.

Table NA.1, 9.2.4(1) UK decision
Perpend joints fully grouted with mortar or ungrouted joints with mechanical interlocking between masonry units may be used. Ungrouted joints without mechanical interlock may only be used subject to appropriate validation.

9.3 Types of construction and behaviour factors

(1) Depending on the masonry type used for the seismic resistant elements, masonry buildings should be assigned to one of the following types of construction:

a) unreinforced masonry construction;

b) confined masonry construction;

c) reinforced masonry construction;

NOTE 1 Construction with masonry systems which provide an enhanced ductility of the structure is also included (see Note 2 to Table 9.1).

NOTE 2 Frames with infill masonry are not covered in this section.

(2) Due to its low tensile strength and low ductility, unreinforced masonry that follows the provisions of EN 1996 alone is considered to offer low-dissipation capacity (DCL) and its use should be limited, provided that the effective thickness of walls, t_{ef}, is not less than a minimum value, $t_{ef,min}$.

NOTE 1 The conditions under which unreinforced masonry that follows the provisions of EN 1996 alone may be used in a country may be found in its National Annex. Such use is recommended only in low seismicity cases (see 3.2.1(4))

NOTE 2 The value ascribed to $t_{ef,min}$ for use in a country of unreinforced masonry that follows the provisions of EN 1996 alone may be found in its National Annex. The recommended values of $t_{ef,min}$ are those in the second column, and second and third rows of Table 9.2.

Table NA.1, 9.3(2) UK decision
There are no restrictions on the use of unreinforced masonry that follows the provisions of BS EN 1996-1:2005 alone.
$t_{ef,min}$ = 170 mm

(3) For the reasons noted in (2) of this clause, unreinforced masonry satisfying the provisions of the present Eurocode may not be used if the value of $a_g \cdot S$ exceeds a certain limit, $a_{g,urm}$.

NOTE The value ascribed to $a_{g,urm}$ for use in a country may be found in its National Annex . This value should not be less than that corresponding to the threshold for the low seismicity cases. The value ascribed to $a_{g,urm}$ should be consistent with the values adopted for the minimum strength of masonry units, $f_{b,min}$, $f_{bh,min}$ and of mortar, $f_{m,min}$. For the values recommended in the Notes to 9.2.2 and 9.2.3, the recommended value of $a_{g,urm}$ is 0,20 g.

Table NA.1, 9.3(3) UK decision
$a_{g,urm}$ = 0,25 g

(4) For types a) to c) ranges of permissible values of the upper limit of the behaviour factor q are given in Table 9.1.

Table 9.1 — Types of construction and behaviour factor

Type of construction	Behaviour factor q
Unreinforced masonry according to EN 1996 alone (recommended only for low seismicity cases).	1,5
Unreinforced masonry according to EN 1998-1	1,5 - 2,5
Confined masonry	2,0 – 3,0
Reinforced masonry	2,5 - 3,0

NOTE 1 The upper limit values ascribed to q for use in a country (within the ranges of Table 9.1) may be found in its National Annex. The recommended values of q are the lower limits of the ranges in Table 9.1.

NOTE 2 For buildings constructed with masonry systems which provide an enhanced ductility of the structure, specific values of the behaviour factor q may be used, provided that the system and the related values for q are verified experimentally. The values ascribed to q for use in a country for such buildings may be found [AC1) in its National Annex of this document (AC1].

Table NA.1, 9.3(4) UK decision

Unreinforced masonry in accordance with BS EN 1998-1: $q = 2,0$

Confined masonry: $q = 2,5$

Reinforced masonry: $q = 3,0$

The behaviour factor q above is linked to the ductility demands on masonry elements and connections, hence to the corresponding design criteria and/or construction rules (see 9.5 and 9.7).

10 Base isolation

10.1 Scope

(1)P This section covers the design of seismically isolated structures in which the isolation system, located below the main mass of the structure, aims at reducing the seismic response of the lateral-force resisting system.

(2) The reduction of the seismic response of the lateral-force resisting system may be obtained by increasing the fundamental period of the seismically isolated structure, by modifying the shape of the fundamental mode and by increasing the damping, or by a combination of these effects. The isolation system may consist of linear or non-linear springs and/or dampers.

(3) Specific rules concerning base isolation of buildings are given in this Section.

10.3 Fundamental requirements

(1)P The fundamental requirements in 2.1 and in the corresponding Parts of this Eurocode, according to the type of structure considered, shall be satisfied.

(2)P Increased reliability is required for the isolating devices. This shall be effected by applying a magnification factor γ_x on seismic displacements of each unit.

NOTE The value to be ascribed to γ_x for use in a country may be found in its National Annex, depending on the type of isolating device used. For buildings the recommended value is γ_x =1,2.

Table NA.1, 10.3(2) UK decision

γ_x = 1,5 for buildings.

The criteria for the seismic design of base-isolated structures are the same as the criteria for the seismic design of non-isolated structures i.e. collapse limitation for the design earthquake and damage limitation for the serviceability earthquake, with the same drift limits.

Bibliography

Standards publications

BS EN 1993-1-10:2005, *Eurocode 3 – Design of steel structures – Part 1-10: Material toughness and through-thickness properties*

BS EN 1996-1-1:2005, *Eurocode 6 – Design of masonry structures – Part 1-1: General rules for reinforced and unreinforced masonry structures*

BS EN 1998-1:2004, *Eurocode 8 – Design of structures for earthquake resistance – Part 1: General rules, seismic actions and rules for buildings*

PD 6698:2008, *Background paper to the UK National Annexes to BS EN 1998-1, BS EN 1998-2, BS EN 1998-4, BS EN 1998-5 and BS EN 1998-6*

Other publications

[1] Institution of Structural Engineers: *Manual for the seismic design of steel and concrete buildings to Eurocode 8*, London: publication expected 2008.

Useful references

A Elghazouli, *Seismic Design of Buildings to Eurocode 8*, ISBN 978 0 415 44762-1, Taylor and Francis (2009)

M Fardis, *Seismic Design, Assessment and Retrofitting of Concrete Buildings based on Eurocode 8*, ISBN: 978 1 4020 9841 3, Springer (2009)

M Fardis, E Carvalho, A Alnashai, E Faccioli, P Pinto and A Plumier, *Designers' Guide to EN 1998-1 and EN 1998-5, Eurocode 8: Design of structures for earthquake resistance – General rules, seismic actions, design rules for buildings, foundations and retaining structures*, ISBN: 0 7277 3348 6, Thomas Telford (2005)

Chapter 9 – Extracts from Eurocode 9: Design of aluminium structures

The extracts in this chapter are taken from EN 1999-1-1:2007+A1:2010: *Eurocode 9: Design of aluminium structures — Part 1-1: General structural rules* and from the National Annex to *Eurocode 9*. The text of EN 1999-1-1:2007 altered by CEN amendment A1 is indicated by [A1) (A1].

The National Annex extracts are taken from *UK National Annex to Eurocode 9: Design of aluminium structures – Part 1-1: General structural rules.*

The full list of the contents of BS EN 1999 follows and is given for reference purposes. (Bold items are covered in this chapter.)

5 Structural analysis
5.1 Structural modelling for analysis
5.1.1 Structural modelling and basic assumptions
5.1.2 Joint modelling
5.1.3 Ground-structure interaction
5.2 Global analysis
5.2.1 Effects of deformed geometry of the structure
5.2.2 Structural stability of frames
5.3 Imperfections
5.3.1 Basis
5.3.2 Imperfections for global analysis of frames
5.3.3 Imperfection for analysis of bracing systems
5.3.4 Member imperfections
5.4 Methods of analysis
5.4.1 General
5.4.2 Elastic global analysis
5.4.3 Plastic global analysis
6 Ultimate limit states for members
6.1 Basis
6.1.1 General
6.1.2 Characteristic value of strength
6.1.3 Partial safety factors
6.1.4 Classification of cross-sections
6.1.5 Local buckling resistance
6.1.6 HAZ softening adjacent to welds
6.2 Resistance of cross-sections
6.2.1 General
6.2.2 Section properties
6.2.3 Tension
6.2.4 Compression
6.2.5 Bending moment
6.2.6 Shear
6.2.7 Torsion
6.2.8 Bending and shear
6.2.9 Bending and axial force
6.2.10 Bending, shear and axial force
6.2.11 Web bearing
6.3 Buckling resistance of members
6.3.1 Members in compression
6.3.2 Members in bending
6.3.3 Members in bending and axial compression
6.4 Uniformed built-up members
6.4.1 General
6.4.2 Laced compression members
6.4.3 Battened compression members
6.4.4 Closely spaced built-up members
6.5 Un-stiffened plates under in-plane loading
6.5.1 General
6.5.2 Resistance under uniform compression
6.5.3 Resistance under in-plane moment
6.5.4 Resistance under transverse or longitudinal stress gradient
6.5.5 Resistance under shear
6.5.6 Resistance under combined action
6.6 Stiffened plates under in-plane loading
6.6.1 General
6.6.2 Stiffened plates under uniform compression
6.6.3 Stiffened plates under in-plane moment
6.6.4 Longitudinal stress gradient on multi-stiffened plates
6.6.5 Multi-stiffened plating in shear
6.6.6 Buckling load for orthotropic plates

1 General

1.1 Scope

1.1.1 Scope of EN 1999

(1)P EN 1999 applies to the design of buildings and civil engineering and structural works in aluminium. It complies with the principles and requirements for the safety and serviceability of structures, the basis of their design and verification that are given in EN 1990 – Basis of structural design.

(2) EN 1999 is only concerned with requirements for resistance, serviceability, durability and fire resistance of aluminium structures. Other requirements, e.g. concerning thermal or sound insulation, are not considered.

(3) EN 1999 is intended to be used in conjunction with:

- EN 1990 "Basis of structural design"
- EN 1991 "Actions on structures"
- European Standards for construction products relevant for aluminium structures
- EN 1090-1: Execution of steel structures and aluminium structures – Part 1: Requirements for conformity assessment of structural components
- EN 1090-3: Execution of steel structures and aluminium structures – Part 3: Technical requirements for aluminium structures

(4) EN 1999 is subdivided in five parts:

EN 1999-1-1 Design of Aluminium Structures: General structural rules.
EN 1999-1-2 Design of Aluminium Structures: Structural fire design.
EN 1999-1-3 Design of Aluminium Structures: Structures susceptible to fatigue.
EN 1999-1-4 Design of Aluminium Structures: Cold-formed structural sheeting.
EN 1999-1-5 Design of Aluminium Structures: Shell structures.

EN 1999 includes the principles necessary to design aluminium structures. The requirements in the code include information to ensure overall stability and strength of structures and individual elements, data to ensure structures are serviceable through their design life and how to ensure the material is durable. The code uses limit state design in conjunction with partial factors. For the design of new structures, EN 1999 should be used together with ENs 1990, 1991 and possibly ENs 1997 and 1998. When aluminium elements are used in structures which include other materials, then the code can be used in conjunction with ENs 1992 (concrete), 1993 (steel), 1994 (composite steel and concrete), 1995 (timber) and 1996 (masonry).

EN 1999-1-1 is intended for use by:

- committees drafting standards for structural design and related product, testing and execution standards;
- clients (e. g. for the formulation of their specific requirements on reliability levels and durability);
- designers and contractors; relevant authorities.

1.1.2 Scope of EN 1999-1-1

A1) (1) EN 1999-1-1 gives basic design rules for structures made of wrought aluminium alloys and limited guidance for cast alloys (see section 3 and Annex C). (A1

NOTE Minimum material thickness may be defined in the National Annex. The following limits are recommended – if not otherwise explicitly stated in this standard:

- components with material thickness not less than 0,6 mm;
- welded components with material thickness not less than 1,5 mm;
- connections with:
  - steel bolts and pins with diameter not less than 5 mm;
  - aluminium bolts and pins with diameter not less than 8 mm;
  - rivets and thread forming screws with diameter not less than 4,2 mm

(2) The following subjects are dealt with in EN 1999-1-1:

Section 1: General
Section 2: Basis of design
Section 3: Materials
Section 4: Durability
Section 5: Structural analysis
Section 6: Ultimate limit states for members
Section 7: Serviceability limit states
Section 8: Design of joints
Annex A Execution classes
Annex B Equivalent T-stub in tension
Annex C Materials selection
Annex D Corrosion and surface protection
Annex E Analytical models for stress strain relationship
Annex F Behaviour of cross section beyond elastic limit
Annex G Rotation capacity
Annex H Plastic hinge method for continuous beams
Annex I Lateral torsional buckling of beams and torsional or flexural-torsional buckling of compression members
Annex J Properties of cross sections
Annex K Shear lag effects in member design
Annex L Classification of connections
Annex M Adhesive bonded connections

(3) Sections 1 to 2 provide additional clauses to those given in EN 1990 "Basis of structural design".

(4) Section 3 deals with material properties of products made of structural aluminium alloys.

(5) Section 4 gives general rules for durability.

(6) Section 5 refers to the structural analysis of structures, in which the members can be modelled with sufficient accuracy as line elements for global analysis.

(7) Section 6 gives detailed rules for the design of cross sections and members.

(8) Section 7 gives rules for serviceability.

(9) Section 8 gives detail rules for connections subject to static loading: bolted, riveted, welded and adhesive bonded connections.

EN 1999-1-1 provides design guidance for wrought aluminium structures, but with limited additional information on cast aluminium alloys but unlike the British Standards which include design guidance on structural elements, EN 1999-1-1 only indicates the principles of design, leaving others to deliver more specific information which could be used directly by design offices.

Scope of part 1-2 of Eurocode 9

This part deals with the design of aluminium structures for the accidental situation of fire exposure. The approach is to adjust the design resistance of elements to take account of their exposure to fire for a particular length of time as set out in EN 1991-1-1 which takes into account the properties of aluminium at elevated temperatures. The design actions are also adjusted for the fire situation (it is unlikely full design loads will exist during a serious fire) in accordance with EN 1991-1-2. Only passive methods of fire protection are considered – active methods are not covered. The code sets out to limit premature collapse of a structure and to limit the spread of fire.

Scope of part 1-3 of Eurocode 9

This part gives the basis for the design of aluminium alloy structures with respect to the limit state of fracture induced by fatigue. The part suggests designers use one of three approaches: a safe life design approach which is a conservative desk top approach, damage tolerant design in which regular inspections of a structure (or element) enable fatigue to be managed in a confident way or thirdly, fatigue design based on the results of testing. The fatigue design presented in this part is not for use in pressurised pipes or vessels.

Scope of part 1-4 of Eurocode 9

Part 1-4 of the code examines cold-formed structural sheeting in aluminium. The rules in this part complement those elsewhere in EN 1999-1 and give the design requirements for cold-formed aluminium sheeting manufactured from hot rolled or cold rolled sheet or strip that has then been cold-formed by such processes as cold-rolled forming or press-breaking. Additional guidance is included to enable the design of stressed-skin elements using aluminium sheeting as a structural diaphragm, but specifically excludes cold-formed C or Z aluminium profiles, and cold formed and welded circular or rectangular hollow sections. Methods are included for design by calculation and for design assisted by testing.

Scope of part 1-5 of Eurocode 9

EN 1999-1-5 applies to the structural design of aluminium structures, stiffened and unstiffened, that have the form of a shell of revolution or of a round panel in monocoque structures. Design of these structures should be undertaken in accordance with the relevant parts of EN 1999 and with cognizance of supplementary information on shells given in EN 1993-1-6 and the relevant application parts. The provisions in EN 1999-1-5 apply to axisymmetric shells (cylinders, cones, spheres) and associated circular or annular plates and beam section rings and stringer stiffeners where they form part of the complete structure.

Scope of National annexes to parts 1-1, 1-2, 1-3, 1-4 and 1-5

These provide UK decisions on Nationally Determined Parameters, UK decisions on the status of EN 1999 informative annexes; and references to non-contradictory complementary information.

1.5 Terms and definitions

(1) The definitions in EN 1990 1.5 apply.

(2) The following terms are used in EN 1999-1-1 with the following definitions:

1.5.1
frame
the whole or a portion of a structure, comprising an assembly of directly connected structural members, designed to act together to resist load; this term refers to both moment-resisting frames and triangulated frames; it covers both plane frames and three-dimensional frames

1.5.2
sub-frame
a frame that forms part of a larger frame, but is be treated as an isolated frame in a structural analysis

1.5.3
type of framing
terms used to distinguish between frames that are either:

- **semi-continuous**, in which the structural properties of the members and connections need explicit consideration in the global analysis
- **continuous**, in which only the structural properties of the members need be considered in the global analysis
- **simple**, in which the joints are not required to resist moments

1.5.4
global analysis
the determination of a consistent set of internal forces and moments in a structure, which are in equilibrium with a particular set of actions on the structure

1.5.5
system length
distance in a given plane between two adjacent points at which a member is braced against lateral displacement, or between one such point and the end of the member

1.5.6
buckling length
length of an equivalent uniform member with pinned ends, which has the same cross-section and the same elastic critical force as the verified uniform member (individual or as a component of a frame structure)

1.5.7
shear lag effect
non uniform stress distribution in wide flanges due to shear deformations; it is taken into account by using a reduced "effective" flange width in safety assessments

1.5.8
capacity design
design based on the plastic deformation capacity of a member and its connections providing additional strength in its connections and in other parts connected to the member

1.6 Symbols

(1) For the purpose of this standard the following apply.

Additional symbols are defined where they first occur.

NOTE Symbols are ordered by appearance in EN 1999-1-1. Symbols may have various meanings.

Section 1 General

x – x axis along a member
y – y axis of a cross-section
z – z axis of a cross-section
u – u major principal axis (where this does not coincide with the y-y axis)
v – v minor principal axis (where this does not coincide with the z-z axis)

Section 2 Basis of design

P_k nominal value of the effect of prestressing imposed during erection
G_k nominal value of the effect of permanent actions
X_k characteristic values of material property

X_n nominal values of material property
R_d design value of resistance
R_k characteristic value of resistance
γ_M general partial factor
γ_{Mi} particular partial factor
γ_{Mf} partial factor for fatigue
η conversion factor
a_d design value of geometrical data

Section 3 Materials

f_o characteristic value of 0,2 % proof strength
f_u characteristic value of ultimate tensile strength
f_{oc} characteristic value of 0,2 % proof strength of cast material
f_{uc} characteristic value of ultimate tensile strength of cast material
A_{50} elongation value measured with a constant ref. length of 50 mm, see EN 10 002
$A = A_{5,65\sqrt{A_0}}$ elongation value measured with a reference length $5,65\sqrt{A_0}$, see EN 10 002
A_0 original cross-section area of test specimen
$f_{o,haz}$ 0,2 % proof strength in heat affected zone, HAZ
$f_{u,haz}$ ultimate tensile strength in heat affected zone, HAZ
$\rho_{o,haz}$ $= f_{o,haz} / f_o$ ratio between 0,2 % proof strength in HAZ and in parent material
$\rho_{u,haz}$ $= f_{u,haz} / f_u$ ratio between ultimate strength in HAZ and in parent material
BC buckling class
n_p exponent in Ramberg-Osgood expression for plastic design
E modulus of elasticity
G shear modulus
v Poisson's ratio in elastic stage
α coefficient of linear thermal expansion
ρ unit mass

Section 5 Structural analysis

α_{cr} factor by which the design loads would have to be increased to cause elastic instability in a global mode
F_{Ed} design loading on the structure
F_{cr} elastic critical buckling load for global instability mode based on initial elastic stiffness
H_{Ed} design value of the horizontal reaction at the bottom of the storey to the horizontal loads and fictitious horizontal loads
V_{Ed} total design vertical load on the structure on the bottom of the storey
$\delta_{H,Ed}$ horizontal displacement at the top of the storey, relative to the bottom of the storey
h storey height, height of the structure
$\bar{\lambda}$ non dimensional slenderness
N_{Ed} design value of the axial force
ϕ global initial sway imperfection
ϕ_0 basic value for global initial sway imperfection
α_h reduction factor for height h applicable to columns
α_m reduction factor for the number of columns in a row
m number of columns in a row
e_0 maximum amplitude of a member imperfection
L member length
$e_{0,d}$ design value of maximum amplitude of an imperfection
M_{Rk} characteristic moment resistance of the critical cross section
N_{Rk} characteristic resistance to normal force of the critical cross section
q equivalent force per unit length
δ_q in-plane deflection of a bracing system
q_d equivalent design force per unit length
M_{Ed} design bending moment
k factor for $e_{o,d}$

Section 6 Ultimate limit states for members

γ_{M1} partial factor for resistance of cross-sections whatever the class is
γ_{M1} partial factor for resistance of members to instability assessed by member checks
γ_{M2} partial factor for resistance of cross-sections in tension to fracture
b width of cross section part

t thickness of a cross-section part
β width-to-thickness ratio b/t
η coefficient to allow for stress gradient or reinforcement of cross section part
ψ stress ratio
σ_{cr} elastic critical stress for a reinforced cross section part
σ_{cr0} elastic critical stress for an un-reinforced cross section part
R radius of curvature to the mid-thickness of material
D diameter to mid-thickness of tube material
β_1, β_2, β_3 limits for slenderness parameter
ε $= \sqrt{250 / f_o}$, coefficient
z_1 distance from neutral axis to most severely stressed fibre
z_2 distance from neutral axis to fibre under consideration
C_1, C_2 constants
ρ_c reduction factor for local buckling
b_{haz} extent of HAZ
T_1 interpass temperature
α_2 factor for b_{haz}

6.2 Resistance of cross sections

$\sigma_{x,Ed}$ design value of the local longitudinal stress
$\sigma_{y,Ed}$ design value of the local transverse stress
τ_{Ed} design value of the local shear stress
N_{Ed} design normal force
$M_{y,Ed}$ design bending moment, y-y axis
$M_{z,Ed}$ design bending moment, z-z axis
N_{Rd} design values of the resistance to normal forces
$M_{y,Rd}$ design values of the resistance to bending moments, y-y axis
$M_{z,Rd}$ design values of the resistance to bending moments, z-z axis
s staggered pitch, the spacing of the centres of two consecutive holes in the chain measured parallel to the member axis
p spacing of the centres of the same two holes measured perpendicular to the member axis
n number of holes extending in any diagonal or zig-zag line progressively across the member or part of the member
d diameter of hole
A_g area of gross cross-section
A_{net} net area of cross-section
A_{eff} effective area of cross-section
[A1) *Deleted text* (A1]
$N_{t,Rd}$ design values of the resistance to tension force
$N_{o,Rd}$ design value of resistance to general yielding of a member in tensions
$N_{u,Rd}$ design value of resistance to axial force of the net cross-section at holes for fasteners
$N_{c,Rd}$ design resistance to normal forces of the cross-section for uniform compression
M_{Rd} design resistance for bending about one principal axis of a cross-section
$M_{u,Rd}$ design resistance for bending of the net cross-section at holes
$M_{o,Rd}$ design resistance for bending to general yielding
α shape factor
W_{el} elastic modulus of the gross section (see 6.2.5.2)
W_{net} elastic modulus of the net section allowing for holes and HAZ softening, if welded
W_{pl} plastic modulus of gross section
W_{eff} effective elastic section modulus, obtained using a reduced thickness t_{eff} for the class 4 parts
$W_{el,haz}$ effective elastic modulus of the gross section, obtained using a reduced thickness $\rho_{o,haz}t$ for the HAZ material
$W_{pl,haz}$ effective plastic modulus of the gross section, obtained using a reduced thickness $\rho_{o,haz}t$ for the HAZ material
$W_{eff,haz}$ effective elastic section modulus, obtained using a reduced thickness $\rho_c t$ for the class 4 parts or a reduced thickness $\rho_{o,haz}t$ for the HAZ material, whichever is the smaller
$\alpha_{3,u}$ shape factor for class 3 cross section without welds
$\alpha_{3,w}$ shape factor for class 3 cross section with welds
V_{Ed} design shear force

V_{Rd} design shear resistance
A_v shear area
η_v factor for shear area
h_w depth of a web between flanges
t_w web thickness
A_e the section area of an un-welded section, and the effective section area obtained by taking a reduced thickness $\rho_{o,haz}t$ for the HAZ material of a welded section
T_{Ed} design value of torsional moment
T_{Rd} design St. Venant torsion moment resistance
$W_{T,pl}$ plastic torsion modulus
$T_{t,Ed}$ design value of internal St. Venant torsional moment
$T_{w,Ed}$ design value of internal warping torsional moment
$\tau_{t,Ed}$ design shear stresses due to St. Venant torsion
$\tau_{w,Ed}$ design shear stresses due to warping torsion
$\sigma_{w,Ed}$ design direct stresses due to the bimoment B_{Ed}
B_{Ed} bimoment
$V_{T,Rd}$ reduced design shear resistance making allowance for the presence of torsional moment
$f_{o,V}$ reduced design value of strength making allowance for the presence of shear force
$M_{v,Rd}$ reduced design value of the resistance to bending moment making allowance for the presence of shear force

6.3 Buckling resistance

N_{Rd} resistance of axial compression force
$M_{y,Rd}$ bending moment resistance about y-y axis
$M_{z,Rd}$ bending moment resistance about z-z axis
η_0, γ_0, ξ_0, ψ exponents in interaction formulae
ω_0 factor for section with localized weld
ρ reduction factor to determine reduced design value of the resistance to bending moment making allowance of the presence of shear force
$N_{b,Rd}$ design buckling resistance of a compression member
κ factor to allow for the weakening effect of welding
χ reduction factor for relevant buckling mode
ϕ value to determine the reduction factor χ
α imperfection factor
$\bar{\lambda}_0$ limit of the horizontal plateau of the buckling curves
N_{cr} elastic critical force for the relevant buckling mode based on the gross cross sectional properties
i radius of gyration about the relevant axis, determined using the properties of the gross cross-section
$\bar{\lambda}$ relative slenderness
$\bar{\lambda}_T$ relative slenderness for torsional or torsional-flexural buckling
N_{cr} elastic torsional-flexural buckling force
k buckling length factor
$M_{b,Rd}$ design buckling resistance moment
χ_{LT} reduction factor for lateral-torsional buckling
ϕ_{LT} value to determine the reduction factor χ_{LT}
α_{LT} imperfection factor
$\bar{\lambda}_{LT}$ non dimensional slenderness for lateral torsional buckling
M_{cr} elastic critical moment for lateral-torsional buckling
$\bar{\lambda}_{0,LT}$ plateau length of the lateral torsional buckling curve
η_c, γ_c, ξ_c, ψ_c exponents in interaction formulae
ω_x, $\omega_{x,LT}$ factors for section with localized weld
$\bar{\lambda}_{haz}$, $\bar{\lambda}_{haz,LT}$ relative slenderness parameters for section with localized weld
x_s distance from section with localized weld to simple support or point of contra flexure of the deflection curve for elastic buckling from an axial force

6.4 Uniform built-up compression members

L_{ch} buckling length of chord
h_0 distance of centrelines of chords of a built-up column
a distance between restraints of chords
α angle between axes of chord and lacings
i_{min} minimum radius of gyration of single angles

A_{ch}	area of one chord of a built-up column
$N_{ch,Ed}$	design chord force in the middle of a built-up member
M_{Ed}^{1}	design value of the maximum moment in the middle of the built-up member
I_{eff}	effective second moment of area of the built-up member
S_v	shear stiffness of built-up member from the lacings or battened panel
n	number of planes of lacings
A_d	area of one diagonal of a built-up column
d	length of a diagonal of a built-up column
A_v	area of one post (or transverse element) of a built-up column
I_{ch}	in plane second moment of area of a chord
I_{bl}	in plane second moment of area of a batten
μ	efficiency factor
i_y, i_z	radius of gyration (y-y axis and z-z axis)

6.5 Un-stiffened plates under in-plane loading

v_1	reduction factor for shear buckling
k_τ	buckling coefficient for shear buckling

6.6 Stiffened plates under in-plane loading

c	elastic support from plate
l_w	half wave-length in elastic buckling
χ	reduction factor for flexural buckling of sub-unit
I_{eff}	second moment of area off effective cross section of plating for in-plane bending
y_{st}	distance from centre of plating to centre of outermost stiffener
B_x	bending stiffness of orthotropic plate in section x = constant
B_y	bending stiffness of orthotropic plate in section y = constant
H	torsional stiffness of orthotropic plate
I_L	second moment of area of one stiffener and adjacent plating in the longitudinal direction
I_{xT}	torsional constant of one stiffener and adjacent plating in the longitudinal direction
a	half distance between stiffeners
t_1, t_2	thickness of layers in orthotropic plate
s	developed width of stiffeners and adjacent plate
$\tau_{cr,g}$	shear buckling stress for orthotropic plate
ϕ, η_h	factors

6.7 Plate girders

b_f	flange width
h_w	web depth = clear distance between inside flanges
b_w	depth of straight portion of a web
t_w	web thickness
t_f	flange thickness
I_{st}	second moment of area of gross cross-section of stiffener and adjacent effective parts of the web plate
b_1, b_2	distances from stiffener to inside flanges (welds)
a_c	half wave length for elastic buckling of stiffener
ρ_v	factor for shear buckling resistance
η	factor for shear buckling resistance in plastic range
λ_w	slenderness parameter for shear buckling
$V_{w,Rd}$	shear resistance contribution from the web
$V_{f,Rd}$	shear resistance contribution from the flanges
$k_{\tau,st}$	contribution from the longitudinal stiffeners to the buckling coefficient k_τ
$k_{\tau 1}$	buckling coefficient for subpanel
c	factor in expression for $V_{f,Rd}$
$M_{f,Rd}$	design moment resistance of a cross section considering the flanges only
A_{f1}, A_{f2}	cross section area of top and bottom flange
F_{Ed}	design transverse force
F_{Rd}	design resistance to transverse force
L_{eff}	effective length for resistance to transverse force
l_y	effective loaded length for resistance to transverse force
χ_F	reduction factor for local buckling due to transverse force
s_s	length stiff bearing under transverse force

λ_F slenderness parameter for local buckling due to transverse force
k_F buckling factor for transverse force
γ_s relative second moment of area of the stiffener closest to the loaded flange
I_{sl} second moment of area of the stiffener closest to the loaded flange
m_1, m_2 parameters in formulae for effective loaded length
l_e parameter in formulae for effective loaded length
$M_{N,Rd}$ reduced moment resistance due to presence of axial force
A_w cross section area of web
A_{fc} cross-section area of compression flange
k factor for flange induced buckling
r radius of curvature
h_f distance between centres of flanges

6.8 Members with corrugated webs
b_1, b_2 flange widths
t_1, t_2 flange thicknesses
ρ_z reduction factor due to transverse moments in the flanges
M_z transverse bending moment in the flanges
$\rho_{c,g}$ reduction factor for global buckling
$\lambda_{c,g}$ slenderness parameter for global buckling
$\tau_{cr,g}$ shear buckling stress for global buckling
$\rho_{c,l}$ reduction factor for local buckling
$\lambda_{c,l}$ slenderness parameter for local buckling
$\tau_{cr,l}$ shear buckling stress for local buckling
a_0, a_1, a_2, a_3, a_{max} widths of corrugations

Section 7 Serviceability limit state
I_{ser} effective section moment of area for serviceability limit state
I_{eff} section moment of area for the effective cross-section at the ultimate limit state
σ_{gr} maximum compressive bending stress at the serviceability limit state based on the gross cross section

Section 8 Design of connections
$\gamma_{M3} \rightarrow \gamma_{M7}$ partial safety factors
γ_{Mw} partial safety factor for resistance of welded connection
γ_{Mp} partial safety factor for resistance of pin connection
γ_{Ma} partial safety factor for resistance of adhesive bonded connection
γ_{Mser} partial safety factor for serviceability limit state
[A1) *Deleted text* (A1]
$e_1 \rightarrow e_4$ edge distances
p, p_1, p_2 spacing between bolt holes
d diameter of fastener
d_0 hole diameter
$V_{eff,1,Rd}$ design block tearing resistance for concentric loading
$V_{eff,2,Rd}$ design block tearing resistance for eccentric loading
A_{nt} net area subject to tension
A_{nv} net area subject to shear
A_1 area of part of angle outside the bolt hole
β_2, β_3 reduction factors for connections in angles
$F_{v,Ed}$ design shear force per bolt for the ultimate limit state
$F_{v,Ed,ser}$ design shear force per bolt for the serviceability limit state
$F_{v,Rd}$ design shear resistance per bolt
$F_{b,Rd}$ design bearing resistance per bolt
$F_{s,Rd,ser}$ design slip resistance per bolt at the serviceability limit state
$F_{s,Rd}$ design slip resistance per bolt at the ultimate limit state
$F_{t,Ed}$ design tensile force per bolt for the ultimate limit state
$F_{t,Rd}$ design tension resistance per bolt
$N_{net,Rd}$ design, resistance of section at bolt holes
$B_{t,Rd}$ design tension resistance of a bolt-plate assembly
f_{ub} characteristic ultimate strength of bolt material
f_{ur} characteristic ultimate strength of rivet material

A_0 — cross section area of the hole
A — gross cross section of a bolt
A_s — tensile stress area of a bolt
k_2 — factor for tension resistance of a bolt
d_m — mean of the across points and across flats dimensions of the bolt head or the nut or if washers are used the outer diameter of the washer, whichever is smaller
t_p — thickness of the plate under the bolt head or the nut
$F_{p,C}$ — preloading, force
μ — slip factor
n — number of friction interfaces
β_{Lf} — reduction factor for long joint
L_j — distance between the centres of the end fasteners in a long joint
β_p — reduction factor for fasteners passing through packings
a, b — plate thickness in a pin connection
c — gap between plates in a pin connection
f_w — characteristic strength of weld metal
$\sigma_\perp$ — normal stress perpendicular to weld axis
$\sigma_\parallel$ — normal stress parallel to weld axis
τ, $\tau_\parallel$ — shear stress parallel to weld axis
$\tau_\perp$ — shear stress perpendicular to weld axis
γ_{Mw} — partial safety factor for welded joints
L_w — total length of longitudinal fillet weld
$L_{w,eff}$ — effective length of longitudinal fillet weld
a — effective throat thickness
σ_{haz} — design normal stress in HAZ, perpendicular to the weld axis
τ_{haz} — design shear stress in HAZ
$f_{v,haz}$ — characteristic shear strength in HAZ

Annex A Execution classes

U — utilization grade

Annex B Equivalent T-stub in tension

$F_{u,Rd}$ — tension resistance of a T-stub flange
B_u — tension resistance of a bolt-plate assembly
B_o — conventional bolt strength at elastic limit
A_s — stress area of bolt
I_{eff} — effective length
e_{min} — minimum edge distance
m — distance from weld toe to centre of bolt

Annex C Materials selection

$\sigma_{eq,Ed}$ — equivalent design stress for castings
$\sigma_{x,Ed}$ — design stress in x-axis direction for castings
$\sigma_{y,Ed}$ — design stress in y-axis direction for castings
$\tau_{xy,Ed}$ — design shear stress for castings
σ_{Rd} — design resistance for castings
$\gamma_{Mo,c}$, $\gamma_{Mu,c}$ — partial factors for yields strength and ultimate strength castings respectively
$\gamma_{M2,co}$, $\gamma_{M2,cu}$ — partial factors for yields strength and ultimate strength for bearing resistance of bolts, rivets in castings
$\gamma_{Mp,co}$, $\gamma_{Mp,cu}$ — partial factors for yields strength and ultimate strength for bearing resistance of pins in castings

Annex E Analytical model for stress-strain relationship

The symbols are defined in the Annex

Annex F Behavior of cross-sections beyond elastic limit

α_0 — geometrical shape factor
α_5, α_{10} — generalized shape factors corresponding to ultimate curvature values $\chi_u = 5\chi_{cel}$ and $\chi_u = 10\chi_{el}$
$\alpha_{M,red}$ — correction factor for welded class 1 cross section

Annex G Rotation capacity

χ_u ultimate bending curvature
χ_{el} elastic bending curvature ($= \chi_{0,2}$)
ξ ductility factor
M_o elastic bending moment corresponding to the attainment of the proof stress f_o
m, k numerical parameters
R rotation capacity
θ_p, θ_{el} and θ_u, plastic rotation, elastic rotation and maximum plastic rotation corresponding to ultimate curvature χ_u

Annex H Plastic hinge method for continuous beams

η parameter depending on geometrical shape factor and conventional available ductility of the material
α_ξ shape factor α_5 or α_{10}
a, b, c coefficients in expression for η

Annex I Lateral torsional buckling of beams and torsional or flexural-torsional buckling of compression members

I_t torsion constant
I_w warping constant
I_z second moment of area of minor axis
k_z end condition corresponding to restraints against lateral movement
k_w end condition corresponding to rotation about the longitudinal axis
k_y end condition corresponding to restraints against movement in plane of loading
κ_{wt} non-dimensional torsion parameter
ς_g relative non-dimensional coordinate of the point of load application
ς_j relative non-dimensional cross section mono-symmetry parameter
μ_{cr} relative non-dimensional critical moment
z_a coordinate of the point of load application related to centroid
z_s coordinate of the shear centre related to centroid
z_g coordinate of the point of load application related to shear centre
z_j mono-symmetry constant
c depth of a lip
ψ_f mono-symmetry factor
h_f distance between centrelines of flanges
h_s distance between shear centre of upper flange and shear centre of bottom flange
I_{fc} second moment of area of the compression flange about the minor axis of the section
I_{ft} second moment of area of the tension flange about the minor axis of the section
C_1, C_2, C_3, $C_{1,1}$, C_{12} coefficients in formulae for relative non-dimensional critical moment
$N_{cr,y}$, $N_{cr,z}$, $N_{cr,T}$ elastic flexural buckling load (y-y and z-z axes) and torsional buckling load
i_s polar radius of gyration
α_{yw}, α_{zw} coefficients in equation for torsional and torsional-flexural buckling
k, λ_t coefficients in formula for relative slenderness parameter $\bar{\lambda}_T$
λ_0, s, X coefficients to calculate λ_t

Annex J Properties of cross sections

β, δ, γ fillet or bulb factors
b_{sh} width of flat cross section parts
α fillet or bulb factor; angle between flat section parts adjacent to fillets or bulbs
D diameter of circle inscribed in fillet or bulb
NOTE Notations for cross section constants given in J.4 and are not repeated here

Annex K Shear lag effects in member design

b_{eff} effective width for shear lag
β_s effective width factor for shear lag
κ notional width-to-length ratio for flange
A_{st} area of all longitudinal stiffeners within half the flange width
$\alpha_{st,1}$ relative area of stiffeners = area of stiffeners divided by centre to centre distance of stiffeners
s_e loaded length in section between flange and web
[A1] b_0 width of outstand or half width of internal cross-section part
L_e points of zero bending moment [A1]

Annex L Classification of joints

F load, generalized force force
F_u ultimate load, ultimate generalized force
v generalized deformation
v_u deformation corresponding to ultimate generalized force

Annex M Adhesive bonded connection

$f_{v,adh}$ characteristic shear strength values of adhesives
τ average shear stress in the adhesive layer
γ_{Ma} material factor for adhesive bonded joint

1.7 Conventions for member axes

(1) In general the convention for member axes is:

x-x – along the member
y-y – axis of the cross-section
z-z – axis of the cross-section

(2) For aluminium members, the conventions used for cross-section axes are:

- generally:
  y-y – cross-section axis parallel to the flanges
  z-z – cross-section axis perpendicular to the flanges
- for angle sections:
  y-y – axis parallel to the smaller leg
  z-z – axis perpendicular to the smaller leg
- where necessary:
  u-u – major principal axis (where this does not coincide with the y-y axis)
  v-v – minor principal axis (where this does not coincide with the z-z axis)

(3) The symbols used for dimensions and axes of aluminium sections are indicated in Figure 1.1.

(4) The convention used for subscripts, which indicate axes for moments is: "Use the axis about which the moment acts."

NOTE All rules in this Eurocode relate to principal axis properties, which are generally defined by the axes y-y and z-z for symmetrical sections and by the u-u and v-v axis for unsymmetrical section such as angles.

When designing aluminium elements, using the correct axes is essential to avoid failure. The clause on this aspect of design as well as a diagram to clarify the axes for most common elements is included as an aid to design.

1.8 Specification for execution of the work

(1) A specification for execution of the work should be prepared that contains all necessary technical information to carry out the work. This information should include execution class(es), whether any non-normative tolerances in EN 1090-3 should apply, complete geometrical information and of materials to be used in members and joints, types and sizes of fasteners, weld requirements and requirements for execution of work. EN 1090-3 contains a checklist for information to be provided.

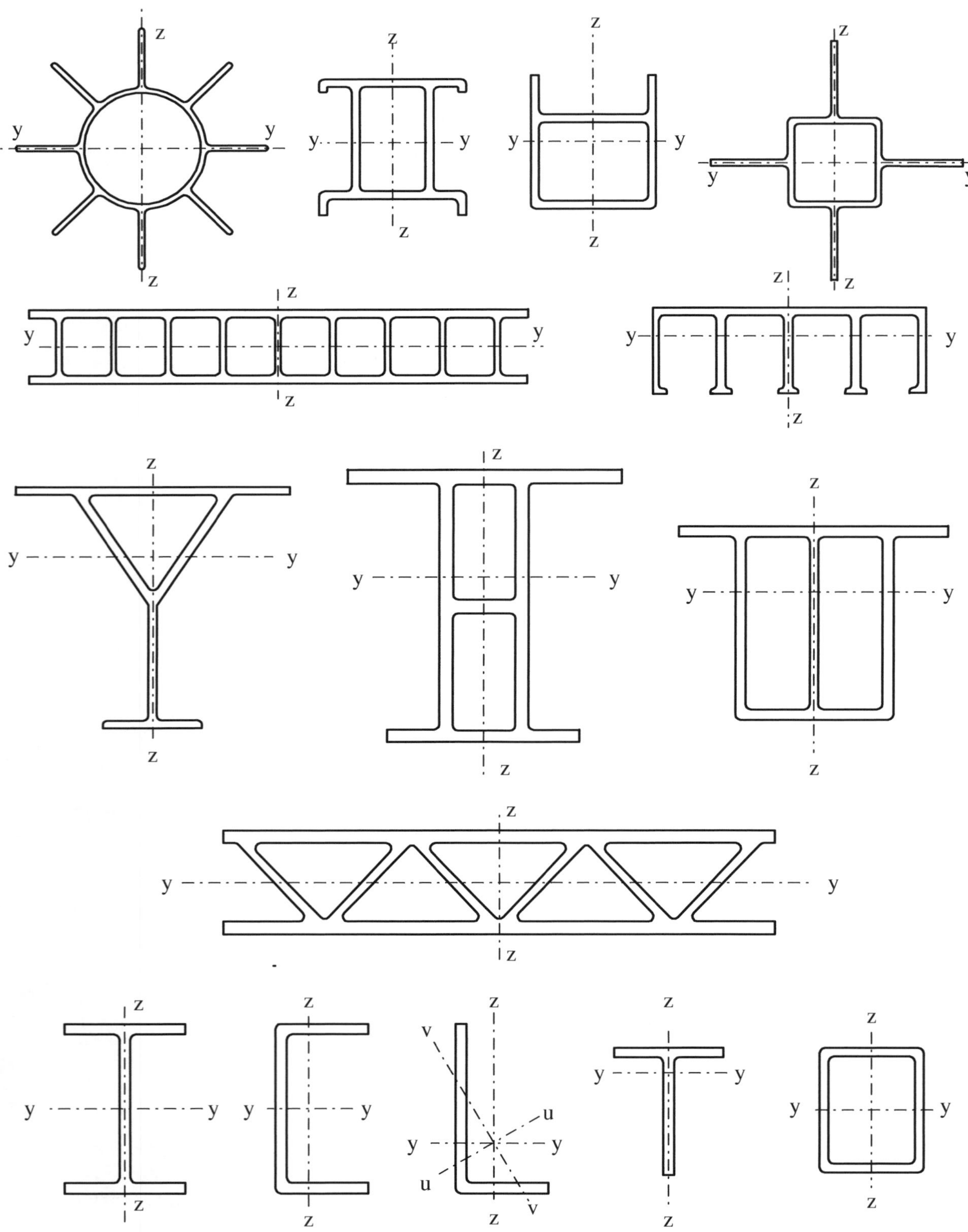

Figure 1.1 — Definition of axes for various cross-sections

2 Basis of design

2.1 Requirements

2.1.1 Basic requirements

(1)P The design of aluminium structures shall be in accordance with the general rules given in EN 1990.

(2)P The supplementary provisions for aluminium structures given in this section shall also be applied.

(3)P The basic requirements of EN 1990 section 2 shall be deemed to be satisfied where limit state design is used in conjunction with the partial factor method and the load combinations given in EN 1990 together with the actions given in EN 1991.

(4) The rules for resistances, serviceability and durability given in the various parts of EN 1999 should be applied.

In addition to the basic requirements given in 2.1.1 for aluminium structures, they should be designed to take account of reliability management which is the procedure whereby designers and executors ensure building work is to an appropriate standard for particular circumstances. Further, in the design of aluminium structures, corrosion, fatigue, wearing and accidental actions should be considered and designed for.

The design of aluminium structures is based on limit state ideas as specified in EN 1990 and by using those principles the design resistances of elements, and hence the resistance of aluminium structures as specified in EN 1999-1-1 can be evaluated.

Actions for the design of aluminium structures should be taken from EN 1991 and the actions to be considered in the erection stage should be obtained from EN 1991-1-6. To combine actions and partial factors for actions see Annex A to EN 1990. Geometrical data for cross sections and systems may be taken from product standards or drawings for the execution according to EN 1090-3 and treated as nominal values. In certain situations the effect of 'local' actions on design should be included but the relevant National Annex will point this out.

Design values should be adjusted to take account of geometrical imperfections specified in this standard which may be due to one or both of:

- the effects of geometrical imperfections of members as governed by geometrical tolerances in product standards or the execution standard or the effects of structural imperfections from fabrication and erection,
- residual stresses, variations of the yield strength and heat-affected zones.

3 Materials

3.1 General

(1) The material properties given in this section are specified as characteristic values. They are based on the minimum values given in the relevant product standard.

(2) Other material properties are given in the ENs listed in 1.2.1.

3.2 Structural aluminium

3.2.1 Range of materials

(1) This European standard covers the design of structures fabricated from aluminium alloy material listed in Table 3.1a for wrought alloys conforming to the ENs listed in 1.2.3.1. For the design of structures of cast aluminium alloys given in Table 3.1b, see 3.2.3.1.

NOTE Annex C gives further information for the design of structures of cast aluminium alloys.

The UK National annex has been pragmatic about materials and includes the following advice.

Table NA.1, 3.2.1(1) UK decision

To enable the use of materials held in stock which were produced prior to the adoption of European material standards, it is permitted to use aluminium alloys listed in the British Standards tabulated in PD 6702-1[1)]. This provision is subject to approval of the designer and the use of the values for 0.2% proof stress and minimum tensile strength given in PD 6702-1 for the alloy in question, rather than the values in BS EN 1999-1-1:2007, Table 3.2a, Table 3.2b and Table 3.2c, when calculating the design resistance of the relevant material.

[1)] In preparation.

Table 3.1a — Wrought aluminium alloys for structures

Alloy designation		Form of product	Durability rating[3)]
Numerical	Chemical symbols		
EN AW-3004	EN AW-AlMn1Mg1	SH, ST, PL	A
EN AW-3005	EN AW-AlMn1Mg0,5	SH, ST, PL	A
EN AW-3103	EN AW-Al Mn1	SH, ST, PL, ET, EP, ER/B	A
EN AW-5005 / 5005A	EN AW-AlMg1(B) / (C)	SH, ST, PL	A
EN AW-5049	EN AW-AlMg2Mn0,8	SH, ST, PL	A
EN AW-5052	EN AW-Al Mg2,5	SH, ST, PL, ET[2)], EP[2)], ER/B, DT	A
EN AW-5083	EN AW-Al Mg4,5Mn0,7	SH, ST, PL, ET[2)], EP[2)], ER/B, DT, FO	A[1)]
EN AW-5454	EN AW-Al Mg3Mn	SH, ST, PL, ET[2)], EP[2)], ER/B	A
EN AW-5754	EN AW-Al Mg3	SH, ST, PL, ET[2)], EP[2)], ER/B, DT, FO	A
EN AW-6060	EN AW-Al MgSi	ET,EP,ER/B,DT	B
EN AW-6061	EN AW-Al Mg1SiCu	SH, ST,PL,ET,EP,ER/B,DT	B
EN AW-6063	EN AW-Al Mg0,7Si	ET, EP, ER/B,DT	B
EN AW-6005A	EN AW-Al SiMg(A)	ET, EP, ER/B	B
EN AW-6082	EN AW-Al Si1MgMn	SH, ST, PL, ET, EP, ER/B, DT, FO	B
EN AW-6106	EN AW-AlMgSiMn	EP	B
EN AW-7020	EN AW-Al Zn4,5Mg1	SH, ST, PL, ET, EP, ER/B, DT	C
EN AW-8011A	EN AW-AlFeSi	SH, ST, PL	B

Key:
SH - Sheet (EN 485)
ST - Strip (EN 485)
PL - Plate (EN 485)
ET - Extruded Tube (EN 755)
EP - Extruded Profiles (EN 755)
ER/B - Extruded Rod and Bar (EN 755)
DT - Drawn Tube (EN 754)
FO - Forgings (EN 586)

1) See Annex C: C2.2.2(2)

2) Only simple, solid (open) extruded sections or thick-walled tubes over a mandrel (seamless)

3) See 4, Annex C and Annex D

Table 3.1b — Cast aluminium alloys for structures

Alloy designation		Durability rating[1)]
Numerical	Chemical symbols	
EN AC-42100	EN AC-Al Si7Mg0,3	B
EN AC-42200	EN AC-Al Si7Mg0,6	B
EN AC-43000	EN AC-Al Si10Mg(a)	B
EN AC-43300	EN AC-AlSi9Mg	B
EN AC-44200	EN AC-Al Si12(a)	B
EN AC-51300	EN AC-Al Mg5	A

1) see 4, Annex C and Annex D

NOTE 1 For other aluminium alloys and temper than those listed, see the National Annex.

NOTE 2 For advice on the selection of aluminium alloys see Annex C.

Table 3.1a specifies wrought aluminium products whereas details on cast aluminium materials are given in Table 3.1b. Wrought products are forged or hammered into shape from an aluminium ingot whereas when cast the molten material is poured into a mould. Of the wrought products shown in Table 3.1a, some are suitable for structural applications, others can be heat treated whilst each product is classified in terms of durability. The wrought products denoted EN AW-5049, EN AW-5052, EN AW-5454, EN AW-5754 and EN AW-5083 are recommended for structural applications, have durability rating A but cannot be heat treated. The alloys EN AW-6082, EN AW-6061, EN AW-6005A, EN AW-6106, EN AW-6063 and EN AW-6060 are also suitable for structural applications and have durability rating B. The alloy EN AW-7020 too, is suitable for general structural applications and has durability rating C. All the 6 and 7 series materials suitable for structural use can be heat treated. EN AW-8011A is also suitable for heat treatment and is used in the building industry especially for facades. It is possible, though unusual, to use some cast aluminium materials in structural elements but certain additional design rules should be observed as indicated in Appendix C. These special design rules are only applicable to cast parts which have geometry and applied actions where buckling cannot occur. The cast component should not be formed by bending or welded or machined with sharp internal corners.

Tables 3.1a and 3.1b categorise aluminium products into three durability ratings; A, B and C in descending order of durability, which are used to determine the need and degree of protection required. Table D.1 summarises the protection needed for the various durability ratings. It should be noted that this table refers to aluminium not in contact with other aluminium alloys, metals, timber, plaster, concrete etc. In these cases more stringent requirements on protecting aluminium are specified.

3.2.2 Material properties for wrought aluminium alloys

(1) Characteristic values of the 0,2% proof strength f_o and the ultimate tensile strength f_u for wrought aluminium alloys for a range of tempers and thicknesses are given in Table 3.2a for sheet, strip and plate products; Table 3.2b for extruded rod/bar, extruded tube and extruded profiles and drawn tube and Table 3.2c for forgings. The values in Table 3.2a, b and c, as well as in Table 3.3 and Table 3.4 (for aluminium fasteners only) are applicable for structures subject to service temperatures up to 80°C.

NOTE Product properties for electrically welded tubes according to EN 1592-1 to 4 for structural applications are not given in this standard. The National Annex may give rules for their application. Buckling class B is recommended.

(2) For service temperatures between 80°C and 100°C reduction of the strength should be taken in account.

Table NA.1 3.2.2(1) UK decision

The tube can conservatively be treated as having a longitudinal weld laid with the MIG process for its full length, and with buckling class B when using BS EN 1999-1-1:2007, 6.1.4.4, 6.1.5, and 6.3.1.

NOTE 1 The National Annex may give rules for the reduction of the characteristic values to be applied. For temperatures between 80°C and 100°C the following procedure is recommended:

All characteristic aluminium resistance values (f_o, f_u, $f_{o,haz}$ and $f_{u,haz}$) may be reduced according to

$$X_{kT} = [1 - k_{100}(T - 80) / 20]\, X_k \tag{3.1}$$

where:

X_k is the characteristic value of a strength property of a material
X_{kT} is the characteristic strength value for the material at temperature T between 80°C and 100°C
T is the highest temperature the structure is operating
k_{100} = 0,1 for strain hardening alloys (3xxx-alloys, 5xxx-alloys and EN AW 8011A)
k_{100} = 0,2 for precipitation hardening material (6xxx-alloys and EN AW-7020)

At 100°C generally Buckling Class B is applicable for all aluminium alloys. For temperatures between 80°C and 100°C interpolation between Class A and Class B should be done.

NOTE 2 Between 80°C and 100°C the reduction of the strength values is recoverable, e.g. the materials regain its strength when the temperature is dropping down. For temperatures over 100°C also a reduction of the elastic modulus and additionally time depending, not recoverable reductions of strength should be considered.

Table NA.1 3.2.2(2) UK decision

Use the recommended procedure, subject to confirmation that the alloy is suitable for use at the relevant temperature.

NOTE Certain alloys are susceptible to stress corrosion cracking at elevated temperatures – e.g. see C.2.2.2 relating to EN AW-5083.

(3) Characteristic values for the heat affected zone (0,2% proof strength $f_{o,haz}$ and ultimate tensile strength $f_{u,haz}$) are also given in Table 3.2a to 3.2c and also reduction factors (see 6.1.6), buckling class (used in 6.1.4 and 6.3.1) and exponent in Ramberg-Osgood expression for plastic resistance.

Table 3.2a — Characteristic values of 0,2% proof strength f_o, ultimate tensile strength f_u (unwelded and for HAZ), min elongation A, reduction factors $\rho_{o,has}$ and $\rho_{u,haz}$ in HAZ, buckling class and exponent n_p for wrought aluminium alloys – Sheet, strip and plate

Alloy EN-AW	Temper 1)	Thickness 1) mm	f_o 1)	f_u	A_{50} 1) 6)	$f_{o,haz}$ 2)	$f_{u,haz}$ 2)	HAZ-factor 2)		BC 4)	n_p 1), 5)
			N/mm²		%	N/mm²		$\rho_{o,haz}$ 1)	$\rho_{u,haz}$		
3004	H14 ∣ H24/H34	≤ 6 ∣ 3	180 ∣ 170	220	1 ∣ 3	75	155	0,42 ∣ 0,44	0,70	B	23 ∣ 18
	H16 ∣ H26/H36	≤ 4 ∣ 3	200 ∣ 190	240	1 ∣ 3			0,38 ∣ 0,39	0,65	B	25 ∣ 20
3005	H14 ∣ H24	≤ 6 ∣ 3	150 ∣ 130	170	1 ∣ 4	56	115	0,37 ∣ 0,43	0,68	B	38 ∣ 18
	H16 ∣ H26	≤ 4 ∣ 3	175 ∣ 160	195	1 ∣ 3			0,32 ∣ 0,35	0,59	B	43 ∣ 24
3103	H14 ∣ H24	≤ 25 ∣ 12,5	120 ∣ 110	140	2 ∣ 4	44	90	0,37 ∣ 0,40	0,64	B	31 ∣ 20
	H16 ∣ H26	≤ 4	145 ∣ 135	160	1 ∣ 2			0,30 ∣ 0,33	0,56	B	48 ∣ 28
5005/ 5005A	O/H111	≤ 50	35	100	15	35	100	1	1	B	5
	H12 ∣ H22/H32	≤ 12,5	95 ∣ 80	125	2 ∣ 4	44	100	0,46 ∣ 0,55	0,80	B	18 ∣ 11
	H14 ∣ H24/H34	≤ 12,5	120 ∣ 110	145	2 ∣ 3			0,37 ∣ 0,40	0,69	B	25 ∣ 17
5052	H12 ∣ H22/H32	≤ 40	160 ∣ 130	210	4 ∣ 5	80	170	0,50 ∣ 0,62	0,81	B	17 ∣ 10
	H14 ∣ H24/H34	≤ 25	180 ∣ 150	230	3 ∣ 4			0,44 ∣ 0,53	0,74	B	19 ∣ 11
5049	O / H111	≤ 100	80	190	12	80	190	1	1	B	6
	H14 ∣ H24/H34	≤ 25	190 ∣ 160	240	3 ∣ 6	100	190	0,53 ∣ 0,63	0,79	B	20 ∣ 12
5454	O/H111	≤ 80	85	215	12	85	215	1	1	B	5
	H14∣H24/H34	≤ 25	220 ∣ 200	270	2 ∣ 4	105	215	0,48 ∣ 0,53	0,80	B	22 ∣ 15
5754	O/H111	≤ 100	80	190	12	80	190	1	1	B	6
	H14∣H24/H34	≤ 25	190 ∣ 160	240	3 ∣ 6	100	190	0,53 ∣ 0,63	0,79	B	20 ∣ 12
5083	O/H111	≤ 50	125	275	11	125	275	1	1	B	6
		50<t≤80	115	270	14 3)	115	270			B	
	H12∣H22/H32	≤ 40	250 ∣ 215	305	3 ∣ 5	155	275	0,62 ∣ 0,72	0,90	B	22 ∣ 14
	H14∣H24/H34	≤ 25	280 ∣ 250	340	2 ∣ 4			0,55 ∣ 0,62	0,81	A	22 ∣ 14
6061	T4 / T451	≤ 12,5	110	205	12	95	150	0,86	0,73	B	8
	T6 / T651	≤ 12,5	240	290	6	115	175	0,48	0,60	A	23
	T651	12,5<t≤80	240	290	6 3)						
6082	T4 / T451	≤ 12,5	110	205	12	100	160	0,91	0,78	B	8
	T61/T6151	≤12,5	205	280	10	125	185	0,61	0,66	A	15
	T6151	12,5<t≤100	200	275	12 3)			0,63	0,67	A	14
	T6/T651	≤ 6	260	310	6			0,48	0,60	A	25
		6<t≤12,5	255	300	9			0,49	0,62	A	27
	T651	12,5<t≤100	240	295	7 3)			0,52	0,63	A	21
7020	T6	≤ 12,5	280	350	7	205	280	0,73	0,80	A	19
	T651	≤ 40			9 3)						
8011A	H14 ∣ H24	≤ 12,5	110 ∣ 100	125	2 ∣ 3	37	85	0,34 ∣ 0,37	0,68	B	37 ∣ 22
	H16 ∣ H26	≤ 4	130 ∣ 120	145	1 ∣ 2			0,28 ∣ 0,31	0,59		33 ∣ 33

1) If two (three) tempers are specified in one line, tempers separated by "∣" have different technological values but separated by "/" have same values. (The tempers show differences for f_o, A and n_p.).

2) The HAZ-values are valid for MIG welding and thickness up to 15mm. For TIG welding strain hardening alloys (3xxx, 5xxx and 8011A) up to 6 mm the same values apply, but for TIG welding precipitation hardening alloys (6xxx and 7xxx) and thickness up to 6 mm the HAZ values have to be multiplied by a factor 0,8 and so the ρ-factors. For higher thickness – unless other data are available – the HAZ values and ρ-factors have to be further reduced by a factor 0,8 for the precipitation hardening alloys (6xxx and 7xxx) and by a factor 0,9 for the strain hardening alloys (3xxx, 5xxx and 8011A). These reductions do not apply in temper O.

3) Based on A $(= A_{5,65\sqrt{A_o}})$, not A_{50}.

4) BC = buckling class, see 6.1.4.4, 6.1.5 and 6.3.1.

5) n-value in Ramberg-Osgood expression for plastic analysis. It applies only in connection with the listed f_o-value.

6) The minimum elongation values indicated do not apply across the whole range of thickness given, but mostly to the thinner materials. In detail see EN 485-2.

Table 3.2b — Characteristic values of 0,2% proof strength f_o and ultimate tensile strength f_u (unwelded and for HAZ), min elongation A, reduction factors $\rho_{o,haz}$ and $\rho_{u,haz}$ in HAZ, buckling class and exponent n_p for wrought aluminium alloys – Extruded profiles, extruded tube, extruded rod/bar and drawn tube

Alloy EN-AW	Product form	Temper	Thick-ness t mm 1) 3)	f_o 1)	f_u 1)	A 5) 2)	$f_{o,haz}$ 4)	$f_{u,haz}$ 4)	HAZ-factor 4)		BC 6)	n_p 7)
				N/mm²		%	N/mm²		$\rho_{o,haz}$	$\rho_{u,haz}$		
5083	ET, EP,ER/B	O / H111, F, H112	$t \leq 200$	**110**	**270**	12	110	270	1	1	B	5
	DT	H12/22/32	$t \leq 10$	200	280	6	135	270	0,68	0,96	B	14
		H14/24/34	$t \leq 5$	235	300	4			0,57	0,90	A	18
5454	ET, EP,ER/B	O/H111 F/H112	$t \leq$ **25**	85	200	16	85	200	1	1	B	5
5754	ET, EP,ER/B	O/H111 F/H112	$t \leq$ **25**	80	180	14	80	180	1	1	B	6
	DT	H14/ H24/H34	$t \leq 10$	180	240	4	100	180	0,56	0,75	B	16
6060	EP,ET,ER/B	T5	$t \leq$ **5**	120	160	8	50	80	0,42	0,50	B	17
	EP		$5 < t \leq 25$	100	140	8			0,50	0,57	B	14
	ET,EP,ER/B	T6	$t \leq$ **15**	**140**	**170**	8	60	100	0,43	0,59	A	24
	DT		$t \leq 20$	160	215	12			0,38	0,47	A	16
	EP,ET,ER/B	T64	$t \leq$ **15**	120	180	12	60	100	0,50	0,56	A	12
	EP,ET,ER/B	T66	$t \leq$ **3**	160	215	8	65	110	0,41	0,51	A	16
	EP		$3 < t \leq 25$	150	195	8			0,43	0,56	A	18
6061	EP,ET,ER/B	T4	$t < 25$	110	180	15	95	150	0,86	0,83	B	8
	DT		$t < 20$	110	205	16				0,73	B	8
	EP,ET,ER/B	T6	$t \leq 25$	240	260	8	115	175	0,48	0,67	A	55
	DT		$t < 20$	240	290	10				0,60	A	23
6063	EP,ET,ER/B	T5	$t \leq$ **3**	130	175	8	60	100	0,46	0,57	B	16
	EP		$3 < t \leq 25$	110	160	**7**			0,55	0,63	B	13
	EP,ET,ER/B	T6	$t \leq$ **25**	**160**	**195**	**8**	65	110	0,41	0,56	A	24
	DT		$t \leq 20$	190	220	10			0,34	0,50	A	31
	EP,ET,ER/B	T66	$t \leq$ **10**	200	245	**8**	75	130	0,38	0,53	A	22
	EP		$10 < t \leq 25$	180	225	8			0,42	0,58	A	21
	DT		$t \leq 20$	195	230	10			0,38	0,57	A	28
6005A	EP/O, ER/B	T6	$t \leq$ **5**	225	270	8	115	165	0,51	0,61	A	25
			$5 < t \leq 10$	215	260	8			0,53	0,63	A	24
			$10 < t \leq 25$	200	250	8			0,58	0,66	A	20
	EP/H, ET	T6	$t \leq 5$	**215**	**255**	8			0,53	0,65	A	26
			$5 < t \leq$ **10**	**200**	**250**	8			0,58	0,66	A	20
6106	EP	T6	$t \leq 10$	200	250	8	95	160	0,48	0,64	A	20

Table 3.2b — Continued

Alloy EN-AW	Product form	Temper	Thickness t mm 1) 3)	f_o 1)	f_u 1)	A 5) 2)	$f_{o,haz}$ 4)	$f_{u,haz}$ 4)	HAZ-factor 4)		BC 6)	n_p 7)
				N/mm²		%	N/mm²		$\rho_{o,haz}$	$\rho_{u,haz}$		
6082	EP,ET,ER/B	T4	$t \le$ **25**	110	205	14	100	160	0,91	0,78	B	8
	A1⟩ EP ⟨A1	T5	$t \le 5$	230	270	8	125	185	0,54	0,69	B	28
	A1⟩ EP ⟨A1	T6	$t \le 5$	250	290	8	125	185	0,50	0,64	A	32
	ET		$5 < t \le$ **15**	260	310	10			0,48	0,60	A	25
	ER/B	T6	$t \le 20$	250	295	8			0,50	0,63	A	27
			$20 < t \le 150$	260	310	8			0,48	0,60	A	25
	DT	T6	$t \le 5$	255	310	8			0,49	0,60	A	22
			$5 < t \le 20$	240	310	10			0,52	0,60	A	17
7020	EP,ET,ER/B	T6	$t \le$ **15**	290	350	10	205	280	0,71	0,80	A	23
	EP,ET,ER/B	T6	$15 < t <$ **40**	**275**	350	10			0,75	0,80	A	19
	DT	T6	$t \le 20$	280	350	10			0,73	0,80	A	18

Key: EP - Extruded profiles; EP/O - Extruded open profiles; EP/H - Extruded hollow profiles; ET - Extruded tube; ER/B - Extruded rod and bar; DT - Drawn tube

1): Where values are quoted in **bold** greater thicknesses and/or higher mechanical properties may be permitted in some forms see ENs and prENs listed in 1.2.1.3. In this case the $R_{p0,2}$ and R_m values can be taken as f_o and f_u. If using such higher values the corresponding HAZ-factors ρ have to be calculated acc. to expression (6.13) and (6.14) with the same values for $f_{o,haz}$ and $f_{u,haz}$.

2): Where minimum elongation values are given in **bold**, higher minimum values may be given for some forms or thicknesses.

3): According to A1⟩ EN 755-2:2008: ⟨A1 following rule applies: *"If a profile cross-section is comprised of different thicknesses which fall in more than one set of specified mechanically property values, the lowest specified value should be considered as valid for the whole profile cross-section."* Exception is possible and the highest value given may be used provided the manufacturer can support the value by an appropriate quality assurance certificate.

4): The HAZ-values are valid for MIG welding and thickness up to 15 mm. For TIG welding strain hardening alloys A1⟩ (3xxx and 5xxx) ⟨A1 up to 6 mm the same values apply, but for TIG welding precipitation hardening alloys (6xxx and 7xxx) and thickness up to 6 mm the HAZ values have to be multiplied by a factor 0,8 and so the ρ-factors. For higher thickness – unless other data are available – the HAZ values and ρ-factors have to be further reduced by a factor 0,8 for the precipitation hardening alloys (6xxx and 7xxx) alloys and by a factor 0,9 for strain hardening alloys (3xxx, 5xxx and 8011A). These reductions do not apply in temper O.

5) $A = A_{5,65\sqrt{A_o}}$

6) BC = buckling class, see 6.1.4.4, 6.1.5 and 6.3.1.

7) n-value in Ramberg-Osgood expression for plastic analysis. It applies only in connection with the listed f_o-value (= minimum standardized value).

Table 3.2c — Characteristic values of 0,2% proof strength f_o, ultimate tensile strength f_u (unwelded and for HAZ), minimum elongation *A* and buckling class for wrought aluminium alloys – Forgings

Alloy EN-AW	Temper	Thick-ness up to mm	Direction	f_o	f_u	$f_{o,haz}$ 1)	$f_{u,haz}$ 1)	A 3)	Buckling class
				N/mm²				%	
5754	H112	150	Longitudinal (L)	80	180	80	180	15	B
5083	H112	150	Longitudinal (L)	120	270	120	270	12	B
			Transverse (T)	110	260	110	260	10	B
6082	T6	100	Longitudinal (L)	260	310	125 2)	185 2)	6	A
			Transverse (T)	250	290			5	A

1) $\rho_{o,haz}$; $\rho_{u,haz}$ to be calculated according to expression (6.13) and (6.14)
2) For thicknesses over 15 mm (MIG-welding) or 6 mm (TIG-welding) see table 3.2.b footnote 4).
3) $A = A_{5,65\sqrt{A_o}}$

3.2.3 Material properties for cast aluminium alloys

3.2.3.1 General

(1) EN 1999-1-1 is not generally applicable to castings.

NOTE 1 The design rules in this European standard are applicable for gravity cast products according to Table 3.3 if the additional and special rules and the quality provisions of Annex C, C.3.4 are followed.

NOTE 2 The National Annex may give rules for quality requirements for castings.

Table NA.1 3.2.3.1(1) UK decision

Use the recommendations given in Annex C.

3.2.3.2 Characteristic values

(1) The characteristic values of the 0,2% proof strength f_o and the ultimate tensile strength f_u for sand and permanent mould cast aluminium to be met by the caster or the foundry in each location of a cast piece are given in Table 3.3. The listed values are 70% of the values of EN 1706:2008, which are only valid for separately cast test specimens [A1⟩ (see 6.3.3.2 of EN 1706:1998). ⟨A1]

NOTE The listed values for A_{50} in Table 3.3 are 50 % of the elongation values of EN 1706:1998, which are only valid for separately cast test specimens (see 6.3.3.2 EN 1706:1998).

Table 3.3 — Characteristic values of 0,2% proof strength f_o and ultimate tensile strength f_u for cast aluminium alloys – Gravity castings

Alloy	Casting process	Temper	f_o (f_{oc}) N/mm²	f_u (f_{uc}) N/mm²	A_{50} % [1)]
EN AC-42100	Permanent mould	T6	147	203	2,0
	Permanent mould	T64	126	175	4
EN AC-42200	Permanent mould	T6	168	224	1,5
	Permanent mould	T64	147	203	3
EN AC-43000	Permanent mould	F	63	126	1,25
EN AC-43300	Permanent mould	T6	147	203	2,0
	Sand cast	T6	133	161	1,0
	Permanent mould	T64	126	175	3
EN AC-44200	Permanent mould	F	56	119	3
	Sand cast	F	49	105	2,5
EN AC-51300	Permanent mould	F	70	126	2,0
	Sand cast	F	63	112	1,5
1) For elongation requirements for the design of cast components, see C.3.4.2(1).					

3.2.5 Design values of material constants

(1) The material constants to be adopted in calculations for the aluminium alloys covered by this European Standard should be taken as follows:

- modulus of elasticity E = 70 000 N/mm²;
- shear modulus G = 27 000 N/mm²;
- Poisson's ratio ν = 0,3;
- coefficient of linear thermal expansion $\alpha = 23 \times 10^{-6}$ per °C;
- unit mass ρ = 2 700 kg/m³.

(2) For material properties in structures subject to elevated temperatures associated with fire see EN 1999-1-2.

Dimensional tolerances for aluminium elements are given in separate material standards listed in 1.2.3.3 and 1.2.3.4.

3.3 Connecting devices

3.3.1 General

(1) Connecting devices should be suitable for their specific use.

(2) Suitable connecting devices include bolts, friction grip fasteners, solid rivets, special fasteners, welds and adhesives.

NOTE For adhesives, see Annex M.

The design and material requirements for connections in aluminium structures and elements are given in Sections 3.3, Section 8 (Design of joints – weld thickness and bolt sizes etc) and Annex L and M of the code.

In sub Sections 3.3.2 and 3.3.3 connecting devices are defined as bolted, riveted, welded and those formed using adhesives. Further classification includes friction grip fasteners or pre-loaded bolts, special fasteners and self tapping and self drilling screws and blind rivets, this latter class being limited to use in thin walled structures. According to Table 3.4 rivets may be formed using specific aluminium alloy grades whereas bolts can again be manufactured using specific aluminium alloys but steel and stainless steel to specific requirements are also permitted, the diameters of all these connections being restricted according to the table.

Table NA.1 3.3.2(3) UK decision

Use the recommendations given in Annex C.

Table NA.1 3.3.2.2(1) UK decision

To enable the use of (HSFG) bolts held in stock which were produced prior to the adoption of European material standards, it is permitted to use bolts listed in the British Standards tabulated in PD 6702-1. This provision is subject to approval of the designer and the use of the relevant values for preload rather than the standard values given in BS EN 1090 (in preparation) and BS EN 1090-3.

Sub Section 3.3.4 discusses welding aluminium elements and provides rules to ensure the weld fill material and the parent aluminium alloy are compatible as mismatches result in cracking of the weld material in the joints. Tables 3.5 and 3.6 and design requirements given is Section 8 expand on the guidance. Sub Section 3.3.4 informs the reader that guidance on adhesives can be found in Annex M.

Annex L of the code classifies aluminium joints. A connection is defined as the location at which two or more members at a joint in a structure are interconnected. In some cases beams will be connected into the web of a column whereas in other instances the column flange will carry the beam. A connection can be thought of as a system which fastens a given member(s) into the remaining parts of a structure. A joint, by contrast comprises basic components (or structural elements) assembled so that internal forces and moments can be transferred between them. It can also comprise what is termed a web panel which helps to transfer the forces (see Figure L.1). The designer will influence how this occurs through his design assumptions and the nature of a joint will influence how rigid, strong or ductile a connection in a structure is.

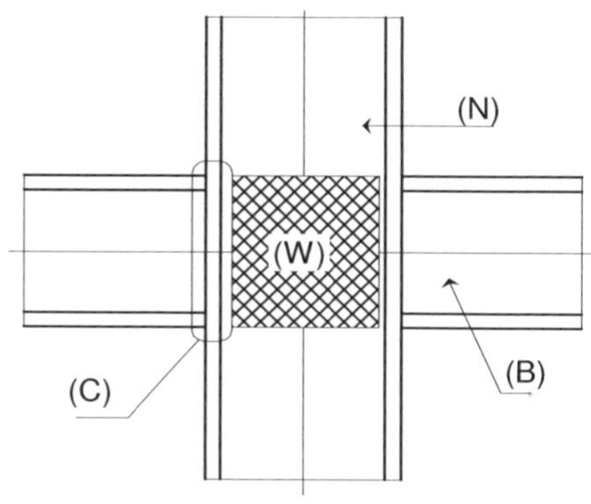

Welded joint
Joint = web panel in shear + connections
Components: welds, column flanges

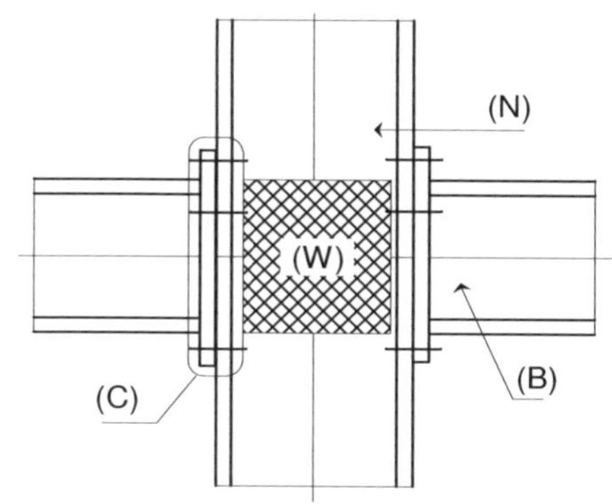

Bolted joint
Joint = web panel in shear + connections
Components: welds, end-plates, bolts, column flanges

(C) Connection, (W) web panel in shear, (N) column, (B) beam

Figure L.1 — Definition of "connection" and "joint"

4 Durability

(1) The basic requirements for durability are given in EN 1990.

NOTE For aluminium in contact with other material, recommendations are given in Annex D.

(2) Under normal atmospheric conditions, aluminium structures made of alloys listed in Tables 3.1a and 3.1.b can be used without the need for surface protection to avoid loss of load-bearing capacity.

NOTE Annex D gives information on corrosion resistance of aluminium and guidelines for surface protection of aluminium, as well as information on conditions for which a corrosion protection is recommended.

(3) Components susceptible to corrosion and subject to aggressive exposure, mechanical wear or fatigue should be designed such that inspection, maintenance and repair can be carried out satisfactorily during the design life. Access should be available for service inspection and maintenance.

(4) The requirements and means for execution of protective treatment undertaken off-site and on-site are given in EN 1090-3.

(5) The excecution specification should describe the extent, type and execution procedure for a selected protective treatment.

Annex D [informative] – Corrosion and surface protection

The following is a summary of the recommendations given in Annex D.

The corrosion resistance of aluminium alloys is attributable to the protective oxide film which forms on the surface of the metal immediately on exposure to air. This film is normally invisible and relatively inert. As it forms naturally on exposure to air or oxygen, and in many complex environments containing oxygen the protective film is thus self sealing. In mild environments an aluminium surface will retain its original appearance for years, and no protection is needed for most alloys. In moderate industrial conditions there will be a darkening and roughening of the surface. As the atmosphere becomes more aggressive such as in certain strongly acidic or strongly alkaline environments, the surface discoloration and roughening will be worse with visible white powdery surface oxides and the oxide film may itself be soluble. In these situations, the metal ceases to be fully protected and added protection is necessary. These conditions may also occur in crevices due to high local acid or alkaline conditions, but locations having this extreme effect are relatively few in number. In coastal and marine environments the surface will roughen and acquire a grey, stone-like, appearance, and protection of some alloys is necessary. Where aluminium is immersed in water special precautions may be necessary.

Where surface attack does occur corrosion time curves for aluminium and aluminium alloys usually follow an exponential form, with an initial loss of reflectivity after slight weathering. After this there is very little further change over very extensive periods. On atmospheric exposure, the initial stage may be a few months or two to three years, followed by little, if any, further change over periods of twenty, thirty or even eighty years. Such behaviour is consistent for all external freely exposed conditions and for all internal or shielded conditions, except where extremes of acidity or alkalinity can develop. Tropical environments are in general no more harmful to aluminium than temperate environments, although certain 5xxx-alloys are affected by long exposure to high ambient temperatures, particularly if in a marine environment.

Generally the structure should be designed according to known practice for avoiding corrosion. The possibility of galvanic corrosion and crevice corrosion should be evaluated and avoided due to proper design. All parts should be well drained. If a decorative appearance of aluminium is required to be kept for a long time the suitable surface treatments are organic coatings (liquid coating, powder coating) and anodic oxidation. The excecution specification should define the detail requirements. Deviations of colour appearance should be taken into account and should be agreed and defined e.g. by limit samples. Differences in appearance may occur by different lots of semi-products, by different lots of coating material and by different coaters. For the selection of suitable surface treatments the different behaviours of the systems concerning repairability, weathering resistance and cleanability should be taken in account. Specifications for anodic oxidation are given in EN 12373-1.

To assess if aluminium needs to be protected, the materials' durability rating is determined using Tables 3.1a and 3.1b, then based on this the required corrosion protection can be determined using Table D.1. In evaluating the need for protection from corrosion, the external environment needs to be assessed, and the specific location of the aluminium in a structure is studied and needs to be taken into account. For example, if there are crevasses or structural details which allow water or other agents to collect near or against aluminium alloys.

In the cases where different aluminium alloys are in contact or aluminium alloys and other materials especially metals are in contact or the washings from other metals may be in contact with aluminium, additional protection to the alloy is required as indicated in Table D.2. The Annex also informs on how to protect the alloys of aluminium when in contact with concrete, masonry, plaster, timber, soil, general chemicals used in building and insulating materials.

5 Structural analysis

5.1 Structural modelling for analysis

5.1.1 Structural modelling and basic assumptions

(1) Analysis should be based upon calculation models of the structure that are appropriate for the limit state under consideration.

(2) The calculation model and basic assumptions for the calculations should reflect the structural behaviour at the relevant limit state with appropriate accuracy and reflect the anticipated type of behaviour of the cross sections, members, joints and bearings.

5.1.2 Joint modelling

(1) The effects of the behaviour of the joints on the distribution of internal forces and moments within a structure, and on the overall deformations of the structure, may generally be neglected, but where such effects are significant (such as in the case of semi-continuous joints) they should be taken into account.

(2) To identify whether the effects of joint behaviour on the analysis need be taken into account, a distinction may be made between three joint models as follows:

- simple, in which the joint may be assumed not to transmit bending moments;
- continuous, in which the stiffness and/or the resistance of the joint allow full continuity of the members to be assumed in the analysis;
- semi-continuous, in which the behaviour of the joint needs to be taken into account in the analysis

NOTE Recommendations for the various types of joints are given in Annex L.

5.1.3 Ground-structure interaction

(1) Account should be taken of the deformation characteristics of the supports where significant.

NOTE EN 1997 gives guidance for calculation of soil-structure interaction.

5.2 Global analysis

5.2.1 Effects of deformed geometry of the structure

(1) The internal forces and moments may generally be determined using either:

- first-order analysis, using the initial geometry of the structure or
- second-order analysis, taking into account the influence of the deformation of the structure.

(2)P The effects of the deformed geometry (second-order effects) shall be considered if they increase the action effects significantly or modify significantly the structural behaviour.

(3) First order analysis may be used for the structure, if the increase of the relevant internal forces or moments or any other change of structural behaviour caused by deformations can be neglected. This condition may be assumed to be fulfilled, if the following criterion is satisfied:

$$\alpha_{cr} = \frac{F_{cr}}{F_{Ed}} \geq 10 \qquad (5.1)$$

where:

α_{cr} is the factor by which the design loading would have to be increased to cause elastic instability in a global mode

F_{Ed} is the design loading on the structure

F_{cr} is the elastic critical buckling load for global instability mode based on initial elastic stiffness.

NOTE The national Annex may give a different criterion for the limit of α_{cr} for neglecting the influence of second order effects.

Table NA.1 5.2.1(3) UK decision

Use the recommended value.

(4) The effects of shear lag and of local buckling on the stiffness should be taken into account if this significantly influences the global analysis.

NOTE Recommendations how to allow for shear lag are given in Annex K.

(5) The effects on the global analysis of the slip in bolt holes and similar deformations of connection devices like studs and anchor bolts on action effects should be taken into account, where relevant and significant.

5.2.2 Structural stability of frames

(1) If according to 5.2.1 the influence of the deformation of the structure has to be taken into account. (2) to (6) should be applied to consider these effects and to verify the structural stability.

(2) The verification of the stability of frames or their parts should be carried out considering imperfections and second order effects.

(3) According to the type of frame and the global analysis, second order effects and imperfections may be accounted for by one of the following methods:

a) both totally by the global analysis,
b) partially by the global analysis and partially through individual stability checks of members according to 6.3,
c) for basic cases by individual stability checks of equivalent members according to 6.3 using appropriate buckling lengths according to the global buckling mode of the structure.

(4) Second order effects may be calculated by using an analysis appropriate to the structure (including step-by-step or other iterative procedures). For frames where the first sway buckling mode is predominant first order elastic analysis should be carried out with subsequent amplification of relevant action effects (e.g. bending moments) by appropriate factors.

(5) In accordance with 5.2.2(3) a) and b) the stability of individual members should be checked according to the following:

a) If second order effects in individual members and relevant member imperfections (see 5.3.4) are totally accounted for in the global analysis of the structure, no individual stability check for the members according to 6.3 is necessary.
b) If second order effects in individual members or certain individual member imperfections (e.g. member imperfections for flexural and/or lateral torsional buckling, see 5.3.4) are not totally accounted for in the global analysis, the individual stability of members should be checked according to the relevant criteria in 6.3 for the effects not included in the global analysis. This verification should take account of end moments and forces from the global analysis of the structure, including global second order effects and global imperfections (see 5.3.2) where relevant and may be based on a buckling length equal to the system length, see Figure 5.1 (d), (e), (f) and (g).

(6) Where the stability of a frame is assessed by a check with the equivalent column method according to 6.3 the buckling length values should be based on a global buckling mode of the frame accounting for the stiffness behaviour of members and joints, the presence of plastic hinges and the distribution of compressive forces under the design loads. In this case internal forces to be used in resistance checks are calculated according to first order theory without considering imperfections, see Figure 5.1 (a), (b) and (c).

When undertaking frame anlaysis the first step is to decide if the frame is braced or un-braced. Braced frames are constructed with lateral bracing in the form of diagonal ties or shear walls included in the structure and these elements carry lateral forces imposed on the structure via the floors which act as horizontal diaphragms (plates) to the foundations. It is a design decision as to whether a structure would be braced or un-braced and this decision is usually taken at a very early stage. The analysis of braced and un-braced frames are very different and in practice, most frames are braced. With aluminium, whole framed buildings are rarely built using this material but frames for storage or part frames to support ceilings or similar applications will require designers to make the same decisions.

Once the decision on whether a frame is braced or unbraced has been made, the internal forces can be determined using one of two techniques. If the structure is unlikely to deform significantly, and rules are included in the code to ascertain when deformation is significant 5.2.1(3), then what is termed a first order analysis should be undertaken. This means analyse the structure elastically and use the results to determine element size. In some cases the effect of imperfections should be included in the element design as noted in 5.2.2(5). If the rules indicate deformations are important then the analysis of the structure should include for these but in addition the effect of imperfections should be allowed for while analyzing the structure and clause 5.3 summarises how this should be undertaken.

5.3 Imperfections

5.3.1 Basis

(1)P Appropriate allowances shall be considered to cover the effects of imperfections, including residual stresses and geometrical imperfections such as lack of verticality, lack of straightness, lack of flatness, lack of fit and any unspecified eccentricities present in joints of the unloaded structure.

NOTE A1⟩ Geometrical imperfections in accordance with the essential tolerances given in EN 1090-3 are considered in the resistance formulae, the buckling curves and the γ_M-values in EN 1999. ⟨A1

(2) Equivalent geometric imperfections, see 5.3.2 and 5.3.3, should be used, with values which reflect the possible effects of all type of imperfections. In the equivalent column method according to 5.3.4 the effects are included in the resistance formulae for member design.

(3) The following imperfections should be taken into account:

a) global imperfections for frames and bracing systems
b) local imperfections for individual members

5.3.2 Imperfections for global analysis of frames

(1) The assumed shape of global imperfections and local imperfections may be derived from the elastic buckling mode of a structure in the plane of buckling considered.

(2) Both in and out of plane buckling including torsional buckling with symmetric and asymmetric buckling shapes should be taken into account in the most unfavourable direction and form.

(3) For frames sensitive to buckling in a sway mode the effect of imperfections should be allowed for in frame analysis by means of an equivalent imperfection in the form of an initial sway imperfection and individual bow imperfections of members. The imperfections may be determined from:

a) global initial sway imperfections, see Figure 5.1(d):

$$\phi = \phi_0 \alpha_h \alpha_m \tag{5.2}$$

where:

ϕ_0 is the basic value: $\phi_0 = 1/200$

α_h is the reduction factor for height h applicable to columns:

$\alpha_h = \dfrac{2}{\sqrt{h}}$ but $\dfrac{2}{3} \leq \alpha_h \leq 1{,}0$

h is the height of the structure in meters

α_m is the reduction factor for the number of columns in a row: $\alpha_m = \sqrt{0{,}5\left(1+\dfrac{1}{m}\right)}$

m is the number of columns in a row including only those columns which carry a vertical load N_{Ed} not less than 50% of the average value of the column in the vertical plane considered.

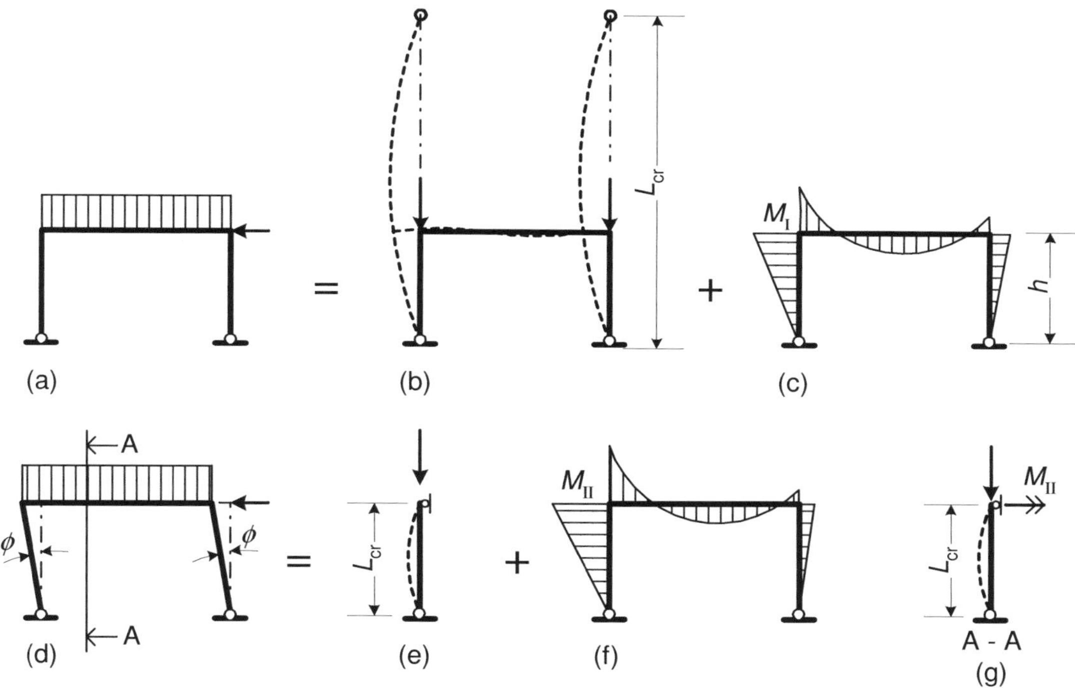

The equivalent column method is illustrated by (a), (b) and (c), where (a) is system and load, (b) is equivalent column length and (c) is the first order moment.

The equivalent sway method is illustrated by (d), (e), (f) and (g), where (d) is system, load and displacement, (e) is initial local bow and buckling length for flexural buckling, (f) is second order moment including moment from sway imperfection and (g) is initial local bow and buckling length for lateral-torsional buckling.

Figure 5.1 — Equivalent buckling length and equivalent sway imperfections

b) relative initial local bow imperfections of members for flexural buckling

$$e_0/L \qquad (5.3)$$

where L is the member length

NOTE The values e_0/L may be chosen in the National Annex. Recommended values are given in Table 5.1.

Table 5.1 — Design values of initial bow imperfection e_0/L

Buckling class acc. to Table 3.2	Elastic analysis	Plastic analysis
	e_0/L	e_0/L
A	1/300	1/250
B	1/200	1/150

Table NA.1 5.3.2(3) UK decision

Use the recommended value.

(4) For building frames sway imperfections may be disregarded where

$$H_{Ed} \geq 0{,}15\ V_{Ed} \qquad (5.4)$$

where:

H_{Ed} is the design value of the horizontal force
V_{Ed} is design value of the vertical force.

(5) For the determination of horizontal forces to floor diaphragms the configuration of imperfections as given in Figure 5.2 should be applied, where ϕ is a sway imperfection obtained from expression (5.2) assuming a single storey with height h, see (3) a).

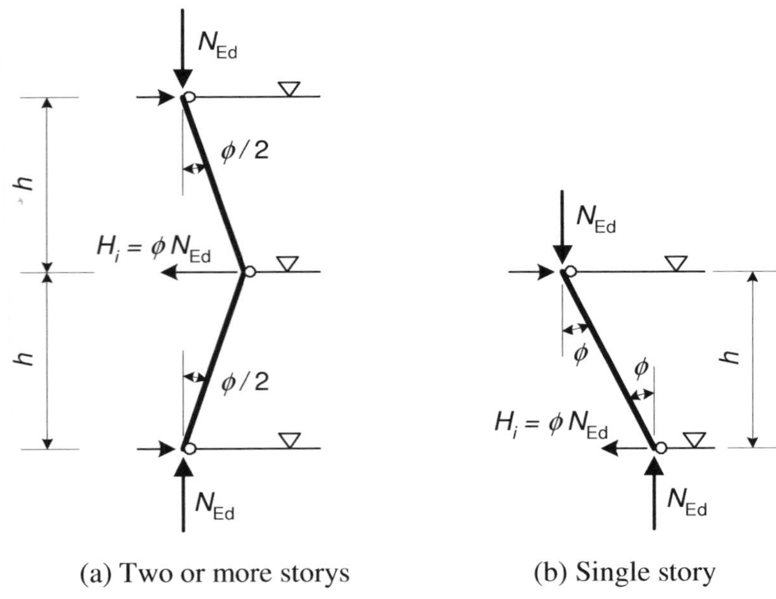

(a) Two or more storys (b) Single story

Figure 5.2 — Configuration of sway imperfections ϕ for horizontal forces on floor diaphragms

(6) When performing the global analysis for determining end forces and end moments to be used in member checks according to 6.3 local bow imperfections may be neglected. However, for frames sensitive to second order effects local bow imperfections of members additionally to global sway imperfections (see 5.2.1(3)) should be introduced in the structural analysis of the frame for each compressed member where the following conditions are met:

- at least one moment resistant joint at one member end
- $\bar{\lambda} > 0{,}5\sqrt{\dfrac{Af_o}{N_{Ed}}}$ (5.5)

where:

N_{Ed} is the design value of the compression force

$\bar{\lambda}$ is the in-plane relative slenderness calculated for the member considered as hinged at its ends

NOTE Local bow imperfections are taken into account in member checks, see 5.2.2 (3) and 5.3.4.

(7) The effects of initial sway imperfection and bow imperfections may be replaced by systems of equivalent horizontal forces, introduced for each column, see Figure 5.2 and Figure 5.3.

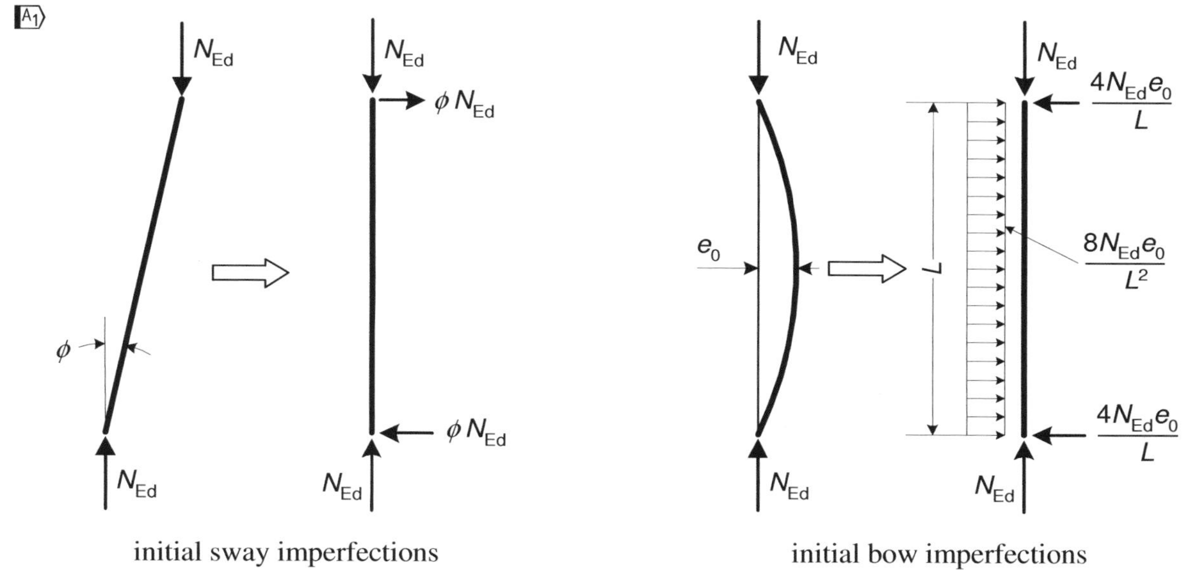

Figure 5.3 — Replacement of initial imperfections by equivalent horizontal forces A1

(8) These initial sway imperfections should apply in all relevant horizontal directions, but need only be considered in one direction at a time.

(9) Where, in multi-storey beam-and-column building frames, equivalent forces are used they should be applied at each floor and roof level.

(10) The possible torsional effects on a structure caused by anti-symmetric sways at the two opposite faces, should also be considered, see Figure 5.4.

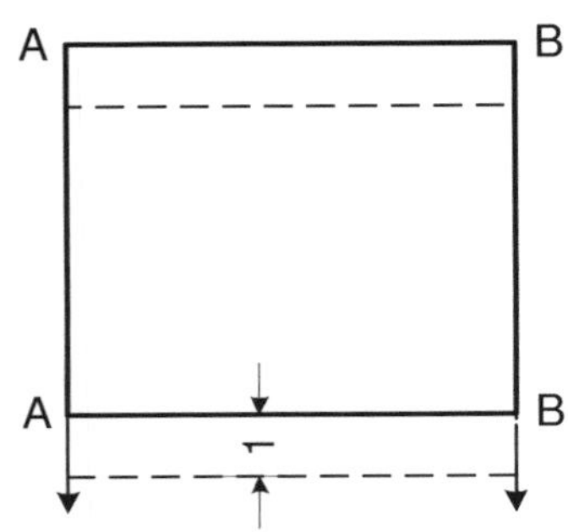

(a) Faces A-A and B-B sway in same direction

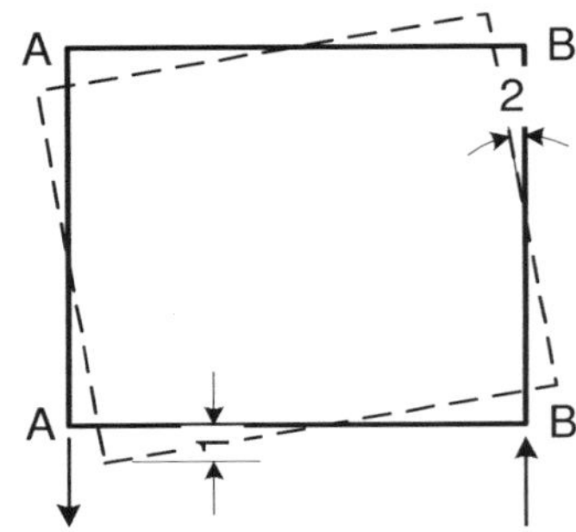

(b) Faces A-A and B-B sway in opposite direction

1 *translational sway,* 2 *rotational sway*

Figure 5.4 — Translational and torsional effects (plan view)

(11) As an alternative to (3) and (6) the shape of the elastic critical buckling mode η_{cr} of the structure or of the verified member may be applied as a unique global and local imperfection. The equivalent geometrical imperfection may be expressed in the form:

A1⟩ $$\eta_{init}(x) = e_0 \frac{N_{cr,m}}{EI_m \left|\eta''_{cr,m}\right|} \eta_{cr}(x) \quad (5.6)$$ ⟨A1

where:

$$e_0 = \alpha(\bar{\lambda}_m - \bar{\lambda}_0)\frac{M_{Rk,m}}{N_{Rk,m}} \frac{1 - \frac{\chi\bar{\lambda}_m^2}{\gamma_{M1}}}{1 - \chi\bar{\lambda}_m^2} \quad \text{for } \bar{\lambda}_m > \bar{\lambda}_0 \quad (5.7)$$

A1⟩ and m denotes the cross-section where $\left|\eta''_{cr}\right|$ reaches its maximum in the case of uniform normal force and uniform cross-section; ⟨A1

α is the imperfection factor for the relevant buckling curve, see Table 6.6;

$\bar{\lambda}_m = \sqrt{\frac{N_{Rk,m}}{N_{cr,m}}}$ is the relative slenderness of the structure;

$\bar{\lambda}_0$ is the limit given in Table 6.6;

χ is the reduction factor for the relevant buckling curve, see 6.3.1.2;

$N_{cr,m} = \alpha_{cr} N_{Ed,m}$ is the value of axial force in cross-section m when the elastic critical buckling was reached;

α_{cr} is the minimum force amplifier for the axial force configuration N_{Ed} in members to reach the elastic critical buckling;

$M_{Rk,m}$ is the characteristic moment resistance of the cross-section m according to (6.25) 6.2.5.1;

$N_{Rk,m}$ is the characteristic normal force resistance of the cross-section m according to (6.22) 6.2.4;

A1⟩ $EI_m \left|\eta''_{cr,m}\right|$ is the bending moment due to η_{cr} at the cross-section m; ⟨A1

η''_{cr} is the second derivative of $\eta_{cr}(x)$

NOTE 1 For calculating the amplifier α_{cr} the members of the structure may be considered to be loaded by axial forces N_{Ed} only that result from the first order elastic analysis of the structure for the design loads.

NOTE 2 A1⟩ The ratio $\frac{1}{EI_m \left|\eta''_{cr,m}\right|}$ may be replaced by $\frac{\left|\eta^{II}\right|_{max}}{\left|M^{II}_{\eta cr,m}\right| \left|\eta_{cr}\right|_{max}}$ ⟨A1

where:

A1⟩ $|\eta_{cr}|_{max}$ is the maximum value of the amplitude of the buckling mode of the structure (arbitrary value may be taken); ⟨A1

A1⟩ $|\eta^{II}|_{max}$ is the maximum deflection of the structure calculated using second order analysis (symbolised by II) for the structure with the imperfection in the shape of the elastic critical buckling mode η_{cr} with maximum amplitude $|\eta_{cr}|_{max}$; ⟨A1

$M^{II}_{\eta cr,m}$ is the bending moment in cross-section m calculated as given for $|\eta^{II}|_{max}$.

The bending moments in the structure due to η_{init} (x) with allowing for second order effects may be then calculated from:

$$M^{II}_{\eta init}(x) = \frac{e_0 N_{cr,m} |\eta^{II}|_{max}}{|M^{II}_{\eta cr,m}| |\eta_{cr}|_{max}} M^{II}_{\eta cr}(x) \tag{5.8}$$

NOTE 3 Formula (5.6) is based on the requirement that the imperfection η_{init} having the shape of the elastic buckling mode η_{cr}, should have the same maximum curvature as the equivalent uniform member.

5.3.3 Imperfection for analysis of bracing systems

(1) In the analysis of bracing systems which are required to provide lateral stability within the length of beams or compression members the effects of imperfections should be included by means of an equivalent geometric imperfection of the members to be restrained, in the form of an initial bow imperfection:

$$e_0 = \alpha_m L/500 \tag{5.9}$$

where:

L is the span of the member and

$$\alpha_m = \sqrt{0,5\left(1+\frac{1}{m}\right)} \tag{5.10}$$

in which m is the number of members to be restrained.

(2) For convenience, the effects of the initial bow imperfections of the members to be restrained by a bracing system, may be replaced by the equivalent stabilising force as shown in Figure 5.5:

$$q_0 = \Sigma N_{Ed} 8 \frac{e_0 + \delta_q}{L^2} \tag{5.11}$$

where:

δ_q is the inplane deflection of the bracing system due to q_0 plus any external loads calculated from first order analysis.

NOTE 1 δ_q may be taken as 0 if second order theory is used.

NOTE 2 As δ_q in (5.11) depends on q_0, it results in an iterative procedure.

(3) Where the bracing system is required to stabilise the compression flange of a beam of constant height, the force N_{Ed} in Figure 5.5 may be obtained from:

$$N_{Ed} = M_{Ed}/h \quad (5.12)$$

where:

M_{Ed} is the maximum moment in the beam
h is the overall depth of the beam.

NOTE Where a beam is subjected to external compression, this should be taken into account.

(4) At points where beams or compression members are spliced, it should also be verified that the bracing system is able to resist a local force equal to $\alpha_m N_{Ed}/100$ applied to it by each beam or compression member which is spliced at that point, and to transmit this force to the adjacent points at which that beam or compression member is restrained, see Figure 5.6.

(5) For checking for the local force according to clause (4), any external loads acting on bracing systems should also be included, but the forces arising from the imperfection given in (1) may be omitted.

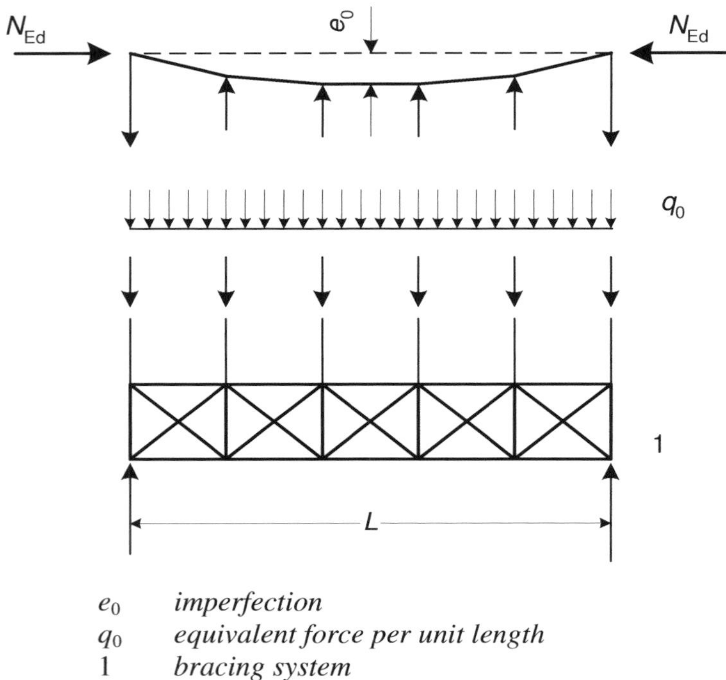

e_0 *imperfection*
q_0 *equivalent force per unit length*
1 *bracing system*

The force N_{Ed} is assumed uniform within the span L of the bracing system. For non-uniform forces this is slightly conservative.

Figure 5.5 — Equivalent stabilising force

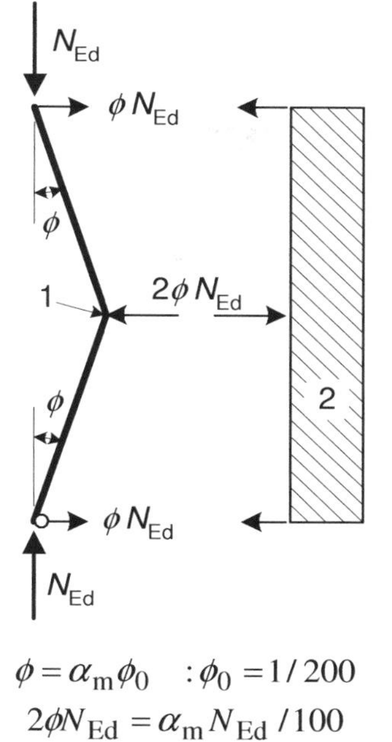

$\phi = \alpha_m \phi_0 \quad : \phi_0 = 1/200$

$2\phi N_{Ed} = \alpha_m N_{Ed} / 100$

1 *splice*, 2 *bracing system*

Figure 5.6 — Bracing forces at splices in compression members

5.3.4 Member imperfections

(1) The effects of imperfections of members described in 5.3.1(1) are incorporated within the formulas given for buckling resistance for members, see section 6.3.1.

(2) Where the stability of members is accounted for by second order analysis according to 5.2.2(5)a) for compression members imperfections [A1⟩ e_0 ⟨A1] according to 5.3.2(3)b) or 5.3.2(5) or (6) should be considered.

(3) For a second order analysis taking account of lateral torsional buckling of a member in bending the imperfections may be adopted as [A1⟩ ke_0, where e_0 ⟨A1] is the equivalent initial bow imperfection of the weak axis of the profile considered. In general an additional torsional imperfection need not to be allowed for.

NOTE The National Annex may choose the value of k. The value $k = 0,5$ is recommended.

Table NA.1 UK decision
Use the recommended value.

Imperfections are usually allowed for in both braced and unbraced frames when according to 5.2.1(3) deformations are significant but if horizontal forces to the structure H_{Ed} exceed 0,15 of the design value of the vertical force V_{Ed} then the impact of imperfections may be ignored, the assumption here being that the horizontal forces will be significantly more dominant than any imperfection. One other exception to allowing for the use of imperfections is when the stability of a frame is assessed by a check with the equivalent column method. Techniques to allow for imperfections include providing an equivalent imperfection in the form of an initial sway imperfection and individual bow imperfections for members or using a system of equivalent horizontal forces for each column as shown in Figures 5.2 and 5.3 in the code.

5.4 Methods of analysis

5.4.1 General

(1) The internal forces and moments may be determined using either

a) elastic global analysis
b) plastic global analysis.

NOTE For finite element model (FEM) analysis see EN 1993-1-5.

(2) Elastic global analysis may be used in all cases.

(3) Plastic global analysis may be used only where the structure has sufficient rotation capacity at the actual location of the plastic hinge, whether this is in the members or in the joints. Where a plastic hinge occurs in a member, the member cross sections should be double symmetric or single symmetric with a plane of symmetry in the same plane as the rotation of the plastic hinge and it should satisfy the requirements specified in 5.4.3. Where a plastic hinge occurs in a joint the joint should either have sufficient strength to ensure the hinge remains in the member or should be able to sustain the plastic resistance for a sufficient rotation.

NOTE 1 Information on rotation capacity is given in Annex G.

NOTE 2 Only certain alloys have the required ductility to allow sufficient rotation capacity, see 6.4.3(2).

5.4.2 Elastic global analysis

(1) Elastic global analysis is based on the assumption that the stress-strain behaviour of the material is linear, whatever the stress level is.

NOTE For the choice of a semi-continuous joint model see 5.1.2.

(2) Internal forces and moments may be calculated according to elastic global analysis even if the resistance of a cross section is based on its plastic resistance.

(3) Elastic global analysis may also be used for cross sections, the resistances of which are limited by local buckling.

5.4.3 Plastic global analysis

(1) Plastic global analysis should not be used for beams with transverse welds on the tension side of the member at the plastic hinge locations.

NOTE For plastic global analysis of beams recommendations are given in Annex H.

(2) Plastic global analysis should only be used where the stability of members can be assured, see 6.3.

Elastic analysis of frames may be used in all cases but plastic analysis is permitted under certain conditions.

6 Ultimate limit states for members

6.1 Basis

6.1.1 General

(1)P Aluminium structures and components shall be proportioned so that the basic design requirements for the ultimate limit state given in Section 2 are satisfied. The design recommendations are for structures subjected to normal atmospheric conditions.

6.1.2 Characteristic value of strength

(1) Resistance calculations for members are made using characteristic value of strength as follows:

f_o is the characteristic value of the strength for bending and overall yielding in tension and compression

f_u is the characteristic value of the strength for the local capacity of a net section in tension or compression

(2) The characteristic value of the 0,2% proof strength f_o and the ultimate tensile strength f_u for wrought aluminium alloys are given in 3.2.2.

6.1.3 Partial safety factors

(1) The partial factors γ_M as defined in 2.4.3 should be applied to the various characteristic values of resistance in this section as follows:

Table 6.1 — Partial safety factors for ultimate limit states

resistance of cross-sections whatever the class is:	γ_{M1}
resistance of members to instability assessed by member checks:	
resistance of cross-sections in tension to fracture:	γ_{M2}
resistance of joints:	See Section 8

NOTE 1 Partial factors γ_{Mi} may be defined in the National Annex. The following numerical values are recommended:

γ_{M1} = 1,10
γ_{M2} = 1,25

NOTE 2 For other recommended numerical values see EN 1999 Part 1-2 to Part 1-5. For structures not covered by EN 1999 Part 1-2 to Part 1-5 the National Annex may give information.

Table NA.1 UK decision

Use the recommended value.

6.1.4 Classification of cross-sections

6.1.4.1 Basis

(1) The role of cross-section classification is to identify the extent to which the resistance and rotation capacity of cross-sections is limited by its local buckling resistance.

NOTE See also Annex F.

6.1.4.2 Classification

(1) Four classes of cross-sections are defined, as follows:

- Class 1 cross-sections are those that can form a plastic hinge with the rotation capacity required for plastic analysis without reduction of the resistance.

NOTE Further information on class 1 cross-sections is given in Annex G.

- Class 2 cross-sections are those that can develop their plastic moment resistance, but have limited rotation capacity because of local buckling.
- Class 3 cross-sections are those in which the calculated stress in the extreme compression fibre of the aluminium member can reach its proof strength, but local buckling is liable to prevent development of the full plastic moment resistance.
- Class 4 cross-sections are those in which local buckling will occur before the attainment of proof stress in one or more parts of the cross-section.

(2) In Class 4 cross-sections effective thickness may be used to make the necessary allowances for reduction in resistance due to the effects of local buckling, see 6.1.5.

(3) The classification of a cross-section depends on the width to thickness ratio of the parts subject to compression.

(4) Compression parts include every part of a cross-section that is either totally or partially in compression under the load combination considered.

(5) The various compression parts in a cross-section (such as web or a flange) can, in general, be in different classes. A cross-section is classified according to the highest (least favourable) class of its compression parts.

(6) The following basic types of thin-walled part are identified in the classification process:

a) flat outstand parts;
b) flat internal parts;
c) curved internal parts.

These parts can be un-reinforced, or reinforced by longitudinal stiffening ribs or edge lips or bulbs (see Figure 6.1).

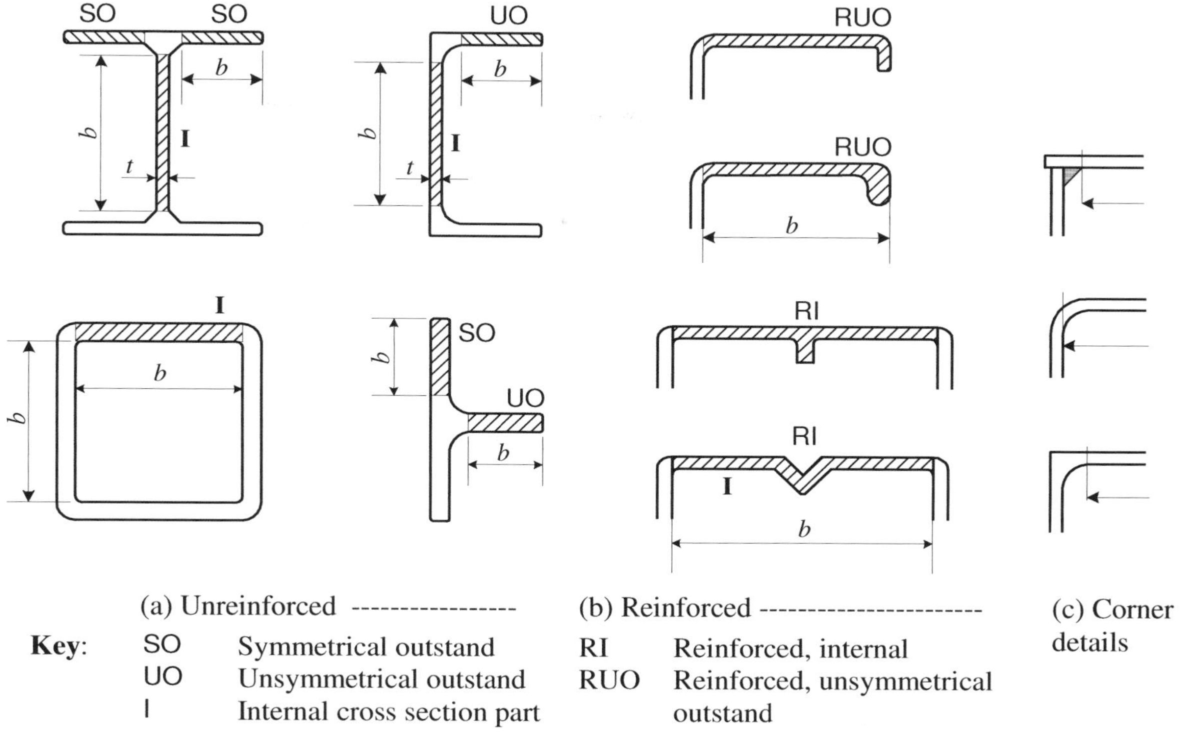

Figure 6.1 — Types of cross-section parts

Additional information on the classification of sections can be found in Annexes F and G.

6.1.4.3 Slenderness parameters

(1) The susceptibility of an un-reinforced flat part to local buckling is defined by the parameter β, which has the following values:

a) flat internal parts with no stress gradient or flat outstands with no stress gradient or peak compression at toe $\qquad \beta = b/t \qquad$ (6.1)

b) internal parts with a stress gradient that results in a neutral axis at the centre $\qquad \beta = 0{,}40b/t \qquad$ (6.2)

c) internal parts with stress gradient and outstands with peak compression at root $\qquad \beta = \eta b/t \qquad$ (6.3)

where:

b is the width of a cross-section part
t is the thickness of a cross-section
η is the stress gradient factor given by the expressions:

$\eta = 0{,}70 + 0{,}30\psi \qquad (1 \geq \psi \geq -1),$ (6.4)

$\eta = 0{,}80/(1-\psi) \qquad (\psi < -1)$, see Figure 6.2 (6.5)

where

ψ is the ratio of the stresses at the edges of the plate under consideration related to the maximum compressive stress. In general the neutral axis should be the elastic neutral axis, but in checking whether a section is class 1 or 2 it is permissible to use the plastic neutral axis.

NOTE All cross section parts are considered simply supported when calculating the parameters β even if the cross section parts are elastically restrained or clamped.

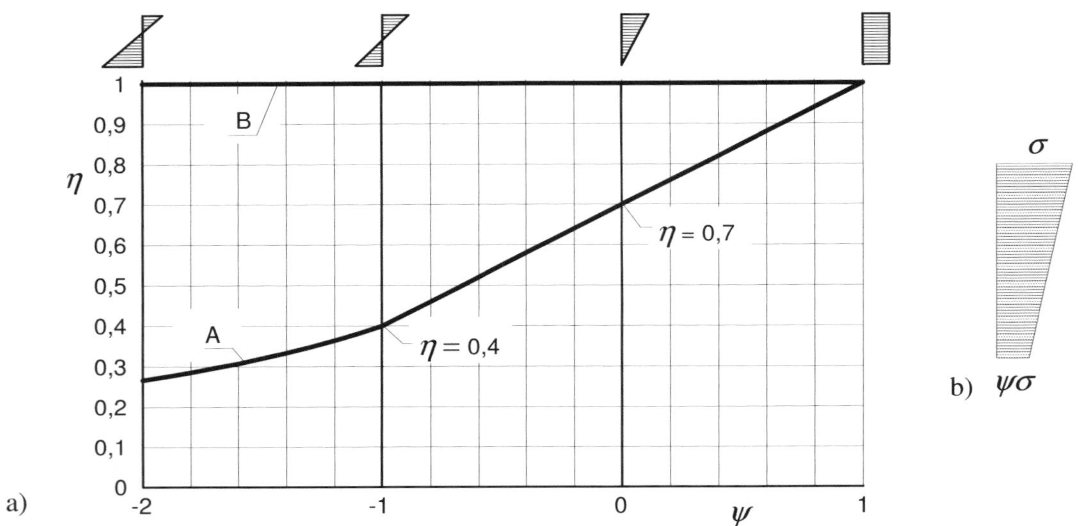

Figure 6.2 — Flat internal parts under stress gradient, values of η.
For internal parts or outstands (peak compression at root) use curve A.
For outstands (peak compression at toe) use line B.

(2) When considering the susceptibility of a reinforced flat part to local buckling, three possible buckling modes should be considered, as shown in Figure 6.3. Separate values of β should be found for each mode. The modes are:

a) Mode 1: the reinforced part buckles as a unit, so that the reinforcement buckles with the same curvature as the part. This mode is often referred to as distortional buckling.
b) Mode 2: the sub-parts and the reinforcement buckle as individual parts with the junction between them remaining straight.
c) Mode 3: this is a combination of Modes 1 and 2 in which sub-part buckles are superimposed on the buckles of the whole part. This is indicated in Figure 6.3(c).

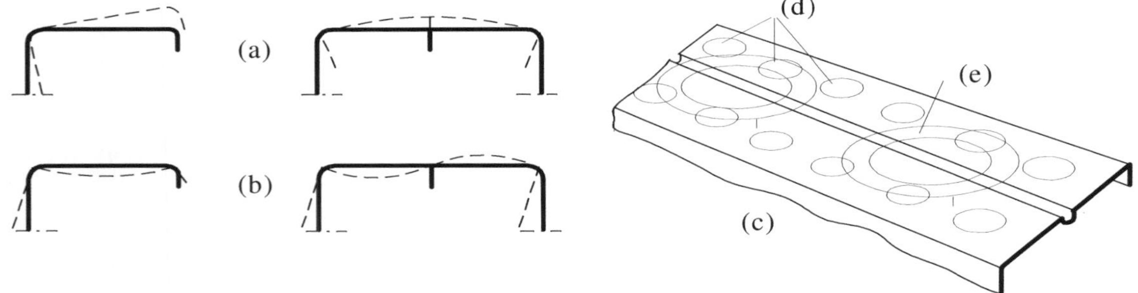

(a) Mode 1, (b) mode 2, (c) mode 3, (d) sub-part buckles, (e) whole reinforced part buckles.

Figure 6.3 — Buckling modes for flat reinforced parts

(3) Values of β are found as follows:

a) Mode 1, uniform compression, standard reinforcement:
When the reinforcement is a single-sided rib or lip of thickness equal to the part thickness t,

$$\beta = \eta \frac{b}{t} \tag{6.6}$$

where η is given in expressions (6.7a), (6.7b) or (6.7c), or is read from Figure 6.4(a), (b) or (c). In this figure the depth c of the rib or lip is measured to the inner surface of the plate.

$$\eta = \frac{1}{\sqrt{1+0,1(c/t-1)^2}}$$ (Figure 6.4a) (6.7a)

$$\eta = \frac{1}{\sqrt{1+2,5\frac{(c/t-1)^2}{b/t}}} \geq 0,5$$ (Figure 6.4b) (6.7b)

$$\eta = \frac{1}{\sqrt{1+4,5\frac{(c/t-1)^2}{b/t}}} \geq 0,33$$ (Figure 6.4c) (6.7c)

b) Mode 1, uniform compression, non-standard reinforcement:
With any other single shape of reinforcement, the reinforcement is replaced by an equivalent rib or lip equal in thickness to the part (t). The value of c for the equivalent rib or lip is chosen so that the second moment of area of the reinforcement about the mid-plane of the plate part is equal to that of the non-standard reinforcement about the same plane. An alternative method is given in 6.6.

c) Mode 1, uniform compression, complex reinforcement:
For unusual shapes of reinforcement not amenable to the analysis described above,

$$\beta = \frac{b}{t}\left(\frac{\sigma_{cr0}}{\sigma_{cr}}\right)^{0,4} \qquad (6.8)$$

σ_{cr} is the elastic critical stress for the reinforced part assuming simply supported edges
σ_{cr0} is the elastic critical stress for the unreinforced part assuming simply supported edges.

d) Mode 1, stress gradient:
The value of β is found from the expression (6.8), where σ_{cr} and σ_{cr0} now relate to the stress at the more heavily compressed edge of the part.

e) Mode 2:
The value of β is found separately for each sub-part in accordance with 6.1.4.3(1).

(4) The susceptibility of a uniformly compressed shallow curved unreinforced internal part to local buckling is defined by β, where:

$$\beta = \frac{b}{t}\frac{1}{\sqrt{1+0,006\frac{b^4}{R^2t^2}}} \qquad (6.9)$$

R is radius of curvature to the mid-thickness of material
b is developed width of the part at mid-thickness of material
t is thickness.

The above treatment is valid if $R/b > 0,1b/t$. Sections containing more deeply curved parts require special study or design by testing.

(5) The susceptibility of a thin-walled round tube to local buckling, whether in uniform compression or in bending is defined by β, where:

$$\beta = 3\sqrt{\frac{D}{t}} \qquad (6.10)$$

D = diameter to mid-thickness of tube material.

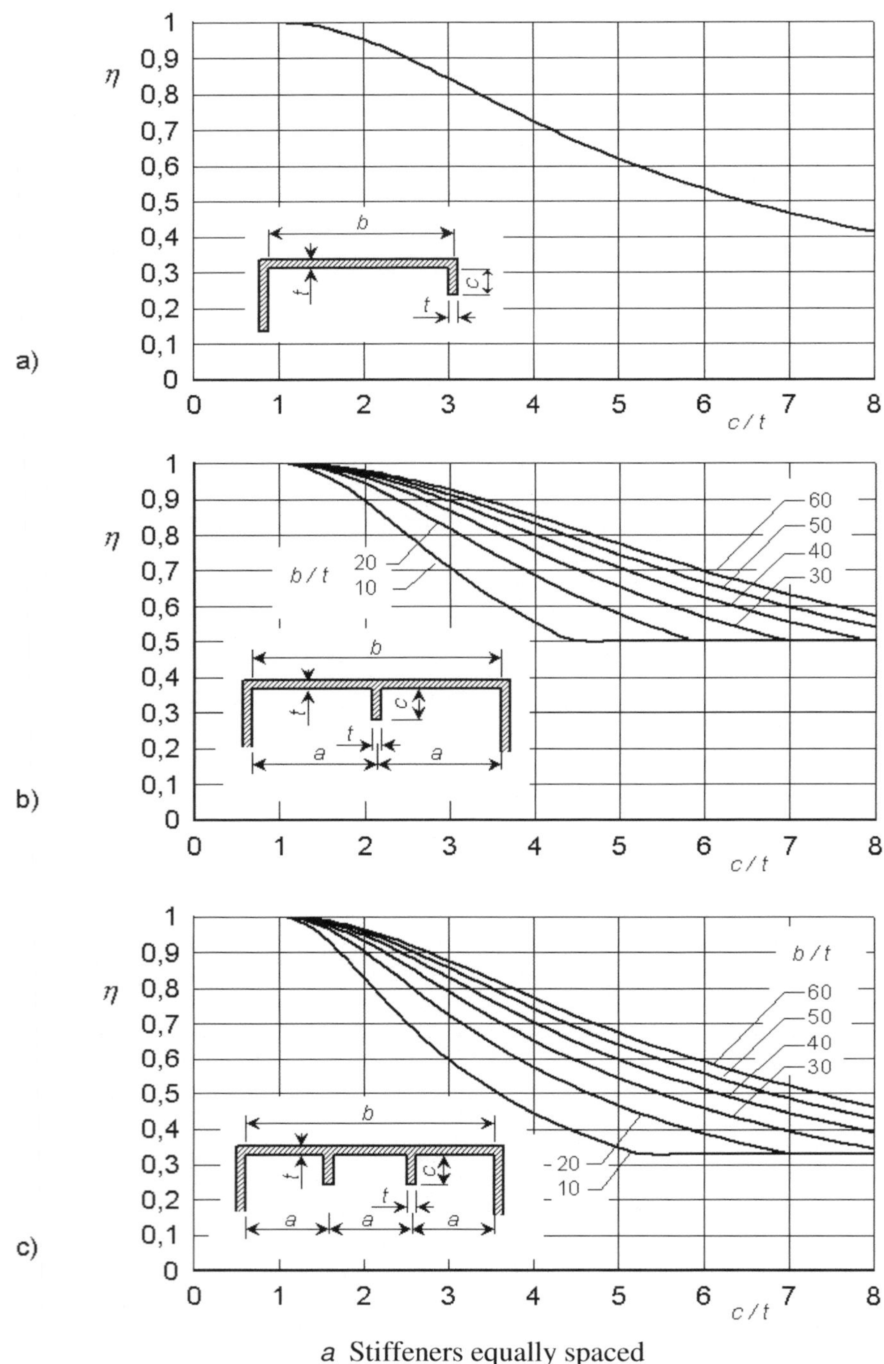

a Stiffeners equally spaced

Figure 6.4 — Values of η for reinforced cross section parts

6.1.4.4 Classification of cross-section parts

(1) The classification of parts of cross-sections is linked to the values of the slenderness parameter β as follows:

Parts in beams

$\beta \leq \beta_1$: class 1
$\beta_1 < \beta \leq \beta_2$: class 2
$\beta_2 < \beta \leq \beta_3$: class 3
$\beta_3 < \beta$: class 4

Parts in struts

$\beta \leq \beta_2$: class 1 or 2
$\beta_2 < \beta \leq \beta_3$: class 3
$\beta_3 < \beta$: class 4

(2) Values of β_1, β_2 and β_3 are given in Table 6.2.

Table 6.2 — Slenderness parameters β_1/ε, β_2/ε and β_3/ε

Material classification according to Table 3.2	Internal part			Outstand part		
	β_1/ε	β_2/ε	β_3/ε	β_1/ε	β_2/ε	β_3/ε
Class A, without welds	11	16	22	3	4,5	6
Class A, with welds	9	13	18	2,5	4	5
Class B, without welds	13	16,5	18	3,5	4,5	5
Class B, with welds	10	13,5	15	3	3,5	4
$\varepsilon = \sqrt{250/f_o}$, f_o in N/mm^2						

(3) In the Table 6.2, a cross-section part is considered with welds if it contains welding at an edge or at any point within its width. However, a cross-sections part may be considered as without welds if the welds are transversal to the member axis and located at a position of lateral restraint.

NOTE In a cross-section part with welds the classification is independent of the extent of the HAZ.

(4) When classifying parts in members under bending, if the parts are less highly stressed than the most severely stressed fibres in the section, a modified expression $\varepsilon = \sqrt{(250 / f_o) / (z_1 / z_2)}$ may be used. In this expression, z_1 is the distance from the elastic neutral axis of the effective section to the most severely stressed fibres, and z_2 is the distance from the elastic neutral axis of the effective section to the part under consideration. z_1 and z_2 should be evaluated on the effective section by means of an iterative procedure (minimum two steps).

6.1.5 Local buckling resistance

(1) Local buckling in class 4 members is generally allowed for by replacing the true section by an effective section. The effective section is obtained by employing a local buckling factor ρ_c to factor down the thickness. ρ_c is applied to any uniform thickness class 4 part that is wholly or partly in compression. Parts that are not uniform in thickness require a special study.

(2) The factor ρ_c is given by expressions (6.11) or (6.12), separately for different parts of the section, in terms of the ratio β/ε, where β is found in 6.1.4.3, ε is defined in Table 6.2 and the constants C_1 and C_2 in Table 6.3. The relationships between ρ_c and β/ε are summarised in Figure 6.5.

$$\rho_c = 1{,}0 \qquad \text{if } \beta \leq \beta_3 \tag{6.11}$$

$$\rho_c = \frac{C_1}{(\beta/\varepsilon)} - \frac{C_2}{(\beta/\varepsilon)^2} \qquad \text{if } \beta > \beta_3 \tag{6.12}$$

Table 6.3 – Constants C_1 and C_2 in expressions for ρ_c

Material classification according to Table 3.2	Internal part		Outstand part	
	C_1	C_2	C_1	C_2
Class A, without welds	32	220	10	24
Class A, with welds	29	198	9	20
Class B, without welds	29	198	9	20
Class B, with welds	25	150	8	16

(3) For flat outstand parts in unsymmetrical cross-sections (Figure 6.1), ρ_c is given by the above expressions for flat outstand in symmetrical sections, but not more than $120/(\beta/\varepsilon)^2$.

(4) For reinforced cross-section parts: Consider all possible modes of buckling, and take the lower value of ρ_c. In the case of mode 1 buckling the factor ρ_c should be applied to the area of the reinforcement as well as to the basic plate thickness. See also 6.7. For reinforced outstand cross section part use curve for outstands, otherwise curve for internal cross section part.

(5) For the determination of ρ_c in sections required to carry biaxial bending or combined bending and axial load, see notes in 6.3.3(4).

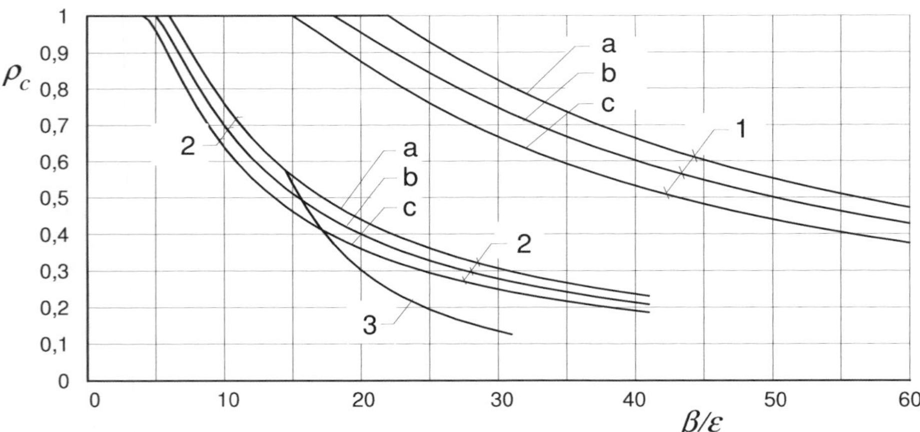

1 Internal parts and round tubes, 2 Symmetrical outstands, 3 Un-symmetrical outstands
a) class A, without welds,
b) class A, with welds or class B, without welds
c) class B, with welds

Figure 6.5 — Relationship between ρ_c and β/ε for outstands, internal parts and round tubes

Local buckling is not generally a problem in most structural elements but class 4 elements need special consideration as the various components making up the section are slender. In these elements, local buckling can occur.

6.1.6 HAZ softening adjacent to welds

6.1.6.1 General

(1)P In the design of welded structures using strain hardened or artificially aged precipitation hardening alloys the reduction in strength properties that occurs in the vicinity of welds shall be allowed for.

(2) Exceptions to this rule, where there is no weakening adjacent to welds, occur in alloys in the O-condition; or if the material is in the F condition and design strength is based on O-condition properties.

(3) For design purposes it is assumed that throughout the heat affected zone (HAZ) the strength properties are reduced on a constant level.

NOTE 1 The reduction affects the 0,2% proof strength of the material more severely than the ultimate tensile strength. The affected region extends immediately around the weld, beyond which the strength properties rapidly recover to their full unwelded values.

NOTE 2 Even small welds to connect a small attachment to a main member may considerably reduce the resistance of the member due to the presence of a HAZ. In beam design it is often beneficial to locate welds and attachments in low stress areas, i.e. near the neutral axis or away from regions of high bending moment.

NOTE 3 For some heat treatable alloys it is possible to mitigate the effects of HAZ softening by means of artificial ageing applied after welding.

6.1.6.2 Severity of softening

(1) The characteristic value of the 0,2% proof strengths $f_{o,haz}$ and the ultimate strength $f_{a,haz}$ in the heat affected zone are listed in Table 3.2. Table 3.2 also gives the reduction factors

$$\rho_{o,haz} = \frac{f_{o,haz}}{f_o} \qquad (6.13)$$

$$\rho_{u,haz} = \frac{f_{u,haz}}{f_u} \qquad (6.14)$$

NOTE Values for other alloys and tempers must be found and defined by testing. If general values are wanted, testing series are necessary to allow for the fact that material from different manufactures of semi products may vary in chemical composition and therefore may show different strength values after welding. In some cases it is also possible to derive strength values from values of well-known alloys by interpolation.

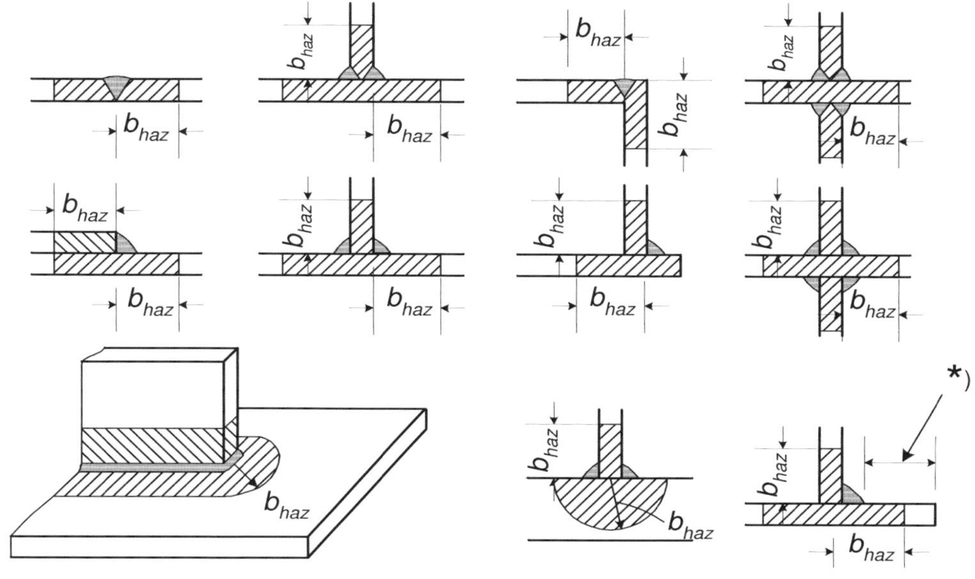

*) If this distance is less than $3b_{haz}$ assume that the HAZ extends to the full width of outstand, see 6.1.6.3(7)

Figure 6.6 — The extent of heat-affected zones (HAZ)

(2) The values of $f_{o,haz}$ and [A1) $f_{u,haz}$ (A1] in Table 3.2 are valid from the following times after welding, providing the material has been held at a temperature not less than 10°C:

- 6xxx series alloys 3 days
- 7xxx series alloys 30 days.

NOTE 1 If the material is held at a temperature below 10°C after welding, the recovery time will be prolonged. Advice should be sought from manufacturers.

NOTE 2 The severity of softening can be taken into account by the characteristic value of strength $f_{o,haz}$ and $f_{u,haz}$ in the HAZ (Table 3.2) as for the parent metal, or by reducing the assumed cross-sectional area over which the stresses acts with the factors $\rho_{o,haz}$ and $\rho_{u,haz}$ (Table 3.2). Thus the characteristic resistance of a simple rectangular section affected by HAZ softening can be expressed as $Af_{u,haz} = (\rho_{u,haz} A)\, f_u$ if the design is dominated by ultimate strength or as $Af_{o,haz} = (\rho_{o,haz} A)\, f_o$ if the design is dominated by the 0,2% proof strength.

The extent to which heat affected zones intrude into the parent material also needs to be considered. A number of factors influence this penetration including, among others:

- type of weld,
- thickness of parent material,
- the cooling regime applied,
- whether multi-pass welds were used and welds close to each other resulting in the overlapping of HAZ zones.

Section 6.1.6.3 includes rules to allow for the extent of HAZ intrusion.

6.2 Resistance of cross-sections

6.2.1 General

(1)P The design value of an action effect in each cross-section shall not exceed the corresponding design resistance and if several action effects act simultaneously the combined effect shall not exceed the resistance for that combination.

(2) Shear lag effects should be included by an effective width. Local buckling effects should be included by an effective thickness, see 6.1.5. As an alternative, equivalent effective width may also be used.

NOTE For the effect of shear lag, see Annex K.

(3) The design values of resistance depend on the classification of the cross-section.

(4) Verification according to elastic resistance may be carried out for all cross-sectional classes provided the effective cross-sectional properties are used for the verification of class 4 cross-sections.

(5) For the resistance the following yield criterion for a critical point of the cross-section may be used unless other interaction formulae apply, see 6.2.7 to 6.2.10.

$$\left(\frac{\sigma_{x,Ed}}{f_o / \gamma_{M1}}\right)^2 + \left(\frac{\sigma_{z,Ed}}{f_o / \gamma_{M1}}\right)^2 - \left(\frac{\sigma_{x,Ed}}{f_o / \gamma_{M1}}\right)\left(\frac{\sigma_{z,Ed}}{f_o / \gamma_{M1}}\right) + 3\left(\frac{\tau_{Ed}}{f_o / \gamma_{M1}}\right)^2 \le C \tag{6.15}$$

$$\frac{\sigma_{x,Ed}}{f_o / \gamma_{M1}} \le 1, \quad \frac{\sigma_{z,Ed}}{f_o / \gamma_{M1}} \le 1 \text{ and } \frac{\sqrt{3}\tau_{Ed}}{f_o / \gamma_{M1}} \le 1 \qquad \text{(6.15a, b, c)}$$

where:

$\sigma_{x,Ed}$ is the design value of the local longitudinal stress at the point of consideration
$\sigma_{z,Ed}$ is the design value of the local transverse stress at the point of consideration
τ_{Ed} is the design value of the local shear stress at the point of consideration
$C \ge 1$ is a constant, see NOTE 2

NOTE 1 The verification according to 6.2.1(5) can be conservative as it only partially allow for plastic stress distribution, which is permitted in elastic design. Therefore it should only be performed where the interaction on the basis of resistances cannot be performed.

NOTE 2 The constant C in criterion (6.15) may be defined in the National Annex. The numerical value C = 1,2 is recommended.

Table NA.1 6.2.1(5)

Use the recommended value.

Section 6.2 through to 6.2.11 provides information on the resistance of cross sections including data on bending, compressive, shear, torsional and tension effects, as well as various combinations of these. The resistance of the section is considered in isolation so the impact of the boundary conditions, slenderness (long as opposed to short elements) etc. are not considered in this part. Section 6.3 provides information on element design where the impact of boundary conditions, slenderness and other effects are examined.

6.2.2 Section properties

6.2.2.1 Gross cross-section

(1) The properties of the gross cross-section (A_g) should be found by using the nominal dimensions. Holes for fasteners need not be deducted, but allowance should be made for larger openings. Splice materials and battens should not be included.

6.2.2.2 Net area

(1) The net area of a cross-section (A_{net}) should be taken as the gross area less appropriate deductions for holes, other openings and heat affected zones.

(2) For calculating net section properties, the deduction for a single fastener hole should be the [A1) *Deleted text* (A1] cross-sectional area of the hole in the plane of its axis. For countersunk holes, appropriate allowance should be made for the countersunk portion.

(3) Provided that the fastener holes are not staggered, the total area to be deducted for the fastener holes should be the maximum sum of the sectional areas of the holes in any cross-section perpendicular to the member axis (see failure plane 1 in Figure 6.7).

NOTE The maximum sum denotes the position of the critical failure line.

(4) Where the fastener holes are staggered, the total area to be deducted for fastener holes should be the greater of (see Figure 6.7):

a) the deduction for non-staggered holes given in (3)
b) a deduction taken as $\sum t\, d - \sum t\, b_s$ where b_s is the lesser of

$$s^2/(4p) \quad \text{or} \quad 0{,}65s \tag{6.16}$$

where:

- d is the diameter of hole
- s is staggered pitch, the spacing of the centres of two consecutive holes in the chain measured parallel to the member axis
- p is the spacing of the centers of the same two holes measured perpendicular to the member axis
- t is the thickness (or effective thickness in a member containing HAZ material).

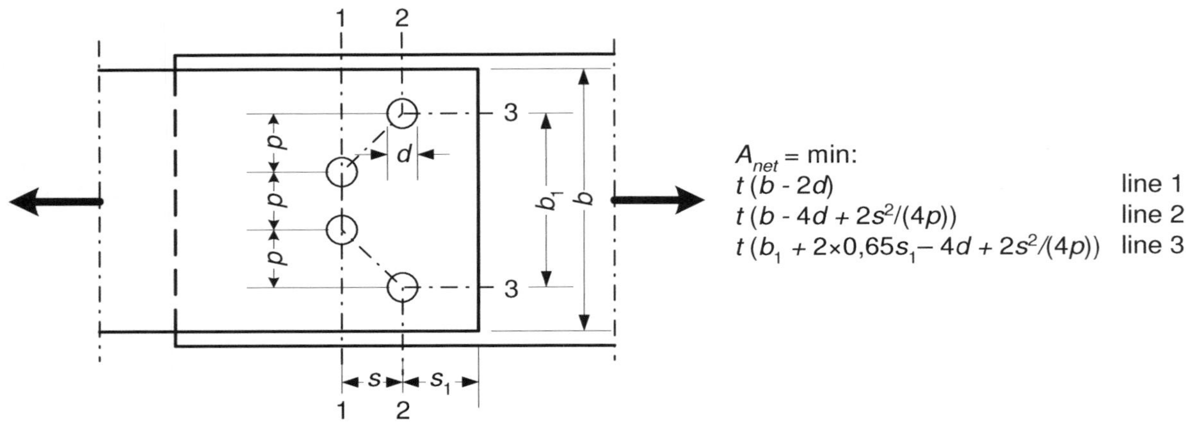

Figure 6.7 — Staggered holes and critical fracture lines 1, 2 and 3

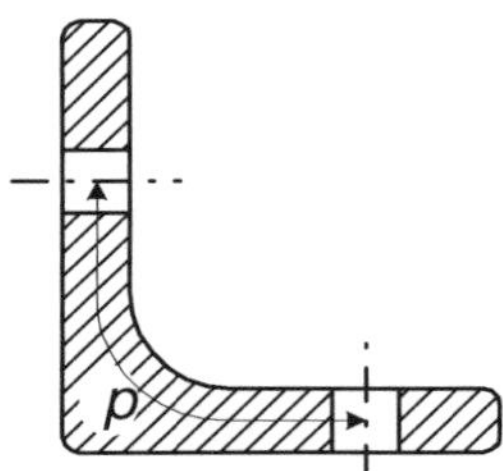

Figure 6.8 — Angles with holes in both legs

(5) In an angle or other member with holes in more than one plane, the spacing p should be measured along the center of thickness of the material (see Figure 6.8).

6.2.2.3 Shear lag effects

(1) The effect of shear lag on the buckling and rupture resistance of flanges should be taken into account.

NOTE Recommendations for the effect of shear lag are given in Annex K.

6.2.3 Tension

(1)P The design value of the tensile force N_{Ed} shall satisfy:

$$\frac{N_{Ed}}{N_{t,Rd}} \leq 1,0 \tag{6.17}$$

[A1] NOTE Eccentricity due to the shift of centroidal axis of asymmetric welded sections may be neglected. [A1]

(2) The design tension resistance of the cross-section $N_{t,Rd}$ should be taken as the lesser of $N_{o,Rd}$ and $N_{u,Rd}$ where:

a) general yielding along the member: $N_{o,Rd} = A_g f_o/\gamma_{M1}$ (6.18)
b) local failure at a section with holes: $N_{u,Rd} = 0,9A_{net} f_u/\gamma_{M2}$ (6.19a)
c) local failure at a section with HAZ: $N_{u,Rd} = A_{eff} f_u/\gamma_{M2}$ (6.19b)

where:

A_g is either the gross section or a reduced cross-section to allow for HAZ softening due to longitudinal welds. In the latter case A_g is found by taking a reduced area equal to $\rho_{o,haz}$ times the area of the HAZ, see 6.1.6.2

A_{net} is the net section area, with deduction for holes and a deduction if required to allow for the effect of HAZ softening in the net section through the hole. The latter deduction is based on the reduced thickness of $\rho_{u,haz}t$

A_{eff} is the effective area based on the reduced thickness of $\rho_{u,haz}t$.

(3) For angles connected through one leg see [A1) 8.5.2.3 (A1]. Similar consideration should also be given to other types of sections connected through outstands such as T-sections and channels.

(4) For staggered holes, see 6.2.2.2.

6.2.4 Compression

(1) P The design value of the axial compression force N_{Ed} shall satisfy:

$$\frac{N_{Ed}}{N_{c,Rd}} \leq 1{,}0 \tag{6.20}$$

[A1) NOTE Eccentricity due to the shift of centroidal axis of asymmetric welded sections may be neglected. (A1]

(2) The design resistance for uniform compression $N_{c,Rd}$ should be taken as the lesser of $N_{u,Rd}$ and $N_{c,Rd}$ where:

a) in sections with unfilled holes $N_{u,Rd} = A_{net}f_u/\gamma_{M2}$ (6.21)

b) other sections $N_{c,Rd} = A_{eff}f_o/\gamma_{M1}$ (6.22)

in which:

A_{net} is the net section area, with deductions for unfilled holes and HAZ softening if necessary. See 6.2.2.2. For holes located in reduced thickness regions the deduction may be based on the reduced thickness, instead of the full thickness.

A_{eff} is the effective section area based on reduced thickness allowing for local buckling and HAZ softening but ignoring unfilled holes.

6.2.5 Bending moment

6.2.5.1 Basis

(1)P The design value of the bending moment M_{Ed} at each cross section shall satisfy

$$\frac{M_{Ed}}{M_{Rd}} \leq 1{,}0 \tag{6.23}$$

[A1) NOTE Eccentricity due to the shift of centroidal axis of asymmetric welded sections may be neglected. (A1]

(2) The design resistance for bending about one principal axis of a cross section M_{Rd} is determined as the lesser of $M_{u,Rd}$ and $M_{c,Rd}$ where:

$M_{u,Rd} = W_{net}f_u/\gamma_{M2}$ in a net section and (6.24)

$M_{c,Rd} = \alpha W_{el}f_o/\gamma_{M1}$ at each cross-section (6.25)

where:

α is the shape factor, see Table 6.4

W_{el} is the elastic modulus of the gross section (see 6.2.5.2)

W_{net} is the elastic modulus of the net section allowing for holes and HAZ softening, if welded (see 6.2.5.2). The latter deduction is based on the reduced thickness of $\rho_{u,haz}t$.

Table 6.4 — Values of shape factor α

Cross-section class	Without welds	With longitudinal welds
1	W_{pl} / W_{el} *)	$W_{pl,haz} / W_{el}$ *)
2	W_{pl} / W_{el}	$W_{pl,haz} / W_{el}$
3	$\alpha_{3,u}$	$\alpha_{3,w}$
4	W_{eff} / W_{el}	$W_{eff,haz} / W_{el}$
*) NOTE These formulae are on the conservative side. For more refined value, recommendations are given in Annex F		

In Table 6.4 the various section moduli W and $\alpha_{3,u}$, $\alpha_{3,w}$ are defined as:

W_{pl} plastic modulus of gross section

W_{eff} effective elastic section modulus, obtained using a reduced thickness t_{eff} for the class 4 parts (see 6.2.5.2)

$W_{el,haz}$ effective elastic modulus of the gross section, obtained using a reduced thickness $\rho_{o,haz}t$ for the HAZ material (see 6.2.5.2)

$W_{pl,haz}$ effective plastic modulus of the gross section, obtained using a reduced thickness $\rho_{o,haz}t$ for the HAZ material (see 6.2.5.2)

$W_{eff,haz}$ effective elastic section modulus, obtained using a reduced thickness $\rho_c t$ for the class 4 parts or a reduced thickness $\rho_{o,haz}t$ for the HAZ material, whichever is the smaller (see 6.2.5.2)

$\alpha_{3,u} = 1$ or may alternatively be taken as:

$$\alpha_{3,u} = \left[1 + \left(\frac{\beta_3 - \beta}{\beta_3 - \beta_2}\right)\left(\frac{W_{pl}}{W_{el}} - 1\right)\right] \tag{6.26}$$

$\alpha_{3,w} = W_{el,haz}/W_{el}$ or may alternatively be taken as:

$$\alpha_{3,w} = \left[\frac{W_{el,haz}}{W_{el}} + \left(\frac{\beta_3 - \beta}{\beta_3 - \beta_2}\right)\left(\frac{W_{pl,haz} - W_{el,haz}}{W_{el}}\right)\right] \tag{6.27}$$

where:

β is the slenderness parameter for the most critical part in the section

β_2 and β_3 are the limiting values for that same part according to Table 6.2.

A1) The critical part is determined by the lowest value of β_2/β. (A1

(3) Refer to 6.2.8 for combination of bending moment and shear force.

(4) In addition, the resistance of the member to lateral-torsional buckling should also be verified, see 6.3.2.

The design cross section will be affected by the presence of holes or HAZ softening. In general, class 1, 2 and 3 sections with holes can be dealt with in accordance with 6.2.2.1 and 6.2.2.2. For all classes of section affected by HAZ and for class 4 sections with holes, additional rules in accordance with 6.2.5.2 should be applied.

6.2.6 Shear

(1)P The design value of the shear force V_{Ed} at each cross-section shall satisfy:

$$\frac{V_{Ed}}{V_{Rd}} \leq 1{,}0 \tag{6.28}$$

where:

V_{Rd} is the design shear resistance of the cross-section.

(2) For non-slender sections, $h_w/t_w < 39\varepsilon$, see 6.5.5(2)

$$V_{Rd} = A_v \frac{f_o}{\sqrt{3}\gamma_{M1}} \tag{6.29}$$

where A_v is the shear area, taken as:

a) For sections containing shear webs

$$A_v = \sum_{i=1}^{n}\left[(h_w - \sum d)(t_w)_i - (1-\rho_{o,haz})b_{haz}(t_w)_i\right] \tag{6.30}$$

where:

h_w	is the depth of the web between flanges.
b_{haz}	is the total depth of HAZ material occurring between the clear depth of the web between flanges. For sections with no welds, $\rho_{o,haz} = 1$. If the HAZ extends the entire depth of the web panel $b_{haz} = h_w - \Sigma d$
t_w	is the web thickness
d	is the diameter of holes along the shear plane
n	is the number of webs.

b) For a solid bar and a round tube

$$A_v = \eta_v A_e \tag{6.31}$$

where:

η_v	= 0,8 for a solid bar
η_v	= 0,6 for a round tube
A_e	is the full section area of an unwelded section, and the effective section area obtained by taking a reduced thickness $\rho_{o,haz}t$ for the HAZ material of a welded section.

(3) For slender webs and stiffened webs, see 6.7.4 – 6.7.6.

(4) Where a shear force is combined with a torsional moment, the shear resistance V_{Rd} should be reduced as specified in 6.2.7(9).

EN 1999-1-1 obviously includes guidance on elements subject to torsion. As these members are not likely to occur in practical situations very often, the guidance on them has been excluded from designs including only bonding moments and shear forces but can be viewed in section 6.2.7. Further guidance when elements are subject to shear force and torsional moments can be viewed in 6.2.7.

6.2.8 Bending and shear

(1) Where a shear force is present allowance should be made for its effect on the moment resistance.

(2) If the shear force V_{Ed} is less than half the shear resistance V_{Rd} its effect on the moment resistance may be neglected except where shear buckling reduces the section resistance, see 6.7.6.

(3) Otherwise the reduced moment resistance should be taken as the design resistance of the cross-section, calculated using a reduced strength

$$f_{o,V} = f_o(1 - (2V_{Ed} / V_{Rd} - 1)^2) \tag{6.38}$$

where V_{Rd} is obtained from 6.2.6.

The code then somewhat unusually offers additional guidance for particular types of section and class giving specific equations for the moment of resistance $M_{V,Rd}$ using the reduced strength as can be seen in 6.2.8(4) and 6.2.8(5) and if torsion as well as bending and shear are included section 6.2.8(7) [erroneously in the code as 6.2.8(3) but corrected by the July amendment] indicates the procedure.

6.2.9 Bending and axial force

6.2.9.1 Open cross-sections

(1) For doubly symmetric cross-sections (except solid sections, see 6.2.9.2) the following two criterions should be satisfied:

$$\left(\frac{N_{Ed}}{\omega_0 N_{Rd}}\right)^{\xi_0} + \frac{M_{y,Ed}}{\omega_0 M_{y,Rd}} \leq 1{,}00 \qquad (6.40)$$

$$\left(\frac{N_{Ed}}{\omega_0 N_{Rd}}\right)^{\eta_0} + \left(\frac{M_{y,Ed}}{\omega_0 M_{y,Rd}}\right)^{\gamma_0} + \left(\frac{M_{z,Ed}}{\omega_0 M_{z,Rd}}\right)^{\xi_0} \leq 1{,}00 \qquad (6.41)$$

where:

η_0 = 1,0 or may alternatively be taken as $\alpha_z^2 \alpha_y^2$ but $1 \leq \eta_0 \leq 2$ (6.42a)

γ_0 = 1,0 or may alternatively be taken as α_z^2 but $1 \leq \gamma_0 \leq 1{,}56$ (6.42b)

ξ_0 = 1,0 or may alternatively be taken as α_y^2 but $1 \leq \xi_0 \leq 1{,}56$ (6.42c)

N_{Ed} is the design values of the axial compression or tension force

$M_{y,Ed}$ and $M_{z,Ed}$ are the bending moments about the y-y and z-z axis

N_{Rd} = $A_{eff} f_o / \gamma_{M1}$, see 6.2.4

$M_{y,Rd}$ = $\alpha_y W_{y,el} f_o / \gamma_{M1}$

$M_{z,Rd}$ = $\alpha_z W_{z,el} f_o / \gamma_{M1}$

α_y, α_z are the shape factors for bending about the y and z axis, with allowance for local buckling and HAZ softening from longitudinal welds, see 6.2.5

ω_0 = 1 for sections without localized welds or holes. Otherwise, see 6.2.9.3.

NOTE For classification of cross section, see 6.3.3(4).

6.2.10 Bending, shear and axial force

(1) Where shear and axial force are present, allowance should be made for the effect of both shear force and axial force on the resistance of the moment.

(2) Provided that the design value of the shear force V_{Ed} does not exceed 50% of the shear resistance V_{Rd} no reduction of the resistances defined for bending and axial force in 6.2.9 need be made, except where shear buckling reduces the section resistance, see 6.7.6.

(3) Where V_{Ed} exceeds 50% of V_{Rd} the design resistance of the cross-section to combinations of moment and axial force should be reduced using a reduced yield strength

$$(1 - \rho) f_o \qquad (6.46)$$

for the shear area where:

$$\rho = (2V_{Ed}/V_{Rd} - 1)^2 \qquad (6.47)$$

and V_{Rd} is obtained from 6.2.6(2).

NOTE Instead of applying reduced yield strength, the calculation may also be performed applying an effective plate thickness.

6.2.11 Web bearing

(1) This clause concerns the design of webs subjected to localised forces caused by concentrated loads or reactions applied to a beam. For un-stiffened and longitudinally stiffened web this subject is covered in 6.7.5.

(2) For transversely stiffened web, the bearing stiffener, if fitted, should be of class 1 or 2 section. It may be conservatively designed on the assumption that it resists the entire bearing force, unaided by the web, the stiffener being checked as a strut (see 6.3.1) for out-of-plane column buckling and local squashing, with lateral bending effects allowed for if necessary (see 6.3.2). See also 6.7.8.

6.3 Buckling resistance of members

In section 6.3 procedures to design aluminium members subject to compression, bending or a combination of bending and compression are given. The process requires the resistance of the section to be evaluated first but then the influence of boundary conditions, slenderness, and loading are included.

6.3.1 Members in compression

(1) Members subject to axial compression may fail in one of three ways:

a)	flexural	(see 6.3.1.1 to 6.3.1.3)
b)	torsional or flexural torsional	(see 6.3.1.1 and 6.3.1.4)
c)	local squashing	(see 6.2.4)

NOTE Check a) should always be made. Check b) is generally necessary but may be waived in some cases. Check c) is only necessary for struts of low slenderness that are significantly weakened locally by holes or welding.

6.3.1.1 Buckling resistance

(1)P A compression member shall be verified against both flexural and torsional or torsional-flexural buckling as follows:

$$\frac{N_{Ed}}{N_{b,Rd}} \leq 1,0 \qquad (6.48)$$

where:

N_{Ed} is the design value of the compression force
$N_{b,Rd}$ is the design buckling resistance of the compression member

(2) The design buckling resistance of a compression member $N_{b,Rd}$ should be taken as:

$$N_{b,Rd} = \kappa \chi A_{eff} f_o / \gamma_{M1} \qquad (6.49)$$

where:

χ is the reduction factor for the relevant buckling mode as given in 6.3.1.2.
κ is a factor to allow for the weakening effects of welding. For longitudinally welded member κ is given in Table 6.5 for flexural buckling and $\kappa = 1$ for torsional and torsional-flexural buckling. In case of transversally welded member $\kappa = \omega_x$ according to 6.3.3.3 [A1) $\kappa = 1$ if there are no welds (A1].
A_{eff} is the effective area allowing for local buckling for class 4 cross-section. For torsional and torsional-flexural buckling see Table 6.7.
A_{eff} $= A$ for class 1, 2 or 3 cross-section

6.3.1.2 Buckling curves

(1) For axial compression in members the value of χ for the appropriate value of $\bar{\lambda}$ should be determined from the relevant buckling curve according to:

[A1⟩ $$\chi = \frac{1}{\phi + \sqrt{\phi^2 - \bar{\lambda}^2}} \text{ but } \chi \leq 1,0$$ ⟨A1] (6.50)

where:

$$\phi = 0,5(1 + \alpha(\bar{\lambda} - \bar{\lambda}_0) + \bar{\lambda}^2)$$

$$\bar{\lambda} = \sqrt{\frac{A_{eff} f_o}{N_{cr}}}$$ (6.51)

α is an imperfection factor

$\bar{\lambda}_0$ is the limit of the horizontal plateau

N_{cr} is the elastic critical force for the relevant buckling mode based on the gross cross-sectional properties

[A1⟩ NOTE In a member with a local weld the slenderness parameter $\bar{\lambda}_{haz}$ according to 6.3.3.3(3) should be used for the section with the weld. ⟨A1]

(2) The imperfection factor α and limit of horizontal plateau $\bar{\lambda}_0$ corresponding to appropriate buckling curve should be obtained from Table 6.6 for flexural buckling and Table 6.7 for torsional or torsional-flexural buckling.

(3) Values of the reduction factor χ for the appropriate relative slenderness $\bar{\lambda}$ may be obtained from Figure 6.11 for flexural buckling and Figure 6.12 for torsional or torsional-flexural buckling.

(4) For slenderness $\bar{\lambda} \leq \bar{\lambda}_0$ or for $N_{Ed} \leq \bar{\lambda}_0^2 N_{cr}$ the buckling effects may be ignored and only cross-sectional check apply.

Table 6.5 — Values of κ factor for member with longitudinal welds

Class A material according to Table 3.2	Class B material according to Table 3.2
$\kappa = 1 - \left(1 - \frac{A_1}{A}\right)10^{-\bar{\lambda}} - \left(0,05 + 0,1\frac{A_1}{A}\right)\bar{\lambda}^{1,3(1-\bar{\lambda})}$ with $A_1 = A - A_{haz}(1 - \rho_{o,haz})$ in which A_{haz} = area of HAZ	$\kappa = 1$ if $\bar{\lambda} \leq 0,2$ $\kappa = 1 + 0,04(4\bar{\lambda})^{(0,5-\bar{\lambda})} - 0,22\bar{\lambda}^{1.4(1-\bar{\lambda})}$ if $\bar{\lambda} > 0,2$

Table 6.6 — Values of α and $\bar{\lambda}_0$ for flexural buckling

Material buckling class according to Table 3.2	α	$\bar{\lambda}_0$
Class A	0,20	0,10
Class B	0,32	0,00

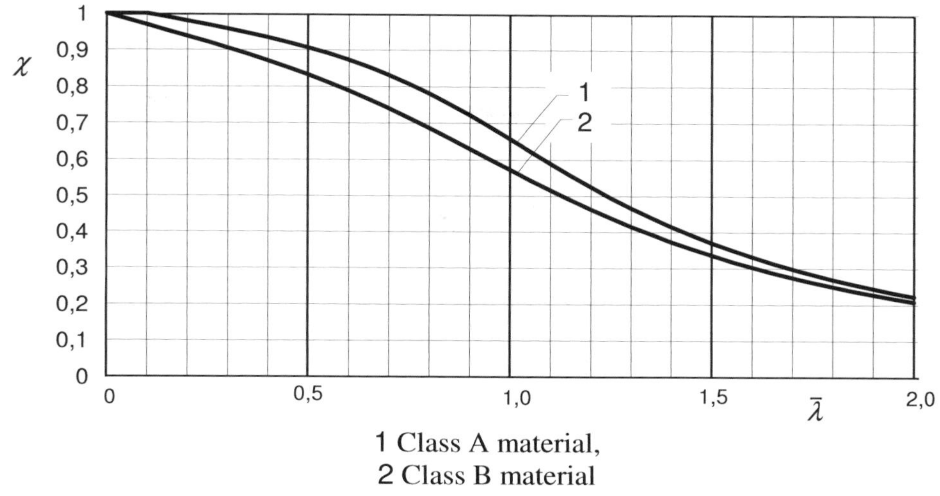

1 Class A material,
2 Class B material

Figure 6.11 — Reduction factor χ for flexural buckling

Table 6.7 — Values of α, $\bar{\lambda}_0$ and A_{eff} for torsional and torsional-flexural buckling

Cross-section	α	$\bar{\lambda}_0$	A_{eff}
General[1)]	0,35	0,4	A_{eff} [1)]
Composed entirely of radiating outstands[2)]	0,20	0,6	A [2)]

1) For sections containing reinforced outstands such that mode 1 would be critical in terms of local buckling (see 6.1.4.3(2)), the member should be regarded as "general" and A_{eff} determined allowing for either or both local buckling and HAZ material.

2) For sections such as angles, tees and cruciforms, composed entirely of radiating outstands, local and torsional buckling are closely related. When determining A_{eff} allowance should be made, where appropriate, for the presence of HAZ material but no reduction should be made for local buckling i.e. $\rho_c = 1$.

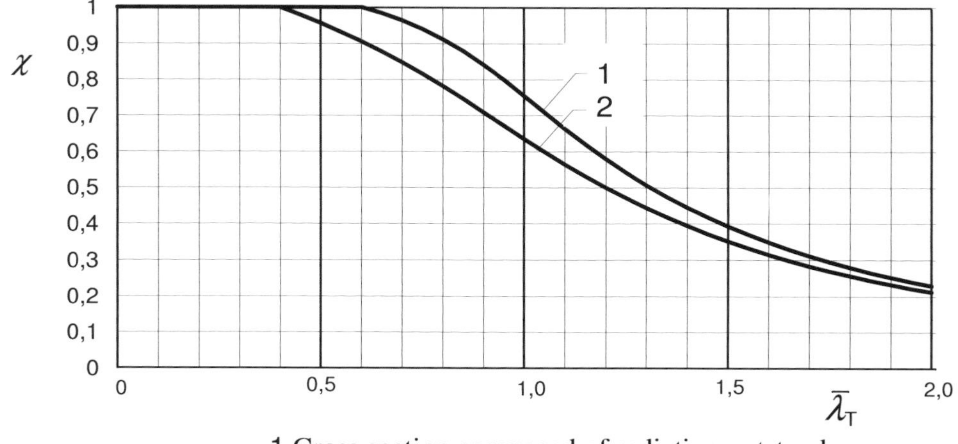

1 Cross section composed of radiating outstands,
2 General cross section

Figure 6.12 — Reduction factor χ for torsional and torsional-flexural buckling

6.3.1.3 Slenderness for flexural buckling

A1 (1) The relative slenderness $\bar{\lambda}$ is given by:

$$\bar{\lambda} = \sqrt{\frac{A_{\mathrm{eff}} f_{\mathrm{o}}}{N_{\mathrm{cr}}}} = \frac{L_{\mathrm{cr}}}{i} \frac{1}{\pi} \sqrt{\frac{A_{\mathrm{eff}}}{A} \frac{f_{\mathrm{o}}}{E}} \tag{6.52}$$

where:

L_{cr} is the buckling length in the buckling plane considered

i is the radius of gyration about the relevant axis, determined using the properties of gross cross-section.

(2) The buckling length L_{cr} should be taken as kL, where L is the length between points of lateral support; for a cantilever, L is its length. The value of k, the buckling length factor for members, should be assessed from knowledge of the end conditions. Unless more accurate analysis is carried out, Table 6.8 should be used.

NOTE The buckling length factors k are increased compared to the theoretical value for fixed ends to allow for various deformations in the connection between different structural parts.

Table 6.8 — Buckling length factor *k* for struts

End conditions	*k*
1. Held in position and restrained in direction at both ends	0,7
2. Held in position at both ends and restrained in direction at one end	0,85
3. Held in position at both ends, but not restrained in direction	1,0
4. Held in position at one end, and restrained in direction at both ends	1,25
5. Held in position and restrained in direction at one end, and partially restrained in direction but not held in position at the other end	1,5
6. Held in position and restrained in direction at one end, but not held in position or restrained at the other end	2,1

A1

6.3.1.4 Slenderness for torsional and torsional-flexural buckling

(1) For members with open cross-sections account should be taken of the possibility that the resistance of the member to either torsional or torsional-flexural buckling could be less than its resistance to flexural buckling.

NOTE The possibility of torsional and torsional-flexural buckling may be ignored for the following:

a) hollow sections
b) doubly symmetrical I-sections
c) sections composed entirely of radiating outstands, e.g. angles, tees, cruciforms, that are classified as class 1 and 2 in accordance with 6.1.4

(2) The relative slenderness $\bar{\lambda} = \bar{\lambda}_T$ for torsional and torsional-flexural buckling should be taken as:

$$\bar{\lambda} = \sqrt{\frac{A_{\mathrm{eff}} f_{\mathrm{o}}}{N_{\mathrm{cr}}}} \tag{6.53}$$

where:

A_{eff} is the cross-section area according to Table 6.7

N_{cr} is the elastic critical load for torsional buckling, allowing for interaction with flexural buckling if necessary (torsional-flexural buckling)

NOTE Values of N_{cr} and $\bar{\lambda}_T$ are given in Annex I.

6.3.1.5 Eccentrically connected single-bay struts

(1) Providing the end attachment prevents rotation in the plane of the connected part and no deliberate bending is applied, the following types of eccentrically connected strut may be designed using a simplified approach. This represents an alternative to the general method for combined bending and compression of 6.3.3:

a) single angle connected through one leg only;
b) back to back angles connected to one side of a gusset plate;
c) single channel connected by its web only;
d) single tee connected by its flange only.

(2) Where flexural buckling using 6.3.1.1 out of the plane of the attached part(s) is checked, the eccentricity of loading should be ignored and the value of $N_{b,Rd}$ should be taken as 40% of the value for centroidal loading.

(3) The value for a) should be that about the axis parallel to the connected part(s). For torsional buckling no change to the method of 6.3.1.1 and 6.3.1.4 is necessary.

6.3.2 Members in bending

(1) The following resistances should normally be checked:

a) bending (see 6.2.5), including, where appropriate, allowance for coincident shear (see 6.2.8);
b) shear (see 6.2.6 and 6.2.8);
c) web bearing (see 6.7.5);
d) lateral torsional buckling (see 6.3.2.1).

(2) Due account should be taken of the class of cross-section (see 6.1.4), the presence of any heat affected zones (see 6.1.5) and the need to allow for the presence of holes (see 6.2.5).

(3) For members required to resist bending combined with axial load reference is made to 6.3.3.

(4) Biaxial bending combined with axial load is covered under 6.2.9 and 6.3.3. If there is no axial force the term with N_{Ed} should be deleted.

6.3.2.1 Buckling resistance

NOTE Lateral torsional buckling need not be checked in any of the following circumstances:

a) bending takes place about the minor principal axis and at the same time the load application is not over the shear centre;
b) the member is fully restrained against lateral movement throughout its length;
c) the relative slenderness $\bar{\lambda}_{LT}$ (see 6.3.2.3) between points of effective lateral restraint is less than 0,4.

(1)P A laterally unrestrained member subject to major axis bending shall be verified against lateral-torsional buckling as follows:

$$\frac{M_{Ed}}{M_{b,Rd}} \leq 1,0 \tag{6.54}$$

where:

M_{Ed} is the design value of the bending moment
$M_{b,Rd}$ is the design buckling resistance moment.

(2) The design buckling resistance moment of laterally un-restrained member should be taken as:

$$M_{b,Rd} = \chi_{LT} \alpha W_{el,y} f_o / \gamma_{M1} \quad (6.55)$$

where:

$W_{el,y}$ is the elastic section modulus of the gross section, without reduction for HAZ softening, local buckling or holes
α is taken from Table 6.4 subject to the limitation $\alpha \le W_{pl,y}/W_{el,y}$
χ_{LT} is the reduction factor for lateral torsional buckling (see 6.3.2.2).

6.3.2.2 Reduction factor for lateral torsional buckling

(1) The reduction factor for lateral torsional buckling χ_{LT} for the appropriate relative slenderness $\bar{\lambda}_{LT}$ should be determined from:

$$\chi_{LT} = \frac{1}{\phi_{LT} + \sqrt{\phi_{LT}^2 - \bar{\lambda}_{LT}^2}} \text{ but } \chi_{LT} \le 1 \quad (6.56)$$

where:

$$\phi_{LT} = 0{,}5\left[1 + \alpha_{LT}(\bar{\lambda}_{LT} - \bar{\lambda}_{0,LT}) + \bar{\lambda}_{LT}^2\right] \quad (6.57)$$

α_{LT} is an imperfection factor
$\bar{\lambda}_{LT}$ is the relative slenderness
$\bar{\lambda}_{0,LT}$ is the limit of the horizontal plateau
M_{cr} is the elastic critical moment for lateral-torsional buckling.

(2) The value of α_{LT} and $\bar{\lambda}_{0,LT}$ should be taken as:

$\alpha_{LT} = 0{,}10$ and $\bar{\lambda}_{0,LT} = 0{,}6$ for class 1 and 2 cross-sections
$\alpha_{LT} = 0{,}20$ and $\bar{\lambda}_{0,LT} = 0{,}4$ for class 3 and 4 cross-sections.

(3) Values of the reduction factor χ_{LT} for the appropriate relative slenderness $\bar{\lambda}_{LT}$ may be obtained from Figure 6.13.

(4) For slenderness $\bar{\lambda}_{LT} \le \bar{\lambda}_{0,LT}$ or for $M_{Ed} \le \bar{\lambda}_{0,LT}^2 M_{cr}$ the buckling effects may be ignored and only cross-sectional check apply.

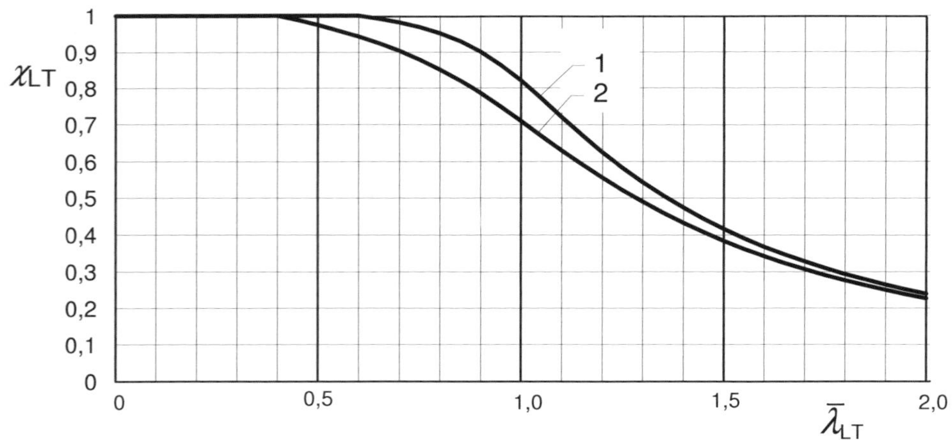

1 Class 1 and 2 cross sections,
2 Class 3 and 4 cross sections

Figure 6.13 — Reduction factor for lateral-torsional buckling

6.3.2.3 Slenderness

(1) The relative slenderness parameter $\bar{\lambda}_{LT}$ should be determined from

$$\bar{\lambda}_{LT} = \sqrt{\frac{\alpha W_{el,y} f_o}{M_{cr}}} \tag{6.58}$$

where:

α is taken from Table 6.4 subject to the limitation $\alpha \le W_{pl,y}/W_{el,y}$.
M_{cr} is the elastic critical moment for lateral-torsional buckling.

(2) M_{cr} is based on gross cross-sectional properties and takes into account the loading conditions, the real moment distribution and the lateral restraints.

NOTE Expressions for M_{cr} for certain sections and boundary conditions are given in Annex I.1 and approximate values of $\bar{\lambda}_{LT}$ for certain I-sections and channels are given in Annex I.2.

6.3.2.4 Effective lateral restraints

(1) Bracing systems providing lateral restraint should be designed according to 5.3.3.

NOTE Where a series of two or more parallel members require lateral restraint, it is not adequate merely to tie the compression flanges together so that they become mutually dependent. Adequate restraint will be provided only by anchoring the ties to an independent robust support, or by providing a triangulated bracing system. If the number of parallel members exceeds three, it is sufficient for the restraint system to be designed to resist the sum of the lateral forces derived from the three largest compressive forces only.

6.3.3 Members in bending and axial compression

(1) Unless second order analysis is carried out using the imperfections as given in 5.3.2, the stability of uniform members should be checked as given in the following clause, where a distinction is made for:

- members that are not susceptible to torsional deformations, e.g. circular hollow sections or sections restrained from torsion (flexural buckling only);
- members that are susceptible to torsional deformations, e.g. members with open cross-sections not restrained from torsion (lateral-torsional buckling or flexural buckling).

(2) Two checks are in general needed for members that are susceptible to torsional deformations:

- flexural buckling;
- lateral-torsional buckling.

(3) For calculatation of the resistance N_{Rd}, $M_{y,Rd}$ and $M_{z,Rd}$ due account of the presence of HAZ-softening from longitudinal welds should be taken. (See 6.2.4 and 6.2.5.) The presence of localized HAZ-softening from transverse welds and the presence of holes should be taken care of according to 6.3.3.3 and 6.3.3.4 respectively.

(4) All quantities in the interaction criterion should be taken as positive.

NOTE 1 Classification of cross-sections for members with combined bending and axial forces is made for the loading components separately according to 6.1.4. No classification is made for the combined state of stress.

NOTE 2 A cross-section can belong to different classes for axial force, major axis bending and minor axis bending. The combined state of stress is taken care of in the interaction expressions. These interaction expressions can be used for all classes of cross-section. The influence of local buckling and yielding on the resistance for combined loading is taken care of by the capacities in the denominators and the exponents, which are functions of the slenderness of the cross-section.

NOTE 3 Section check is included in the check of flexural and lateral-torsional buckling if the methods in 6.3.3.1 and 6.3.3.5 are used.

6.3.3.1 Flexural buckling

(1) For a member with open doubly symmetric cross-section (solid sections, see (2)), one of the following criterions should be satisfied:

– For major axis (y-axis) bending:

$$\left(\frac{N_{Ed}}{\chi_y \omega_x N_{Rd}}\right)^{\xi_{yc}} + \left(\frac{M_{y,Ed}}{\omega_0 M_{y,Rd}}\right) \leq 1,00 \qquad (6.59)$$

– For minor axis (z-axis) bending:

$$\left(\frac{N_{Ed}}{\chi_z \omega_x N_{Rd}}\right)^{\eta_c} + \left(\frac{M_{z,Ed}}{\omega_0 M_{z,Rd}}\right) \leq 1,00 \qquad (6.60)$$

where:

η_c = 0,8 or may alternatively be taken as $\eta_c = \eta_0 \chi_z$ but $\eta_c \geq 0,8$ (6.61a)
ξ_{yc} = 0,8 or may alternatively be taken as $\xi_{yc} = \xi_0 \chi_y$ but $\xi_{yc} \geq 0,8$ (6.61b)
ξ_{zc} = 0,8 or may alternatively be taken as $\xi_{zc} = \xi_0 \chi_z$ but $\xi_{zc} \geq 0,8$ (6.61c)
η_0 and ξ_0 are according to 6.2.9.1
$\omega_x = \omega_0 = 1$ for beam-columns without localized welds and with equal end moments. Otherwise, see [A1) 6.3.3, 6.3.3.4 and 6.3.3.5 (A1] respectively.

(2) For solid cross-sections criterion (6.60) may be used with the exponents taken as 0,8 or

$\eta_c = 2\chi$ but $\eta_c \geq 0,8$ (6.61d)
$\xi_c = 1,56\chi$ but $\xi_c \geq 0,8$ (6.61e)

(3) Hollow cross-sections and tubes should satisfy the following criterion:

$$\left(\frac{N_{Ed}}{\chi_{min} \omega_x N_{Rd}}\right)^{\psi_c} + \frac{1}{\omega_0}\left[\left(\frac{M_{y,Ed}}{M_{y,Rd}}\right)^{1,7} + \left(\frac{M_{z,Ed}}{M_{z,Rd}}\right)^{1,7}\right]^{0,6} \leq 1,00 \qquad (6.62)$$

where $\psi_c = 0,8$ or may alternatively be taken as $1,3\chi_y$ or $1,3\chi_z$ depending on direction of buckling, but $\psi_c \geq 0,8$. $\chi_{min} = \min(\chi_y, \chi_z)$

(4) For other open monosymmetrical cross sections, bending about either axis, expression (6.59) may be used with ξ_{yc}, $M_{y,Ed}$, $M_{y,Rd}$ and χ_y replaced by ξ_{zc}, $M_{z,Ed}$, $M_{z,Rd}$ and χ_z.

(5) The notations in the criterions (6.59) to (6.62) are:

N_{Ed} is the design value of the axial compressive force
$M_{y,Ed}$, $M_{z,Ed}$ are the design values of bending moment about the y- and z-axis. The moments are calculated according to *first order theory*
$N_{Rd} = A f_o/\gamma_{M1}$ or $A_{eff} f_o/\gamma_{M1}$ for class 4 cross-sections. For members with longitudinal welds but without localized welds $N_{Rd} = \kappa A f_o/\gamma_{M1}$ or $\kappa A_{eff} f_o/\gamma_{M1}$, see 6.3.1.
χ_y and χ_z are the reduction factor for buckling in the z-x plane and the y-x plane, respectively
$M_{y,Rd} = \alpha_y W_y f_o/\gamma_{M1}$ bending moment capacity about the y-axis
$M_{z,Rd} = \alpha_z W_z f_o/\gamma_{M1}$ bending moment capacity about the z-axis
α_y, α_z are the shape factors, but α_y and α_z should not be taken larger than 1,25. See 6.2.5 and 6.2.9.1(1)

6.3.3.2 Lateral-torsional buckling

(1) Members with open cross-section symmetrical about major axis, centrally symmetric or doubly symmetric cross-section, the following criterion should satisfy:

$$\left(\frac{N_{ed}}{\chi_z \omega_x N_{Rd}}\right)^{\eta_c} + \left(\frac{M_{y,Ed}}{\chi_{LT} \omega_{xLT} M_{y,Rd}}\right)^{\gamma_c} + \left(\frac{M_{z,Ed}}{\omega_0 M_{z,Rd}}\right)^{\xi_{zc}} \leq 1,00 \qquad (6.63)$$

where:

N_{Ed} is the design value of axial compression force
$M_{y,Ed}$ is bending moment about the y-axis. In the case of beam-columns with hinged ends and in the case of members in non-sway frames, $M_{y,Ed}$ is moment of the *first order*. For members in frames free to sway, $M_{y,Ed}$ is bending moment according to *second order* theory.
$M_{z,Ed}$ is bending moment about the z-axis. $M_{z,Ed}$ is bending moment according to *first order* theory
$N_{Rd} = Af_o/\gamma_{M1}$ or $A_{eff}f_o/\gamma_{M1}$ for class 4 cross-sections. For members with longitudinal welds but without localized welds $N_{Rd} = \kappa Af_o/\gamma_{M1}$ or $\kappa A_{eff}f_o/\gamma_{M1}$, see 6.3.1.
χ_z is the reduction factor for buckling when one or both flanges deflects laterally (buckling in the x-y plane or lateral-torsional buckling) based on (6.68a) in section with localized weld
$M_{y,Rd} = \alpha_y W_{y,el} f_o/\gamma_{M1}$ = bending moment capacity for y-axis bending
$M_{z,Rd} = \alpha_z W_{z,el} f_o/\gamma_{M1}$ = bending moment capacity for z-axis bending
α_y, α_z are the shape factors but α_y and α_z should not be taken larger than 1,25. See 6.2.5 and 6.2.9.1(1)
χ_{LT} is the reduction factor for lateral-torsional buckling
η_c = 0,8 or alternatively $\eta_0 \chi_z$ but $\eta_c \geq 0,8$
γ_c = γ_0
ξ_{zc} = 0,8 or alternatively $\xi_0 \chi_z$ but $\xi_{zc} \geq 0,8$
where η_0, γ_0 and ξ_0 are defined according to the expression in 6.2.9.1.
ω_x, ω_0 and ω_{xLT} = HAZ-softening factors, see 6.3.3.3 or factors for design section, see 6.3.3.5.

(2) The criterion for flexural buckling, see 6.3.3.1, should also be satisfied.

Clauses 6.3 – 6.3.3.2 include design procedures for elements in bending, compression or a combination of bending and compression and will include most elements likely to be encountered in practice. The clauses do not include data on the impact of HAZ effects, reduction of the section through including holes, unequal end moments or lateral loads on aluminium beams/column elements, information on which is included in clauses 6.3.3.3 – 6.3.3.5.

Aluminium elements can be formed by building up or combining a number of components using what are termed laces or battens or by joining closely spaced components at regular intervals along their lengths. Further, aluminium plate girders can be manufactured by welding together aluminium plates to form an I beam for example. In some plate girders, a corrugated web is desirable to stiffen the element. Design of these elements follows the basic rules described thus far, but additional requirements pertinent to the made up element also need to be considered as described in 6.4, 6.7 and 6.8.

A common technique of using aluminium plates in a structure is to attach them into a frame but to use the in-plane bending resistance of the plate structurally. The method by which the plates are fixed to the frame affects the boundary conditions and the analysis. Further, stiffened plates under in-plane forces are often required in aluminium. The specific design requirements for these specialist elements are given in clauses 6.5 and 6.6.

7 Serviceability limit states

7.1 General

(1)P An aluminium structure shall be designed and constructed such that all relevant serviceability criteria are satisfied.

(2) The basic requirements for serviceability limit states are given in 3.4 of EN 1990.

(3) Any serviceability limit state and the associated loading and analysis model should be specified for a project.

(4) Where plastic global analysis is used for the ultimate limit state, plastic redistribution of forces and moments at the serviceability limit state may occur. If so, the effects should be considered.

NOTE The National Annex may give further guidance.

Table NA.1 7.1(4) UK recommendation

Certain members might experience permanent strains from serviceability loadings if designed to maximum utilization at the ultimate limit state. It is recommended that extreme fibre stresses are checked at serviceability loads for members subject to combined axial and bending effects. Further guidance is given in PD 6702-1.

7.2 Serviceability limit states for buildings

7.2.1 Vertical deflections

(1) With reference to EN 1990 – Annex A1.4 limits for vertical deflections according to Figure A1.1 in EN 1990 should be specified for each project and agreed with the owner of the construction work.

NOTE The National Annex may specify the limits.

7.2.2 Horizontal deflections

(1) With reference to EN 1990 – Annex A1.4 limits for horizontal deflections according to Figure A1.2 in EN 1990 should be specified for each project and agreed with the owner of the construction work.

NOTE The National Annex may specify the limits.

In clauses 7.2.1 and 7.2.2 the UK National Annex refers the reader to EN 1990 and its National Annex and PD 6702-1 for further guidance.

7.2.3 Dynamic effects

(1) With reference to EN 1990 – Annex A1.4.4 the vibrations of structures on which the public can walk should be limited to avoid significant discomfort to users, and limits should be specified for each project and agreed with the owner of the construction work.

NOTE The National Annex may specify limits for vibration of floors.

Table NA.1 7.2.3(1) UK recommendation

Certain values are given in BS EN 1990 and the National Annex to BS EN 1990. The National Annex to BS EN 1995 also gives values and guidance. PD 6702-1 gives further guidance.

7.2.4 Calculation of elastic deflection

(1) The calculation of elastic deflection should generally be based on the properties of the gross cross-section of the member. However, for slender sections it may be necessary to take reduced section properties to allow for local buckling (see section 6.7.5). Due allowance of effects of partitioning and other stiffening effects, second order effects and changes in geometry should also be made.

(2) For class 4 sections the following effective second moment of area I_{ser}, constant along the beam may be used

$$I_{ser} = I_{gr} - \frac{\sigma_{gr}}{f_o}(I_{gr} - I_{eff}) \tag{7.1}$$

where:

- I_{gr} is the second moment of area of the gross cross-section
- I_{eff} is the second moment of area of the effective cross-section at the ultimate limit state, with allowance for local buckling, [A1) see 6.2.5.2 (A1]
- σ_{gr} is the maximum compressive bending stress at the serviceability limit state, based on the gross cross-section (positive in the formula).

(3) Deflections should be calculated making also due allowance for the rotational stiffness of any semi-rigid joints, and the possible recurrence of local plastic deformation at the serviceability limit state.

8 Design of joints

8.1 Basis of design

8.1.1 Introduction

(1)P All joints shall have a design resistance such that the structure remains effective and is capable of satisfying all the basic design requirements given in 2.

(2) The partial safety factors γ_M for joints should be applied to the characteristic resistance for the various types of joints.

NOTE Numerical values for γ_M may be defined in the National Annex. Recommended values are given in Table 8.1.

Table NA.1 8.1.1(2)

Use γ_{Mw} = 1,35. For other safety factors use the recommended values.

A1 Table 8.1 — Recommended partial factors γ_M for joints

Resistance of members and cross-sections	γ_{M1} and γ_{M2} see 6.1.3
Resistance of bolt connections	γ_{M2} = 1,25
Resistance of rivet connections	
Resistance of plates in bearing	
Resistance of pin connections	γ_{Mp} = 1,25
Resistance of welded connections	γ_{Mw} = 1,25
Slip resistance, see 8.5.9.3 - for serviceability limit states - for ultimate limit states	 $\gamma_{Ms,ser}$ = 1,1 $\gamma_{Ms,ult}$ = 1,25
Resistance of adhesive bonded connections	$\gamma_{Ma} \geq$ 3,0
Resistance of pins at serviceability limit state	$\gamma_{Mp,ser}$ = 1,0

A1

(3) Joints subject to fatigue should also satisfy the rules given in EN 1999-1-3.

8.1.2 Applied forces and moments

(1) The forces and moments applied to joints at the ultimate limit state should be determined by global analysis conforming to 5.

(2) These applied forces and moments should include:

- second order effects;
- the effects of imperfections (see 5.3);
- the effects of connection flexibility

NOTE For the effect of connection flexibility, see Annex L.

8.1.3 Resistance of joints

(1) The resistance of a joint should be determined on the basis of the resistances of the individual fasteners, welds and other components of the joint.

(2) Linear-elastic analysis should generally be used in the design of the joint. Alternatively non-linear analysis of the joint may be employed provided that it takes account of the load deformation characteristics of all the components of the joint.

(3) If the design model is based on yield lines such as block shear i.e., the adequacy of the model should be demonstrated on the basis of physical tests.

8.1.4 Design assumptions

(1) Joints may be designed by distributing the internal forces and moments in whatever rational way is best, provided that:

(a) the assumed internal forces and moments are in equilibrium with the applied forces and moments;
(b) each part in the joint is capable of resisting the forces or stresses assumed in the analysis;
(c) the deformations implied by this distribution are within the deformation capacity of the fasteners or welds and of the connected parts, and
(d) the deformations assumed in any design model based on yield lines are based on rigid body rotations (and in-plane deformations) which are physically possible.

(2) In addition, the assumed distribution of internal forces should be realistic with regard to relative stiffness within the joint. The internal forces will seek to follow the path with the greatest rigidity. This path should be clearly identified and consistently followed throughout the design of the joint.

(3) Residual stresses and stresses due to tightening of fasteners and due to ordinary accuracy of fit-up need not usually be allowed for.

8.1.5 Fabrication and execution

(1) Ease of fabrication and execution should be considered in the design of all joints and splices.

(2) Attention should be paid to:

- the clearances necessary for safe execution;
- the clearances needed for tightening fasteners;
- the need for access for welding;
- the requirements of welding procedures, and
- the effects of angular and length tolerances on fit-up.

(3) Attention should also be paid to the requirements for:

- subsequent inspection;
- surface treatment, and
- maintenance.

Requirements to execution of aluminium structures are given in prEN 1090-3.

8.2 Intersections for bolted, riveted and welded joints

(1) Members meeting at a joint should usually be arranged with their centroidal axes intersecting at a point.

(2) Any kind of eccentricity in the nodes should be taken into account, except in the case of particular types of structures where it has been demonstrated that it is not necessary.

8.3 Joints loaded in shear subject to impact, vibration and/or load reversal

(A1) (1) Where a joint loaded in shear is subject to frequent impact or significant vibration either welding, preloaded bolts, injection bolts or other types of bolts, which effectively prevent movement and loosening of fastener, should be used.

(2) Where slipping is not acceptable in a joint because it is subject to reversal of shear load (or for any other reason), preloaded bolts in a slip-resistant connection (category B or C as appropriate, see 8.5.3), fitted bolts or welding should be used.

(3) For wind and/or stability bracings, bolts in bearing type connections (category A in 8.5.3) may be used. (A1)

8.4 Classification of joints

NOTE Recommendations for classification of joints are given in Annex L.

8.5 Connections made with bolts, rivets and pins

8.5.1 Positioning of holes for bolts and rivets

(1) The positioning of holes for bolts and rivets should be such as to prevent corrosion and local buckling and to facilitate the installation of the bolts or rivets.

(2) In case of minimum end distances, minimum edge distances and minimum spacings no minus tolerances are allowed.

(3) The positioning of the holes should also be in conformity with the limits of validity of the rules used to determine the design resistances of the bolts and rivets.

(4) Minimum and maximum spacing, end and edge distances are given in Table 8.2.

Table 8.2 — Minimum, regular and maximum spacing, end and edge distances

1	2	3	4	5
Distances and spacings, see Figures 8.1 and 8.2	Minimum	Regular distance	Maximum[1) 2) 3)]	
			Structures made of aluminium according to Table 3.1a	
			Aluminium exposed to the weather or other corrosive influences	Aluminium not exposed to the weather or other corrosive influences
End distance e_1	$1{,}2d_0$ [6)]	$2{,}0d_0$	$4t + 40$ mm	The larger of $12t$ or 150 mm
Edge distance e_2	$1{,}2d_0$ [6)]	$1{,}5d_0$	$4t + 40$ mm	The larger of $12t$ or 150 mm
End distance e_3 for slotted holes [4)]	Slotted holes are not recommended. Slotted holes of category A see 8.5.1(4) – (10)			
Edge distance e_4 for slotted holes [4)]	Slotted holes are not recommended Slotted holes of category A see 8.5.1(4) – (10)			
Compression members (see Figure 8.2): Spacing p_1	$2{,}2d_0$	$2{,}5d_0$	Compression members: The smaller of $14t$ or 200 mm	Compression members: The smaller of $14t$ or 200 mm
Tension members (see Figure 8.3): Spacing p_1, $p_{1,0}$, $p_{1,i}$	$2{,}2d_0$	$2{,}5d_0$	Outer lines: The smaller of $14t$ or 200 mm Inner lines: The smaller of $28t$ or 400 mm	1,5 times the values of column 4
Spacing p_2 [5)]	$2{,}4d_0$	$3{,}0d_0$	The smaller of $14t$ or 200 mm	The smaller of $14t$ or 200 mm

1) Maximum values for spacings, edge and end distances are unlimited, except in the following cases:
- for compression members in order to avoid local buckling and to prevent corrosion in exposed members and;
- for exposed tension members to prevent corrosion.

2) The local buckling resistance of the plate in compression between the fasteners should be calculated according to 6.4 as column like buckling by using 0,6 p_1 as buckling length. Local buckling between the fasteners need not to be checked if p_1/t is smaller than 9ε. The edge distance should not exceed the maximum to satisfy local buckling requirements for an outstand part in the compression members, see 6.4.2 - 6.4.5. The end distance is not affected by this requirement.

3) t is the thickness of the thinner outer connected part.

4) Slotted holes are not recommended, slotted holes of category A see 8.5.1 (5).

5) For staggered rows of fasteners a minimum line spacing $p_2 = 1{,}2d_0$ may be used, if the minimum distance between any two fasteners in a staggered row is $p_1 = 2{,}4d_0$, see Figure 8.2.

6) The minimum values of e_1 and e_2 should be specified with no minus deviation but only plus deviations.

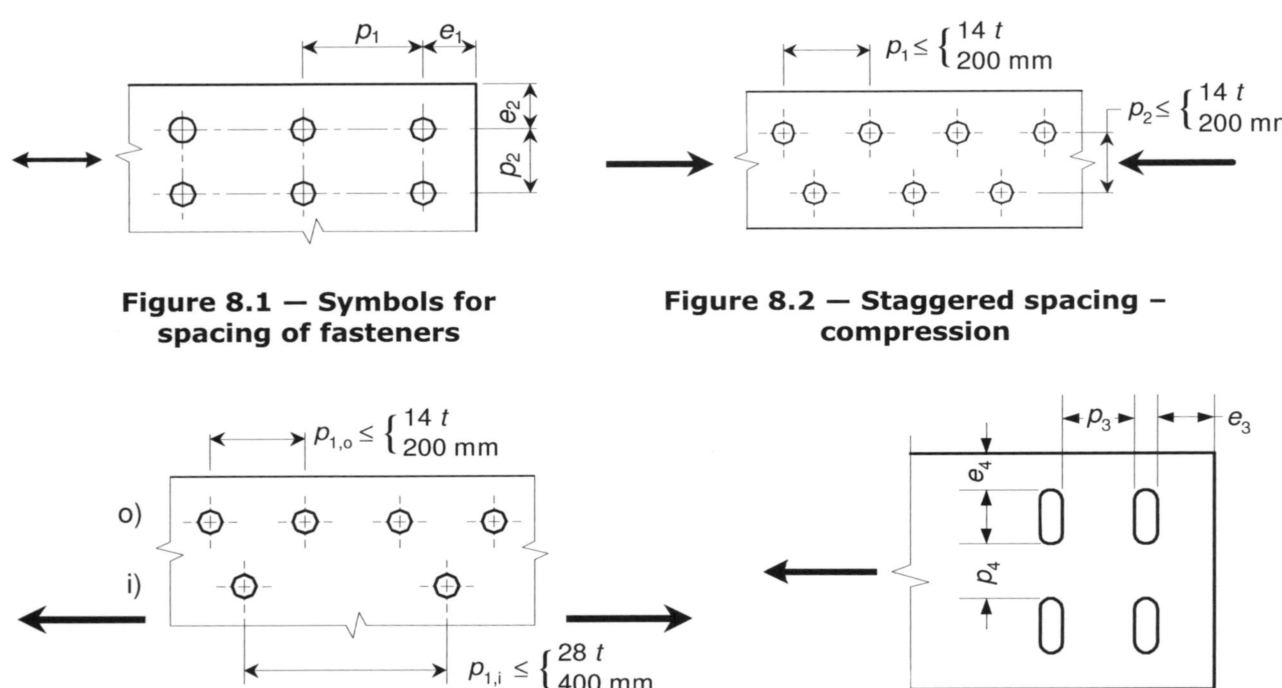

Figure 8.1 — Symbols for spacing of fasteners

Figure 8.2 — Staggered spacing - compression

o) outer line, i) inner line

Figure 8.3 — Spacing in tension member

Figure 8.4 — Slotted holes

The use of slotted holes to connect aluminium elements is not recommended. If this procedure is unavoidable strict guidelines (8.5.1(5) – 8.5.1(11)) should be observed. These guidelines can also be used if oversized holes are required. Sometimes with aluminium elements, a phenomenon known as block tearing can occur. This results when a cluster of bolts causes failure of the jointed material along a row of bolts usually in shear. To avoid block tearing, the information in clause 8.5.2.2 should be followed.

8.5.3 Categories of bolted connections

8.5.3.1 Shear connections

(1) The design of a bolted connection loaded in shear should conform to one of the following categories, see Table 8.4.

(2) **Category A: Bearing type**
In this category protected steel bolts (ordinary or high strength type) or stainless steel bolts or aluminium bolts or aluminium rivets should be used. No preloading and special provisions for contact surfaces are required. [A1) *Deleted text* (A1]

(3) **Category B: Slip-resistant at serviceability limit state**
In this category preloaded high strength bolts with controlled tightening in conformity with prEN 1090-3 should be used. Slip should not occur at the serviceability limit state. The combination of actions to be considered should be selected from 2.3.4 depending on the load cases where resistance to slip is required. The design serviceability shear load should not exceed the design slip resistance, obtained from 8.5.9. [A1) *Deleted text* (A1]

(4) **Category C: Slip resistant at ultimate limit state**
In this category preloaded high strength bolts with controlled tightening in conformity with prEN 1090-3 should be used. Slip should not occur at the ultimate limit state. [A1) *Deleted text* (A1]

(5) In addition, at the ultimate limit state the design plastic resistance of the net section at bolt holes $N_{net,Rd}$ should be taken as:

$$N_{net,Rd} = 0{,}9 A_{net} f_u / \gamma_{M2} \tag{8.6}$$

Table 8.4 — Categories of bolted connections

Shear connections		
Category	Criteria	Remarks
A; bearing type	$F_{v,Ed} \le F_{v,Rd}$ $F_{v,Ed} \le F_{b,Rd}$ $\Sigma F_{v,Ed} \le N_{net,Rd}$	No preloading required. All grades from 4.6 to 10.9. $N_{net,Rd} = 0{,}9 A_{net} f_u / \gamma_{M2}$
B; slip resistant at serviceability	$F_{v,Ed,ser} \le F_{s,Rd,ser}$ $F_{v,Ed} \le F_{v,Rd}$ $F_{v,Ed} \le F_{b,Rd}$ $\Sigma F_{v,Ed} \le N_{net,Rd}$ $\Sigma F_{v,Ed,ser} \le N_{net,Rd,ser}$	Preloaded high strength bolts. No slip at the serviceability limit state. $N_{net,Rd} = 0{,}9 A_{net} f_u / \gamma_{M2}$ $N_{net,Rd,ser} = A_{net} f_o / \gamma_{M1}$
C; slip resistant at ultimate	$F_{v,Ed} \le F_{s,Rd}$ $F_{v,Ed} \le F_{b,Rd}$ $\Sigma F_{v,Ed} \le N_{net,Rd}$ A1) $\Sigma F_{v,Ed} \le N_{net,Rd,ser}$ (A1	Preloaded high strength bolts. No slip at the ultimate limit state. $N_{net,Rd} = 0{,}9 A_{net} f_u / \gamma_{M2}$ $N_{net,Rd,ser} = A_{net} f_o / \gamma_{M1}$
Tension connections		
Category	Criterion	Remarks
D; non-preloaded	$F_{t,Ed} \le F_{t,Rd}$ $F_{t,Ed} \le B_{p,Rd}$	Bolt class from 4.6 to 10.9.
E; preloaded	$F_{t,Ed} \le F_{t,Rd}$ $F_{t,Ed} \le B_{p,Rd}$	Preloaded 8.8 or 10.9 bolts.

Key:
- $F_{v,Ed}$ design shear force per bolt for the ultimate limit state
- $F_{v,Ed,ser}$ design shear force per bolt for the serviceability limit state
- $F_{v,Rd}$ design shear resistance per bolt
- $F_{b,Rd}$ design bearing resistance per bolt
- $F_{s,Rd,ser}$ design slip resistance per bolt at the serviceability limit state
- $F_{s,Rd}$ design slip resistance per bolt at the ultimate limit state
- $F_{t,Ed}$ design tensile force per bolt for the ultimate limit state
- $F_{t,Rd}$ design tension resistance per bolt
- A_{net} net area, see 6.2.2.2 (tension members only)
- $B_{p,Rd}$ design resistance for punching resistance, see Table 8.5.

8.5.3.2 Tension connections

(1) The design of a bolted connection loaded in tension should conform with one of the following categories, see Table 8.4.

(2) **Category D: Connections with non-preloaded bolts**
In this category bolts from class 4.6 up to and including class 10.9 or aluminium bolts or stainless steel bolts should be used. No preloading is required. This category should not be used where the connections are frequently subjected to variations of tensile loading. However, they may be used in connections designed to resist normal wind loads.

(3) **Category E: Connections with preloaded high strength bolts**
In this category preloaded high strength bolts with controlled tightening in conformity with prEN 1090-3 should be used. Such preloading improves fatigue resistance. However, the extent of the improvement depends on detailing and tolerances.

(4) For tension connections of both categories D and E no special treatment of contact surfaces is necessary, except where connections of category E are subject to both tension and shear (combination E-B or E-C).

8.5.4 Distribution of forces between fasteners

(1) The distribution of internal forces between fasteners due to the bending moment at the ultimate limit state should be proportional to the distance from the centre of rotation and the distribution of the shear force should be equal, see Figure 8.7(a), in the following cases:

- category C slip-resistant connections;
- other shear connections where the design shear resistance $F_{v,Rd}$ of a fastener is less than the design bearing resistance $F_{b,Rd}$.

(2) In other cases the distribution of internal forces between fasteners due to the bending moment at the ultimate limit state may be assumed plastic and the distribution of the shear force may be assumed equal, see Figure 8.7(b).

(3) In a lap joint, the same bearing resistance in any particular direction should be assumed for each fastener up to a maximum length of max $L = 15\ d$, where d is the nominal diameter of the bolt or rivet. For $L > 15\ d$ see 8.5.11.

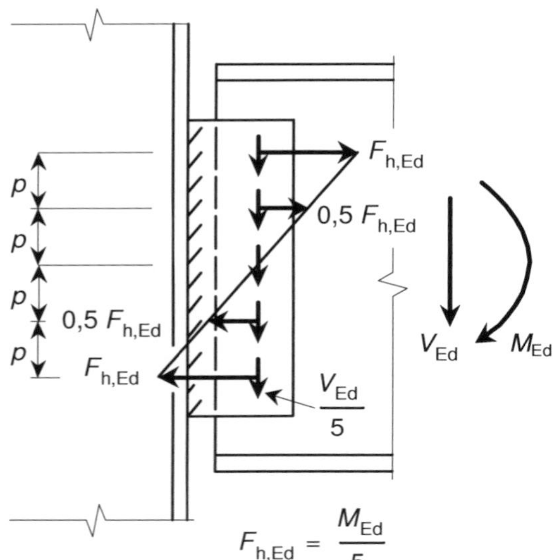

(a) Elastic load distribution
Distribution proportional to distance from centre of rotation

$$F_{v,Ed} = \sqrt{\left(\frac{M_{Ed}}{5p}\right)^2 + \left(\frac{V_{Ed}}{5}\right)^2} \quad (8.7)$$

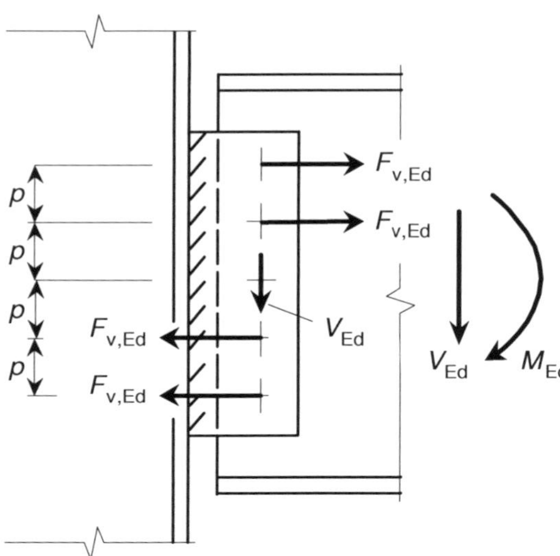

(b) Plastic load distribution
Possible plastic distribution with one fastener resisting V_{Ed} and four resisting M_{Ed}

$$F_{v,Ed} = \frac{M_{Ed}}{6p} \quad (8.8)$$

Figure 8.7 — Example of distribution of loads between fasteners (five bolts)

8.5.5 Design resistances of bolts

(1) The design resistances given in this clause apply to standard manufactured steel bolts, stainless steel bolts and aluminium bolts according to Table 3.4 which conform, including corresponding nuts and washers, to the reference standards listed in prEN 1090-3. For aluminium bolts the additional requirements of C.4.1 should be followed.

(2)P At the ultimate limit state the design shear force $F_{v,Ed}$ on a bolt shall not exceed the lesser of:

- the design shear resistance $F_{v,Rd}$;
- the design bearing resistance $F_{b,Rd}$ of that bolt with the minimum bearing capacity of the connection, both as given in Table 8.5.

(3)P At the ultimate limit state the design tensile force $F_{t,Ed}$, inclusive of any force due to prying action, shall not exceed the design tension resistance $B_{t,Rd}$ of the bolt-plate assembly.

(4) Bolts subject to both shear force and tensile force should in addition be verified as given in Table 8.5.

(5)P The design tension resistance of the bolt-plate assembly $B_{t,Rd}$ shall be taken as the smaller of the design tension resistance $F_{t,Rd}$ of the bolt given in Table 8.5 and the design punching shear resistance of the bolt head and the nut in the plate, $B_{p,Rd}$ obtained from Table 8.5.

Table 8.5 — Design resistance for bolts and rivets

Failure mode	Bolts	Rivets
Shear resistance per shear plane:	$F_{v,Rd} = \dfrac{\alpha_v \, f_{ub} \, A}{\gamma_{M2}}$ (8.9) - where the shear plane passes through the threaded portion of the bolt (A is the tensile stress area of the bolt A_S): - for steel bolts with classes 4.6, 5.6 and 8.8: $\alpha_v = 0,6$ - for steel bolts with classes 4.8, 5.8, 6.8 and 10.9, stainless steel bolts and aluminium bolts: $\alpha_v = 0,5$ - where the shear plane passes through the unthreaded portion of the bolt (A is the gross cross section of the bolt): $\alpha_v = 0,6$ f_{ub} = characteristic ultimate strength of the bolt material	$F_{v,Rd} = \dfrac{0,6 \, f_{ur} \, A_0}{\gamma_{M2}}$ (8.10) f_{ur} = characteristic ultimate strength of the rivet material A_0 = cross sectional area of the hole
Bearing resistance 1) 2) 3) 4) 5) 6)	$F_{b,Rd} = \dfrac{k_1 \, \alpha_b \, f_u \, d \, t}{\gamma_{M2}}$ (8.11) where α_b is the smallest of α_d or $\dfrac{f_{ub}}{f_u}$ or 1,0; but $\leq 0,66$ for slotted holes (8.12) in the direction of the load transfer: - for end bolts: $\alpha_d = \dfrac{e_1}{3d_0}$; for inner bolts: $\alpha_d = \dfrac{p_1}{3d_0} - \dfrac{1}{4}$; (8.13 and 8.14) perpendicular to the direction of the load transfer: - for edge bolts: k_1 is the smallest of $2,8\dfrac{e_2}{d_0} - 1,7$ or 2,5 (8.15) - for inner bolts: k_1 is the smallest of $1,4\dfrac{p_2}{d_0} - 1,7$ or 2,5 (8.16) f_u is the characteristic ultimate strength of the material of the connected parts f_{ub} is the characteristic ultimate strengths of the bolt material d is the bolt diameter d_0 is the hole diameter e_1, e_2, p_1, p_2 see Figure 8.1 5)	
Tension resistance	$F_{t,Rd} = \dfrac{k_2 \, f_{ub} \, A_s}{\gamma_{M2}}$ (8.17) where $k_2 = 0,9$ for steel bolts, $k_2 = 0,50$ for aluminium bolts and $k_2 = 0,63$ for countersunk steel bolts,	$F_{t,Rd} = \dfrac{0,6 \, f_{ur} \, A_0}{\gamma_{M2}}$ (8.18) For solid rivets with head dimensions according to Annex C, Figure C.1 or greater on both sides.
Punching shear resistance	$B_{p,Rd} = 0,6 \, \pi \, d_m \, t_p \, f_u / \gamma_{M2}$ (8.19) where: d_m is the mean of the across points and across flats dimensions of the bolt head or the nut or if washers are used the outer diameter of the washer, whichever is smaller; t_p is the thickness of the plate under the bolt head or the nut; f_u characteristic ultimate strength of the member material.	
Combined shear and tension	$\dfrac{F_{v,Ed}}{F_{v,Rd}} + \dfrac{F_{t,Ed}}{1,4 \, F_{t,Rd}} \leq 1,0$ (8.20)	

[1] The bearing resistance $F_{b,Rd}$ for bolts

- in oversized holes according to prEN 1090-3 is 0,8 times the bearing resistance for bolts in normal holes,
- in short slotted holes, where the longitudinal axis of the slotted hole is perpendicular to the direction of the force transfer and the length of the slotted hole is not more than 1,5 times the diameter of the round part of the hole, is 0,80 times the bearing resistance for bolts in round, normal holes.
- in long slotted holes, where the longitudinal axis of the slotted hole is perpendicular to the direction of the force transfer and the length of the slotted hole is between 1,5 times the hole diameter and 2,5 times the hole diameter of the round part of the hole, is 0,65 times the bearing resistance for bolts in round, normal holes.

[2] For countersunk bolts:

- the bearing resistance $F_{b,Rd}$ should be based on a plate thickness t equal to the thickness of the connected plate minus half the depth of the countersinking,

[3] In addition to bearing resistance, the net section resistance needs to be checked

[4] If the load on a bolt is not parallel to the edge, the bearing resistance may be verified separately for the bolt load components parallel and normal to the end.

[5] Aluminium bolts should not be used in connections with slotted holes.

[6] For slotted holes replace d_0 by (d + 1 mm), e_1 by ($e_3 + d/2$), e_2 by ($e_4 + d/2$), p_1 by ($p_3 + d$) and p_2 by ($p_4 + d$) where p_3, p_4, e_3 and e_4 are found in Figure 8.4.

(6) The design resistances for tension and for shear through the threaded portion given in Table 8.5 are restricted to bolts with rolled threads. [A1) For bolts with cut threads, the relevant values from Table 8.5 should be reduced by multiplying them by a factor of 0,85. (A1]

[A1) (7) The values for design shear resistance $F_{v,Rd}$ given in Table 8.5 apply only where the bolts are used in holes with nominal clearances not exceeding those for standard holes as specified in EN 1090-3. For oversized holes and slotted holes $F_{v,Rd}$ is reduced by a factor of 0,7. (A1]

Subclauses 8.5.3 – 8.5.5 categorise bolted connections, describe how forces are distributed between bolts when more than one is used and provide details on the design resistance of single and groups of bolts. The categories of shear resistance connectors are described, these being simple type bearing connectors, where the shear strength of the bolts and the bearing or crushing of the material being jointed resist the forces, and slip resistant bolt connectors. With the slip resistant connectors, bolts clamp the two parts of the joint, the force of clamping being higher when the slip resistance at ultimate loads is required than at serviceability loading. For certain types of connection, the distribution of forces between bolts in a joint when the joint is subject to a moment may be assumed to be proportional to the distance of the bolt from the centre of rotation of the joint (assumed elastic behaviour) or in other situations plastic behaviour may be assumed. In lap joints of up to a certain length, the same force may be assumed to exist in each fastener (bolt or rivet). When determining the resistance of bolts, elastic theory is generally employed to determine resistances but additional factors to allow for prying, crinkling of material etc. are included as noted in Table 8.5. Connecting aluminium using rivets is undertaken in accordance with subclause 8.5.6.

8.6 Welded connections

8.6.1 General

(1) In the design of welded joints consideration should be given both to the strength of the welds and to the strength of the HAZ.

(2) The design guidance given here applies to:

- the welding process MIG and TIG for material thicknesses according to Table 3.2a and Table 3.2b [A1) *Deleted text* (A1];
- quality level according to prEN 1090-3;
- combinations of parent and filler metal as given in 3.3.4;
- structures loaded with predominantly static loads.

(3) If – in case of primary load bearing members – the above conditions are not fulfilled special test pieces should be welded and tested, which should be agreed upon by the contracting parties.

(4) If for secondary or non load-bearing members a lower quality level has been specified lower design strength values should be used.

Both an MIG and a TIG weld involve a process where the concentrated heat of an electric arc is used to join together metals by fusion of the parent metal using a consumable electrode. The MIG (Metal Inert Gas) weld process, fuses the metal by heating with an arc. A TIG (Tungsten Inert Gas) weld, on the other hand, functions by joining metals through the process of heating with tungsten electrodes that do not become part of the completed weld. In general MIG welding is faster than using the TIG process and requires less experience.

8.6.2 Heat-affected zone (HAZ)

(1) For the following classes of alloys a heat-affected zone should be taken into account ([A1) see also 6.1.6 (A1]):

- heat-treatable alloys in temper T4 and above (6xxx and 7xxx series);
- non-heat-treatable alloys in any work-hardened condition (3xxx, 5xxx and 8xxx series).

(2) The severity and extent (dimensions) of HAZ softening given in [A1) 6.1.6 (A1] should be taken into account. Both severity and extent are different for TIG and MIG welding. For TIG welding a higher extent (larger HAZ area) and more severe softening due to the higher heat-input should be applied.

(3) The characteristic strengths $f_{u,haz}$ for the material in the HAZ are given in Table 3.2. The characteristic shear strength in the HAZ is defined as: $f_{v,haz} = f_{u,haz}/\sqrt{3}$.

Both fillet and butt welds are permissible although butt welds which do not penetrate through the full depth of an element should only be used in secondary and non-load bearing members. With butt welds the design is based on elastic theory but there are additional factors which reduce the allowable shear in the weld and allowance for the HAZ next to the weld should be made. With fillet welds, design is again based on elastic theory and stresses are determined across the throat thickness of the weld. Joining aluminium elements using adhesives or hybrid connections may be undertaken provided 8.7 – 8.9 are observed.

Table NA.1 8.9(3) UK recommendation

Refer to PD 6702-1 and PD 6705-3 for other processes such as friction stir or laser welding.

Bibliography

Standards publications

For dated references, only the edition cited applies. For undated references, the latest edition of the referenced document (including any amendments) applies.

BS EN 1090-2, *Execution of steel structures and aluminium structures – Part 2: Technical requirements for steel structures*[1)]

BS EN 1090-3:2008, *Execution of steel structures and aluminium structures – Part 3: Technical requirements for aluminium structures*

BS EN 1990:2002, *Eurocode 0: Basis of structural design*

BS EN 1991 (all parts), *Eurocode 1: Actions on structures*

PD 6702-1, *Recommendations for the design of aluminium structures to BS EN 1999*[1)]

PD 6705-3, *Recommendations for the execution of aluminium structures to BS EN 1090-3*[1)]

[1)] In preparation.

Useful references

Dwight J, *Aluminium design and construction*. ISBN 0 419 15710 7. London: Spon., 2002.

Mazzolani, Frederico M, *Aluminium Structural Design*. ISBN 978 3 211 00456 2. Springer, 2003.

Muller, Ulrich, *Introduction to Structural Aluminium Design*. ISBN 978 184995 007. Whittles Publishing, 2010.